"MERCY HOSPITAL" FIRST ONE IN GARY

BEST WISHES
ALWAYS TO MY
FRIEND MONSIGNOR
SEMANCIK —
Paul Bomberger

Monsignor
Semancik,
Enjoy the book!

MONSIGNOR SEMANCIK —
THANK YOU FOR YOUR
SUPPORT —

Monsignor Semancik, —
Thank you for all of your support
and encouragement in making St.
Mary Medical Center a 'top choice'
for health care in NWI.
Enjoy!
                    Sincerely,
                    Janice

Community Healthcare System®

ST. MARY Medical Center

1500 S. Lake Park Ave., Hobart, Indiana 46342

St. Mary Medical Center – A Mission of Mercy, a Century of Care

Compliments of:

Janice Ryba, CEO and Administrator
St. Mary Medical Center

St. Mary Medical Center

A Mission of Mercy, a Century of Care

St. Mary Medical Center

A MISSION OF MERCY, A CENTURY OF CARE

Copyright © 2010 by Community Foundation of Northwest Indiana, Inc.
905 Ridge Road
Munster, IN 46321
Phone: (219) 947-6011
Fax: (219) 947-6144
Internet: www.comhs.org

Other hospital history publications through
Community Foundation of Northwest Indiana, Inc.:
The Community Hospital – An Impossible Dream, © 2007
St. Catherine Hospital – A Family, © 2009

Library of Congress Control Number: 2010913047
Bomberger, Jane
St. Mary Medical Center – A Mission of Mercy, a Century of Care

ISBN #978-0-9714601-8-8

362.110977299

Print management by HeuleGordon Inc.
Printed in Korea

Marking Time source: www.infoplease.com
Milestones of the 20th Century
Facts about the 20th Century (by George Ochoa and Melinda Corey)
The Eventful Century – Milestones of Medicine (Reader's Digest)
Milestones in Health and Medicine (Anne S. Harding)
Chronicle of the 20th Century

Proceeds from the sale of this book go toward the
St. Mary Medical Center Endowment Fund.

1500 S. Lake Park Ave., Hobart, Indiana 46342
www.comhs.org

St. Mary Medical Center

A Mission of Mercy, a Century of Care

A HISTORY
BY

Jane Bomberger

GRAPHIC DESIGN
BY

Joseph A. Gonzalez

St. Mary Medical Center

A Mission of Mercy, a Century of Care

IT'S BEEN *Said* IN 2009...

"(St. Mary Medical Center) has had as its main mission the care of the people – Mercy was its name!"

Robert S. Martino, M.D.
ORTHOPEDIC SURGEON
MERCY HOSPITAL
(BEGAN IN 1965 IN GARY)

IT'S BEEN *Said* IN 2009...

"I really love what I do. I love working with people. I love helping people and I just feel that this is my calling. I owe St. Mary's everything. This is the only job I have ever had in my entire life and that is why if I have to work 20 hours a day with no pay, I would do it because I owe St. Mary/Community Healthcare System everything. They truly have blessed me and my family."

Claudia Dixon
FOOD SERVICE SUPERVISOR
MERCY HOSPITAL
(BEGAN IN 1973 IN GARY)

IT'S BEEN *Said* IN 2009...

"St. Mary Medical Center is a place where people in good conscience can bring their family members to be cared for at our hospital with no hesitation or reservation. Your husband, son, daughter, mother, aunt, sister, uncle should know that we do a great job. It doesn't mean that the outcome is always the one we all want but St. Mary Medical Center is proud to (stand on its fine reputation among our friends and neighbors)."

Zlatan Stepanovic, M.D.
CARDIOLOGIST
DIRECTOR OF CONGESTIVE HEART FAILURE CLINIC
ST. MARY MEDICAL CENTER
(BEGAN IN 1997 IN HOBART)

IT'S BEEN *Said* IN 2009...

"My St. Mary's story starts with my birth at the old Mercy Hospital in Gary in 1968. My family has been coming to St. Mary Medical Center for as long as I can remember. It has always been our hometown hospital. It has completed the whole cycle of life because I have been here for hospice situations and my daughter's birth and anywhere in between – heart attacks, my uncle's surgery – so we've all come here for generations."

Robert Boby
EMERGENCY MEDICAL SERVICES COORDINATOR
ST. MARY MEDICAL CENTER
(BEGAN IN 2003 IN HOBART)

Foreword
by
WILLIAM K. SCHENCK
PRESIDENT, BOARD OF DIRECTORS, ST. MARY MEDICAL CENTER
BOARD MEMBER, COMMUNITY FOUNDATION OF NORTHWEST INDIANA, INC.

St. Mary Medical Center has a long and distinguished history and the future promises to continue in that tradition.

More than 30 years ago, I taught my first class at Indiana University Northwest in the library of what was then the hospital's Gary location. Even then, it was evident that Mercy Hospital and its equipment were in serious need of upgrading. Thus, a second facility of the Ancilla Domini Sisters opened in Hobart years later, although this was not accomplished without a few bumps in the road.

Today, St. Mary Medical Center is part of Community Healthcare System, and thanks to the outstanding leadership and vision of Donald Powers and John Gorski, it is a beautiful state-of-the-art facility serving the healthcare needs of east Lake County and west Porter County.

In addition to the facilities mentioned above, St. Mary Medical Center now has a top-notch medical staff, an outstanding board of directors, and a team of dedicated employees and volunteers, all of whom are committed to the service of our patients in a friendly, personalized, and efficient manner.

It has been an honor for me to follow in the footsteps of Bob Welsh and Milt Triana in leading this team as we plan and build for the future with construction of a new Emergency Department. Of course the day-to-day operation of the hospital demands a dedicated, effective administrator and Janice Ryba fills that role with distinction.

I am very proud of St. Mary Medical Center and of the small part I am playing in its continuing outstanding history of service.

Preface

This publication, tracing St. Mary Medical Center's history from the early 1900s, has been compiled from every available resource. To the credit of those who took the time to preserve hospital information, we have retrieved memorabilia and photos that portray a century of medical advancements and hospital care. As the book was assembled, letters requesting additional information were sent out, scores of staff members, physicians, local residents, and community leaders were interviewed and department heads were asked to submit write-ups for their areas within the hospital. We also visited the Poor Handmaids of Jesus Christ archives at the University of Notre Dame library and talked with some of the Sisters at the Motherhouse in Donaldson, Indiana. Additional information was obtained from the Calumet Region Archives of Indiana University Northwest, the St. Mary Medical Center Auxiliary, the Hobart History Museum, the Gary Public Library, and the St. Mary Medical Center warehouse. Every attempt was made to reach as many people as possible. While accuracy is of utmost importance, we apologize for any errors found in this book.

Judging a Book by its Title

In the fall of 2009, Mary Fetsch, director of Marketing and Community Relations, distributed the notice below as an opportunity for hospital staff members to name the St. Mary Medical Center history book and win a complimentary copy of the book upon publication.

The title, selected by Hospital CEO and Administrator, Janice L. Ryba, is:

"St. Mary Medical Center – A Mission of Mercy, a Century of Care"

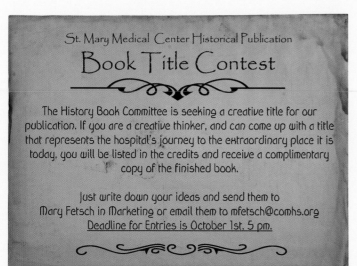

The title is a compilation of similar phrasing from four participants:

A Mission of Mercy
Bobbi Homola
St. Mary Medical Center: A Mission of Mercy

A Century of Care
Sister Mary O'Hara, OP
St. Mary Medical Center: A Century of Devoting Caring Service

Kris Shocaroff
St. Mary's Hospital: A Region Icon Celebrating a Century of Care

Donna Wasko
Celebrating a Century of Caring

BOOK TITLE CONTEST WINNERS
Shown (l-r): Sister Mary O'Hara, OP, Pastoral Care; Kris Shocaroff, Case Management; Bobbi Homola, Food and Nutrition; and Donna Wasko, Heart Ambulatory Clinic

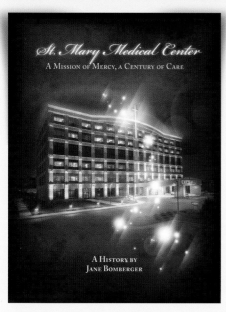

Congratulations to the winners!

Acknowledgements

Debra Jenkins has been an integral part of the book since the day the project began. She is one of the finest how-to, go-to people anyone could imagine. When Debra first began working at St. Mary Medical Center in Gary in 1985, one of her mentors said, "Just do your best," and to the admiration of all those who know her and work with her, Debra has lived up to that advice every day. It is with pride that she is named editor of this book.

Graphic Designer Joseph Gonzalez has worked tirelessly on both the design of this book and two previously published histories within Community Healthcare System called *The Community Hospital – An Impossible Dream* and *St. Catherine Hospital – A Family*. As a member of the marketing team for Community Foundation of Northwest Indiana, Inc. (CFNI), Joe's talent is evident and admired by all. Sincere thanks are extended to Joe for his time, energy, patience, and creativity with our third hospital history book.

Sister Mary Ellen Goeller, PHJC, has been an important resource for information at both the Motherhouse in Donaldson, Indiana, and at the St. Mary Medical Center campus. We appreciate her knowledge and willingness to locate resources, track down facts, and relay information to and from the good Sisters of Donaldson, Indiana.

Mary Jaroscak, longtime historian and auxiliary volunteer, has assisted us on behalf of the St. Mary Medical Center Auxiliary with care, assistance, and firsthand knowledge. Special to this research have been invaluable scrapbooks that members have made and preserved since the auxiliary's inception.

Dr. John T. Scully has provided much key information and recollections beginning in the early days of Gary. His correspondence and phone calls have contributed to both the factual and human elements of the book. We thank him for his time, suggestions, enthusiasm, and succinct recall.

Members of the St. Mary Medical Center history book committee have been very supportive with this project. In appreciation of their time and expertise, they are:

Dee Bedella – Coordinator, Sleep Lab/Community Liaison
Barbara Blejski – Director, Medical Staff
Mary Fetsch – Director, Marketing and Community Relations
Karen Gerke – Director, Surgical Services
Yvonne Hoff – Director, Human Resources
Debra Jenkins – Regional Assistant, Mission Effectiveness
Roz Jevtic – Marketing Assistant,
   Marketing and Community Relations

Janice L. Ryba – CEO and Administrator
Jim Wade – Manager, Plant Operations
Dianne Whiting – Executive Assistant to
   the Administrator and Board of Directors
Elizabeth Yee – Vice President, Clinical
   Ancillary Services

Thank you, Mary Fetsch and Roz Jevtic, for the hours and hours you spent taking hospital photos, unearthing historical data, recommending resources, and lending an extra hand.

We also extend our thanks to:

• Indiana University Northwest Archivist Stephen McShane, for his assistance with contributions from the university archives. His knowledge and interest in history are contagious!

• Archivist Wm. Kevin Cawley and his staff for their generous assistance at the University of Notre Dame Archives. The Poor Handmaids of Jesus Christ kept careful, type-written records pertaining to the history of Mercy Hospital and St. Mary Medical Center. Their entries and other historical materials are carefully stored in the university archives in South Bend, Indiana. We obtained much of that information from a campus visit and gratefully acknowledge their assistance throughout this publication.

• The *Post-Tribune* and *The Times* newspapers for permission to reprint photos, stories, and information from designated publications. We appreciate their cooperation with all three CFNI history books.

• Virginia Curtis and Elin Christianson of the Hobart Historical Society for generously sharing a lot of Hobart community information and hospital history materials.

• David Hess, Indiana Room Librarian of the Gary Public Library for his kindness, time, and generosity with valuable library resources.

WE ALSO EXTEND OUR THANKS TO (CONTINUED):

• LeeAnn Shea, Regional Manager of Transcription for Community Healthcare System, and Jil Cannon, Transcription Supervisor at St. Mary Medical Center, for their management of taped interviews from hospital staff members, civic leaders, and local citizens. LeeAnn, Jil, and their transcriptionists are to be commended for their cooperation, accuracy, and the incredible number of hours they contributed toward the book project. Transcriptionists include:

Joe Danton	Amy Mangold
Marcia Davidson	Lori O'Neal
Laura Eaton	Diane Reed
Diane Gilbert	Annette Sanderson
Stephanie Hicks	Julie Storey
Laura Hollister	Donna Swanson
Shannon Liesch	

• Mylinda Cane, Regional Director of Marketing and Corporate Communications for Community Healthcare System, for her care and support with the book project.

• Peg Schoon for her detailed, accurate indexing of this book.

• Proofreaders: **Mylinda Cane**, Regional Director, Marketing and Corporate Communications
    Linda Buzinec, St. Mary Medical Center Board member
    Mary Fetsch, Director, Marketing and Corporate Communications
    Lisa Field, St. Mary Medical Center Board member
    Tammie R. Finn-Jones, Vice President and Chief Nursing Officer
    Ramona Fissinger, Vice President, Health Data Support Services
    Janice L. Ryba, CEO and Administrator
    Kay Schenck, Community Volunteer
    Mary Sudicky, Vice President Finance and Chief Financial Officer
    Dianne Whiting, Executive Assistant to the Administrator and Board of Directors
    Elizabeth Yee, Vice President, Clinical Ancillary Services

Thank you all for your speed-reading, cogent comments, and assistance in meeting deadlines.

Additionally, we want to recognize the following people for their permission to use information in the book, their e-mails, editing and computer skills, photos, past records, recollections, and/or time-honored scrapbooks – all so important to this history:

Ismael "Izzy" Alicea	Jack Kamen, M.D.
John Almasy	Maryann Kerr
Connie Blaine	Debbie Krejci
Raymond Carmody, M.D.	Dorothy Lawver
John E. Carter, M.D.	Bruce Lovell
Pat DeMunck	Toni Mola
Julie Dowd	Alice Nedoff
Mary Ellen Donovan	Nancy Nye
Rosemarie Ehrhardt	Teresa Pedroza
Karen Gerke	Helen Petrovich
Carla Good	Evelyn Ryan
Sister Nora Hahn, PHJC	Vivian Fugate Springer
Susan Harmening	Jo Toigo
Betty Higgins	Shirley Makivich Urbanek
Nancy Higgins	Grace Veliz
Bobbi Homola	
Paul Jancarich	
Mary Jaroscak	

Finally, while all those who were interviewed for this book are too numerous to mention, we nevertheless thank you for graciously donating your time, knowledge, and resources. Your participation is invaluable.

Table of Contents

ST. MARY MEDICAL CENTER – A MISSION OF MERCY, A CENTURY OF CARE

ADVICE FROM ERMA BOMBECK:

"Never go to a doctor whose office plants have died."

"St. Mary Medical Center

has a long and distinguished

history and the future promises

to continue in that tradition."

William K. Schenck
PRESIDENT, BOARD OF DIRECTORS
ST. MARY MEDICAL CENTER

St. Mary Medical Center –
A Mission of Mercy, a Century of Care

A CHRONOLOGY 1906 - 2010

1906 ——————————————————————————————————————— 1922

On April 18, the city of Gary, Indiana was founded.

Gary's first hospital came into being. The hospital's origins date back to a converted wood-frame, four-unit apartment building at 624-34 Carolina Street donated by U.S. Steel's Gary Land Company to Mercy Hospital. The hospital was organized by a group of Franciscan sisters from Burlington, Iowa. The hospital opened on November 13.

Mercy Hospital accepted its first patient between November 20 and 26.

The Saint Mary Mercy Hospital School of Nursing was organized.

On May 21, the groundbreaking ceremony was held for the new Mercy Hospital at 540 Tyler Street – on land donated by the Illinois Steel Company.

In November, the Order of the Poor Handmaids of Jesus Christ assumed responsibility of the old hospital and the new hospital site under construction on the 500 block of Tyler Street.

During World War I, four graduates of St. Mary's Mercy School of Nursing gave their services to their country. (Source: Donaldson, Indiana Archives)

On December 9, the new St. Mary Mercy Hospital opened.

March 1, the Saint Mary Mercy Hospital Lay Advisory Board was founded.

The first Medical Advisory Board for the new Saint Mary Mercy Hospital was formed. Members were Theodore Templin, M.D.; George W. Gannon, M.D.; Charles W. Yarrington, M.D.; Harry W. Long, M.D.; Dr. Frank Michael, M.D.; Ira Miltimore, M.D.; and Ernst Schaible, M.D.

| 1906 | 1907 | 1912 | 1913 | 1914 | 1915 | 1922 |

1923 — 1955

Ground was broken for a new nurses' residence. In later years, with increased student registration, the attic was converted into living quarters, nurses' rooms were added above the porch, and an elevator was installed. It was erected in 1924.

On May 12, Hospital Day, Mercy Hospital's new south Wing opened to the public.

November 5, The National Catholic Hospital Association (of which Mercy Hospital was a member) held its national convention at St. Catherine's Hospital.

American College of Surgeons gave high rating to Lake County institutions – St. Catherine's Hospital (the largest with 360 beds) and Mercy Hospital among them.

On May 5, the approval of a $61,800 Federal Works Administration (FWA) grant to finance the bulk of a $113,000 projected addition to Mercy Hospital was announced by Congressman Ray J. Madden.

Medical staff accepted application for staff privileges by Benjamin F. Grant, M.D., the hospital's first black physician.

African-American students were admitted to St. Mary's Mercy School of Nursing.

A north wing addition provided 18 more beds, a third delivery room and facilities for the Pediatric Department.

In June, the Saint Mary Mercy Hospital Women's Auxiliary was organized by the Mercy Hospital Junior League.

A new laundry building was built.

The hospital's main entrance was remodeled, increasing space in the administrative office, medical library, record file room, central service department, newborn and premature nursery, the cafeteria and space for 16 more patient beds.

August 21, Miss Janice Coefield became the first African-American in Lake County to receive her diploma from the St. Mary's Mercy School of Nursing.

| 1923 | 1928 | 1930 | 1932 | 1944 | 1947 | 1952 | 1953 | 1955 |

St. Mary Mercy Hospital celebrated its golden jubilee – 50 years of healthcare in Gary.

A $139,000 grant from the Ford Foundation allowed for expansion of the Clinical Laboratory Department.

A $13,000 addition included a cellar for the Dietary Department and an underground passageway from the convent to the Sisters' dining room.

A $40,000 addition for the X-ray Department included a radiographic room, one deep therapy room, and lavatory facilities.

A $60,000 heating conversion changed the system from oil to gas.

August 20 marked the commemoration of the 50 years of service of the Poor Handmaids of Jesus Christ in Gary. (CHJC, University of Notre Dame Archives).

The Inhalation Therapy Department, initiated by Jack M. Kamen, M.D., was one of 10 such departments in the country with a full-time physician director. It was a "first" for Gary and the Calumet Region in fighting cardiac and thoracic diseases.

In August, construction began on a new seven-bed Intensive Care Unit and modernization for the north U.S. Steel section of the hospital's first floor.

In February, the $43,000 Intensive Care Unit opened.

In April, the Gary Joint Hospital Fund initiated a $4 million fund raising campaign to be divided between St. Mary Mercy and Methodist hospitals. The campaign involved matching funds from U.S. Steel.

Paul C. Bellendorf became the first lay chief executive officer of Mercy Hospital, succeeding Sister Cornelia Leible, PHJC, who had served in that role for nearly 16 years.

1956   **1958**   **1959**   **1962**   **1963**   **1964**   **1965**   **1967**

1968

1972

In June, to make way for the new hospital building, demolition began on the chapel, existing buildings, and houses on Fillmore Street.

On August 15, a groundbreaking ceremony was held for the new $6.5 million dollar hospital expansion.

In August, St. Mary Medical Center's School of Nursing held graduation for its last class.

In January, renovation began on the new Radiology Department.

In February, the $500,000 Radiology Department was completed.

Mercy Hospital's heliport was a large red medical cross symbol on the playground/parking lot of Holy Angels School.

In September, construction began on a new six-bed Coronary Care Unit on the Tyler Street side of First Floor North.

On December 16, an open house was held for the newly relocated and expanded Materials Management Department.

On April 2 and 3, an open house was held for the new $300,000 Coronary Care Unit.

In August, an Employee Fund Drive was launched and topped $100,000 in donations for St. Mary Mercy Hospital Southeast in Hobart, Indiana.

On November 28, a groundbreaking ceremony was held for the new St. Mary Mercy Hospital Southeast in Hobart.

On December 27, patients were admitted to the newly completed third floor wing of the new Gary hospital expansion.

A group of physicians formed a corporation and operated the Emergency Room under a contract at St. Mary Mercy Hospital.

In February, the Laboratory Department was the first to move into the new hospital wing.

On February 22, the new Dietary Department opened.

1968   1969   1970   1971   1972

On April 15, 1973, the new satellite hospital, St. Mary Medical Center Southeast, opened in Hobart.

1972 ———————————————— 1974

On March 6, the new 4West Medical-Surgical patient floor was activated.

On April 9, the new chapel was dedicated and the first Mass was celebrated there.

On May 21, the dedication and open house ceremonies were held for the new hospital west wing.

On July 21, the new surgical suite on the main floor of the new wing was activated and the 3East patient floor opened.

On August 23, the first open heart surgery in a Gary hospital was performed in the new Open Heart Surgery Suite.

April 15, the new satellite hospital, St. Mary Medical Center Southeast, opened in Hobart.

On April 24, the first patient was admitted to the new St. Mary Mercy Hospital Southeast.

In June, Paul R. Kaiser became the new hospital administrator.

Mary Gulyassy was appointed associate administrator of the Hobart facility.

In March, the Gary hospital received permission from the Federal Aviation Association to operate the first area heliport for the emergency evacuation of patients.

On June 1, the Gary hospital's Obstetrical Department and nursery closed.

In August, the Hobart hospital became the official Eye Collection Center for the Indiana Lions Eye Bank, Inc.

In August, the new six-bed Cardiovascular Post-operative Nursing Unit opened.

St. Mary Mercy Hospital's name was legally changed to St. Mary Medical Center and the corporate, legal name of the two hospital sites officially became St. Mary Medical Center of Gary-Hobart, Inc.

In December, remodeling of the Pediatric Department in Gary was completed.

1972   1973   1974

> "Every time I visited St. Mary's in Gary or in Hobart I always felt so welcomed. Everyone went out of their way to make sure you had whatever you needed."
>
> *Sister Annemarie Kampwerth*, PHJC
> FORMER PROVINCIAL

1975 —————————————————————————————— 1977

In April, the new heart catheterization room opened at the Gary hospital.

In May, renovation began at St. Mary Medical Center – Gary on the Orthopedic Unit, 2South.

On December 12, the new Stromberg–Carlson Communications System was installed at the Gary hospital.

In June, the new Electroencephalographs (EEG) Department opened in Gary.

In July, the new $65,000 12-bed Intermediate Care Unit opened.

In July, a closed circuit television system was installed at the Gary location.

In November, the Gary warehouse on Fifth and Tyler Street was razed and turned into a 45-car parking lot.

In March, the name of the in-house hospital publication was changed from *Acts of Mercy* to *Acts and Facts*. (Note: "The focus initially became internal communication. There were two newsletters. They both came out once a month but they were... staggered. *Acts and Facts* was taken outside, off-set printed, and distributed to employees via the cafeteria. The other one, also distributed in the cafeteria, was simply typewritten and included departmental reporters from the nursing floor, respiratory therapy, X-ray, etc. Each area contributed and it was kind of a gossip column.") Mike Adler, former Director of Public Relations

In May, the Alcoholism Treatment Program, with housing for 22 patients, opened on the 3North wing at the Gary hospital.

In May, the $6.4 million Hobart hospital expansion was announced and would include a Medical Arts Building and ancillary services.

In August, the Gary Community Mental Health Center began operating from the 3South wing of the Gary hospital.

In August, the Pain Center was begun at the Gary hospital by Jack M. Kamen, M.D., and was one of four such clinics in Indiana.

In August, St. Mary Medical Center Gary-Hobart became the first area hospitals to go on a computerized system to register patients. (Cathode Ray Tube, CRT)

In August, a major $260,000 renovation of the laundry facilities at both Gary and Hobart hospitals was completed.

1975   1976   1977

> *"It is not as important to do great things in life as it is to do small things with great love."* ~ Mother Teresa

1978

A new group of physicians was appointed to staff the Emergency Room of the two hospitals. (CHJC, University of Notre Dame Archives)

On April 16, Mother Mary Katherine Kasper, PHJC, foundress of the Poor Handmaids of Jesus Christ, was beatified by Pope Paul VI in Rome.

In May, the St. Mary Medical Center Auxiliary celebrated its 25th Anniversary.

On May 23, a newly renovated Intensive Care Unit, located on the fourth floor of the Gary hospital.

Approval was secured for the Hobart expansion project and ground was broken in September over the objections of the Office of Civil Rights. (CHJC, University of Notre Dame Archives)

On November 27, the Intermediate Care Unit for treatment of post-critical care patients opened in Gary on 4West with 12 beds.

1979

On March 7, the newly refurbished cafeteria serving area opened at the St. Mary Medical Center – Gary.

On March 12, newly expanded departments of Radiology and Emergency opened as part of the first phase of St. Mary Medical Center's $6.8 million construction project in Hobart.

1980

In January, Indiana's first Quality Assurance Program was inaugurated.

In February, the St. Mary Medical Center Auxiliary donated $180,400.

In March, Mother General Fabiola, PHJC, of Germany, visited St. Mary Medical Center as part of a world tour.

In May, a Perfect Attendance Program was announced at both hospitals.

In June, a Hewlett Packard Care Computer was installed at both hospitals – a first in Northwest Indiana.

In September, "Rooming In" began for mothers and newborns in the OB Department in Hobart.

In December, Nuclear Cardiography began within nuclear medicine.

"The patients of St. Mary Medical Center and Community Healthcare System will be well served by these values for another 100 years!"

John Gorski
Chief Operating Officer
Community Healthcare System

1981

In January, the Employee of the Year Program began with Elizabeth Brown.

In February, the St. Mary Medical Center Auxiliary donated $185, 000.

In April, "Huggy Bear," a child-sized teddy bear, joined the hospital as a guide for pediatric tours.

In June, Mary Gulyassy became interim associate administrator.

On June 14, the mobile CT Scanner was dedicated and service began to patients at both hospitals.

On July 4, the Intensive Care Unit closed at St. Mary Medical Center – Gary.

In August, the Ambulatory Care Center opened.

In December, a physician newsletter, *The Chart*, was published.

1982

In February, the St. Mary Medical Center Auxiliary donated $190,000.

In March, Administrator John Dandridge, Jr., began at St. Mary Medical Center Gary and Hobart.

In May, the St. Mary Medical Center CT Scanner won honorable mention in the graphic design competition sponsored by *Fleet Owner Magazine*.

In August, Cardiac Rehabilitation Phase II opened at the hospital's Gary site.

In November, St. Mary Medical Center – Gary observed 75 Years of medical care and community service.

In November, St. Mary Medical Center - Gary installed the Auto-Microbic System, a computer used in space flights to monitor the health of astronauts.

In December, the St. Mary Medical Center Radiology Department in Gary was re-dedicated to Sister Willibalda Heidt, PHJC, a pioneer in radiologic technology.

1983

In April, St. Mary Medical Center - Hobart, celebrated its 10th anniversary.

In October, the hospital opened a new warehouse.

In January, the Ambulatory Care Center was dedicated as the Turner-Grutka Ambulatory Care Center.

In February, the auxiliary set a record with a $240,000 donation to St. Mary Medical Center.

The Obstetrics Department at the Hobart campus closed.

In August/September, St. Mary Medical Center was chosen for Wells Fargo gamefields promotion by the National Fitness campaign.

In November, the Collins DS/560 Pulmonary Function machines were installed in Hobart, representing state-of-the-art testing for pulmonary patients.

In February, the Diagnostic Outpatient Center opened on the Hobart campus housing the first Magnetic Resonance Imager (MRI) in the area.

St. Mary Medical Center Hobart opened the Digestive Disorders Unit.

In October, St. Mary Medical Center Gary and Hobart introduced the Employee Assistance Program (EAP) to help individuals cope with their problems.

St. Mary Medical Center Auxiliary donated a transport bus to the hospital.

On April 16, St. Mary Medical Center - Hobart opened a new Pediatric Department.

The sponsors of St. Catherine Hospital and St. Mary Medical Center Gary and Hobart consolidated their boards to form Lakeshore Health System. John R. Birdzell was named chief executive officer for the three hospitals.

In February, St. Mary Medical Center and St. Catherine Hospital open a wellness center known as WellSource in Southlake Mall.

On September 1, an emergency triple coronary bypass, the first of its kind at the Cardiac Catheterization Laboratory in Hobart, was performed on a 70-year-old man, one month ahead of its scheduled opening.

On October 25, the Hobart hospital opened a new state-of-the-art Cardiac Catherization Laboratory.

St. Mary Medical Center Hobart opened a new Rehabilitative Therapy Suite.

1984

1985

1986

1987

"A dominant aspect of our mission is to continue to grow and mutually meet the needs of our community."

Janice L. Ryba
CEO AND ADMINISTRATOR
ST. MARY MEDICAL CENTER

On February 14, Gary hospital opened the first phase of the new Emergency Center that gave access from Fifth Avenue.

In June, lithotripsy came to Lakeshore hospitals.

Ancilla Systems, Inc. announced the appointment of Thomas L. Gleason as chairman of the board of directors for Lakeshore Health System.

In August, a helipad was added at St. Mary in Hobart through donations from the Fraternal Order of Police Lodge 121, Veterans of Foreign Wars Post 5365, and Boyd Construction Company.

In January, St. Mary Medical Center in Hobart opened The Birthing Suites.

The Podiatric Residency Program was established at St. Mary Medical Center.

Gary's first Magnetic Resonance Imaging (MRI) services were introduced.

March 19, the hospitals of Lakeshore Health System introduced The Urology Center of Northwest Indiana.

Lifeline (an emergency response system) came to St. Mary Medical Center.

St. Mary Medical Center in Gary opened the new state-of-the-art Cardiac Rehabilitation Center.

On March 21, St. Mary Medical Center Hobart opened the Health & Rehabilitation Spectrum.

On August 17, St. Mary Medical Center in Hobart opened its new Chest Pain Emergency Center.

St. Mary Medical Center in Hobart performed the first thoracoscopy in Northwest Indiana on a 22-year-old male.

In November, the new Outpatient Service Center at St. Mary Medical Center in Hobart was unveiled.

On November 19, St. Mary Medical Center Gary and Hobart became smoke-free within the hospitals.

1988   1989   1990   1991   1992

St. Mary Medical Center in Hobart was the first hospital in the area to offer two new technologies to help in the fight against cancer – Monoclonal antibody scanning and Matastron.

Beth Kaminski was named chief executive officer of St. Mary Medical Center.

On March 6, Ancilla Systems Incorporated and its affiliate, Lakeshore Health System, announced their intention to sell St. Mary Medical Center in Gary.

On March 19, The Coalition on Healthcare in Gary, a group of Gary doctors, ministers and community leaders, brought federal suit against St. Mary Medical Center, Ancilla Systems Incorporated, and Lakeshore Health System alleging that the hospital owners violated civil rights assurances they made to provide equal facilities and services at the Hobart and Gary hospitals.

On May 24, Ancilla Systems Incorporated, Lakeshore Health System and Summit Medical Management, Inc. announced the signing of a letter of intent for Summit to buy St. Mary Medical Center, Gary, and rename it Northwest Family Center.

In July, St. Mary introduced the Picker International Prism 3000XP triple-head nuclear medicine imaging camera.

On February 22, 16 months after Summit purchased St. Mary Medical Center in Gary, they informed employees that owners would opt to either sell the hospital – possibly to a physician group – convert it into a long-term acute care facility, or close it within 60 to 90 days.

The St. Mary Medical Center Foundation was created as a funding vehicle for the hospital.

Milt Triana was named chief executive officer of St. Mary Medical Center.

St. Mary Medical Center installed Payrollmation to modernize the payroll process, improve accuracy, and record-keeping.

On June 23, St. Mary added direct deposit to its array of employee benefits.

The Garden Café, operated by St. Mary Medical Center Auxiliary, opened.

1993

1994

1995

"In medicine, you are able to get people back to sort of a state of normalcy.

Once we have done the surgery or treatment and they're pretty much pain free, they are very relieved and grateful. That is probably the best part about it all - when they say they have their life back."

Scott A. Andrews, M.D.
ORTHOPEDIC SURGEON
MEDICAL STAFF PRESIDENT, 2008-2010

In January, St. Mary Medical Center opened The Collective Image.

In January, Ancilla Home Health of St. Mary Medical Center was introduced.

St. Mary Medical Center opened an Electrophysiology (EP) department.

In December, St. Mary Medical Center opened a new Joint Replacement Center.

St. Mary Medical Center opened The Heart-Vascular Center of Portage.

In October, St. Mary Medical Center became one of the first hospitals in Northwest Indiana to offer Coronary Intravascular Ultrasound (IVUS).

On November 3, a groundbreaking ceremony was held for the Linden House of St. Mary Medical Center.

St. Mary Medical Center celebrated 25 years of growth and success with medical care and community service.

The Physician Office Building was constructed primarily to house physician offices.

In March, the Transitional Care Unit (TCU) was established to accommodate patients requiring a longer length of stay.

On January 1, St. Mary Medical Center became the sponsor hospital to an Emergency Medical Service housed at the Lakes of the Four Seasons (LOFS) Fire Department.

St. Mary Medical Center sold 1/3 acre of land to ABC Academy for the development of a child daycare center.

In September, St. Mary Medical Center sold 3.96 acres of land to Hobart Retirement, LLC, for construction of an independent living retirement facility known as Brentwood Assisted Living.

In October, St. Mary Medical Center unveiled its new helipad.

St. Mary Medical Center expanded with a new Merrillville Family Health Center.

1996   1997   1998   1999

2000

Through the Well City USA project, Hobart, Indiana was awarded Well City status.

In the spring, *Post-Tribune* readers voted St. Mary Medical Center the "Best Hospital in Northwest Indiana" as part of the newspaper's first "Neighbor's Choice" awards for local businesses.

On June 1, Lake Park Surgicare, LLC, opened as a joint venture of St. Anthony Medical Center, St. Mary Medical Center and approximately 20 surgeons.

St. Mary Medical Center's Obstetrics Department began offering midwife services.

St. Mary Medical Center introduced new approaches to emergency care by implementing parallel registration, a fast-track system, on-site test results, a computerized tracking system, and a dedicated children's area.

2001

St. Mary Medical Center offered Baby Net on its website.

St. Mary Medical Center introduced a new feature to its web site – "Ask a Doc" – to provide answers to specific healthcare questions and concerns.

On April 1, St. Mary Medical Center opened the Winfield Family Health Center.

The St. Mary Medical Center Auxiliary donated a new hydrotherapy tub in the Labor and Delivery ward.

St. Mary Medical Center dedicated the Intensive Care Unit (ICU) to John T. Scully, M.D.

On October 17, the Community Foundation, Inc. (CFI), parent company of The Community Hospital, announced the acquisition of two Northwest Indiana hospitals operated by Ancilla Systems Incorporated. The foundation name was later changed to Community Foundation of Northwest Indiana, Inc. (CFNI). Under the banner of Community Healthcare System, The Community Hospital, St. Catherine Hospital, and St. Mary Medical Center were integrated to offer a network of collective, quality medical services.

In December, Peter Mavrelis, M.D., and John Mirro, M.D., performed the first gastric outlet obstruction.

2002

St. Mary Medical Center became the first hospital in Lake County to utilize the TriVex surgery performed by Cardiovascular Surgeon, Benjamin Tang, M.D.

St. Mary added a new MRI to the Portage Outpatient Health Center.

In the spring, St. Mary Medical Center issued its last *Neighborly Care* publication. It was replaced with a new quarterly publication, *Vim & Vigor Magazine*.

Community Foundation of Northwest Indiana, Inc. sought planning approval to begin construction for a multi-million dollar, six-story, New Patient Tower to be built at St. Mary Medical Center in Hobart.

On March 3, The Collective Image closed.

The newly-named Center for Imaging and Radiation Oncology (CIRO) was acquired to provide MRI testing and radiation oncology.

In September, the New Patient Tower was completed.

St. Mary Medical Center received national quality recognition from HealthGrades®, the nation's leading independent rating agencies for hospital quality. The prestigious honor was repeated in 2006, 2007 and 2008.

The Family Birthing Center underwent a $1.5 million renovation.

In July, St. Mary Medical Center Laboratory incorporated the Total Laboratory Automation (TLA) system.

Gastroenterologists at St. Mary Medical Center were the only specialists in Northwest Indiana to offer a new procedure called esophagoscopy for patients suffering from chronic Gastro-Esophageal Reflux Disease (GERD).

The Lung Center at St. Mary Medical Center was sanctioned by the American Lung Association of Indiana.

On October 10, St. Mary Medical Center opened the Women's Diagnostic Center.

St. Mary Medical Center remodeled and opened 3East as a Medical/Surgical Unit.

St. Mary Medical Center opened its Same Day Surgery/Endoscopy Unit on 2East.

St. Mary Medical Center offered carotid artery stenting.

St. Mary introduced new technology called CartoMerge™ Image Integration Module to treat patients for electrical malfunctions of the heart.

St. Mary Medical Center began offering full-field digital mammography.

In June, the Podiatric Residency Program ended at St. Mary Medical Center.

On August 2, St. Mary Medical Center opened the new Sleep Diagnostics facility.

2003

2003

2004

2005

2006

2007

2007

2007

St. Mary Medical Center was the only hospital in Northwest Indiana that provided a new hip resurfacing procedure using the ReCap® Femoral Resurfacing System offered by Dr. Michael Leland, an orthopedic surgeon.

St. Mary Medical Center Laboratory, together with the laboratories from St. Catherine Hospital and Community Hospital, received its first College of American Pathologists (CAP) System Laboratory accreditation.

St. Mary Medical Center offered remote defibrillator monitoring systems through the Electrophysiology (EP) Lab.

Janice L. Ryba was named CEO and administrator of St. Mary Medical Center.

For its Emergency Department and Cardiac Catheterization Lab that remained below the national benchmark set at 90 minutes, St. Mary Medical Center was selected as a finalist in the 2007 BKD Indiana Excellence Awards competition.

2008

St. Mary Medical Center was featured in the October edition of *Advance for Nurses* as a "top hospital" in the magazine's second annual Readers' Choice survey for the Greater Chicago and metropolitan areas of Wisconsin and Indiana.

St. Mary Medical Center was one of only four hospitals in the United States selected to implement CartoSound, a system that allows for more advanced, precise mapping of arrhythmias by combining ultrasound with CT scan images.

On November 19, St. Mary Medical Center was a recognized finalist at the 2008 BKD Indiana Excellence Awards in Indianapolis for their groundbreaking program in Same-Day Mammography Results.

St. Mary Medical Center was awarded two Press Ganey Compass Awards for patient satisfaction improvements in the areas of Ambulatory Surgery and Outpatient Services.

The Society of Innovators of Northwest Indiana recognized Community Healthcare System hospitals as part of its "Class of Innovators" in providing same-day results for mammogram screenings and breast biopsies. Community Hospital in Munster, St. Catherine Hospital in East Chicago and St. Mary Medical Center in Hobart were selected as the Chanute Prize recipients for team innovation.

St. Mary Medical Center introduced a new model of care through the addition of The Joint Academy on the hospital's Orthopedic Unit.

Community Hospital and St. Mary Medical Center were among a small number of hospitals in the country to use CARTOSOUND™ imaging technology.

Gastroenterologists on staff at St. Mary Medical Center were among the first in Indiana to use the SpyGlass Direct Visualization System.

The three hospitals of the Community Healthcare System were the first in Northwest Indiana to introduce VeinViewer, a revolutionary technology making it easier to detect veins for drawing blood and inserting IVs.

A new spinal procedure called eXtreme Lateral Interbody Fusion (XLIF®) came to St. Mary Medical Center.

St. Mary Medical Center began using a new cool blue laser called CLiRpath® to eliminate blockages in arteries of the leg.

"St. Mary Medical Center is the largest employer in Hobart and the major provider of healthcare but that just touches the surface. St. Mary's is a 'Great Neighbor'!"

Mike Adams
EXECUTIVE DIRECTOR, HOBART CHAMBER OF COMMERCE

A Mission of Mercy, a Century of Care
A CHRONOLOGY 1906 - 2010

2009 ———————————————————————————————————— 2010

On January 29, St. Mary Medical Center was honored as the 2008 Large Business of the Year by the Hobart Chamber of Commerce.

Pictured {LEFT TO RIGHT}:
Hobart Chamber of Commerce Executive Director Mike Adams;
St. Mary Medical Center CEO and Administrator Janice L. Ryba;
and U.S. Representative Pete Visclosky, D-Merrillville

In January, St. Mary Medical Center unveiled its new $3 million technologically-advanced Cardiac Catheterization Laboratory.

On January 29, St. Mary Medical Center was honored as the 2008 Large Business of the Year by the Hobart Chamber of Commerce.

On March 26, St. Mary Medical Center opened its Special Imaging Building.

In May, St. Mary Medical Center opened its new Wound/Ostomy/Continence Center.

A new therapy called VitalStim®, became available at St. Mary Medical Center.

St. Mary Medical Center was the first hospital in Northwest Indiana to begin using the RF Surgical Detection System™ for tracking and locating surgical sponges.

In the fall, St. Mary Medical Center became the sponsoring hospital for the Hobart Fire Department Emergency Medical Services (EMS) division.

On October 28, St. Mary Medical Center held a groundbreaking on a new $12.5 million Emergency Department expansion and renovation.

Community Healthcare System received Thomson Reuter's national recognition for hospital quality and efficiency as one of the nation's top performing health systems.

Surgeons at St. Mary Medical Center performed the first operations using a new procedure for treatment of gastroesophageal reflux disease (GERD).

In January, St. Mary began offering outpatient surgical services at the new Outpatient Surgery at Lake Park facility – formerly Lake Park Surgicare, LLC.

2008   2009   2010

Mercy Hospital and St. Mary Medical Center
ROSTER OF ADMINISTRATORS

St. Mary Medical Center Administrators | Mercy Hospital in Gary

Sister Lydia Kroeger, PHJC	1913-1915
Sister Alphonsina Still, PHJC	1915-1929
Sister Engelberta Peters, PHJC	1929-1933
Sister Flavia Schmitz, PHJC	1933-1939
Sister Tharsilla Kunigunda, PHJC	1939-1945
Sister Alphonsina Still, PHJC	1945-1951

Sister M. Milburg, PHJC
1951-1955

Mother Mary Therese Kellerman, PHJC
1955-1961

Sister Cornelia Leible, PHJC
1961-1967

Paul C. Bellendorf
1967-1973

Paul R. Kaiser
1973 – 1981
(GARY AND HOBART)

Mary Gulyassy, 1981
Interim Associate Administrator
(GARY AND HOBART)

John Dandridge, Jr.
1982-1986
(GARY AND HOBART)

John Birdzell
1986-1993
(GARY AND HOBART)

Beth Kaminski
1993-1995

Milton Triana
1995-2007

Janice L. Ryba
2007 – PRESENT

A Message
from
JANICE L. RYBA
CHIEF EXECUTIVE OFFICER AND ADMINISTRATOR
ST. MARY MEDICAL CENTER

IT HAS BEEN A PRIVILEGE FOR ME TO SERVE AS ADMINISTRATOR OF ST. MARY MEDICAL CENTER FOR NEARLY THREE YEARS.

It is especially gratifying to be a part of this organization at a time when we celebrate more than 100 years of the hospital's commitment and service to Northwest Indiana and the city of Hobart.

St. Mary Medical Center has a proud history of clinical excellence, community service, and compassionate patient care. These are the common threads that have guided our efforts over our long and distinguished history.

One might characterize us as being a "friendly community" hospital. We were founded in 1907 to provide health care services to thousands of immigrants who flocked here to work in the new steel mills and refineries of the region. Northwest Indiana became a proud "melting pot" of people with different religious and racial backgrounds, all of whom wanted to work, raise families, and establish homes in the Calumet Area.

Over the years, business and industries have come and gone, ethnic balances have shifted, the economy of the area has prospered at times and suffered at other times. Through all this change, however, St. Mary Medical Center has grown and expanded its reach. In 1973, after 66 years of service in the Gary community, land was purchased from Bess M. Hayward at a fraction of the cost and allowed the organization to expand to the growing communities to the south and east – caring for patients, without regard for their social status, religion, ethnicity, or ability to pay.

On behalf of the Sisters, medical staff, board members, volunteers, and employees who carry on the mission inherited from our predecessors, we express pride in knowing we have contributed, in some small measure, to the remarkable list of achievements that highlight St. Mary Medical Center's rich and distinguished history.

We celebrate a century of caring at St. Mary Medical Center, in anticipation of even greater achievements and innovation in the future under the sponsorship and commitment to excellence of Community Healthcare System.

IT'S BEEN *Said* IN 2009...

"When you talk about a work/life balance and you work at a facility like St. Mary, the spirit of your work is never really separated from your life."

Janice L. Ryba
CEO AND ADMINISTRATOR
ST. MARY MEDICAL CENTER

About
JANICE L. RYBA
CHIEF EXECUTIVE OFFICER AND ADMINISTRATOR
ST. MARY MEDICAL CENTER

With more than 28 years of healthcare experience, Janice L. Ryba, JD, MJ, MHA, was originally employed by Community Hospital in February 1984 as a senior technologist in the Hematology Department of Laboratory Services. Since then, continuing to "advance from within," she has held various management and leadership positions during a time of significant growth at Community Hospital.

From 2001 – 2007, Janice served as vice president for Community Healthcare System, the three-hospital conglomerate comprised of Community Hospital in Munster, St. Catherine Hospital in East Chicago, and St. Mary Medical Center in Hobart. Her responsibilities have included broad clinical and support services for Rehabilitation Services, Neurodiagnostics, Acute Rehabilitation Centers, Quality/Risk Management, and Medical Staff Services for the three healthcare facilities. Janice's role in Quality/Risk Management helped shape the foundation for standards and national distinctions for quality healthcare.

In 2007, Janice was appointed CEO and administrator of St. Mary Medical Center, overseeing the 190-bed not-for-profit hospital in Hobart, Indiana. Janice has served on several local organizations including the Quality of Life Council and participates as a member of the American College of Healthcare Executives (ACHE), the American Health Lawyers Association (AHLA), and the Indiana Hospital Association (IHA).

She holds a Juris Doctor from John Marshall Law School in Chicago, a Master of Jurisprudence in Health Law from Loyola University, as well as a Master of Health Administration from Governors State University. Janice's background, experience and focus no doubt allow her to take St. Mary Medical Center and its people into the next century of care.

A native of Chicago, Illinois, Janice resides in Munster, Indiana with her husband, Randy.

Dianne Whiting, Executive Assistant to the Administrator (seated) and Janice L. Ryba, St. Mary Medical Center CEO and Administrator.

IT'S BEEN *Said* IN 2009...

"When Janice Ryba was promoted in August 2007 to CEO and administrator of St. Mary Medical Center, it was a profound privilege to be asked to join her as her executive assistant. A ten-year relationship with someone – working side by side day after day – breeds an understanding of Janice as a wonderful mentor, boss and friend.

"In the two short years since arriving at St. Mary Medical Center, Janice completed the $4.5 million CT/MRI Imaging Building and will next complete a $12.5 million Emergency Department Renovation/Expansion project.

"Intelligent and so knowledgeable in expansive healthcare issues, Janice is well respected and admired not only by our hospital leadership and staff members, but also by physicians as well. They know her as a competent leader and a go-getter and I assist her and observe with pride as she digs into getting things done – no matter what the project or issue may be. Working in combination with dedicated St. Mary personnel, Janice can accomplish anything."

Dianne Whiting
EXECUTIVE ASSISTANT TO THE ADMINISTRATOR AND BOARD OF DIRECTORS
ST. MARY MEDICAL CENTER
(BEGAN IN 2000 AT COMMUNITY HOSPITAL)

CEO *on the* GO

A Physician Chili Cook-Off was held in January 2009 in the Waterfall Café. Physicians entered their favorite chili recipes which were judged on the balance of spice, consistency, overall taste, and appearance. The winner – John Dolatowski, M.D. – was selected by (l-r) judges Ryan Smith, chef; Stephen Karol, M.D.; Janice L. Ryba, CEO and administrator; and Sister Mary Ellen Goeller, PHJC, regional director of Mission Integration. Mark Simaga, M.D., was awarded second place.

Shown in 2007 in support of the Juvenile Diabetes Research Foundation fund-raising efforts are (l-r) Director of Medical Records Jo Toigo who was also a JDRF chicken sale event organizer; Railcats Coach Joe "Moose" Gates; CEO and Administrator Janice L. Ryba; and CFNI Senior Vice-President/Chief Administration Officer John Mybeck who served as JDRF Northwest Indiana Walk Chairman.

A Cobbler Bake-off Contest was held in October 2009. Employees entered their favorite cobblers to the judges who were (l-r): Janice L. Ryba, CEO and administrator; Ryan Smith, chef; and Carol Ochwat, contract specialist.

This was an event held in September 2009 where St. Mary Medical Center participated in the Breast Cancer Tea given by the Pink Ribbon Society. Shown (l-r) are Bharat Barai, M.D.; Jonathan Patterson, D.O.; Jerome March, M.D.; and Janice L. Ryba, CEO and administrator. The Pink Ribbon Society was established in 2003 and is dedicated to supporting men and women in the Lake, Porter, Jasper and Newton counties in Northwest Indiana whose lives have been touched by breast cancer.

With April as Donate Life Month, this photo was taken in 2009 in recognition of Organ Tissue Donations. Shown here (l-r) are Alice Jenkins; Mike Henderson; Janice L. Ryba, CEO and administrator; Ed Jagiela; and Sister Mary O'Hara, OP.

"We will probably expand into Porter County sooner or later. I think you'll see that the system in Lake County is going to continue to grow. We will be the pacesetter for what is to come, I'm sure. Our main concern is bringing the finest healthcare available to the people who live in our service area."

– DONALD S. POWERS

Donald S. Powers
PRESIDENT *and* CEO
COMMUNITY FOUNDATION OF NORTHWEST INDIANA, INC.

Donald S. Powers, as president and CEO of Community Foundation of Northwest Indiana, Inc., oversees the not-for-profit organization that provides leadership and resources for the enhancement of health and the quality of life in Northwest Indiana.

Mr. Powers is one of the original directors and president of Community Foundation, Inc., the organization that became known as Community Foundation of Northwest Indiana, Inc., in 2001. Before either foundation was formed, he served as secretary and subsequently as president of The Community Hospital board of directors.

Among the businesses of Community Foundation of Northwest Indiana, Inc., are three not-for-profit hospitals in Northwest Indiana – The Community Hospital in Munster, St. Catherine Hospital in East Chicago and St. Mary Medical Center in Hobart – all of which merged in the fall of 2001 to become Community Healthcare System.

At Community Hospital's inception, Mr. Powers – already a local real estate developer – was the managing partner of a land development trust that donated the largest corporate gift to Community Hospital's building campaign – five acres of the needed 15-acre parcel and approximately $20,000 in cash to improve the construction site where Community Hospital now stands. He personally paid the hospital's insurance premiums during its lean years. "I was so involved in trying to keep it financially afloat that I didn't worry too

much about the future – the present was very demanding," Mr. Powers would later note.

The success of Community Hospital has fueled the development of a multi-million dollar medical corridor in Northwest Indiana that contains many of the hospital's ventures, including medical office buildings and a medically-based fitness center. Mr. Powers oversaw the reinvestment of over $300 million in Community Hospital to add new medical technology and services that respond to the community's need for premier health care close to home.

Under the direction of Mr. Powers, the Munster Medical Research Foundation founded the Community Cancer Research Foundation, Inc., a not-for-profit organization dedicated to improving the quality of life for cancer patients in the community with both research and resources available to residents of Northwest Indiana and beyond. The Foundation also includes the Cancer Resource Centre where cancer patients and their loved ones can receive free support and educational services.

Through Mr. Powers' leadership, Community Foundation of Northwest Indiana, Inc., has supported numerous local charities and economic development and has funded medical scholarships for area universities. The organization helped provide a home for the visual and performing arts and constructed an 11-acre memorial park honoring the men and women who serve our country.

"The people of St. Mary Medical Center – the administration, the staff, physicians, volunteers and patients – have not stopped pushing us to reach even higher."

– JOHN GORSKI

John Gorski
CHIEF OPERATING OFFICER
COMMUNITY HEALTHCARE SYSTEM

The history of St. Mary Medical Center has been shaped by much change, spanning more than 100 years from the beginning of the first hospital in Gary to the secondary hospital site in Hobart. This book accounts for the advances in medical care St. Mary helped to bring to area patients, as well as the many challenges it has faced providing care to all who have come through its doors.

When we came together in 2001 as one healthcare system – Community Hospital in Munster; St. Catherine Hospital in East Chicago; and St. Mary Medical Center in Hobart – change was indeed our first order of business. It wasn't an easy time, blending together the distinct cultures of three hospitals, accessing each other's strengths, and evaluating what improvements could be made.

There were many investments needed at St. Mary, including the daunting task of rebuilding all of its patient floors. The hospital had been promised many things over the years, but much had not materialized. As a result, there was a fair amount of skepticism about what changes might come from the formation of the new healthcare system.

The New Patient Tower – an investment of more than $40 million – was the initial down payment on the promise Community Healthcare System made to strengthen healthcare in Northwest Indiana. The people of St. Mary Medical Center – the administration, the staff, physicians, volunteers and patients – have not stopped pushing us to reach even higher.

Perhaps most remarkable about the story of St. Mary Medical Center is what hasn't changed. A legacy of devotion, integrity and compassion lives on through a new generation of leaders, hospital staff and physicians. The patients of St. Mary Medical Center and Community Healthcare System will be well served by these values for another 100 years!

Community Healthcare System

Caring *as* one

October 17, 2001

To our Healthcare Family:

Today marks the beginning of a new relationship between Community Hospital , St. Catherine Hospital and St. Mary Medical Center. These three hospitals will form a new, multi-site healthcare system in Northwest Indiana. With your help, *Community Healthcare System*, will be recognized as one of the leading quality providers in the region.

The goal of integrating these three hospitals under one system is to improve the quality of care, reduce healthcare costs, secure a larger market and provide for the continued availability of capital for replacement and growth. We have found through our many months of careful planning, there is a lot to gain by cooperating, rather than competing and duplicating efforts.

As with any new beginning, there are many questions and issues to resolve. To some of these, we know the answers. For others, we will turn to our employees, physicians, patients and the community to help us determine new directions for this health system. We welcome your input and questions...

We look forward to working with all of our employees to create a better, stronger community-based healthcare system. Caring as one.

Sincerely,

Donald S. Powers
Chairman, President and Chief Executive Officer

In the year of the acquisition, 2001, a mug exemplifying "Caring for the Community" said: *In recognition of St. Mary Medical Center May the Poor Handmaids of Jesus Christ Health Care Mission Continue to Flourish*

St. Mary Medical Center in Hobart and St. Catherine Hospital in East Chicago were acquired from Ancilla Systems Incorporated in October 2001 by Community Foundation of Northwest Indiana, Inc. The two hospitals, together with Community Hospital in Munster, formed Community Healthcare System. Poor Handmaids of Jesus Christ Provincial, Sister Jolise May, PHJC (left), presented commemorative plaques to each hospital. Also shown {LEFT TO RIGHT} are CFNI Assistant to the President John Mybeck; St. Mary Medical Center Administrator Milt Triana; and Sister Kathleen Quinn, PHJC. Not pictured: St. Catherine Hospital Administrator Jo Ann Birdzell.

"In accepting these plaques, I ask that you please know that the goal of Community Foundation of Northwest Indiana is to continue to make St. Catherine Hospital and St. Mary Medical Center grow in spirit and tradition," Mybeck said during hospital chapel services. "These plaques and the services today demonstrate the loyalty and commitment that I hope we can continue to exemplify. We will do all in our power to extend the good care to the community that the Poor Handmaids of Jesus Christ have provided throughout the years."

Neighborly Care, SPRING 2002

"The best thing that ever happened to St. Mary's in recent years is the acquisition. I'll be honest; I was not totally in favor of it. As a board member of what was then Community Foundation, Inc. (CFI), George Watson and I probably were the two guys who resisted it the most – mainly because my history with St. Catherine was such that I knew the physical shape it was in. It was an old, old hospital. The Sisters didn't like to spend money for modernization. In healthcare today, you've got to keep up. If you're going to attract bright young doctors you've got to have the newest equipment. It's what they learned on, what they trained on.

"Don Powers came in and he knew, and knows, that you have to spend money. You have to keep your properties up. They've got to look good and they've got to be good. And he spent the money that had to be spent on both hospitals – probably more on St. Mary's because he built the new wing. As far as the need goes and as far as Don's philosophy, it hasn't ended and it won't end."

Bill Schenck, President, Board of Directors
St. Mary Medical Center Board Member
Community Foundation of Northwest Indiana, Inc.

"By profession I am an educator. My involvement with the healthcare ministry of our congregation was as a board member of Ancilla Systems Incorporated (ASI) and its affiliate hospitals. I was on various committees for the health system. I was elected into leadership and became more directly involved in the development and growth and future planning of the hospital system. I was elected as provincial for eight years – was located in Donaldson, Indiana – and I was very involved in Ancilla Systems.

"We really struggled financially since several of our hospitals served a poorer population. We began to look at possible partners – Community Hospital or the Franciscan group or Holy Cross Sisters – people who could really join us in the ministry. Through Beth Kaminski (former CEO of Ancilla Systems Incorporated) it certainly was an opportunity to partner with Community Hospital, a hospital that was considered the premier hospital in the area. We also began to think about our role in healthcare because we knew that we could not continue to compete in what was happening between and among neighboring hospitals. We began to rethink where we should be as a religious order. That is how HealthVisions came to be and Sojourner Truth and Nazareth Home – all with hands-on ministry that goes back to our roots. If the hospitals were in good hands we could do this.

"I call it a change in sponsorship. At the time of the acquisition we knew this was the way to go in order to maintain quality healthcare in the area as well as to follow a new way for the congregation to participate in healthcare. As a congregation along with Ancilla Systems, we just did not have the financial resources to do things better. Transitioning our hospitals was difficult to do but in the long run it didn't take long for us to realize that this was the right decision. I would hope we all had a bit of healthy grieving. Our participation in healthcare is being rejuvenated and regenerated and we're moving on."

Sr. Jolise May, PHJC
General Superior of the International Congregation
of the Poor Handmaids of Jesus Christ
Dernbach, Germany

Sr. Jolise May, PHJC
General Superior
of the International
Congregation of
the Poor Handmaids
of Jesus Christ
Dernbach, Germany

COMMUNITY FOUNDATION OF NORTHWEST INDIANA, INC.
ORGANIZATION CHART

AS OF
DECEMBER 2009

Ridgewood Arts
Foundation, Inc.
(6)

Community Foundation of
Northwest Indiana, Inc.
(2)

Community
Resources, Inc.
(3)

St. Catherine
Hospital, Inc.
(4)

Munster Medical
Research Foundation, Inc.
d/b/a The Commuity Hospital
(1)

Community
Village, Inc.
(7)

St. Mary
Medical Center, Inc.
(8)

CVPA Holding
Corporation
(5)

Community
Cancer Research
Foundation, Inc.
(9)

COMMUNITY FOUNDATION OF NORTHWEST INDIANA, INC.
AND RELATED COMPANIES DETAILS AS OF DECEMBER 2009

Ref.	Entity	Abbreviation	Date of Incorporation	Fiscal Year End	Tax Status	Date of Tax Exemption
1.	Munster Medical Research Foundation, Inc. d/b/a/ The Community Hospital	MMRF or CH	December 28, 1964	June 30	501(c)(3)	July 13, 1965
2.	Community Foundation of Northwest Indiana, Inc. (Formerly known as Community Foundation, Inc. – CFI)	CFNI	January 7, 1985	June 30	501(c)(3)	July 2, 1985
3.	Community Resources, Inc.	CRI	September 2, 1985	June 30	For profit	Taxable
4.	St. Catherine Hospital, Inc.	SCH or STC	April 22, 1988	June 30	501(c)(3)	August 31, 2001
5.	CVPA Holding Corporation	CVPA	December 6, 1994	June 30	501(c)(3)	January 4, 2001
6.	Ridgewood Arts Foundation, Inc.*	RAF	December 7, 1994	June 30	501(c)(3)	March 9, 1995
7.	Community Village, Inc.	CVI	May 19, 1995	June 30	501(c)(3)	February 5, 1996
8.	St. Mary Medical Center, Inc.	SMMC	November 11, 1996	June 30	501(c)(3)	September 15, 1997
9.	Community Cancer Research Foundation, Inc.**	CCRF	April 9, 2001	June 30	501(c)(3)	November 21, 2001

* Successor organization to Memorial Recreation and Education Foundation, Inc. (MREF)
  which existed from June 4, 1984 through December 31, 1996

** Successor organization to Community Hospital Cancer Research Foundation, Inc.

Represented here are the physicians who have served as Medical Staff presidents at St. Mary Medical Center from 1927-2010. While photos were not available of each individual, we have collected quotes, pictures and recollections from and about many of them. Consecutive photos are included from 1971-2010 and their numbers indicate the year of each presidency.

Medical Staff Presidents
St. Mary Medical Center - 1927 – 2010

Consecutive photos not available:

1927 Robert Bills, M.D.	1938 Charles Pettibone, M.D.	1949 David B. Templin, M.D.	1960 Henry Lebioda, M.D.
1928 Robert Bills, M.D.	1939 James Chevigny, M.D.	1950 William Troutwine, M.D.	1961 James Reynolds, M.D.
1929 B. Harris, M.D.	1940 Preston Vye, M.D.	1951 Milton May, M.D.	1962 James Reynolds, M.D.
1930 B. Harris, M.D.	1941 Raymond Carmody, M.D.	1952 Joseph Carbone, M.D.	1963 Richard Purcell, M.D.
1931 C. M. Regher, M.D.	1942 Carl Bendler, M.D.	1953 William Horst, M.D.	1964 Frank Monroe, M.D.
1932 Grover L. Verplank, M.D.	1943 John Bercham, M.D.	1954 William Horst, M.D.	1965 Charles Yast, M.D.
1933 Walter Behn, M.D.	1944 Carl Bendler, M.D.	1955 John Mirro, M.D.	1966 Marvin Bernard, M.D.
1934 H. Baitinger, M.D.	1945 Robert J. Bills, M.D.	1956 Lawrence Kudele, M.D.	1967 Alvin Jahns, M.D.
1935 George Gannon, M.D.	1946 Leo Cooper, M.D.	1957 Joseph Sala, M.D.	1968 Walfred Nelson, M.D.
1936 Harry Parker, M.D.	1947 Joseph Donchess, M.D.	1958 John Reed, M.D.	1969 William Glover, M.D.
1937 Frank Michael, M.D.	1948 Ladislaus Danielski, M.D.	1959 Frank Spellman, M.D.	1970 Joseph Ornelas, M.D.

Consecutive photos available:

1. John Brincko, M.D	1971	
2. Archie Kresek, M.D.	1972	
3. Walter Sala, M.D.	1973	
4. Robert Young, M.D.	1974	
5. Alexander S. Williams, III, M.D.	1975, 1989	
6. Robert Martino, M.D.	1976	
7. William Nowlin, M.D.	1977	
8. John Wylie, M.D.	1978	
9. Pierre Gilles, M.D.	1979	
10. Raffy Hovanessian, M.D.	1980	
11. Felipe Chua, M.D.	1981	
12. Arun Goel, M.D.	1982	
13. John O. Carter, M.D.	1983	
14. Rodolfo Jao, M.D.	1984	
15. Keshav Aggarwal, M.D.	1985	
16. John Kolettis, M.D.	1986	
17. Vijay Dave, M. D.	1987	
18. John Reed, M.D.	1988	
19. Prinn Stang, M.D.	1990	
20. Erwin Gomez, M.D.	1991	
21. William Forgey, M.D.	1992	
22. Harsh Dalal, M.D.	1993	
23. Paul Nyongani, M.D.	1994	
24. Heratch Doumanian, M.D.	1995	
25. Nazzal Obaid, M.D.	1996, 1997	
26. Koppolu Sarma, M.D.	1998, 1999	
27. Oscar dela Paz, M.D.	2000, 2001	
28. Thach Nguyen, M.D.	2002 – 6/2004	
29. Raja Devanathan, M.D.	7/2004 – 6/2006	
30. Peter Mavrelis, M.D.	7/2006 – 6/2008	
31. Scott Andrews, M.D.	7/2008 – 6/2010	

It's Been Said...

"Later on, board certification in orthopedics was more mandatory and more needed and the major orthopod in our area was Dr. Alvin Jahns (Jankowski until he changed his name to Jahns). Dr. Jahns was one of the first pioneers in the field of orthopedics. He was instrumental in bringing Dr. George Volan, a hand surgeon, to the area. Because of the industrial neighborhood that we lived in, Dr. Volan was very, very busy. Later on, Dr. Dale Olson joined Dr. Jahns. He was followed by Dr. Martino who became a part of that group until he started on his own. Dr. Robert Martino is still around. A partner of his is Dr. Joe Koscielniak who is an orthopod as well…"

Bruce Lovell, X-ray Technologist
Mercy Hospital | (began in 1963 in Gary)

"I did private duty for 17 years – at Mercy Hospital, Methodist in Gary, or St. Catherine's – all three. I lived on Third and Harrison, a block from Mercy. They had a lot of mill accidents and auto accidents. Dr. Joseph Donchess was a good doctor for the mill with the burn cases. I worked a lot."

Margaret Hart Swisher
Auxiliary Member, former RN
Graduate of St. Mary's Mercy School of Nursing, 1943

"Dr. 'Army' Armalavage was also an orthopedic surgeon in those days. Dr. Armalavage was one of the original doctors who started the Gary Clinic. The Gary Clinic was on Harrison Street, 61st and Harrison Street. This was perhaps in 1965 or '67 or '68.

"Our surgeons were Dr. Walter Robinson and Dr. Bill Glover who did a lot of surgery in the 1960s. Also Dr. Robert Milos was there in those days. Dr. Paul Yocum, Jr. was an ophthalmologist, as I recall… They were all here at the time I got there. Dr. William Mott was an orthopedic surgeon as well. There were quite a few doctors but not as many as one would think."

Bruce Lovell, X-ray Technologist
Mercy Hospital
(began in 1963 in Gary)

"The U.S. Steel doctor was Dr. Joseph Donchess, medical director of U.S. Steel starting in the 1930s. He was a three-year All-American at the University of Pittsburgh and trained at Massachusetts General Hospital. He was a superb trauma surgeon and available 24 hours a day. Dr. Milton May was an associate of Dr. Donchess."

John T. Scully, M.D.
Internist, retired
Mercy Hospital
(began in 1955 in Gary)

"I worked in the day when the doctor would get on the elevator and you stepped back for him out of respect."

Margaret Hart Swisher, Auxiliary Member, former RN
Graduate of St. Mary's Mercy School of Nursing, 1943

"My husband, Leo Cooper, was an orthopedic surgeon at Mercy Hospital. Gary in those days was very nice. The west side of Gary was the nicest, I should say. We lived there, all of our friends lived there, and so did most of the staff from the hospital."

Arlene Cooper
longtime Auxiliary Member

"Once we were inside the hospital, when the elevator came down and there was a doctor standing by the elevator to go in, you stepped back and let the doctor go in first and you went in after him. We had a lot of respect for the nuns and the doctors."

Helen Petrovich, R.N
St. Mary Mercy Hospital
(began in Gary in 1934)
(Note: Helen Petrovich was 95 years old at the time of her interview.)

> *"Place your intelligence, your talents,*
> *your enthusiasm, your compassion and*
> *your fortitude at the service of life."*
>
> ~Pope John Paul II

IT'S BEEN *Said* IN 2009...

"Bob was president of the medical staff. I think he was very, very well respected. He was a very dedicated doctor. He really loved his patients and his work. They just gave him anything he wanted in order to make his practice and the hospital a better hospital.

"He took care of most of the nuns in the hospital. I still have cards from the nuns that he operated on. He also was the ophthalmologist for the retirement home for the nuns in Donaldson."

Ruth Young
WIFE OF ROBERT LAWRENCE YOUNG, M.D., OPHTHALMOLOGIST

IT'S BEEN *Said* IN 2009...

"My relationship with the black physicians was good. I had great respect for them. I also was on the staff of Gary Mercy Hospital with a black ophthalmologist, Pierre Gilles, an eye doctor who came from Haiti. He was practicing in Gary Mercy with me. He came before me – maybe around 1965."

Jose H. Roig, MD.
OPHTHALMOLOGIST
MERCY HOSPITAL
(BEGAN IN 1967 IN GARY)

IT'S BEEN *Said* IN 2009...

"Three specialists joined the staff from Cook County Hospital. They were bachelors and lived together when they first arrived. Dr. Joseph Carbone was a pediatrician and chief of pediatrics for many years. He was a brilliant clinician (and also the cook for the three bachelors). Dr. Ray Carmody was an ophthalmologist and a remarkable diagnostician. Dr. James Reynolds was a urologist and an excellent surgeon. These three people contributed greatly to the development of Mercy."

John T. Scully, M.D.
INTERNIST, RETIRED
MERCY HOSPITAL
(BEGAN IN 1955 IN GARY)

IT'S BEEN *Said* IN 2009...

"My son was born here at St. Mary Medical Center in 1981. I received a radiology bill for $500 at that time. I was a young family man and I paid the bill but it was tough to pay. Someone encouraged me to see Dr. Heratch Doumanian concerning the bill (since) he was known to cover all or part of the cost. I was somewhat embarrassed but I finally went and told him about the bill and he said, 'Well, why didn't you come to me?' He asked me to bring him the bill, which I did, and expected that he would return part of the amount. He wrote me a check for the $500 out of his own pocket. That made an impression on me. From the physicians to guys like me, we looked out for each other."

Ismael "Izzy" Alicea
MAINTENANCE WORKER III
ST. MARY MEDICAL CENTER
(BEGAN IN 1979 IN GARY)

IT'S BEEN *Said* IN 2009...

"As a physician in general practice, my husband, Dr. Alexander S. Williams, III, did what he loved most. He provided excellent medical care and a love of his patients. He never shared experiences concerning his patients outside the office. Their visits and records were always confidential.

"He had a lot of respect and always spoke very highly of the entire St. Mary's Mercy Hospital staff. He always believed it took the entire team for excellent medical care – 'physically, mentally and spiritually.' Loving and caring cannot be separated.

"He graduated from Meharry Medical College in 1947, did his internship at Homer G. Phillips Hospital in St. Louis, Missouri, and returned to Gary to start his medical practice. After 50 years of service, he retired in 1998 as Dr. Alexander S. Williams, III, Emeritus. He died in June 2008, and is missed by many."

Hattie Rose Williams
WIFE OF DR. ALEXANDER S. WILLIAMS, III

"Ten years from now St. Mary Medical Center will continue to do incredibly well because the New Patient Tower is as nice as any hotel around and the patients absolutely love it. The place is just full. I think they are going to add some new operating rooms in a few years and it's just going to be busier and busier.

"Community is known as being a wealthy system, and if things need to be done, they are probably going to be done right. They made sure the tower had private rooms which hurt the bed count, I guess, but it's so much better for the patient experience no matter how you look at it."

Scott A. Andrews, M.D.
ORTHOPEDIC SURGEON
MEDICAL STAFF PRESIDENT, 2008
(BEGAN IN 1994 IN HOBART)

"Dr. Henry Lebioda was in family practice. He was very good. He trained one of the Emergency Room doctors, Dr. Phillip Kellar. He was very nice – always professional – never gruff, always gentle."

Alice Williams
COMMUNICATIONS OPERATOR
COMMUNICATION SERVICES
MERCY HOSPITAL
(BEGAN IN 1987 IN GARY)

"We had a young male who was a noncompliant diabetic. Part of the task in medical records at that time was a financial responsibility role. I remember typing his reports frequently. We had two full shelves of just his records. He didn't obey any instructions from his physicians. He would take candy bars that people gave him. They would find him down by the candy machine at the bottom of the stairs. They would tell him to get back up to his room. When he passed, we were having a Utilization Committee meeting with Dr. Vijay Dave as the chairman. He told us the diabetic patient had passed away. You know, we were wearing our 'business hats,' but without him having to direct us or speak, all of us dropped our heads. The moment was somber. He had been nothing but an aggravation, but with his demise, we all felt it. Dr. Dave was an eloquent speaker and chose the right words. He reflected on that moment and said, 'Here we had done nothing but toiled over how to handle him, and without speaking about it, we have all, with our body language, relayed how sad a moment this is.' Then he returned to business again."

Jo Toigo
DIRECTOR, MEDICAL RECORDS
ST. MARY MEDICAL CENTER
(BEGAN IN 1980 IN GARY)

"Dr. Peter Mavrelis and Dr. John Mirro are gastroenterologists. They're wonderful."

Catherine Wiseman, RN
CLINICAL CASE MANAGER
ACUTE REHABILITATION UNIT, retired
ST. MARY MEDICAL CENTER
(BEGAN IN 1975 IN HOBART)

"Dr. Alexander Williams was one of the main physicians in Gary and was always involved with the community. He was a very nice doctor – always very patient and always tried to look for ways to improve our services. He made an impression on me."

Lou Molina
VICE PRESIDENT FINANCE AND CHIEF FINANCIAL OFFICER
COMMUNITY HOSPITAL
(BEGAN IN 1986 IN GARY)

"A growing population in our surrounding communities, as well as the trend to coordinate care under the direction of one doctor, has created a distinct need for primary care in our area. St. Mary Medical Center is fulfilling that need by reaching beyond its four walls with primary care facilities in Portage, Winfield and Merrillville ... Together these primary care facilities form a 'geographic triangle' with St. Mary Medical Center near the core."

Koppolu Sarma, M.D.
RADIATION ONCOLOGIST
Neighborly Care, WINTER 1999

"The communities served by Mercy were Hobart, Crown Point, Lowell and Griffith – in addition to Gary. John Mirro, M.D., was in Lowell and came all the way in to Mercy for deliveries."

John T. Scully, M.D.
INTERNIST, retired
MERCY HOSPITAL
(BEGAN IN 1955 IN GARY)

St. Mary Medical Center

A MISSION OF MERCY, A CENTURY OF CARE

IT'S BEEN *Said* IN 2009...

"History can help explain why the world is the way it is today and how it got that way. If we look around our little world here in Northwest Indiana, we see all kinds of different things that may not make sense. Research the past to understand certain trends and why they happened. For example, why is it that we have one of the busiest transportation networks in the nation? Why do we have heavy industry, particularly steel, wedged between a national park and a state park along our Lake Michigan shoreline? Why did our commercial districts move from downtown Hammond and Gary to the suburban malls along U.S. 30, U.S. 41, and State Road 49? In other words, how did Northwest Indiana get the way it is today? History can provide the answers to help us understand our region in the twenty-first century and plan for the future.

"Certainly healthcare came into our region pretty quickly after settlement began in the mid- to late-nineteenth century and the hospital represents the commitment of developers and corporations to the healthcare of the population. St. Mary Medical Center, in both locations, can be seen as a contributor, a factor in the region's development and also a factor in the region's change."

Stephen G. McShane, ARCHIVIST/CURATOR
CALUMET REGIONAL ARCHIVES | INDIANA UNIVERSITY NORTHWEST

The Early 1900s

GARY AND ITS HOSPITAL

"The streets outside the four small, interconnected houses on the 600 block of Carolina Street hadn't yet been paved. A small staff readied the buildings to become the first hospital in the infant city of Gary, a town born as workers settled to build and man United States Steel.

"The tiny hospital had a capacity of just 20 beds. Among the last chores of the Franciscan Sisters of Burlington, Iowa prior to opening the doors was to mount a small sign which said, 'Mercy Hospital', over the front entrance. The doors opened, prepared to accept patients.

"Although the hospital was sold to the Ancilla Domini Sisters (Poor Handmaids of Jesus Christ), later relocated, expanded many times, and its name eventually changed from Mercy Hospital to St. Mary Medical Center, the hospital doors have always been open to care for the sick and injured."

(Acts & Facts, OCTOBER 1982 ISSUE)

Marking Time...

1907
- Theodore Roosevelt was President of the United States.
- The cost of a first-class stamp was $0.02.
- Radiometric dating found the earth to be 2.2 billion years old.

1908
- Henry Ford, an American industrialist/pioneer automobile manufacturer, developed the first Model T automobile which sold for $850.00.

1909
- The National Association for the Advancement of Colored People (NAACP) was founded by prominent black and white intellectuals and led by W. E. B. DuBois.

A relic of the early days shows the Gary Land Company sign on the side of the building and the post office sign across the front.

CHJC, University of Notre Dame Archives

NOTE: *The Poor Handmaids of Jesus Christ kept careful, type-written records pertaining to the history of Mercy Hospital and St. Mary Medical Center. Their entries and other historical materials are carefully stored at the University of Notre Dame Archives in South Bend, Indiana. Many of their entries are hereafter sited as CHJC according to the archival coding.*

Shown *(right)* is a typical duneland scene in the early 1900s before the city of Gary was founded.
Gary Works Circle
GARY PUBLIC LIBRARY

(Below) Before the city of Gary was founded, the area was occupied by Indian villages, trading posts and other historic points of interest.

CALUMET REGIONAL ARCHIVES, IUN

Little did anyone know in 1907 that the sparse structure on Carolina Street would foster emergent healthcare in both Gary and Hobart, Indiana in the years to follow – and that two hospitals, in their time, would become centerpieces of their communities.

The story of city and hospital are intertwined. Today, thankfully, to peruse historical archives and search forgotten files and talk with longtime hospital employees and local leaders is to step back in time and witness a fascinating story of bygone days when the hospital and city were fledgling entities.

THE CITY – THE BIRTH OF GARY

Excerpted from the *Post-Tribune* in the 1950s is this account of the birth of Gary.

"The Calumet region – destined to become one of the nation's most highly concentrated centers of heavy industry – was a wilderness of swamps, swales and sand dunes, uninhabited and undesirable for many decades after white men first saw it in the last half of the 17th century.

"The region fringes the southwestern curve of Lake Michigan for a distance of 16 to 20 miles and embraces what is now Lake and Porter counties. In the early 1800s, there were (many) Pottawatomie Indian villages scattered throughout the Calumet area but by 1846 most of the Indians had moved to western reservations.

"Until 1840, however, the region was known as Indian country. The presence of Indians and the singular geographic features of the region served as barriers to colonization."

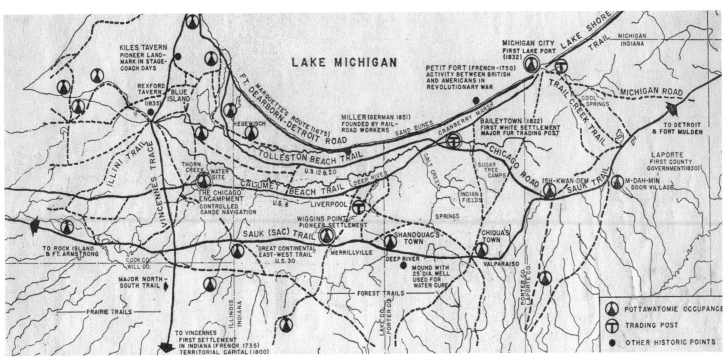

Building began in the city of Gary on April 18, 1906. While rugged wetlands, sand ridges and dunes still dominated the site of the city then, by July of 1907 there were 334 residents who had formed a village. In 1909, Gary was made a fourth-class city and in 1915 was assigned second-class status based on required population. (By 1931, Gary's population would exceed 100,000 people.)

Gary – a City in the Making

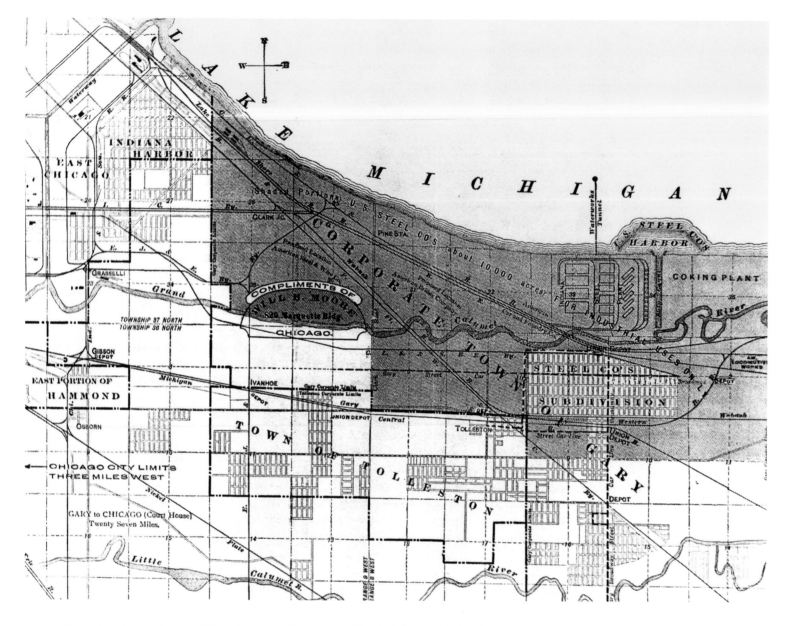

Shown here is an early map of Gary from approximately 1910. The shaded area is labeled the corporate town of Gary. The city's hub, mentioned below – a busy downtown area – also included the Gary National Bank where many physicians maintained offices in early years.

"Notice the small rectangles in the drawing of U.S. Steel's Gary Works up on the shoreline of Gary. Those rectangles represent the plant's Open Hearth furnaces and they are significant because the engineers designing the plant angled them at 35 degrees from the perpendicular. They did so because it made the steelmaking process more efficient than in previous steel plants. It's an example of how Judge Gary wanted this plant to be the most efficient plant in the nation. He was a progressive industrialist, desiring maximum efficiency with as little waste as possible in the new plant.

"A second item to note on the map is the division from the part labeled 'Steel Company's Subdivision.' That area represents the U.S. Steel-built portion of Gary, the part designed and managed by the Gary Land Company, a subsidiary of U.S. Steel. In that part of Gary, the corporation spared no expense, building beautiful neighborhoods and the brand-new downtown commercial district, with the hub at Fifth and Broadway. The Subdivision extended south to the Wabash Railroad tracks/Ninth Avenue. That dividing line is significant, for it separated the U.S. Steel portion of the city from the south side or "Patch" area of Gary, where most of the immigrants, African-Americans, and Latinos had to live, due to the higher cost of living in the U.S. Steel section. Thus, Gary was 'two cities' from the very beginning."

Stephen G. McShane, Archivist/Curator
Calumet Regional Archives
IU Northwest

The Industrial Environment Put to Prose

The following poem was printed in May, 1931, in the 25th anniversary issue of *Gary Works Circle* – a monthly publication for the employees of Gary Works, Illinois Steel Company.

CHJC, University of Notre Dame Archives

Gary

I've talked of dust and fireflies
   And sunset's glow in western skies;
But now I dream of freighted ore
Where smoking chimneys hug the shore
Of henna-colored mounds that rise
Against the turbid eastern skies.

These grimy buildings hold a thrill
A sense that here some human will
Has found a more than human goal
And formed a mighty, living soul.
A fearful presence one can feel
Within this world of flame and steel…

The very ore that lies beside
These belching stacks, may one day ride
Far distant oceans, and the train
That westward bears me home again,
May once have been a heap of ore
Beside this Indiana shore.

And so today, I sing the praise
Of men who wrought in mighty ways!
San Diego Union

The Hospital

This photo, dated May 19, 1908, shows the Mercy Hospital sign just below the front porch roof. The first hospital in Gary opened in 1907.

In November 1907, approximately a year and a half after Gary's settlers had arrived, Father Thomas Francis Jansen, the priest who founded Holy Angels Church – the first Catholic parish in Gary – was visiting Theodore Templin, M.D., in the shack that the doctor called his office. They noticed two Sisters collecting money from local merchants and businesses north of the tracks on Broadway.

FATHER THOMAS FRANCIS JANSEN

Father Thomas Francis Jansen, a Roman Catholic priest, was Gary's first clergyman who "preached from a saddle and said Mass in a dance hall," according to a 1956 article in the *Post-Tribune*. Known for his involvement with Gary's civic affairs and the city's development, Father Jansen – before his death in 1942 – would come to be known as the Right Reverend Monsignor Jansen, Dean of the Gary Deanery.

In the spring of 1907, the pioneer priest secured the second floor of Binzenhoff Hall for services. It was a saloon that was located where City Hall later stood. "His congregation knelt on the dusty dance floor during Mass, then removed the Catholic altar to make room for the Methodists in the afternoon," the *Post-Tribune* story said.

In 1908, Father Jansen organized Holy Angels parish in the offices of the Gary Land Company and oversaw the construction of the combined church/school that was dedicated in 1909.

Father Jansen's plans for a new church in Holy Angels parish were completed after his death by his successor, the Right Reverend Monsignor John A. Sullivan. Father Jansen helped organize and build Mercy Hospital.

Father Thomas Francis Jansen
Reprinted by permission of the
Gary Post-Tribune, MAY 20, 1956

Excerpts included with permission from the *Gary Post-Tribune*, MAY 20, 1956

One of Gary's first physicians, Theodore Templin, M.D., (fourth from the right), is shown in front of the office he occupied with W. F. Walsh, M.D., in the early 1900s. (Templin's name plate is somewhat visible above his head.) The office was located at what is now Broadway and Third. On the far right is Judge E. L. Fitzgerald, Gary's first justice of the peace.
COURTESY OF GARY PUBLIC LIBRARY
Reprinted by permission of the
Gary Post-Tribune – 1956 Jubilee Edition

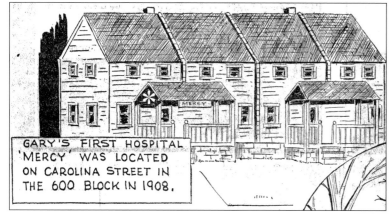

GARY'S FIRST HOSPITAL 'MERCY' WAS LOCATED ON CAROLINA STREET IN THE 600 BLOCK IN 1908.

This drawing of Mercy Hospital, the first facility of its kind in Gary, was published in the *Post-Tribune* in 1956 – the year of Gary's 50th Golden Jubilee celebration.
COURTESY OF GARY PUBLIC LIBRARY
Reprinted by permission of the *Gary Post-Tribune*,
MAY 20, 1956

"Prospect Avenue" in 1907, now known as North Broadway
CHJC, University of Notre Dame Archives

The Sisters were summoned to Dr. Templin's office by the priest and asked if they belonged to an order that conducted hospitals. They were from the Franciscan Sisters of Burlington, Iowa, and were collecting funds for hospitals in other cities. From this chance interview, the Mother Superior of the Burlington Order came to Gary to discuss the possibility of opening a hospital in the new mill town. The Gary Land Company, a subsidiary of the U.S. Steel Corporation, agreed to donate four of the company houses under construction in the 600 block of Carolina Street.

MERCY HOSPITAL'S FIRST BABY

The first baby born at Mercy Hospital on January 26, 1908 was Raymond L. Rearick whose father came to Gary in 1906 to work on the construction of the mills. The baby was born at the hospital site then located at 600 Carolina Street. Pictured here in 1956, Rearick was the oldest of five boys and went on to operate a heating and supply firm in Gary.

Calumet Regional Archives
IU Northwest

A FEW YEARS LATER...

According to archival information, this is a 1913 photo showing the refurbished structure from the original tar paper shacks of St. Mary Mercy Hospital in Gary, Indiana.

Word Gathering, Poor Handmaids of Jesus Christ
NOVEMBER/DECEMBER 1993

With designated units, the Burlington Sisters set out to establish the hospital. Bed and bedding were provided and gradually the four dwellings became usable for hospital purposes. Someone donated an "operating light," or an old-fashioned hanging oil lamp – the type in vogue at the time with crystal prisms hanging from it. A wash boiler, over an oil burner, was where Gary's first physicians sterilized their instruments and apparatus. A $15 operating table completed the hospital's equipment.

Of the four dwellings connected by a long hall at the rear, three of them were used to accommodate 20 patients. The downstairs rooms were converted into wards and three private rooms were on the second floor. A small operating room was in the first house. The fourth house was used for an office, a classroom for student nurses, and quarters for the superintendent and chaplain. There also was a small room occupied by a 14-year-old girl who had been adopted by the Franciscan Sisters. When the Ancilla Domini Sisters (Poor Handmaids of Jesus Christ) took over the hospital in 1913, the girl refused to go with the Franciscan Sisters and remained in Gary. The first patients to be admitted to the hospital at 624-34 Carolina Street were Anna Zink and John Joice, both with typhoid fever. Prevalent in 1907 and 1908, typhoid fever kept the hospital filled to capacity and many were turned away.

One of the long-remembered features of the Carolina Street hospital was its "human" elevator. A husky mill worker named Frank was assigned by the steel company as an orderly at the hospital. Winding stairs in each of the four houses led to patient rooms on the second floor. Since it was impossible to transport a patient on a stretcher, Frank carried them. It was said that he could handle a 300-pound man with ease.

Dorothy Phalen (later Mrs. John Brennan) was the first superintendent of the old hospital. In 1909, Gary Commercial Club sponsored a fund-raising baseball game at Gleason Field and procured $2,600. Dr. Templin, chairman of the drive, also raised $20,000 from physicians and businessmen. With initial funds in hand, the Franciscan Sisters planned a new hospital site – with land donated by Illinois Steel Company – located in the 500 block of Tyler Street. While the construction of the first unit was estimated at $90,000, the actual cost was $120,000.

Additionally, the YMCA sponsored a lecture to benefit the Franciscan Sisters of Mercy Hospital and obtained noted orator and Democratic leader William Jennings Bryan to speak to a maximum crowd. His topic, called "Sign of the Times," was delivered at the Majestic Theater on May 20, 1912, one day before groundbreaking ceremonies for the hospital's construction at 6th and Tyler in Gary. Patrons at the theater paid 50-cents for regular seating, 75-cents for reserved seating and one dollar for box seats.

Notably, substantial help was given to the hospital by United States Steel Corporation. Financial donations along with expensive equipment and furnishings were credited to the goodwill of U.S. Steel leaders. One noted leader was Mr. William P. Gleason, General Superintendent of Gary Works, who had direct charge of the company's development work for at least 25 years.

CHJC, University of Notre Dame Archives

1912 – THE GARY GROUNDBREAKING

MERCY HOSPITAL – 540 TYLER STREET

On May 21, 1912, ground was broken for the first unit of Mercy Hospital. Although dated and obscure, this photo shows the diversified crowd that gathered for the momentous event. Actual work, however, began early in 1914 and was completed by December. It was constructed on land (with an approximate value of $100,000) donated by the Illinois Steel Company.

Courtesy of Gary Public Library
Reprinted by permission of the *Gary Post-Tribune*, MAY 27, 1956

... AND MERCY WAS ITS NAME

On May 21, 1912, groundbreaking ceremonies were held for the first unit of Mercy Hospital on the 500 block of Tyler Street. On November 17, 1913, Sister Magdalena Büttner and Sister Ancilla Varel of the Order of the Poor Handmaids of Jesus Christ from Chicago, and Sisters from Fort Wayne, Indiana, arrived in Gary to take over the hospital from the Franciscan Sisters who lacked funds to continue construction of the new hospital.

Mother Tabitha Schwickert, Provincial of the Order, had been previously contacted at the urgent request of the Right Reverend Bishop Herman Joseph Alerding of Fort Wayne who had agreed to purchase and assume management of the hospital.

This purchase agreement (*right*), dated December 1913, shows the Notary Public certification of the Poor Handmaids of Jesus Christ purchase of "*The Mercy Hospital, Gary, Indiana*" from the Sisters of St. Francis of Sacred Heart.
CHJC, University of Notre Dame Archives

PURCHASE AGREEMENT

No. 3.

State of Iowa :
Des Moines county, : SS.

Before me the undersigned, a Notary Public in and for said County, this 19 day of November, 1913 personally appeared the within named Mother Catherine, Superior of the Sisters of St. Francis of the Sacred Heart, conducting " The Mercy Hospital, Gary, Indiana", who acknowledged the execution of the annexed Contract and Bill of Sale.

Witness my hand and official seal.

Carrie Ingham
Notary Public.

My commission expires _July 4th 1915_

State of Indiana, :
Allen County, : SS.
:

Before me the undersigned a Notary Public in and for said County, this 15th day of November, 1913, personally appeared the within named Mother Tabitha, Provincial of the Poor Handmaids of Jesus Christ, Fort Wayne, Indiana, who acknowledge the execution of the annexed Contract and Bill of Sale.

Witness my hand and official seal.

Lawrence M Dauw
Notary Public

My commission expires _December 6, 1913_

Marking Time... 1912

- The "unsinkable" ocean liner, *Titanic*, sank on maiden voyage after colliding with an iceberg; over 1,500 drowned (Apr. 15).
- *Woodrow Wilson was elected president of the United States.*

The Hospital Purchase Agreement

The purchase agreement read in part: This agreement made and entered into by and between Reverend Mother Catherine, present Superior of the Sisters of St. Francis of the Sacred Heart, Burlington, Iowa of the first part and for and in consideration of the sum of Fourteen Hundred and Fifty ($1,450.00) dollars, lawful money of the United States, to be paid by Reverend Mother Tabitha, Provincial of the Poor Handmaids of Jesus Christ, Fort Wayne, Indiana, of the second part, have bargained and sold, and by these presents do grant and convey unto the said party of the second part all furnishings, furniture and fixtures in and belonging to the Mercy Hospital situated and known as No. 634 Carolina Street, Gary, Indiana… and more specifically described as follows:

Operating room furniture, operating table, dressing tables, pressure sterilizer, steel dressing cabinet, instrument cabinet, hot water tanks, irrigator, instrument sterilizer and all other articles belonging to an operating room – all gauze, cotton and adhesive plaster, which is estimated to be worth ten ($10.00) dollars. Rolltop desk, wardrobe, kitchen range, large and small refrigerator and all kitchen utensils, crockery and cutlery, 39 beds and mattresses, 75 pillows, 200 slips, 60 blankets, 200 sheets, 80 spreads, towels and all linens, eight rockers, seven dressers, 56 chairs, table of nurses' home, three sanitary cots, 12 washstands, nine bedside tables, 26 small tables, several extension tables and all curtains and sashes of windows, three gallons lysol, three gallons glycerine, three and a half gallons peptonoids, two gallons formaldehyde, two and a half gallons lactopepton, all canned goods and jellies, fuel and incubator.

It is further understood and agreed that said second party is to have the hallway, kitchen, dining room and linen room adjoining the main building so long as they wish to use same and at a rental of eight ($8.00) dollars per month.

CHJC, University of Notre Dame Archives

In witness whereof, the said parties to this contract have hereunto set their hands and seals this ___15th___ day of November, in the year One thousand nine hundred and Thirteen.

(seal) *Mother M. Catherine*

(seal) *Mother M. Tabitha, Prov.*

The agreement, dated November 15, 1913, was signed by Mother Catherine and Mother Tabitha, Provincial.
CHJC, University of Notre Dame Archives

"He has half the deed done who has made a beginning."

— Horace

Sister Magdalena Büttner, PHJC
– from Humble Beginnings

Sister Magdalena offered the following account of her arrival.

On November 17, 1913, at 9 o'clock, Sister Ancilla and I arrived in Gary from St. Elizabeth's Hospital in Chicago. We were laiden with heavy baskets of provisions and had quite a long walk before we found the old Mercy Hospital. Miss Phalen, Superintendent, greeted us very kindly and told us to make ourselves at home. The Sisters who were in charge of the place had left two days before. We looked around the hospital… saw the 10 x 20-foot nurses' dining room… the cubby hole the Sisters had used for a refectory, an old rough board nailed to the side of the wall for a table… all rooms – kitchen included – constructed of paper…

(After the tour) we had about two hours before train time so we walked to the depot (we had no idea how far it was). On the way, I mentioned to Sister Ancilla how sorry I felt for the Sisters who were coming, never thinking I was one of the "unfortunate ones" myself. Sister Bartholomew, Sister Lydia, Sister Leonitis and Sister Elvina (a Novice), came in on the 1:40 train from Fort Wayne. We got back to the old hospital in an old jitney bus. The Sisters were just as surprised as we were when they saw the condition of the facility. We managed to find a place for us all for the night but had to use our habits and skirts on the beds to help keep warm.

(The next day) Drs. (Theodore) Templin and (John E.) Metcalf took us over to the new hospital. Construction had been at a standstill. The building was under roof. It was a bitter cold day and things looked dark and gloomy. Some of the contractors said they would have the place ready around the first of March. We were glad to get back to the old place to get warm but didn't succeed very well. The little stove in our refectory went out when we did.

(Badly needed provisions arrived) from St. Elizabeth's Hospital in Chicago the following day. Sister Bartholomew told me I was to remain in Gary with the three I had so much sympathy for. The third morning Sister Leonitis took up her duties in the kitchen and Sister Elvina started house cleaning and is still at it. All the bed linens and coverings were of the poorest kind. (We were told) that Mother Tabitha was going to discontinue the mission in South Bend and send furniture and household goods to us as soon as they could get it shipped.

In the meantime, we did not like to miss Holy Mass every morning so we decided to walk to Holy Angels Church. We went every morning for (more than) two weeks. The brisk morning air seemed to give us a good appetite and cheer our broken spirits. Our appetites were really good and have kept up ever since.

The goods arrived from South Bend around the last of November… Some of the Fathers from Holy Angels Church said Mass almost every morning until Christmas.

Captain Horace Singer Norton

Captain Horace Singer Norton
Calumet Regional Archives, IUN

About a week after we came to Gary, we paid a visit to good Captain Horace Singer Norton. He had promised the Reverend Bishop Alerding to do what he could for us. At our first visit, Sister Lydia and myself were not very favorably impressed. We thought him very stern. It was not long before we realized how kind and good he was, doing all in his power to help us in our struggle. After work started again at the new hospital, he could be found many a day looking after the men at their work.

Through the kindness of the captain, we were made acquainted with Mr. W. P. Gleason, the manager of Illinois Steel Company in Gary. We found another staunch friend in Mr. Gleason. He sent his men to look after the furnaces in the old place, six in all, and supplied us with all the coke (or coal) we needed, even putting it in the basement for us. We were badly in need of money and it was a great help to us not to have to buy coal.

I often wonder what we would have done in Gary without Captain Norton and Mr. Gleason. May our dear Lord reward them both in this world and in the next.

We were supposed to… move on March 1914 but the floors were not laid yet in most of the hospital. Then we were told we would be able to move in May. It was the same story all summer long. One strike after another kept us out until the cold weather came again. The laundry was finished around October 1 and the Sisters started light house-keeping themselves. We sent dinner from the old house for the Sisters and the two men working each day. They kept that up until December 9, 1914, when we moved from the old place on Carolina Street to the new St. Mary Mercy Hospital.

CHJC, University of Notre Dame Archives

Some years later, in the 1920s, William P. Gleason (*left*) and Horace Singer Norton accompanied a lady identified as Queen Marie on a visit to U.S. Steel in Gary.

METHODIST HOSPITAL – A NEIGHBORING FACILITY

During the first half-century of Gary's existence, a number of hospitals were established but by 1956 only two remained – Mercy Hospital and Methodist Hospital. The *Post-Tribune* reported that as early as 1910 local residents felt that Mercy Hospital was inadequate and that a second hospital was needed.

Twenty Gary physicians then joined together to organize the Gary General Hospital and each donated $100 toward the facility that was originally located at 801 Van Buren. In 1914, the hospital site was relocated to 429 Adams to create more space but a campaign to raise funds for the new building was criticized. The board then sought a religious or fraternal organization to take over and finance it. Several years later in 1919, an agreement was reached with the board of trustees of the Methodist Episcopal Hospital and Deaconess Home Association of Indiana to take over the hospital.

Relocated to Sixth and Grant, construction was completed and the former Gary General Hospital was dedicated in May 1923 as the Methodist Hospital of Gary.

THE HOSPITAL OF ILLINOIS STEEL COMPANY

Steel Company Hospital, Gary, Ind.

A PICTURE POSTCARD – STEEL COMPANY HOSPITAL
Built in 1910, Illinois Steel Company had its own industrial hospital to care for mill employees at no charge. Located along the Grand Calumet River on large acreage set aside for medical purposes, the five-story structure was connected by a tunnel to a three-story "power house." By the mid-1950s, the structure was used primarily for first aid and some medical services but the serious cases were sent to other hospitals. A portion of the building was later used by the mill's Accounting Department.

Postcard courtesy of Robert (Bob) Cline

The reverse side of the Steel Company Hospital postcard indicates a one-cent mailing rate (circa early 1900s)

Postcard courtesy of Robert (Bob) Cline

IT'S BEEN *Said* IN 2009...

"This building belonged to the steel company. It was their hospital and the building is actually still there. I believe it was a clinic initially."

Ismael "Izzy" Alicea
MAINTENANCE WORKER III
ST. MARY MEDICAL CENTER
(BEGAN IN 1979 IN GARY)

IT'S BEEN *Said* IN 2009...

"Mercy in Gary was the hospital for Gary Works of U.S. Steel. There was a 15 bed ward on the first floor. There was a huge accident at the mill. The 110-inch flue (or large suction tube) fell. Dr. F. F. Fisher was in charge of the Medical Department at the mill. The flow of patients was so smooth that the problem, though serious, was minimized. (Dr. Fisher later became the vice president at U.S. Steel in Pittsburgh because of the way it was handled.)"

Robert S. Martino, M.D.
ORTHOPEDIC SURGEON
MERCY HOSPITAL (BEGAN IN 1965 IN GARY)

Another hospital located in Gary in the early years was built by Illinois Steel Company in 1910 – an industrial hospital built and maintained by the steel company to care for employees from the mill who were able to receive professional medical care at no charge.

The facility consisted of a five-story main building with a three-story "power house" connected to the main building by a tunnel. It provided for 126 patients and was located along the Grand Calumet River on 14 acres of ground designated by the corporation for hospital needs.

Frank Merritt, M.D., was the hospital's longtime medical director with a staff of four physicians. Later Joseph Donchess, M.D., was chief surgeon for the mills and employed eight physicians.

IT'S BEEN *Said* IN 2009...

"U.S. Steel financed its own area (at Mercy Hospital). They had their own doctor and their own area. It was on the first floor at the north end. If there were mill patients who got hurt on the job, they were brought there."

Mary Ellen Donovan
SECRETARY TO THE DIRECTOR
ST. MARY'S MERCY SCHOOL OF NURSING
(BEGAN IN 1945 IN GARY)

"When I started back in the 1960s orthopedics was kind of a new thing to come about and no one was a board-certified orthopod. Later Dr. Joseph Donchess and Dr. Milton May were the originals. They were based out of U.S. Steel. They had their office at U.S. Steel. U.S. Steel, at that time, paid Mercy Hospital every single day to provide a bed for mill workers who became injured.

"If you had a trauma in the mill and were brought to Mercy Hospital, that bed was there waiting for you. They called it the 'mill ward'. There were three rooms in the mill ward. What I mean by ward is that some large rooms had three beds and some had four beds. The patients were next to each other and all were from U.S. Steel."

Bruce Lovell
X-RAY TECHNOLOGIST
MERCY HOSPITAL | (BEGAN IN 1963 IN GARY)

DID YOU KNOW?

FURTHER MEETING THE NEEDS OF HOSPITALIZATION IN GARY
In January 1929, to meet the needs of Gary's midtown area, St. John's Hospital was opened at 22nd and Massachusetts Street by John MacMitchel, M.D., and Robert M. Hedrick, M.D., both African-American physicians. Dr. MacMitchel died four years later and Dr. Hedrick remained there until his death in 1946. By the mid-1950s, the structure was used as a hotel.

PROMINENT STRUCTURES IN GARY

Gary Public Library in the early days
Calumet Regional Archives, IUN

Emerson School – Gary, Indiana (circa 1920s)
Calumet Regional Archives, IUN

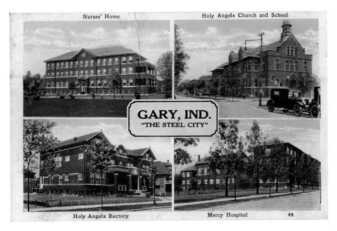

This picture postcard from the late 1920s shows some of the prominent structures of "The Steel City" – (left to right, top to bottom) the Nurses' Home, Holy Angels Church and School, Holy Angels Rectory, and Mercy Hospital (circa 1927-1929)
Calumet Regional Archives, IUN

A Look at the Sisters

A GOOD HABIT

This photo, taken February 22, 1928, shows a group of Mercy Hospital nuns in their habits of the day. This habit was used by the order for more than 100 years – since August 1851 – and it wouldn't be updated until 1964 for the Sisters of Mercy Hospital.

Calumet Regional Archives, IU Northwest

IT'S BEEN *Said* IN 2009... ~~~~~~

"Gary was very poor. Of course our community is noted for taking care of the poor, so we did what we could to help the patients."

Sister Nola Weiner, PHJC, RETIRED
DONALDSON, INDIANA
(WORKED AT MERCY HOSPITAL IN 1940)

A BETTER HABIT

In 1964, the Sisters of Mercy Hospital found a better habit – a new uniform that went into use in August of that year. Modeled here by Sister Cornelia (Leible), PHJC, it consisted of a two-piece suit with a white square headpiece and an attached cloth veil that fell back over the wearer's shoulders. The change was made, the order announced, as part of the movement of the Catholic Church to adopt more modern outfits.

Reprinted by permission of the *Post-Tribune*, AUGUST 7, 1964

SISTERS WHO WERE STATIONED AT
St. Mary's Hospital | Mercy Hospital | St. Mary Mercy Hospital | Lakeshore Health System | St. Mary Medical Center

Sr. Marlene Ardelean	Sr. Gabriel Giesken	Sr. Cornelia Leible	Sr. Loretta Schleper
Sr. Johannetta Bergman	Sr. Mary Ellen Goeller	Sr. Ann Linzmeyer	Sr. Marca Schmak
Sr. Genevieve Biesiada	Sr. Martina Gonya	Sr. Catherine Pavlovich	Sr. Aquinata Theilmann
Sr. Natalie Bleise	Sr. Amadea Hannappel	Sr. Philomene Pawlik	Sr. Catherine Thelen
Sr. Bertram Boeving	Sr. Willibalda Heidt	Sr. Maxelenda Preiss	Sr. Ann Verbick
Sr. Wilma Boeving	Sr. Kathleen Kelley	Sr. Donatilla Roos	Sr. Antoinette Volk
Sr. Judian Breitenbach	Sr. Andre Klein	Sr. Deodilla Roskinski	Sr. Ida Volk
Sr. Omerita Bruck	Sr. Concordia Kneisel	Sr. Lillian Roskinski	Sr. Loretta Volk
Sr. Clarence Caspermeyer	Sr. Margarite Knoch	Sr. Mary Kevin Ryan	Sr. Nola Weiner
Sr. Coelestine Deininger	Sr. Alfreda Kreher	Sr. Wilfreda Ryan	Sr. Inez Wilmering
Sr. Mary Ann Dettmer	Sr. Florence Kuhn	Sr. Sharon Schaefer	Sr. Helen Wojeiechowicz
Sr. Jeanette Cyr	Sr. Odillia LaBocki	Sr. Beata Scherneck	
Sr. Esther Dolezal	Mother Theodolinda Lauf	Sr. Georgine Schleper	

THE POOR HANDMAIDS OF JESUS CHRIST – ANCILLA DOMINI SISTERS

The Poor Handmaids of Jesus Christ is an international congregation of apostolic women religious within the Roman Catholic Church. They minister with the poor, the sick, and children in the United States, Mexico, Germany, England, the Netherlands, India, Brazil, Kenya and Nigeria. With prayer and community living as their foundation, they minister in rural, urban and inner city settings in the Midwest. Focused on partnering in the work of the Spirit, they invite others to join them in various facets of education, pastoral and social work, neighborhood-based health ministries, spiritual guidance and care for the environment. They are recognized more by the love and simplicity with which they serve than by any particular ministry. The corporate legal name of the American Province of the Poor Handmaids of Jesus Christ is Ancilla Domini Sisters.

Source: www.poorhandmaids.org

IT'S BEEN *Said* IN 2009...

"Ancilla Domini Health Service (A.D.H.S.) had its beginning when a group of hospital Sisters met to discuss various hospital practices – especially the benefits of Central Buying. This meeting was held at St. Catherine Hospital in East Chicago. Des Plaines, Illinois was the first office and Elk Grove Village, Illinois was the second office."

Sister Wilma Boeving, PHJC, ASSOCIATE ADMINISTRATOR, RETIRED
MERCY HOSPITAL | (BEGAN IN 1967 IN GARY)

ANCILLA SYSTEMS

A leaf from the linden tree is the corporate symbol of Ancilla Systems. Its significance within the heritage of the Poor Handmaids of Jesus Christ – the sponsoring congregation of Ancilla Systems – dates back to the time of the Blessed Mary Katherine Kasper, founder of the Poor Handmaids of Jesus Christ. She prayed at a simple shrine near her home in Dernbach, Germany that was sheltered by a large linden tree. The single linden leaf represents the personal vocation that was discovered by the founder at her simple place of worship.

MARY KATHERINE KASPER

1851 The Congregation of the Poor Handmaids of Jesus Christ was founded in Dernbach, Germany, in 1851. Its founder was Katherine Kasper – later known as Mother Mary Kasper – who was a German peasant girl born in 1820 to a family of ten and overcame poverty and lack of education to found the order. She began her religious community by building a little house where she and four other young women took their vows as Poor Handmaids of Jesus Christ before Bishop Blum in 1851. In this house they lived together, prayed together, and accepted those who needed help – the sick, the homeless and some orphan children.

CHJC, University of Notre Dame Archives

Designed primarily to care for the "poor sick", as they were known, the congregation also set up elementary and secondary schools in Germany. During the Franco-Prussian War, their activities were extended to military field hospitals in Germany.

In Mother Mary Katherine Kasper's day, there was no known women's role in social service and in her small village no one knew about organized charity. Mother Kasper knew nothing about these things either, but simply responded to the "voice within," as she called it, and reached out to the sick and needy around her.

(*Acts & Facts,* October, 1982)

1868 Difficult as it was for Mother Mary to send the eight Sisters so far away, she would write of their departure for America on July 30, 1868, "With tears in my eyes I watched the vessel from the shore until I lost sight of it." The Catholic order extended itself to the United States in conjunction with the German emigration of that time. Hospitals, schools, orphanages, and homes for the aged were later established in Indiana, Illinois, Wisconsin and Minnesota.

1922 The Motherhouse, home to the American Sisters, was located in Fort Wayne, Indiana from 1868 until 1922 when it was moved to Donaldson, Indiana.

The first eight Sisters to come to America in 1868 were (l-r, top to bottom): Sisters Henrica Boll, Rose Voss, Bella Siewecke, Hyacintha Seiffert, Corona Steib, Eudoxia Bender, Facunda Weber and Matrona Moehring.

Reprinted from "*Called to Mission,*"
Convent Ancilla Domini, Donaldson, Indiana

Hospital Week was marked by "Mother Mary Week" in honor of Mother Mary Kasper. Reverend George T. Meagher, chaplain of the Poor Handmaids Motherhouse in Donaldson, Indiana, published a biography of Mother Mary Kasper called *"With Attentive Ear and Courageous Heart."*

Mother Mary was later beatified in Rome by His Holiness Pope Paul VI. Beatification is the act by which the church, through papal decree, permits public honor under the title of Blessed to a person who has died with a reputation of holiness. Beatification is a preliminary step toward canonization as a saint. The process for Mother Mary's beatification began in 1928, 30 years after her death.

CHJC, University of Notre Dame Archives

NEWS RELEASE

A BEATA FOR OUR TIMES . . .

Mother Mary Katherine Kasper, Foundress of Poor Handmaids, to Be Beatified in Rome, April 16

Through her listening and responding to the "Voice within" Mary Katherine Kasper influenced not only the lives of her fellow German villagers, but of thousands of people continents away. She is to be beatified in Rome on April 16, her humble, Spirit-filled life officially acknowledged as an example for imitation in our day.

For the 400 Poor Handmaids of the American Province, the upcoming event marks a time for celebration, giving of thanks, and reflection. For them, the beatification of this German Fraulein is less an event that looks at one woman's past life, than a challenge to look deeply at their own relationship to the Lord and to measure their dedication alongside her faith.

Note: Mother Mary Kasper was beatified in Rome, as reflected in a document from the University of Notre Dame Archives

CHJC, University of Notre Dame Archives

1980s From their humble 1851 beginning, the Poor Handmaids grew to a congregation in the late 1980s totaling over 2,000 Sisters serving in five countries of the world.
　　　　CHJC, University of Notre Dame Archives

2010 Congregation membership today consists of 660 Sisters in the international congregation and approximately 125 Sisters in the American Province.
　　　　Source: www/poorhandmaids.org

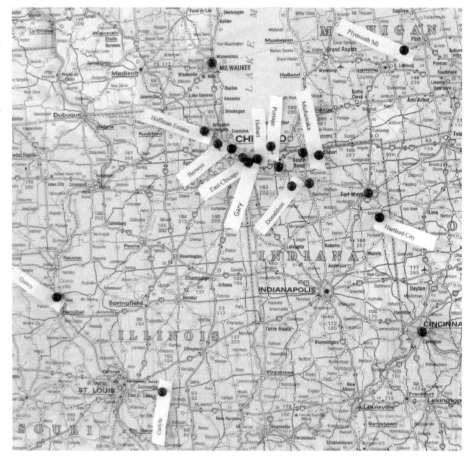

This map shows Poor Handmaids of Jesus Christ Midwest locations in 2010 – concentrated in the Chicagoland area but also including Quincy and Carlisle, Illinois and Plymouth, Indiana.

St. Mary Medical Center
Blessed Mary Katherine Kasper Healthcare Award
Past Recipients

While the list of recipients may be incomplete, known award winners from St. Mary Medical Center are included here.

Jack M. Kamen, M.D.
1979

Alexander S. Williams, M.D.
1982

Paul and Dorothy Heuring
1989

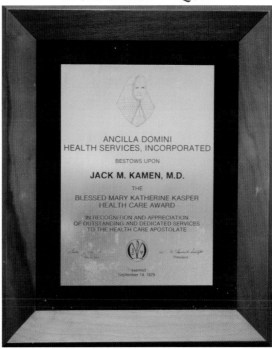

ANCILLA DOMINI
HEALTH SERVICES, INCORPORATED

BESTOWS UPON

JACK M. KAMEN, M.D.

THE
BLESSED MARY KATHERINE KASPER
HEALTH CARE AWARD

IN RECOGNITION AND APPRECIATION
OF OUTSTANDING AND DEDICATED SERVICES
TO THE HEALTH CARE APOSTOLATE

Joni Bucko
1996

John T. Scully, M.D.
1998

"One characteristic of winners is they always look upon themselves as a do-it-yourself project."

- Denis Waitley

The Blessed Mary Catherine Kasper Healthcare Award

In honor of Mother Mary Catherine Kasper, founder of the Poor Handmaids of Jesus Christ, the Blessed Mary Catherine Kasper Healthcare Award was established in 1976 to recognize persons affiliated with Ancilla Systems who have made outstanding contributions to the healthcare ministry. There are two award categories. Religious community, governance, physicians and volunteers is one. The other is devoted solely to employee nominations.

The award is the highest honor that the Board of Directors of Ancilla Systems Incorporated bestows. It is presented to those individuals who have exhibited the same spirit of loving service and unselfish giving as Blessed Mary Catherine Kasper who founded the religious congregation of the Poor Handmaids of Jesus Christ in Dernbach, Germany in 1851.

Recipients are presented with a plaque that represents the Shrine of Heilborn, originally built in 1692, and located south of the Village of Dernbach, Germany. A linden tree was planted at the original shrine more than 300 years ago. It still stands and makes a fitting symbol of growth and stability for Ancilla Systems. The shrine, noted for its simplicity and atmosphere of intimacy, represents the qualities of personal devotion and reverence which are basic to the Poor Handmaids of Jesus Christ.

Source: *Foundation for Growth*, Ancilla Systems 1988 Annual Report

(Note: In the late 1970s, the spelling of Blessed Katherine Kasper's name was changed to Blessed Catherine Kasper and is therefore reflected both ways in this text.)

"When I started working for Ancilla Systems (in 1988) we were the system office for a not-for-profit Catholic organization that owned seven hospitals at that time.

"...Their office was located in Elk Grove Village, Illinois, with approximately 100 employees. When I returned in 1991, the office moved to Chicago and in 1992 to Hobart..."

Molly Lawlor
HR/DEVELOPMENT SERVICES COORDINATOR
ANCILLA SYSTEMS INCORPORATED
(BEGAN IN 1991)

THE MOTHERHOUSE – DONALDSON, INDIANA

The Motherhouse has been located in Donaldson, Indiana since 1922 when it was transferred from Fort Wayne, Indiana. Located 90 miles east of Chicago, Illinois, and 35 miles southwest of South Bend, Indiana, it is home to the Poor Handmaids of Jesus Christ Provincial offices and Sisters living in Catherine's Cottage and Convent Ancilla Domini. Also located there are the Ancilla Beef and Grain Farm; Ancilla College; Catherine Kasper Life Center, which includes Maria Center and Catherine Kasper Home; Earthworks; Lindenwood Retreat and Conference Center, and MoonTree Community.

BY THE HAND OF THE SISTERS

"It is not as important to do great things in life as it is to do small things with great love." – MOTHER TERESA

"It's almost like the presence of the Poor Handmaids of Jesus Christ is built into the walls of the facility. They provided a great cornerstone and foundation for St. Mary and you see that through the employees and our auxiliary which are truly dedicated to that Catholic directive and mission. We are able to maintain this devotion, and I know the community and the Gary Diocese are appreciative that we continue to flourish."

Janice L. Ryba, CEO AND ADMINISTRATOR
ST. MARY MEDICAL CENTER
(BEGAN IN 1984 AT COMMUNITY HOSPITAL)

"The luxury I had in the first few years of being Chairman of Infection Control in Gary was that we had a good number of Sisters (members of the Poor Handmaids of Jesus Christ) as managers or coordinators in the various departments of the hospital. I remember Sisters Esther (Dolezal), Nora (Hahn) and Judian (Breitenbach). I would say their presence added to the efficiency and high quality of patient care in the various clinical wards of the hospital. We miss them."

Rodolfo L. Jao, MD., FIDSA
INTERNAL MEDICINE/INTERNIST
SPECIALTY IN INFECTIOUS DISEASES
MERCY HOSPITAL
(BEGAN IN 1973 IN GARY)

"Before Sister Cornelia left, she was running across the yard from the nursing home to the hospital by the back entrance and found this man having trouble getting this big T.V. out of the door. Sister said, 'Oh let me help you,' and Sister held the door for him and he got the T.V. outside. Later that afternoon she was in her office and read the report that someone had stolen a big T.V. I asked her if she called it 'accessory to the crime.'"

Sister Wilma Boeving, PHJC
ASSOCIATE ADMINISTRATOR, retired
MERCY HOSPITAL, (BEGAN IN 1967 IN GARY)

by Alice Engle Nedoff

St. Mary Mercy Hospital – Gary, Indiana
1942

My friend Dorothy suggested that I apply for a job at Mercy Hospital. She explained that she recorded birth certificates and reported them to the local newspaper. This sounded interesting. The following morning I entered the hospital and was greeted by a receptionist whom I later learned to be Mrs. Pool.

"I came to apply for a job in the Record Room," I told her.
"You must be the woman that Sister Maxelenda (Preiss) is expecting," she replied.

She ushered me to a beautiful room. The room was outfitted in gleaming mahogany furniture that sat on a lovely oriental rug.

"My goodness," I thought. "They treat applicants royally in this hospital."
In a few minutes a nun walked into the room and introduced herself.

"I'm Sister Maxelenda," she said.
"I'm Alice Engle," I replied. "I came to apply for a job in the Record Room."
"What is your background?"
"I had business college training and worked for a time in Dr. Mather's office."
"Will you be able to start tomorrow?"
I was quick to answer, "I'll be here."

The following day, I began my new job. Sister explained that they didn't have interns any longer because of the war, and the young physicians who had been on the staff were in the service. The older physicians had a huge caseload, and I could help by obtaining and recording data in the medical record. I visited patients and gathered information about their recent complaints and past histories. Some of the doctors dictated physical examinations and operative procedures on the new tape recorder located in the department. Many of the doctors, however, did not like using this innovative equipment and dictated reports to me personally. I transcribed all the information and placed the reports on the medical records for physicians' signatures. I also obtained information for birth certificates and reported the data to the newspaper office and to the Board of Health.

The Record Room eventually became the Medical Record Department. It is now more appropriately called Health Information Management. Transcription became a separate department, equipped with the latest in computer technology. The personnel in this department receive and transcribe reports for the ancillary departments within Community Healthcare System.

If St. Mary Mercy Hospital had a Personnel Department in 1942, I would not have had the pleasure of admiring that beautiful room that was set aside for special visitors. Actually, Mrs. Pool took me to this area by mistake. Sister Maxelenda had been expecting the wife of one of the Gary merchants. Sister did not let on that a mistake had been made. She treated me special. This is always a good way to begin a relationship, and for that matter, it is a good way to maintain one.

Alice Engle Nedoff
St. Mary Mercy Hospital – Gary, Indiana
1942

Alice Nedoff, shown as new Medical Records Director in 1973, reviews a hospital policy book during her first day on the job. Administrator Paul Kaiser announced Nedoff's appointment for Mercy Hospital in Gary and Hobart.
Source Unknown

"Sister Flavia (Schmitz) was a cute little thing. She was the boss so you didn't get close to her. The other nuns wore habits in those days. You could hear them coming; they had these big rosaries, and click, click, click, you could hear them coming down the hall. The nurses in those days could not stand around in the hallway and talk – only two at one time. Now, you don't even know who the nurses are by what they wear. We used to wear our caps and uniforms. Every so often they would surprise us at breakfast time and Sister Flavia would be there with a three-foot ruler. You would walk up to her and you stood there and your uniform had to be 12 inches from the floor. In those days, I had coal black hair and had never had a permanent. I would always pull my hair back and put my cap on over it and Sister thought that was just beautiful and would say, 'Now why can't you girls do that?' because the girls had permanents and everything. If you had your hair floating around, you had to wear a hair net. In those days, the Sisters made everybody tow the mark. The student nurses were required to wear black shoes and socks to distinguish them from a graduate nurse."

Helen Petrovich, RN
St. Mary Mercy Hospital
(began in Gary in 1934)
(Note: Helen Petrovich was 95 years old at the time of her interview.)

"Sister Vitalis (Witt), PHJC, was director of the School of Nursing when I was there. She was very strict and we had rules. When I graduated, I said, 'Did you know, Sister Vitalis, I had perfect attendance. I have never missed a day, and I think I should get something.' She said, 'So, you're healthy.' I thought it was an accomplishment.

"The next year I found out she did give an award for a person with perfect attendance (laughs)."

Margaret Hart Swisher
Auxiliary Member, former RN
Graduate of St. Mary's Mercy School of Nursing, 1943

"In 1959 when my son, Kent Williams, was two years old, I brought him into Mercy Hospital for a surgical procedure. At the time the Sisters were taking care of a little boy about six years old. I found out he had been abused and had a mind and body of a three year old. They had been caring for him for about two years. I thought that was quite remarkable of the Sisters, taking care of that little boy."

Alice Williams
Communications Operator, Communication Services
Mercy Hospital
(began in 1987 in Gary)

"Some of the nuns and some of the supervisors at St. Mary's in Gary were going to all the colleges in the area recruiting staff for the new St. Mary's in Hobart. They had a really nice dinner at the Holiday Inn for the Purdue North Central – Michigan City nursing students who would be graduating that year. They were paying about $2.00 more an hour than they were paying in LaPorte so a bunch of us thought, 'Well, let's check it out.' We went to an orientation at St. Mary's in Gary and I just loved the place. The nuns had told us at the dinner that they would pay us $4.50 an hour. That was in 1972. That was really good money. When we started working, though, I don't know what the problem was but they said, 'We'll pay you $4.30. We just weren't able to get the $4.50 an hour.' About three or four months later, I was in the cafeteria and one of the nuns came up to me (as she did with all the nurses) and had a little manila envelope with nickels and dimes and dollar bills and all sorts of money in it. She said, 'Here. This is the money we owe you. We told you your salary would be $4.50 an hour and this makes up for all the time you worked.' They didn't want to go back on their word and I thought, 'I think I'm in the right place here.' I couldn't believe it. It was all in cash and down to the penny."

Karen Gerke, RN
Director of Surgery
St. Mary Medical Center
(began in 1972 in Gary)

"I knew all the nuns. I took one home with me one day. Sister Ann wanted a haircut. I didn't cut her hair but my girlfriend did.

"(Speaking of the nuns), we had a laundry room in Gary and the nuns would sew. They actually sewed and mended the sheets. Anything that was torn up, they would do it. They did all their cleaning, their clothes, everything, nightgowns, and sheets."

Mary Constandars, HEALTH INFORMATION ANALYST
ST. MARY MEDICAL CENTER, (BEGAN IN 1975 IN GARY)

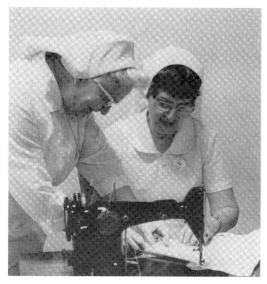

Sisters Beata Scherneck and Ann Verbick work side by side to handle the mending from the two hospitals.
Word-Gathering, SPRING, 1981

"We Sisters were living on the third and fourth floor of the former School of Nursing in Gary. The bishop of the diocese, Bishop Grutka, was planning to move to the Valparaiso area for his retirement. He would be replaced by Bishop Gaughn who decided not to live in Gary. The bishop's house was about three blocks from our hospital… (and) he offered (it) to us. I contacted the Provincial, Sister Stephen, who decided to see the facility before consenting. (Afterwards) she… granted us permission to… move to 'the bishop's house.'

"My brother (had given) us a Springer-Spaniel schnauzer we named Peppy. He went most everywhere with the Sisters and he liked everyone. What was interesting was that he learned not only the names of all the Sisters but also where their rooms were located. One day I instructed the dog to go to Sister Catherine's and bring me her slippers. (He returned) with the slippers! It was then that the play began between Sister Catherine and the dog. That's the truth! The dog died at age 12 and is buried (with a formal burial) behind the garage on the grounds where the Bishop formerly resided."

Sister Mary Bertram Boeving, PHJC, RN
RETIRED

FROM THE PHJC CHRONICLES – MEMORIAL DAY, 1986
Peppy was very ill and died on May 31 about 3:45 p.m. She was buried in the back yard. She is missed by all."
CHJC, University of Notre Dame Archives

"Sister Italia was head of obstetrics; she was extremely kind to everyone. Sister Willibalda was in charge of X-ray and took care of me when I wasn't feeling well one day. She insisted I have a chest X-ray which showed pneumonia. She was very vigilant when I was hospitalized at Mercy for five or six days.

"The Sisters ran everything and were very strict and efficient. The hospital was spotless and they worked hard along with the nurses in every aspect of the hospital's every day functions. They did everything from sterilizing instruments to scrubbing floors. One time in the Operating Room I had struggled with removing a nickel from a young boy's throat for quite some time. When I finally got the nickel out and laid it on the table, I exclaimed, 'There's the damn thing!' Boy did I get a lecture about swearing!"

Raymond Carmody, MD.
OPHTHALMOLOGIST, RETIRED
MERCY HOSPITAL
(BEGAN IN 1935 IN GARY)
NOTE: AT THIS WRITING IN 2009, DR. CARMODY IS 101 YEARS OF AGE. HE RETIRED IN 2001 AT AGE 93 AFTER 70 YEARS OF PRACTICE.

"Sister Philomene and I have a very warm friendship. We are almost like sisters… The patients just loved Sister Philomene because she is so warm. She was very good in dealing with kids. She had a special knack for that. Everybody she met just fell in love with her. She went beyond her job to really make somebody feel good and with her it is automatic. She just has such a huge heart."

Elizabeth Yee
VICE PRESIDENT, CLINICAL ANCILLARY SERVICES
COMMUNITY HOSPITAL
(BEGAN IN 1977 IN GARY)

DID YOU KNOW?

The Mercy Hospital Chronicles
The Poor Handmaids of Jesus Christ kept careful records pertaining to the history of their hospitals. These chronicles were anonymously hand-written by several of the Sisters for many years. Excerpts of their accounts, gratefully obtained from the University of Notre Dame Archives, are interspersed throughout this book. Included here is a series of entries pertaining to the racial situation in the early 1960s.

~ *1914* ~

1914 – MERCY HOSPITAL OPENS

On December 9, 1914, the new St. Mary Mercy Hospital opened. Of interest was a hand-written annual report showing expenses and revenue from December 1913 to December 1914. It is reproduced and transcribed below.

Listing of Financial Costs for the Mission:

Mercy Hospital
Gary, Indiana

Nov. 15 --- Dec. 1 – 1913 -- Dec. 1 -- 1914	
Financial sums as of Nov. 17, 1913	$ 122.00
From patients	6,500.19
Operations of 1 patient	1,005.00
For private nursing care	885.00
Additional staff in laboratory	874.14
Donation from the Motherhouse	400.00
Total:	$9,786.33

A portion of Mercy Hospital's Annual Report from December 1, 1913 to December 1, 1914 was obtained from the University of Notre Dame Archives. Sister Virginia Kampwerth, PHJC, said the difficult-to-decipher report is written in the old "suetterlin script" which is no longer used, showing a total of "the mission's financial costs" for the year at $9,786.33.

MY, HOW HOSPITAL COSTS AND THE ECONOMY HAVE CHANGED!

Mercy Hospital's annual report of 1914 is reproduced here, showing total expenses of $9,378.17 for the year with a remaining sum of $408.16!

Marking Time...1914

- *Federal Trade Commission (FTC) was established in 1915 and responsible for promoting fair competition through the enforcement of certain antitrust laws.*
- *The world's first red and green traffic lights were installed in Cleveland, Ohio.*

- *In his second big-screen appearance, Charlie Chaplin played the Little Tramp, his most famous character.*

A Thriving St. Mary Mercy Hospital – Spanning the Years

On November 17, 1913, the Ancilla Domini Sisters purchased the Tyler Street construction project and assumed management of the hospital. On December 9, 1914, the new St. Mary Mercy Hospital opened. The first section was the North Wing. The South Wing opened April 24, 1928 and the Center-east addition was completed in 1956. Groundbreaking and construction of a new multi-storied wing began on August 15, 1968. Completion of the new 132-bed West Wing in 1972 increased the bed component to 285, thereby providing services to meet ever-increasing community needs. The 184-bed suburban satellite in Hobart opened April 24, 1973.

North Wing – December, 1914
CHJC, University of Notre Dame Archives

North Wing, Fifth Floor addition – 1952
CHJC, University of Notre Dame Archives

South Wing – April 24, 1928
CHJC, University of Notre Dame Archives

Shown here is an early rendering of St. Mary Mercy Hospital from Hall Kane Associates, Inc. Architects, Gary, Indiana

Aerial View – late 1980s
The University of Notre Dame Archives identified this photo to be in the late 1980s. Mercy Hospital in Gary, later named St. Mary Medical Center, was considered the main campus in the early 1970s. Construction began on the west building in 1972 and was completed around 1974. Of note are the Patient Care Towers, and Kasper Hall which was originally the Mercy Hospital School of Nursing. As growth required, the hospital acquired much of the surrounding land.
CHJC, University of Notre Dame Archives

West Wing – 1972
CHJC, University of Notre Dame Archives

SPANNING THE YEARS (CONT'D)

"When they did the New West Tower in Gary, they took out the nuns' quarters and they had a morgue out there in the doctors' parking lot. They took all that out. They started making more changes and they did a nice Emergency Room and surgery and different departments. Dr. Scully had the biggest input when we built ICU – the whole area down there. Physicians had input in the way emergency and surgery areas would look."

Jim Wade, ENGINEERING MANAGER
MERCY HOSPITAL
(BEGAN IN 1960 IN GARY)
NOTE: AT THIS WRITING IN 2009, JIM WADE HAS WORKED AT THE GARY AND HOBART
HOSPITAL SITES FOR 49 YEARS AND IS THE OLDEST ACTIVE EMPLOYEE AT ST. MARY MEDICAL CENTER.

"(It is important that you) have the spiritual care resource within the facility as an integrated part of care for the patients. Our care is not just for the patients but is also for families and staff. I have done counseling for the medical and nursing staff as they have dealt with issues – health issues, staff relationship issues and family issues. So we have a broader ministry than just being in the rooms with the patients although that care is primary. What is very valuable for the staff is that we do respond to those crises situations that occur. Many times the nursing staff here at St. Mary's has said to me 'Jim, how do hospitals manage that don't have chaplains on board?' And I have said, 'I don't know. I'm just glad we're here for you.'"

Jim Stoel, (AKA "JIM THE CHAPLAIN")
ST. MARY MEDICAL CENTER
(BEGAN IN 2000 IN HOBART)

"We once had a terminally ill male patient whose daughter was scheduled to be married a few months later. The doctors were unsure if he would live that long. Sister Mary Ellen Goeller, PHJC, arranged for this man's daughter to get married downstairs in the chapel so her father could attend."

Betty Lane, RN
NURSE MANAGER ONCOLOGY
ST. MARY MEDICAL CENTER
(BEGAN IN 1990 IN HOBART)

"Sister Wilma (PHJC) was the associate administrator and her blood sister, Sister Bertram, was the head of Pastoral Care. Sister Wilma (PHJC) obviously was helping with the day-to-day management of the hospital at the highest of levels and we all know that Pastoral Care is essential in a hospital. People want to reach out. Even if they are not Catholic, when they see a nun they are very apt to look for some advice and some healing words from the Sister."

Mike Adler, FORMER DIRECTOR OF PUBLIC RELATIONS
MERCY HOSPITAL
(BEGAN IN 1977, GARY AND HOBART)

"I have been through two dads passing away – my dad, Thomas Bachinski, in 1998 and my father-in-law, Donald James, who died of the West Nile virus in 2000. My father-in-law was here for three and a half months and we practically lived here. Everyone was just awesome. Sister Mary Ellen is one of my favorite people. She came to my dad's funeral. A plant was sent from administration. I was just overwhelmed that with this large institution they would think to send something for my dad.

"With my father-in-law in the hospital, there were difficult days because he was on a respirator. Chaplain Jim Stoel came around and he was always there for us – holding our hands and hugging us and praying with us. He was such an inspiration and you don't find that in a lot of places."

Joy James, CANCER REGISTRY TECHNICIAN
MERCY HOSPITAL
(BEGAN IN 1973 IN HOBART)

"What do I miss most? (I miss) the family-like, friendly atmosphere of the Mercy medical environment. We all worked together as a cohesive unit and all benefited. The retention of Pastoral Care in this facility provides a hopeful sign for the future."

Jack M. Kamen, MD.
DIRECTOR OF I.C.U, DIRECTOR OF ST. MARY MEDICAL CENTER PAIN CENTER
CHIEF OF DEPARTMENT OF ANESTHESIOLOGY
DIRECTOR OF RESPIRATORY CARE
DIRECTOR OF MEDICAL EDUCATION, RETIRED
MERCY HOSPITAL
(BEGAN IN 1952 AT ST. CATHERINE HOSPITAL)

With Beginnings in Gary • THEN AND NOW

PASTORAL CARE

Contributed by Sister Mary Ellen Goeller, PHJC
Regional Director of Mission Integration

PASTORAL CARE STAFF PHOTO – 2009
PICTURED (L-R): Paul Newman-Jacobs, chaplain;
Sister Mary O'Hara, OP, chaplain; and Jim Stoel, chaplain

PRN CHAPLAINS – 2010
PICTURED (L-R): Diane Marten, Harold Prince, Jim Stoel (Overseer),
Craig Forwalter, and Dee Miller.
NOT PICTURED: Gerry Walworth and Peter Bodnar

Long before Pastoral Care was formalized as a department within St. Mary's Gary and Hobart hospitals, it has been a mainstay of healthcare. When several pioneers of the Poor Handmaids of Jesus Christ arrived at Mercy Hospital in Gary in the early 1900s and started their ministry of nursing care, they also provided for their patients' spiritual needs.

The Sister Superior was the first to identify these needs for patients and their families, sometimes with a loving visit or a prayer. The priest would administer the sacrament of "Extreme Unction" as needed. For those of the Catholic faith, the priest, accompanied by a Sister, would offer communion if someone asked. Sometimes the priest would notify a patient's parish priest, minister, or rabbi according to religious affiliation. These relationships, expected by the Sister Superior and understood and utilized by the floor nurses, were appreciated by patients and patient families.

Medicare was passed into law in July, 1965, and when beneficiaries were first able to sign up for the program a year later, patient documentation for ministry began to take on a new look. As a result of this, years later, the "Sister Patient Visitor" volunteer position was initiated – and among those who served in this capacity were Sister Florence Kuhn, PHJC, and Sister Loretta Volk, PHJC. The nursing staff no longer had time to meet the spiritual needs of their patients. Many hospitals nationwide recognized the need for a Pastoral Care Department within their respective medical facilities and Mercy Hospital answered the need for its own department prior to 1972.

At the same time, as part of any Pastoral Care Department, the Catholic Hospital Association required that hospital chaplains become certified in specialized training. Mercy Hospital Associate Administrator Sister Wilma Boeving, PHJC, enrolled in a St. Louis, Missouri program with Sister Gabriel Giesken, PHJC, for that purpose.

In 1976, Sister Bertram Boeving, PHJC, was assigned as pastoral associate to the Gary hospital and St. Mary Medical Center's Hobart satellite facility. Two years later she was appointed the first Director of Pastoral Care for the Gary/Hobart Hospitals and held this position until 1991. Also added was Sister Philomene Pawlik, PHJC, who had been part of the Pastoral Care staff at St. Catherine Hospital. Along with Father Joseph Herod, C.P.P.S., for the Gary hospital, Father Henry Langhals, C.P.P.S., was at the Hobart facility.

In 1988 to reflect a diversified patient population, the Pastoral Care staff was reorganized to include Reverend Eric Griffis, Reverend Michael Hayden, Reverend Ruben Ferrel, and Reverend Vincent Gray for the Gary and Hobart sites. Also assisting with Catholic patients in part-time positions were Father Mathew Iwauji and Deacon Joe Zemelko. Along with PHJC Sisters Bertram, Gabriel and Philomene, staff additions from other religious orders included Sister Francis Alma Royer, CSJ, Sister Mary O'Hara, OP, and Sister Una O'Meara, OSF. Sister Mary O'Hara, OP, started in the Gary hospital in 1989 and became a full-time Hobart staff member in 1991. Among others who have been staff chaplains in the Pastoral Care Department are Sister Loretta Schelper, PHJC, Lydia Kalb, Kris Graunke, Ruth Harrison, Jim Stoel, and Paul Newman-Jacobs. Mary Rachubinski filled in during the sabbatical of Sister Bertram and took on additional responsibilities as Director of Pastoral Care at both Gary and Hobart hospitals.

As the number of Poor Handmaids of Jesus Christ Sisters was replaced by the laity because fewer women were entering the order, the Director of Pastoral Care reported to the newly-established position of Director of Mission and Philosophy. Father Kenneth Grabner, CSC, then Coordinator of the Alcoholism and Treatment Program, became the first Director of Mission and Philosophy in 1981. Always supportive and cooperative, Father Grabner recognized the importance of immediate spiritual care and counseling for patients, families and staff members. Father Grabner was later replaced by Mary Gulyassy.

In the fall of 1990, Sister Mary Ellen Goeller, PHJC, was hired as the vice president for mission integration. In working with the director of pastoral care and the chaplains, and recognizing the enormity of the chaplains' daily ministry, chaplains were hired to be on-call in the evenings. The chaplains also play a key role in their support of employees, physicians and volunteers. Volunteers now assist in taking Communion to our Catholic patients. Eucharistic Ministers volunteer their time to serve daily.

Another component of pastoral care is grief support. It began as The Consoling Hearts Grief Group – co-sponsored by St. Mary Medical Center and St. Joan of Arc Church and initiated by Father Sammie Maletta, Peggy Gall and Sister Loretta Schelper, PHJC. Currently (in 2010) it is facilitated by Sister Mary O'Hara, OP. Share Your Grief, is led by Chaplain Jim Stoel for hospital staff members who have dealt with tragic deaths, particularly parents who have lost adult children. Since 1978 as part of this reach-out effort, the chaplains mail sympathy cards to the families of staff members and invite them to a Memorial Service in honor of their loved ones. The chaplains serve on committees such as Medical Ethics where policies and difficult cases are discussed and on the Gift of Hope donation committee arising out of their involvement with families' end-of-life experiences.

Local clergy have always been encouraged to visit and administer to their own parishioners. In 1980, former Mercy Hospital Administrator Mary Gulyassy assumed such roles as Director of Mission and Philosophy and Vice President of Mission Effectiveness and encouraged the promotion of good relationships with the hospital and local clergy. The Hobart Ministerial Association initiated monthly lunch meetings whereby church pastors could discuss topics of interest and gain pertinent information about the hospital.

Our Pastoral Care staff continues to minister to all – today and in the future.

"Long before Pastoral Care was formalized as a department within St. Mary's Gary and Hobart hospitals, it has been a mainstay of healthcare."

"We were often called to the Emergency Department for crisis intervention. I remember a case where a woman was coming home from the bank and collapsed at a bus stop. She was a very private person and thus the neighbors did not know about her family. I called the various churches in Gary and finally discovered a priest who knew her family and her background. I was then able to contact the son who lived in Canada."

Sister Mary O'Hara, OP, CHAPLAIN
ST. MARY MEDICAL CENTER
(BEGAN IN 1989 IN GARY)

"I love being a chaplain. I've been in a lot of ministries and I've never loved doing anything as much as hospital chaplain work. There is a lot of grief; there's a lot of heartache but somehow in the midst of all that, you are helping people. You are there for people. My Irish brogue is a bit of a conversation piece. It opens people up to talk about where they are from too. It breaks the communication barrier."

Sister Mary O'Hara, OP, CHAPLAIN
ST. MARY MEDICAL CENTER
(BEGAN IN 1989 IN GARY)

"A female patient came in and received surgery for a malignant growth but the surgery was not able to resolve all of the issues presented to this particular growth. As a consequence, the patient has been hospitalized numerous times. There have been many visits and much time including helping that patient rediscover some kind of contact with the God of eternal life. One of the things the patient said to me recently is, 'Jim, I am scared.' So we talked about what the fears were, what was prompting the fear, and then what resources were available to help deal with those fears. That has been an ongoing relationship and an ongoing care ministry. The patient was discharged from our hospital into VNA Hospice care at the Horton Hospice Center in Valparaiso and it is in my plan to go see the patient at the hospice center. What is also significant is that I got a phone call from the VNA Hospice chaplain... who invited me to come and spend some time with this patient to continue the care that (initially) developed here at the hospital."

Jim Stoel (AKA "JIM THE CHAPLAIN")
ST. MARY MEDICAL CENTER
(BEGAN IN 2000 IN HOBART)

"There was a male patient whose basic healthcare issue was lupus and out of that developed some other health issues... and I spent a lot of time with him and his family. This patient and his wife have been very much involved in a lupus support group for Northwest Indiana and out of contact with them I was asked to do a presentation at the lupus support group – a presentation on spirituality as a support mechanism for coping with health issues. So we have those kinds of developments also where out of caring for patient and families, other opportunities are given to us."

Jim Stoel, (AKA "JIM THE CHAPLAIN")
ST. MARY MEDICAL CENTER
(BEGAN IN 2000 IN HOBART)

Shown here is Father Joseph Herod who was chaplain at the Gary hospital campus beginning in 1980. He was known as a "quiet, unassuming, prayerful man who... invariably succeeded in bringing a little tranquility into even the most troubled situations."
Summary, JUNE 1988

Father Henry J. Langhals is shown in this 1977 photo as he completed eight years of ministering to the sick and injured at St. Mary Medical Center and celebrated his 40-year jubilee in the priesthood. *Acts & Facts,* APRIL, 1977

HORACE SINGER NORTON – LEADER OF THE BOARD

Mercy Hospital was described as a beautiful structure complete with terazza and marble and stairs to the octagon-shaped main lobby from the Tyler Street entrance. Statues and beautiful wood cabinetry were prevalent. The bronzed memorial plaque of Horace Singer Norton hung in the lobby for many years in tribute to the leader of the Lay Advisory Board and its board of directors. It read as follows:

Horace Singer Norton
PRESIDENT
ST. MARY'S MERCY HOSPITAL
ADVISORY BOARD

March 1, 1915 A.D. - August 5, 1947 A.D.

BOARD OF DIRECTORS
1915 to 1947

James B. Bailey	Fred A. Egan
Harry V. Call	William P. Gleason
Fred J. Cassidy	John A. Gross
Michael J. Coyle	Henry G. Hay
James E. Darbaker	John B. Radigan
Charles H. Doorley	Stephen M. Jenks

The *Gary Post-Tribune* eulogized Captain Norton in its newspaper on August 6, 1947, "who had expired the day previous." Norton had headed the Lay Board continuously from 1915 when, with Henry G. Hay, Sr., he directed the organization. "Untold is the valuable assistance rendered by the Lay Advisory Board to St. Mary Mercy Hospital during its developing years, the dark days of depression, and the anxious days of World War II," the article said.

Shown here in November 1947 is the St. Mary's Mercy Hospital Lay Advisory Board. The photo was taken at a reorganization meeting in which Frederick J. Cassidy, a 26-year member, was elected chairman to succeed the late Captain H. S. Norton who had died on August 5. SEATED (L-R) are PHJC Sisters Salesia Schoendienst, Aquinata Theilmann, Vitalis Witt, and Alphonsina Still.
STANDING (L-R) are Judge Fred A. Egan, Frederick J. Cassidy, M. J. Coyle, S. M. Jenks, and John B. Radigan.
Courtesy of Gary Public Library.
Reprinted by permission of the *Gary Post-Tribune*, NOVEMBER 11, 1947

"Tell me and I forget; show me and I remember;
involve me and I understand." ~ANONYMOUS

LAKE COUNTY MEDICAL SOCIETY – EARLY ROOTS

❦ 1906 – Thirty doctors – mostly in Hammond and East Chicago – were already practicing in Lake County when Gary was established.

❦ 1907 – Gary had six physicians – Dr. Theodore Templin, Dr. Harry M. Hosmer, Dr. Charles A. DeLong, Dr. John E. Metcalf, Dr. Ira Miltimore and Dr. Ernst Schaible. It was inferred that these physicians probably formed the nucleus of the St. Mary Mercy Hospital staff.

❦ 1922 – The first Medical Advisory Board for the new St. Mary Mercy Hospital was formed. Members included Theodore Templin, M.D.; George W. Gannon, M.D.; Charles W. Yarrington, M.D.; Harry W. Long, M.D.; Frank Michael, M.D.; Ira Miltimore, M.D.; and Ernst L. Schaible, M.D. The Medical Advisory Committee and the Administrator regulated and guided activities within the hospital to provide the best possible care to the sick and injured. The Hospitalization Standard Movement, known as the "Hospital Betterment Period," was conceived by the American Hospital Association in 1918 and was received by the Supervisory Bodies of St. Mary Mercy Hospital. The effort was to conform to the standards laid down by the American Hospital Association in collaboration with the Catholic Hospital Association.

❦ 1927 – Minutes of the meeting of September 27, 1927, stated that the "by-laws were approved and their adoption favored and signed by Theodore Templin, M.D.; Paul H. Dietrich, M.D.; Grover L. Verplank, M.D.; and George W. Gannon. M.D."

❦ 1947 – A special meeting of the executive committee was called by Sister Alphonsina, PHJC, administrator, regarding the admission of Negro doctors to the staff. Sister informed the doctors "that the Catholic authorities, the Holy Father, and the bishop advised and demanded that the Sisters admit colored doctors to the staff of Mercy Hospital." On July 30, 1947, a *Gary Post-Tribune* article, *"Mercy Taking Negro Medics' Applications,"* appeared in the newspaper and said, "The matter of color no longer will enter into the picture at St. Mary Mercy Hospital as far as doctors being permitted to practice there… The only thing that counts is the qualification of the applicant, be he white or black. The doctors will expect the same performance from all doctors. (Medical staff accepted application for staff privileges by Benjamin F. Grant, M.D., the hospital's first black physician.)

❦ 1957-1958 – The By-Laws, Rules and Regulations were revised and a dental staff was included with the medical staff. The title was changed to The Medical and Dental Staff of St. Mary Mercy Hospital.

❦ 1958 – (Following Dr. Grant in 1947) the first two African-American interns in Gary, Carl Williams, M.D., and G. B. Mitchell, M.D., joined the St. Mary Mercy Hospital medical family… From a nucleus of six physicians, the staff – as reported in the hospital's jubilee edition – had grown to 190 practicing members in a medical facility fully accredited by The Joint Commission.

CHJC, University of Notre Dame Archives

WHAT'S IN A HOSPITAL NAME?

Note: While the hospital in Gary was commonly referred to as Mercy Hospital, it has also been referred to as St. Mary Mercy, St. Mary's Mercy, St. Mary's-Gary, St. Mary Mercy-downtown, St. Mary Medical Center - Gary, or any combination of the aforementioned names.

The Hobart hospital, for a short while before it opened, was called Queen of Peace Hospital. It was later referenced as St. Mary Mercy Southeast, Hobart Mercy, St. Mary Mercy – Hobart and finally came to be known as it is today – St. Mary Medical Center in Hobart.

James Cormican attached the last stainless steel letter above the entrance to St. Mary Medical Center in Gary, formerly known as Mercy Hospital.
Reprinted by permission of the *Post-Tribune,* SEPTEMBER 20, 1974

IT'S BEEN *Said* IN 2009...

"St. Mary's in Gary was never St. Mary's in Gary – it was always called Mercy – just Mercy Hospital. Throughout the period of time preceding 1955 and going way back, it was really Mercy Hospital and not Mercy Gary or anything else. When the satellite hospitals were built for Methodist and Mercy hospitals, Hobart Mercy became St. Mary's in Hobart.

John T. Scully, MD., INTERNIST, RETIRED
MERCY HOSPITAL
(BEGAN IN 1955 IN GARY)

"Originally, the hospital was called Mercy Hospital when it started in Gary in three old buildings. Later, when they built out here in Hobart, it was called St. Mary Medical Center. They changed the name in Gary at the same time, so it was also known as St. Mary Medical Center. In a way, Gary has always been referred to as Mercy Hospital. We still refer to the nursing school as St. Mary's Mercy School of Nursing.

"I guess the Gary facility is the police station down there now. They tore down the nurses' residence, I believe, and now it is a city building."

Mary Ellen Donovan, Secretary to the Director
St. Mary's Mercy School of Nursing
(began in 1945 in Gary)

MERCY HOSPITAL BY-LAWS
– AN INTRODUCTION

"St. Mary Mercy Hospital, Gary, Indiana, is conducted by The Ancilla Domini Sisters, a corporation under the Laws of the State of Indiana for the care of the sick in its vicinity.

"The authority for the administration of the hospital is vested in a governing board composed of members of the parent corporation, The Ancilla Domini Sisters, Motherhouse, in Donaldson, Indiana, which delegates power to a Governing Body of members of the corporation at St. Mary Mercy Hospital.

"Her responsibility for the proper medical care is that of the medical staff. The cooperation and relationship between the governing body and the medical staff is, by very nature of both, very close: Their purpose is one and the same – namely, the care of the sick.

"Christian Charity prompted the establishment of St. Mary Mercy Hospital. Her ethics are governed by the Laws of God, the Natural Law, the principles and policies of the Catholic Hospital Association, and the principles of Medical Ethics of the American Medical Association.

"The Medical Standards of St. Mary Mercy Hospital are guided by those of The Joint Commission."

CHJC, University of Notre Dame Archives

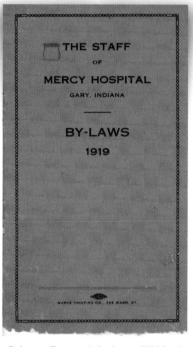

THE STAFF
OF
MERCY HOSPITAL
GARY, INDIANA
——
BY-LAWS
1919

BURKE PRINTING CO., 525 WASH. ST.

Calumet Regional Archives, IU Northwest

By 1965 and in some prior publications, the Gary medical facility was referred to as St. Mary Mercy Hospital, as shown here in the advisory board by-laws stored at the University of Notre Dame Archives.

ST. MARY MERCY HOSPITAL – ADVISORY BOARD BY-LAWS – LATER IN 1965

"The St. Mary Mercy Hospital Lay Advisory Board shall consist of eight (8) members with equal vote with charter members having been appointed by the Administrator of St. Mary Mercy Hospital. The Administrator of Saint Mary Mercy Hospital and members of her council shall be ex-officio members of the advisory board. The bishop of the Diocese of Gary, Indiana shall also be an ex-officio member of the Advisory Board. Ex-officio members of the advisory board shall function without vote.

The St. Mary Mercy Hospital Lay Advisory Board shall consist of outstanding and experienced men in industrial, legal, business and other professional fields. There shall be no less than seven members who shall advise and assist the administrator in financial and business matters pertaining to the hospital. One member of this board shall be elected chairman or president of the board. The administrator and two members of the governing body are representatives of St. Mary Mercy Hospital on this Lay Advisory Board."

CHJC, University of Notre Dame Archives

1912 – St. Mary's Mercy Hospital School of Nursing

Records show that the nursing school was known by several different names. Some have diplomas and literature that refer to it as St. Mary Mercy School of Nursing and others have documentation calling it St. Mary's Mercy School of Nursing. Both names are correct and both are interspersed throughout this book.

School of Nursing – Its History

The School of Nursing was organized in 1912 as an integral part of Mercy Hospital. Due to the ever increasing number of student nurses, a modern fireproof Nurses' Home, fully equipped to meet the latest demands in teaching, was erected in 1924. The School of Nursing was accredited by The Indiana State Board of Nurses' Registration and Nursing Education and by The Catholic Hospital Association. Those applying to the nursing school had to be between 18-35 years of age.

This photo, printed in an early nursing booklet, "*Your Career in Nursing*," shows students entering the Nurses Home. Also printed on the same page is the following message:

*I expect to pass through
this world but once
Any good, therefore, that I
can do; or any kindness
that I can show to any fellow creature,
let me do it now.
Let me not defer or neglect it,
For I shall not pass this way again.*

Anonymous -

Donaldson, Indiana Archives

Marking Time...

1916
- Over 7,000 deaths occurred and 27,363 cases were reported of polio (infantile paralysis) in America's worst polio epidemic.

1917
- U.S. declared war on Germany (Apr. 6) – World War I.
- Between 10-15,000 blacks silently walked down New York City's Fifth Avenue to protest racial discrimination and violence (Jul. 28).

1919
- Eighteenth Amendment of the Constitution (prohibition) was adopted and ratified on January 16.
- Race riots erupted in 26 U.S., including Washington, D.C., and Chicago (July).
- Dial telephones were introduced by the American Telephone and Telegraph Company.

THE SCHOOL OF NURSING
ROSTER OF GRADUATES

A nursing career is for many
"a calling." Shown here is
a nurse in her serenity and
garb of time past.

IT'S BEEN *Said* IN 2009... ~

"There were only two people in the first graduating class of St. Mary's Mercy School of Nursing in 1915. After she left school, Mable Keough (one of the graduates) was a city nurse. She worked in the Health Department for the City of Gary.

"The Cadet Program...was a government issue, paying for the girls to go through the School of Nursing.

"I think it was 1952 when we first took in an African-American girl who was very nice and was a good student. Then we also had to know if the students were Catholic or Protestant but that was never anything that was discussed or promoted. We had a couple of Jewish girls along the way."

Mary Ellen Donovan
SECRETARY TO THE DIRECTOR
ST. MARY'S MERCY SCHOOL
OF NURSING
(BEGAN IN 1945 IN GARY)

Mary Ellen Donovan, former secretary to the director of St. Mary's School of Nursing, compiled a roster of every graduate from the school's first class in 1915 through the final class in 1968 before the school closed. In the early days, records were also kept of each student's religious affiliation and it was noted that only single females were allowed into the school.

1915
Nizan, Sabina
Keough, Mable

1916
Adams, Helen
Carrol, Dorothy
Cross, Catherine
Enright, Elizabeth

1917
Dillon, Valeria
King, Cornelia

1918
Barwiler, Leone
Gordon, Anne
Krause, Florence
Nix, Josephine
Rohyans, Genevieve

1919
Zoll, Anna

1920
Antonella, Sister Mary
Aurelia, Sister Mary
Epper, Hanna
Fitzpatrick, Sara
Flavia, Sister Mary
Gloyeska, Clara
Hannig, Eleanor
McEachern, Ada
McKenna, Hanna
Olps, Matilda
Vayda, Anna
Vayda, Theresa
Warminski, Angeline
Wentzel, Teresa
Wicker, Hedwig

1921
Carroll, Florence
Chodenska, Rose
Gertrude, Sister Mary
Melendy, Fern
Mulligan, Sylvia
Reinoldina, Sister Mary
Sandin, Helga
Swirszinski, Helen
Weis, Emma
Willibalda, Sister Mary

1922
Alzheimer, Elizabeth
Axel, Wilma

Carlson, Gertrude
Krewis, Mildred
Lawrence, Kacid
Meunier, Verna
Morris, Harriet

1923
Beall, Marguerite
Bowser, Lenore
Farnum, Mary
Karr, Emma
Polaski, Mary
Sabo, Rosalie
Sophina, Sister Mary
Theresia, Sister Mary
Thomas, Minnie

1924
Daylor, Marguerite
Lamach, Anna
McGuinos, Ethel
Mosgrove, Anna
Petrosky, Victoria
Poxon, Mary Etta
Sanovicz, Nancy
Sirlin, Elizabeth

1925
Bratton, Lolah
Barnett, Annabelle
Evans, Susan
Navickey, Anna
Schatzley, Naomi
Volk, Catherine

1926
Corpa, Mary Louise
Flannigan, Kathleen
Lynch, Ruth
Malone, Elizabeth
Walsh, Mae

1927
Arnold, Alice
Fagan, Helen
Fleishman, Cecelia
Golkowski, Adeline
Kapsch, Ann
Kapsch, Margaret
Monroe, Marie
Wisher, Teresa
Wishman, Ellyn
Volk, Margaret

1928
Anderson, Helen
Bernard, Lucille
Clark, Madeline
Daerr, Helen
Dellibac, Betty
Larson, Esther
Liss, Carrie
Love, Marie
MacDonald, Elizabeth
Masters, Ruth
Wheale, Edith
Wood, Eva

1929
Billings, Phyllis
Bogesdorfer, Rosana
Bolatoff, Laura
Dittrich, Ada
Hinkle, Mable
Junglen, Margaret
Kapsch, Margaret
Klote, Catherine
Koelzer, Maxelinda
Kopcho, Helen
Kotarski, Alice
LeDue, Winnifred
Nebe, Sophie
Negrelli, Rose
O'Connor, Eileen
Polomcak, Sophie

1930
Berg, Ruth
Coy, Caroline
Glankovic, Agnes
Hammes, Florence
Kopcho, Emma
McMath, Teresa
Manson, Bella
Mazeika, Veronica
Merhar, Ann
Still, Bernadine
Sjaholm, Eleanor
Verdeyen, Emma

1931
Balyard, Grace
Boyd, Vivienne
Campbell, Imogene
Charlton, Mary
Doyle, Estelle
Feasel, Helen
Fox, Susan

Gunder, LaVerne
Johannes, Alma
Kennedy, Mary Regina
Keseric, Emily
Kortokrax, Adelaide
Majcher, Bernice
O'Connor, Margaret
Owen, Pearl
Royal, Ethel
Stewart, Delena
Wright, Gladys
Zimmer, Emma

1932
Bools, Pauline
Dorger, Louise
Gillan, Ruth
Horkavi, Helen
Janscek, Emily
Klouger, Lorraine
Kosky, Viola
Kuzmitz, Frances
Lichtle, Margaret
Malayter, Veronica
Olmstead, Elizabeth
Ooms, Marie
Peterson, Charlotte
Quilling, Charlotte
Rombold, Emma
Smellie, Martha

1933
Carpenter, Lois
Coffeen, Isobel
Crowell, Marion
Detrick, Margaret
Garbon, Victoria
Henderlong, Leone
Henderson, Elsie
Holzmer, Helen
Hopkins, Gladys
Ihnat, Julia
Kristofeck, Bessie
Northcut, Maxine
Rogers, Pauline
Plummer, Vera

1934
Cregg, Catherine
Elisher, Ermine
Glankovic, Mary
Gurband, Lois
Hayden, Margaret
Henderson, Marie
Knapp, Rosemary

Kowal, Olga
Nelson, Genieva
Petrovich, Helen
Pozonovich, Helen
Settlemire, Mary
Stebbins, Dorothy
St. Mary, Lavina

1935
Collins, Margaret
Endicott, Gwendolyn
Jeanette, Sister Mary
Lindquist, Svea
Novotny, Mildred
Schultz, Viola
Slamkowski, Irene
Surovek, Theresa (Sister Cecile)
Timothy, Helen
Wade, Dorothy
Wagner, Madelyn
Witham, Frances

1936
Bayus, Ann M.
Brown, Lucille
Clark, Lail June
Cook, Genevieve J.
Corwell, Kathryn
Gracina, Olga
Gee, Evelyn Van de Lester
Hough, Charlotte
Huttin, Marie
Marciniak, Lottie
Smith, Jeanette
Tyskowski, Frances
Warner, Evelyn

1937
Aydelotte, Helen
Doerr, Margaret
Hendricks, Pearl
Higdon, Frances
Kruzic, Genevieve
Lawlor, Bernadine

McLocklin, Margaret
McTigue, Dorothy
Minger, Maxine
O'Malley, Cecelia
Pilipovich, Martha
Planck, Edna
Reha, Mary

1938
Bartkus, Estelle
Beckman, Anna Irene
Bertha, Catherine
Biblo, Barbara
Davis, Alma
Gaffney, Ada
Kish, Emma
Krupinski, Bertha
Medley, Helen B.
Nywening, Mildred
Ozimec, Mary Anna
Pruvenok, Mary
Radzwicki, Wanda
Spitz, Lovella
Steiner, Frances
Thill, Barbara
Rongers, Margaret
Vygrala, Mary

1939 - February
Farrell, Lillianna
Harper, Wilma
Heilman, Phyllis
Kunert, Verna
Lally, Mary
Stapleton, Sally
Walters, Dorothy

1939
Barnes, Barbara
Cory, Helen
Coughlin, Ruth
Edmonds, Loneata
Golden, Irene
Hullett, Margaret
Kruzick, Ruth

Lane, Agatha
McBride, Laura
McCloskey, Catherine
Mullen, Mary
Noak, Lydia
Roy, Mary Elizabeth
Schnick, Josephine
Schoon, Margaret
Valenas, Eugenia
Wiesemann, Mary E.

1940
Allen, Doris
Armantrout, Rosella
Bendt, Marguerite
Daniels, Ruby
Finn, Marie
Grimala, Louise
Gulbransen, Lillian
Hamsmith, Ruth
Kasarda, Veronica
Marovich, Dorothy
Prentiss, Lucille
Williamson, Constance

1941
Abrahamson, Patricia
Book, Priscilla
Brinzo, Betty
Byrne, Dorothy
Casey, Catherine
Cushman, Charlotte
Delich, Olga
Editz, Eleanor
Ennis, Rita
Entrekin, Dorothy
Fitzpatrick, Ellen
Hard, Helen
Holmquist, Nellie
Horkavi, Irene
Hough, Edith
Jancarich, Violet
Jenda, Ann
Kennedy, Lois
Kriston, Elizabeth
Lindsay, Clara

Markesich, Mary
Michaels, Lillian
Mikovich, Ann
Mordi, Emily
Pekarski, Albertus
Reey, Adella
Sotak, Gizella
Steele, Margaret
Sobotka, Harriet
Troutwine, Dorothy
Turk, Ida
Verplank, Josephine
Weaver, Betty
Webber, Elizabeth

1942
Adamcheck, Joan
Ahrens, Dorothy
Bartz, Helenjean
Fitzpatrick, Patricia
Fry, Lila
Gunn, Kathryn
Hesky, Mildred
Kahler, Phyllis
Keilman, Genevieve
Lanham, Margaret
Lucas, Agnes
McMahon, Marguerite
Martin, Helen
Murphy, Helen
Neises, Marie
Pfaff, Beatrice
Simpson, Marjorie
Sosh, Anna
Stark, Bernice
Willy, Phyllis
Witt, Dorothy

1943
Aubuchon, Mary
Belanger, Gloria
Borsewicz, Stephanie
Corcoran, Frances
Chvostal, Anna
Frishkorn, Mary
Golden, Marjorie
Hart, Margaret
Green, Helen
Jebens, Eleanor
Joint, Lois
Kramer, Madelen
Leake, F. Maxine
Lee, Margaret
Loneski, Eleanor
Lump, Bernice
McChesney, Marguerite
McKown, Anna
Melevin, Bernice
Monnig, Clara
Murray, Betty
Olszewski, Florence
Peterman, Dorothy
Peterman, Emily
Razumich, Katherine

Schiesser, Agnes
Schreiber, Mary
Schutkovske, Betty
Settle, Kathleen
Strubig, Alice
Thompson, Alice
Thompson, Margaret
Utpatel, Eva
Warus, Helen
Williams, Joan
Wirth, Dolores
Ziese, Mary Margaret

1944
Anderson, A. Elizabeth
Berlinger, Mary
Brady, Florence
Boncela, Charlotte
Carew, Gertrude
Donlin, Grace
Dufresne, Hudwig
Frederick, Anna Marie
Freisen, Joan
Galloway, Audrey
Gill, Mary
Graves, Dorothy
Herman, Sophie
Koval, Helen
Koziol, Helen
Lenihan, Mary
Locke, Betty Lou
Lorenz, Eleanor
Love, Dorothy
Marposon, Mary
Mulhern, Mildred
Rowan, Agnes
Tanner, Frances Echard
Sark, Annabelle
Singer, Dorothy
Tyskowski, Marie
Willy, Bernice
Zabowski, Harriet

1945
Anderson, Colleen
Bender, Mary E.
Busselberg, Marian
Capouch, Betty
Dukelow, Mary
Edwards, Mary Patricia
Glankovic, Theresa
Herdegen, Ethel
Lloyd, LaVerne
Mikalauskis, Bernice
Miller, Clara Jane
Ornelas, Consuelo
Rasmussen, Elizabeth
Rongers, Anna Marie
Schiesser, Marie
Smith, Madalyn
Storts, Juanita
Tomyanovich, Betty
Whitehead, Norma
Wilcox, Florence
Wojciehoski, Lucille

1946 – February
Christensen, Catherine
Fletcher, Sarah
Frank, Ruth
Hielscher, Jocelyn
Kindberg, Bettymae
Mele, Mary
Nyhius, Ardelle
Wiegand, Betty

1946
Bayus, Josephine
Bell, Mae
Forrester, Jeanette
Franz, Genevieve
Hawkins, Maxine Rose
Hoffmeister, Patricia
Huff, Marjorie
Kingston, Josephine
Klug, Ethelyn
Kovalcik, Pauline
Luck, Grace
Mikulich, Kathryn
Murphy, Marie
MacPherson, Eileen
Oberle, Margaret
Radville, Eleanor
Roganovich, Violet
Santel, Helen
Schraeder, Doris
Stowers, Doris
Swanson, Lorraine
Swets, Beatrice
Uelmen, Mary
Wilson, Mary Lois

1946 – December
Brooks, Virginia
Charais, Mildred
Cichowlaz, Dolores
Faye, Georgia Deane
Koval, Margaret
Milanovich, Dorothy
Slosarcik, Anne
Urban, Leona
Willy, Arlyene
Wiseman, Margaret

1947 – January
Booher, Esther
Durfos, Irene
Durkin, Mary Jane
Hawkins, Mary Alice
Hughes, Mabel Shaw
Kramazeh, Mary
Mitchell, Lorain
Sadja, Anne
Schest, Wilma
Urbaniak, Irene

1947
Bertucci, Elizabeth
Ferrero, Gloria
Ford, Lillian
Glassford, Catherine

One of the earliest photos available from St. Mary's Mercy Hospital School of Nursing is of the five graduates of the class of 1918. Although their identities are unknown in the photo, they are listed in the roster of graduates as Leone Barwiler, Anne Gordon, Florence Krause, Josephine Nix, and Genevieve Rohyans. The school opened in 1912.
Calumet Regional Archives, IU Northwest

Gunnerson, Naida
Hallman, Violet
Ippolito, Mary
Kovachi, Mary
Krasnansky, Mary
McCormick, Patricia
Matuszewski, Dolores
Murzyn, Theresa
Nomanson, Lenora
Nora, Marie
Nowakowski, Cecelia
Palumbo, Mary
Schreiber, Evelyn
Schuster, Hilda
Sieverding, Gertrude
Sosh, Helene
Steiner, Diane
Vicenzi, Eileen
Visclosky, Helen
Volk, LaPerta
Wells, Josephine
Werline, Betty
Wrobel, Angeline
Zadra, Evelyn

1948 – February
Haugh, Nan
Ligda, Rita
Meyer, Betty
Murphy, Joan
Pattee, Geraldine
Tuttle, Virginia
Slickus, Genevieve

1948
Bartkowiak, Elaine
Bollog, Irene
Bruinsma, E. Helene
Carpenter, Marie Jean
Detterline, Vera
Diaz, Alice

Frederick, Annella
Fugate, Vivian
Granger, Joyce
Huber, Patricia
Keleman, Ethel
Olson, Anita
Palumbo, Grace
Raboin, Gloria
Toretta, Mary Ann
Wallen, Eleanor
Walton, Betty

1949
Kuzma, Mildred
Keeney, Velma
Kirla, Betty
Levy, Helen
Mikos, Bernice
Nomanson, Barbara
Pappas, Marjorie
Rouhselange, Lyra
Sandala, Anne
Stachyra, Lillian
Vincent, Theresa
Winters, Carole Possi

1950
Augustinovich, Pauline
Dernik, Mildred
Glavan, Mary
Grande, Madeline
Harmon, Patsy
Hren, Veronica
Kemp, Alice
O'Keefe, Marguerite
Stephenson, Dorothy
Talbert, Barbara

1951
Borschart, Helen
Eisenhutt, Mary

Elencik, Mildred
Fishcher, Mary C.
Golubic, Terese
Hotuetz, Lorraine
Iussig, Savina
Janowski, Dorothy
Losinski, Ruth
Pawlus, Lucille
Polizzotto, Ann
Richardson, Lorraine
Slingsby, Betty
Stanko, Mary Helen
Starr, Charlotte
Tomaszewski, Eleanor
Vestal, Zoe Ann
Walker, Doris Carol

1952
Cole, Diane
Courtright, Joan
Dalke, Lois
Finucan, Theresa
Gaffney, Kathryn
Gibbons, Phyllis
Gutierrez, Paula
Hubbard, Joan
Lenburg, Vivian
Puscak, Anne
Stempniak, Diane
Sweeney, Theresa
Swingler, Joan
Van Cleave, Janice
Wainman, Patricia
Zimny, Dolores
McEllis, Marie (Urban)

1953
Balucki, Victoria
Coundiff, Marjorie Jean
Demo, Dorothy
Farris, Edna

Linko, Joan
Matthews, Dorothy
McGarry, Maxine
Moblo, Judith
Muldoon, Patricia
Patellis, Katherine
Roberts, Ruth
Sayles, Marilyn
Scubelek, Rose Marie
Welch, Dorothy

1954
Atzhorn, Ruth
Berke, Marilyn
Farrell, Gaynell
Gordon, Joan
Henderson, Patricia
Hutton, Clara
Mang, Eileen
Romanyak, Marianne
Shelton, Barbara
Smith, Doris
Watkins, Patricia

1955
Barkalow, Betty
Beckman, M. Lucille
Bonick, Dolores
Bradford, Barbara
Brandmeier, Mary Ann
Chentnik, Patricia
Coefield, Janice
Donovan, Patricia
Herbst, Loretta
Hesters, Lucille
Inez, Sister M.
Kaster, Mary
Kmetz, Delores
Koldus, Helen
Konieczny, Marie
Kovachi, Florence

Krasnansky, Dorothy
Kretschmer, Barbara
McGarry, Janet
Mattingly, Phyllis
Matuszewski, Barbara
Napierala, Mary Ann
Netzhammer, Jo Ann
Ortiz, Celia
Peas, Phyllis
Piotrowicz, Genevieve
Shaffer, Voande
Wojciehoski, Eva
Wrobel, Dolores

1956
Arzumanian, Mary
Betancourt, Celia
Bratina, Mary Ann
Burke, Barbara
Cammarata, Josephine
Carl, Darlene
Ensminger, Shirley
Ficht, Rita
Holmes, Hazel
Horvath, Frances
Hronec, Theresa
Humenik, Lorraine
Jones, Mary
Kacmar, Betty
Kerns, Rose Marie
Kohley, Mary
Koleszarik, Barbara
Konz, Sandra
Lloyd, Maxine
McCarthy, Sharon
Moneypenny, Mary
Murray, Lucenthia Hayes
Palakovic, Catherine
Quinlan, Nancy
Singleton, Doris
Smith, Carol

Sohovich, Elaine
Spitz, Donna
Torrez, Mary Ann
Vonderhaar, Rose Marie
Williams, Christell

1957
Bianchini, Jeanette
Biggs, Ila Mae Heisterberg
Blakey, Anna M. Craig
Bourque, Joanne
Charbonneau, Evelyn
Chruby, Frances
Deiotte, Celine
Gilliam, Shirley
King, Shirley
Kokos, Dolores
Parot, Lillian
Patnoe, Irene Roberta
Sargent, Sally
Schissler, Judith
Settle, Patricia
Shestak, Joanne
Siurek, Elaine
Spann, Yvonne
Trump, Patricia
Williams, Beverly
Wilson, Gertrude

1958
Adams, Christine
Breitenbach, Margaret
Brown, Joyce
Bumbera, Phyllis
Burke, Joan
Dalton, Delores
Danzy, Marian
DeBie, Marie
Erickson, Joyce
Gibbon, Carole Ann
Greenwood, Elizabeth

In the classroom

Calumet Regional Archives, IUN

Halaschak, Ann Marie
Harenzo, Caroline
Hammes, Marie
Hudak, Patricia Ann
Huseman, Jeannine
Johnson, Jacquelyn
Jones, Mildred
Kowalkowski, Carole
Lulich, Katherine
MacDonald, Geraldine
Melton, Betty Grinstead
Napierala, Catherine
Olszewski, Aurelia
Parr, Catherine
Sanders, Mary Ann
Sebo, Justine

1959
Baker, Eleanor
Chiabai, Anita
Cyr, Kathleen
Farmer, Joyce
Fink, Evelyn
Gregory, Delores Wise
Grube, Mary
Houseknecht, Cherill
Hutts, Doris
Kirla, Veronica
Klaker, Janet
Koleck, Irene
Lindsey, Janet
Magee, Mary
Mattingly, Shirley
Mize, Dorothea
Nadaf, Jeanene
Saklaczynski, Arlene
Smolen, Barbara
Turner, Delores
Whiteman, Joyce

1960
Ambrose, Judith

Broadaway, Lois
Brush, Maryann
Cogley, Ruthann
Csicsko, Janet
Dunn, Martha
Franklin, Delores
Hancock, Imogene
Kachur, Sylvia
Kennedy, Dorothy
Kravets, Darlene
Losinski, Mary Ann
McKenzie, Rose
Morales, Marguerite
Morganelli, Rosemarie
Neely, Audrey
Polito, Barbara
Richter, Charlotte
Sheptak, Julia
Shestak, Elaine
Sotak, Judith
Tolin, Rita

1961
Baker, Maud
Beckham, Rosemary
Brown, Janice Geiselman
Bucko, Sharon
Clements, Beverly
Cook, Virginia
Fehrenbacher, Alice
Gelleott, Janet
Gloodt, Catherine
Harrington, Margaret
Horan, Mary Ann
Hronec, Helen
Huseman, Kay Frances
Johnson, Veolar
Kramer, Dolores
Kruzic, Judith
LeQuia, Melvin
Luniewski, Jeanette
McCrovitz, Samantha
Magdich, Sandra

Malis, Patricia
Melnyk, Carol
Oprzedek, Carol
Petro, Jean
Powell, Ora Dee
Schmelter, Carol
Slivka, Mary Louise
Sullivan, Rosemary
Wineholt, Judith
Zanoni, Josephine
Stryczek, Judith Kopploman

1962
Alvarez, Victoria
Blake, Delores
Brosman, Lorraine
Eaton, Dolores
Eaton, Janice
Grady, Joyce
Graham, Marilyn
McAvoy, Margaret
Moylan, Frances Jane
Parker, Henricine
Plohg, Janice
Plotkin, Elaine
Prentiss, Joan
Robinson, Lillian
Schiralli, Antoinette
Schiralli, Rosalie
Smolen, Rosemary J.
Spence, James Leo
Sul, Felice
Weiland, Judith

1963 – January
Amor, Judith Lollis

1963
Anjanos, Sophie
Bentley, Victoria
Bogee, Lennette
Brown, Patricia
Castro, Gloria

Devitt, Roberta Grodzicki
Doolin, Christine Milenkoff
Douglas, Evelyn Lula
Gabor, Nancy Hathaway
George, Anastasia
Hack, Judith Jefferson
Kaminsky, Patricia
McCarthy, Cornelia
McConnell, Julia
McCormack, Patricia Karch
Pactwa, Linda
Pichel, Velia
Poling, Mary Lou
Quade, Karen
Sanderson, Judith Sohovich
Simko, Janet
Sims, Darlene
Starek, Patricia
Stiener, Margaret

1964
Appel, Marjorie
Boric, Edith
Brennan, Mary Frances
Gordon, Judith
Johnson, Lorine
Kacedan, Charmaine
Kocher, Lucille
Leaser, Paula
Radivan, Loretta
Redigonda, Judith
Schulte, Emily
Ziemniak, Elizabeth

1965
Evans, Patricia
Fassoth, Ann
Fischer, Mary Ann
Fuller, Karen
Glombicki, Caroline
Hellwig, Mary Elizabeth
Johannes, Sandra
Konieczny, Ruth
Lovich, Francine
McPherson, Phyllis
Murphy, Margaret
Reich, Kathleen
Schaller, Laura
Wilson, Beverly

1966
Burdan, Donna
Goold, Elizabeth
Gorski, Elaine Bickel
Grzywana, Diane
Keilman, Rita
Klaub, Rosemary
Lafever, Margaret
Lopeka, Rose
Niedbajlik, Marie
Potter, Idamae (Mrs.)
Puplava, Joan
Simmons, Ilona
Stewart, Ruth Schaller
Zurawik, Diana

1967
Augustine, Mary Ann
Enge, Patricia
Etchison, Michele
Festa, Christine
Garrard, Mary Kathleen
Hellman, Frances
Kirkus, Agnes
Krause, Diane
Liggett, Carol
Miller, Margaret
Robinson, Lynn
Schmitt, Pamela
White, Carol

1968
Adams, Mattie
Augustine, Susan
Barr, Mary Ann
Bode, Shirlee
Boncela, Barbara
Ernst, Helen
Fagen, Phyllis
Green, Mary
Hornyak, Anna
Mann, Judy
Parrish, Laurel
Sabinske, Lenore
Smith, Laura
Wilson, Diane
Yargus, Jean

1969 – class transferred 7/12/68
School closed 8/11/68
Brown, Janet
Coppess, Betty
Dusich, Mary Ann
Grattenthaler, Linda
Hansen, Janice
Johnson, Ruth
Kratschmar, Jo Lynn
Peach, Theresa
Radulovich, Angela
Sabinske, Gayle
Unger, Rita
Wasiuta, Linda
Zimmerman, Mary Ellen

1970 – class transferred 4/19/68
School closed 8/11/68
Abraham, Eileen
Abraham, Kathleen
Branshaw, Doris
Carlesen, Anne Marie
Gomez, Emilia
Howell, Joanne
Kromgols, Diana
Kuplic, Dianne
Mercer, Deborah
Smith, Jeanette
Smith, Kathleen
Ugarte, Patricia
Varga, Kathleen
Walkowiak, Elaine
Wineinger, Judith

Nursing – the 1920s

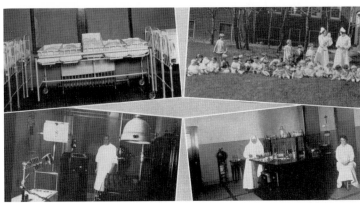

Shown (left to right, top to bottom) in the 1928 edition of the nurses' school yearbook, *"The Pulse,"* are photos of the nursery, some St. Mary's babies, the X-ray Department, and the laboratory.

Calumet Region Archives, IU Northwest

Maxelinda Koelzer graduated from St. Mary's School of
Nursing in 1929. Some of her photos, memorabilia and
scrapbook entries – all preserved in the Calumet Regional
Archives – have been a valuable resource for this book.
Calumet Regional Archives, IU Northwest

In 1928, Maxelinda Koelzer received a letter
from an admiring patient.
Calumet Regional Archives, IU Northwest

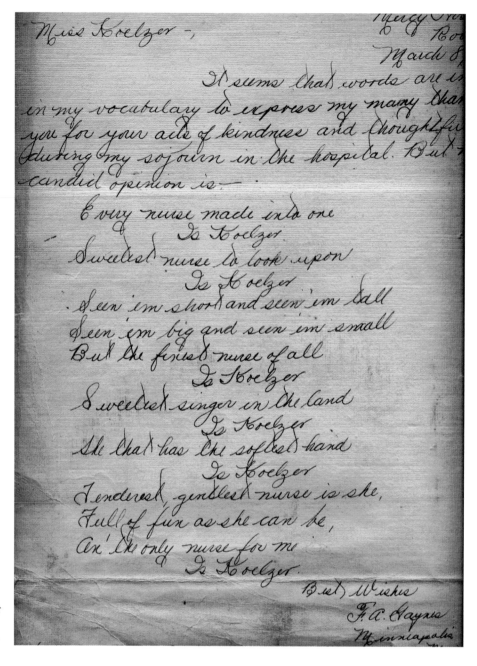

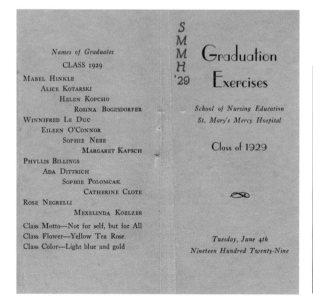

Calumet Regional Archives, IU Northwest

CITY, HOSPITAL AND NURSING

St. Mary's Mercy Hospital and School for Nursing Education, Gary, Indiana

The information contained in this booklet we submit to prospective student nurses, and to those who
have been in the past, and are now, interested in the progress of the institution.

LOCATION

St. Mary's Mercy Hospital is situated in the city
of Gary, Indiana. If one travels south of Chicago
along the shores of Lake Michigan, he soon finds himself in the so-called Calumet District, one of the most
important industrial regions of the United States, of
which Gary, in truth, is the center. Where twenty
years ago the eye detected nothing but the desolate
sand dunes of Northern Indiana, we now behold the
gigantic plants of the U. S. Steel Corporation; the
Illinois Steel Corporation, Tin Mills and Bridge
Works and other various establishments, offering
abundant and profitable employment to many thousands of laborers of different nationalities, all anxious
to become good citizens of God's country.

As a result of such rapid industrial development,
Gary, which was not to be found on the map in 1906,
today boasts of a population of more than 100,000,
and takes just pride in its many churches, schools,
parks and civic improvements.

It deserves to be mentioned, that the city is served
by eight (8) trunk lines, viz; The N. Y. Central, M.
Central, Nickle Plate, Baltimore & Ohio, Pennsyl-
vania, Wabash, Pere Marquette and the Elgin, Joliet
and Eastern, and is therefore, easily accessible from
all points of the West, South and East.

Considering the past development and the present and future possibilities of the Calumet District
and its center, Gary, it can be safely predicted, that,
within the next 25 years there will be but one great
city extending from Chicago east to Michigan City,
Indiana.

Shown here is an excerpt from a bulletin, *"St. Mary's Mercy Hospital and School of Nursing
Education,"* printed around the late 1920s.

Calumet Regional Archives, IU Northwest

Nursing - the 1930s

IT'S BEEN *Said* IN 2009...

"... As a 'probie' we were paid $5.00 a month. Once you became a nurse, the salary was $6.00 for 12 hours for private duty when you first started. You could work for the hospital for room and board for $40.00 a month. That was good. During the Depression, you were glad to get that. Of course I went home and I worked from home after I graduated. I put myself on the registry for private duty."

Helen Petrovich, RN
St. Mary Mercy Hospital
(began in Gary in 1934)
(Note: Helen Petrovich was 95 years old at the time of her interview.)

Shown here are the 1934 graduates of the St. Mary Mercy Hospital School of Nursing. On May 4, 1934, The Gary *Post-Tribune* publicized the event with a headline that read, "11 at Mercy Get Diplomas in Nursing."
Seated (l-r) are Ermine Elisher, Mary Settlemire, Catherine Cregg, and Genieva Nelson.
Standing (l-r) are Mary Glankovic, Helen Petrovich, Marie Henderson, Lois Gurband, Margaret Hayden, Helen Pozonovich, and Olga Kowal.

Photo courtesy of Jancarich family collection

Helen Petrovich, shown at home in 2009, had vivid memories of the St. Mary's Mercy School of Nursing class of 1934.

FIVE MERCY GRADUATES GET STATE CERTIFICATES

Five Gary graduate nurses of Mercy hospital last September, received their state certificates as registered nurses yesterday in the office of County Clerk George W. Sweigert. They were: Margaret Collins, 771 Garfield; Vavina St. Mary, 1300 West 5th; Mildred Novotny, 771 Garfield; Ermine Elischer, 1539 Van Buren, and Helen Petrovich, 1216 Garfield.

Reprinted by permission of the *Post-Tribune*, 1934

Upon Graduation

11 At Mercy Get Diplomas In Nursing

The Nightingale pledge was given to eleven students of the Mercy Hospital School of Nursing Education last night when graduation exercises were held in the K. of C. ballroom, 5th and Madison.

Beginning with solemn high mass yesterday morning in the hospital chapel, the day was filled with class events brought to a conclusion with the ceremony last night. Rev. Joseph Hession of St. Patrick's parish, Fort Wayne, delivered the baccalaureate sermon and the mass and benediction service in the morning. Other priests present were Msgr. Jansen, Rev. H. James Conway, Rev. Edward Sweigart, Rev. Carl Schnitz and Rev. Thomas Daley.

At the noon dinner in honor of the graduating group, the class history was read by Miss Mary Settlemire; the class will and testament was given by Miss Catherine Cregg, and the class prophecy was read by Miss Margaret Collins, junior, class president.

Speaking at the exercises at night, Dr. C. C. Robinson of Indiana Harbor briefly traced the history and growth of Mercy hospital, and Lake Superior Judge Claude V. Ridgely contrasted the nursing done in the dark ages with the scientific methods of today.

Two selections were sung by Florence Guthrie Bader and M. Hobart Bishop, both of whom were accompanied at the piano by Mary Hurley Kitchen. Dr. H. M. Baitinger, president of the Mercy hospital staff, gave the 1934 Florence Nightingale pledge to the class and handed out the diplomas. Dr. L. J. Danieleski, program chairman, presided. Members of the graduating class

included Miss Geneva Nelson, Miss Margaret Hayden, Miss Marie Henderson, Miss Ermine Elisher, Miss Catherine Cregg, Miss Mary Settlemire, Miss Helen Petrovich, Miss Olga Kowal, Miss Helen Pozonvich, Miss Mary Glankovic and Miss Lois Gurband. Miss Emma Carr, obstetrical supervisor, was sponsor for the class.

"The Nightingale pledge was given to eleven students of the Mercy Hospital School of Nursing Education… when graduation exercises were held in the Knights of Columbus ballroom, 5th and Madison. Beginning with solemn high Mass yesterday morning in the hospital chapel, the day was filled with class events brought to a conclusion with the ceremony last night. Speaking at the exercises at night… Lake Superior Judge Claude V. Ridgely contrasted the nursing done in the dark ages with the scientific methods of today."

Reprinted by permission of the
Post-Tribune, May 4, 1934

Posing for a 1934 graduation day photo are (L–R) Helen Pozonovich and Olga Kowal.

Nursing – the 1940s

It's been *Said* in 2009…

"What really helped me was my three years in the school of nursing where I spent hands-on time in the Emergency Room. That helped me more than psychology or any of the lovely things about Shakespeare that I learned to get my degree. It helped throughout my 42-year career."

Margaret Hart Swisher
Auxiliary Member, former RN
Graduate of St. Mary's Mercy School of Nursing, 1943

FOR APPEARANCE SAKE

Vivian Fugate Springer graduated from St. Mary's Mercy School of Nursing in 1948. Her class, she said, was under the "strict" tutelage of Sister Vitalis Witt, PHJC, director of nurses. The class began with 40 students and wound up with 16 graduates. Here are some facts and figures, rules and regulations from the 1940s, as noted by Vivian Fugate Springer.

~ We wore white uniforms, cotton hose, usually heavily darned. There were no nylons in those days.

~ We wore blue capes over our uniforms.

~ No hair on the collar.

~ No finger nail polish.

~ No colored sweaters.

~ Even our shoe strings had to be cleaned and shoes polished daily.

THE SCHEDULE

~ We were in Nurses Training seven days a week for three years with no summers off.

~ In summer time, though, if we had a nickel and a few hours off, we caught the bus to the beach and hopefully there would be someone we knew who would give us a free ride back.

THE RULES

~ There were three girls to every room with one dresser and two small closets (and not that many personal clothes).

~ Doors were locked at 9:00 p.m. and bed check was at 9:30 p.m.

~ No students were allowed to be married or get married.

~ On Sundays, if Sister Vitalis didn't have enough girls lined up to go to Mass, she rang the fire drill bell to add to her numbers.

HOSPITAL MEMORIES

~ Different groups ate in different dining rooms – students, doctors, employees, etc.

~ There were no disposables then. Syringes and needles were washed and sterilized.

~ Needles were sharpened.

~ Gloves were washed and put on a rack to dry, then turned and put in pockets and sterilized.

~ Catheters were washed and put in solution to be sterilized.

~ Bed pans were gathered up on carts and washed by hand as were urinals and wash basins.

~ Turpentine stupes were used for a swollen abdomen. (This was a bucket of warm water and turpentine on a wool cloth that was wrung out and put on the abdomen.)

~ There were not too many antibiotics (like penicillin) at the time. They did not come into use until 1949, usually given as 2,500 units every three or four hours.

~ Patients had lengthy stays in the hospital. New mothers were kept on bed rest for 10 days and on the 10th day were encouraged to sit on the edge of the bed. They went home on the 14th day.

~ Only fathers were allowed to visit the maternity floor and could view their babies through the glass in the nursery during visiting hours.

~ Most babies were bottle fed and were taken to their mothers once a day.

~ Breast fed babies were taken to their mothers every three or four hours.

~ There were 90 to 100 babies in the nursery at one time.

TAKING A HIKE…
Vivian Fugate (Springer) is shown here in 1946 adjusting her cotton stocking. The stretchy material sometimes left "bumps" at the knee.

Shown (l-r) in 1945 are "probies" Vivian Fugate (Springer), Alice Kemp and Anita Olson, roommates in their first year of nursing school. Students wore pointed caps during the first six months of school followed later by square caps. Upon graduation, they received black ribbons for their caps. Nursing capes were dark blue.

World War II – Volunteers and the Cadet Corps

World War II called not only for volunteer nurses but also for additional service on the part of the School of Nursing to train a corps of Cadet Nurses. Before the last-minute formalities of approving Mercy Hospital's participation in the Cadet program were completed, 31 students had registered.

The Motherhouse, Donaldson, Indiana Archives

"I attended St. Mary's Mercy School of Nursing from 1945-1948. Our class was the last class covered by the United States Nurse Cadet Corps. We got to take advantage of this program because we had already passed our entrance exams before the war ended.

"There were not many RNs at the hospitals then because most of them were in the Cadet Corps and then were required to go into active service. After three years of nurses' training you had to serve in some branch of the service for a designated amount of time."

Vivian Fugate Springer, R N, RETIRED
MERCY HOSPITAL
(BEGAN IN 1948 IN GARY)

Joyce Granger, a 1948 nursing school graduate, is shown here in 1945 in the United States Nurse Cadet Uniform.

Shown here in 1946 is the St. Mary Mercy Nursing School graduating class and junior class at Marquette Park Pavilion in Miller, Indiana. Juniors are seated on the right and graduates on the left. Photo courtesy of Kay Comerford who is seated sixth from the back left window at the left table, left side.

A sample class photo, this one from the St. Mary's Mercy Hospital School of Nursing, 1948, shows Director of Nurses Sister Vitalis Witt, PHJC, in the center with nurses in their square caps.

TOP ROW (L-R): Elaine Bartkowiak, Irene Bollog, Helen Bruinsma, Jean Carpenter, Class President Vera Detterline, Alice Diaz, Treasurer Annella Frederick
SECOND ROW FROM TOP (L-R): Vivian Fugate, Joyce Granger, Patricia Huber, and Ethel Keleman
THIRD ROW FROM TOP (L-R): Anita Olson, Gloria Raboin, Mary Ann Toretta and Eleanor Wallen
BOTTOM ROW (L-R): Betty Walton, Barbara Nomanson, and Carol Winters

IT'S BEEN *Said* IN 2009... ⁓⁓⁓⁓⁓⁓⁓⁓⁓⁓⁓⁓⁓⁓⁓⁓⁓⁓⁓⁓⁓

"After graduation in 1948, there were not many cars because of the war and most girls did not drive. If you stayed on and worked at the hospital you could live on the fifth floor – two girls to a room with room, board and laundry for $12.00 a month."

Vivian Fugate Springer, R.N, RETIRED
MERCY HOSPITAL
(BEGAN IN 1948 IN GARY)

Nursing – the 1950s

1955 – Honors and Firsts in Nursing
A superior scholastic record brought top honors for Sister Inez Wilmering (second from left) who was the top graduate of 29 senior students at St. Mary's Mercy Hospital School of Nursing in 1955. She is shown here receiving an award from Director of Nursing Sister Lourdes (Meyer), PHJC. Lucille Beckman (center) was recognized for perfect attendance, and Janice Coefield (right of Beckman) was the first African-American girl to graduate from a Lake County nursing school. Standing far left is Fred Cassidy, who was toastmaster for the graduate banquet in the hospital auditorium. The class of 1955 also included the first married student whereas previously only unmarried students were allowed into the school.

Reprinted by permission of the
Post-Tribune, 1955

IT'S BEEN *Said* IN 2009...

"When the class of 1954 came into training, we were the first ones who got the new uniforms. Our uniform was a pale blue dress and all you got was a wrap-around white apron over the bottom so you were blue and white. All the patients thought we were the cleaning crew so we had to tolerate that. After six months, you were given your cap and a bib that buttoned at the waist so what you had was a full apron over the blue.

"We got our capping after six months and in our junior year we got two blue bars in the corner of the cap. Senior year we had three and then when we graduated, of course, we got our white cap with black bands."

Evelyn Charbonneau Ryan, RN
INFECTION CONTROL, RETIRED
MERCY HOSPITAL
(BEGAN IN 1957 IN GARY)

Shown here in 1955 wearing a typical nurse's cape is Lillian Parot Smith as she stood outside St. Mary's Mercy School of Nursing. Lillian's cape was a gift from another nurse's mother, Anna Zych, after her daughter was killed in a London bombing in World War II.

After the refrains of the school choir's "Ave Maria! O Maiden Mother," diplomas were conferred upon 21 graduates from St. Mary's Mercy School of Nursing class of 1957. Held at Holy Angels Cathedral in Gary, the afternoon's commencement exercises included an address by the Most Reverend Andrew G. Grutka, D. D., bishop of the Gary Diocese. CLASSMATES SHOWN (L-R) IN FRONT ROW: B. Williams, J. Bourque, S. Gilliam, E. Charbonneau, and D. Kokos. MIDDLE ROW (L-R): P. Trump, G. Wilson, E. Siurek, S. King, A. Brown, I. Biggs, S. Sargent, F. Chruby and L. Parot. BACK ROW (L-R): J. Bianchini, Y. Spann, P. Settle, J. Schissler, R. Patnoe, J. Shestak, and C. Deiotte.

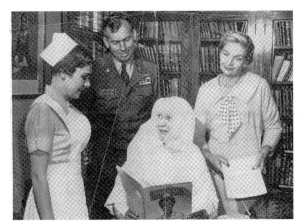

In April 1956, the Army Student Nurse Program (ASNP) was designed to help solve the acute shortage of nurses in the Army. The ASNP provided financial assistance, pay, and allowances of Private First Class (PFC) (E3), to nursing students, both men and women, at the end of their second year in either a three- or four-year program, and at the end of their third year in a five-year program. The schools of nursing were approved by the Department of the Army and accredited by the National League for Nursing. Upon successful completion of the ASNP and state licensure, the participant was commissioned as a second lieutenant in the U.S. Army Reserve and obligated to serve on active duty for two or three years, depending on the length of time in the nursing program.

Joanne Bourque (left), a senior student nurse at Mercy Hospital, was the first student nurse in the nation to enter the Student Nurse Program of the United States Army. She enlisted in the Women's Army Corps Reserve under the Army's new Student Nurse Program. She is shown in this photo in the late 1950s conferring with Sister Lourdes (Meyer), PHJC, as Army Recruiting Sgt. Charley Henderson and Mercy Hospital Recruitment Director Marian Danek watch.

Reprinted by permission of the *Post-Tribune* (undated)

NURSING – THE 1960S

IT'S BEEN *Said* IN 2009...

"I think all my classmates would agree that the best time in Nurses' Training was the time spent on our three affiliations – experience in Psychiatry at the Westville Indiana State Hospital; experience in Maternity and Childbirth at the Chicago Maternity Center (where we went with the doctors into the Projects to assist in home deliveries); and experience in learning TB Nursing at the Chicago Municipal Tuberculosis Sanitarium in Chicago."

Kay (Huseman) Marciniak, R.N
ST. MARY MERCY SCHOOL OF NURSING
(CLASS OF 1961)

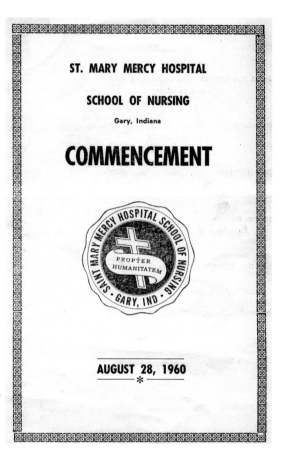

ST. MARY MERCY HOSPITAL

SCHOOL OF NURSING

Gary, Indiana

COMMENCEMENT

SAINT MARY MERCY HOSPITAL SCHOOL OF NURSING · GARY, IND ·
PROPTER HUMANITATEM

AUGUST 28, 1960

The 1960 graduating class of the School of Nursing held its commencement at Holy Angels Cathedral in Gary. A total of 22 students participated in graduating exercises in August of that year. The Most Reverend Andrew G. Grutka, D. D., bishop of the Gary Diocese, conferred diplomas upon the graduates.

The nursing class of 1964 was one of the last classes of St. Mary's Mercy School of Nursing. The school closed in 1968. Pictured (l-r): Mary Frances Brennan, Lorine Johnson, Emily Schulte, Judith Gordon, Lucille Kocher, Charmaine Kacedan, Paula Leaser, Judith Redigonda, Elizabeth Ziemniak, Loretta Radivan, Marjorie Appel, and Edith Boric.

Calumet Regional Archives, IU Northwest

"HOME"/EDUCATION FOR THE NURSING STUDENTS

St. Mary's Mercy Hospital School of Nursing

540 TYLER STREET
GARY 3, INDIANA

August 1957

Dear Applicant,

Your application for admission to the St. Mary Mercy School of Nursing has been accepted. The class will be admitted on August 26. Please report to the School Office on the main floor of the Nurses Home on that date between 2 and 4 p.m. without further notice. Should it be inconvenient for you to come in on this date, arrangements can be made for you to come in a day or two earlier if you will let us know of the change. All baggage sent to the school by express or parcel post must be prepaid and plainly labeled with the full name of the owner.

Uniforms and towels will be laundered by the hospital. The students must provide their own towels, wash cloths and soap. Bed linen, blankets and pillows are provided by the school. Students may do personal laundry in a laundry room in the Nurses Home which is furnished with automatic washers, conventional type washing machine, dryers, irons and ironing boards.

It is advisable that all articles of clothing and other items be clearly marked with name tapes or in indelible ink.

The cost for the first year of nurses training is approximately $400 this year. The cost for the three years is approximately $600. The cost of textbooks, uniforms and cape might subject this amount to change. We will expect a down payment of $210 on the date of entry unless the student has made other arrangements or intends to make other arrangements should there be a financial problem.

A charge of $10 is made for the closet and the room keys. The key deposit will be refunded at the termination of nurses training upon return of the keys.

Students who withdraw during the first year of nurses training are charged board and room on the basis of $1.00 per day for room plus all cafeteria costs during the time they are in residence.

Please return the remainder of your application blanks as soon as possible by return mail if you have not already done so. We must have the application forms on file for our own use before you enter. Should you have any further questions, please feel free to call or write.

Very sincerely yours,

Sister M. Lourdes, R. N.
Director, School of Nursing

Notably, this letter of acceptance to the School of Nursing in August, 1957, signed by the school's director, Sister Lourdes (Meyer), PHJC, states that the cost for the first year of nurses training is approximately $400.

The School of Nursing residence was not built when the school first opened. In 1923, ground was broken for the new structure. In later years, with increased student registration, the attic was converted into living quarters; nurses' rooms were added above the porch, and an elevator was installed. It was erected in 1924.

A view of the Nurses Home shows a vintage car of the 1930s parked on a side street.

The dining room   Calumet Regional Archives, IU Northwest

Reading room at the home of the student nurses.

Calumet Regional Archives, IU Northwest

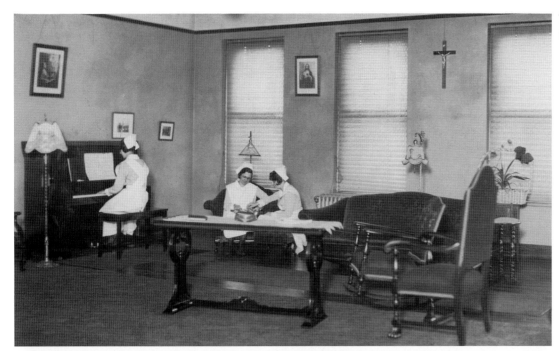

The ancillary room
Calumet Regional Archives, IU Northwest

"BIG SISTERS" HAND OUT CAPS
Shown here in 1958 is a capping ceremony held at Holy Angels Cathedral on Seventh Avenue and Tyler Street in Gary. Caps were awarded upon completion of designated studies and each year a stripe was added to the cap. Seniors wore caps with three stripes on them. "Big sisters" were all second year nursing students who gave caps to first year nursing students.

Rosemarie (Morganelli) Ehrhardt attended the St. Mary Mercy Hospital School of Nursing from 1957-1960. These two photos show the interior of a typical room where she and other student nurses lived.

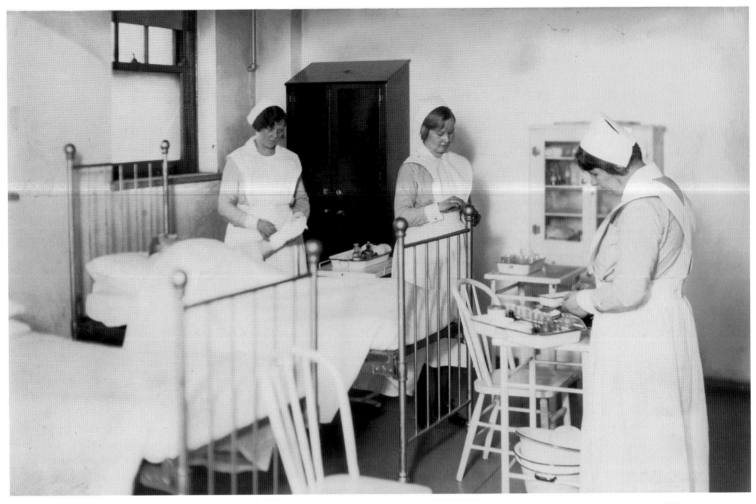

Nursing students with patients

Calumet Regional Archives, IU Northwest

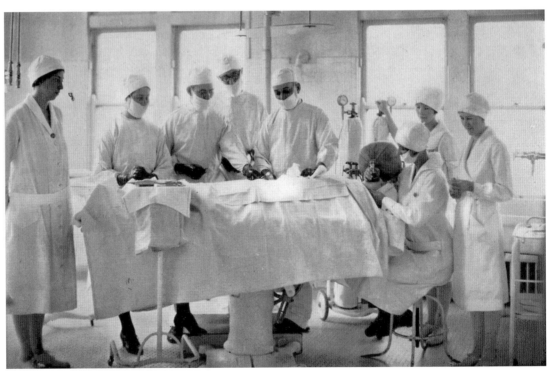

Mercy Hospital Operating Room, 1928

Calumet Regional Archives, IU Northwest

THE GROTTO

IT'S BEEN *Said* IN 2009...

"The grotto was beautiful. It was in between the hospital and the nurses' home and there was a tunnel that connected between both places that you could go through and it sheltered the nurses. Otherwise, you had to go outside. The grotto was situated in a curved area between the two buildings. The purpose of it was spiritual. It was a Catholic hospital and I would say that three quarters of us students were Catholic. We went to Mass in the morning and everyone had breakfast together. Eventually the grotto had no purpose because the nursing school closed in 1968 with its last graduating class. The grotto was torn down in the mid to late 1970s when the space was needed for the remodeling of the Emergency Room."

Rosemarie Ehrhardt
CASE MANAGER, RETIRED
ST. MARY MEDICAL CENTER
(BEGAN IN 1960 IN GARY)

IT'S BEEN *Said* IN 2009...

"I lived just down the road from the nursing school. The hospital was on Fifth and Tyler and I lived on Third and Tyler. I remember walking this way to school and I always noticed the grotto on the south side of the hospital. It was taken down during construction to the new West building in order to make way for the new Emergency entrance."

Ismael "Izzy" Alicea
MAINTENANCE WORKER III
ST. MARY MEDICAL CENTER
(BEGAN IN 1979 IN GARY)

Shown here is a 1958 winter time photo of the grotto that was located between Mercy Hospital and the Nurses Home. It was built by carpenter Leslie Frazee from cement pieces from the hospital. His wife, Agnes Frazee, worked at the hospital as a cook. Inside the grotto was the Blessed Virgin Mary rail. The grotto was taken down in the late 1960s around the time of the West Wing construction that was completed in 1971.

Standing in front of the grotto in late summer are 21 members of the St. Mary Mercy School of Nursing – class of 1959.
STANDING (L-R): Irene Koleck, Cherill Houseknecht, Evelyn Fink, Joyce Whiteman, Doris Hutts, Dorothea Mize, Jeanene Nadaf, Joyce Farmer, Anita Chiaibai, Eleanor Baker, Dolores Gregory, Veronica Kirla, Janet Klaker, Janet Lindsey, and Arlene Saklaczynski.
SEATED (L-R): Delores Turner, Kathleen Cyr, Mary Magee, Shirley Mattingly, Mary Grube, and Barb Smolen.
The Conferring of Diplomas was held at Holy Angels Cathedral, Seventh Avenue and Tyler Street, in Gary.

AUGUST 5, 1959

Nursing Class of 1932 – 50 Years Later

In 1982, the St. Mary Mercy School of Nursing class of 1932 held a week-long 50th reunion full of alumnae banquets, Hobart hospital tours, and "do you remember" chatter that included (in the *Hobart Gazette* of June 16, 1982) "how we had to stand up when a doctor came into the classroom," "how doctors expected undivided attention," "the 10:00 p.m. curfew… and how the (dragon) housemother would lock the door promptly and report us for detention at two minutes after…," "how we were paid six dollars a month for our work while we were learning… and ten dollars a month after we learned!"… "and washing patient beds and scrubbing instruments… and how we had to pay for any broken thermometers and syringes."

My, how nursing has changed!

Florence Nightingale was the first director of the Nightingale Training School. Shown here is a lamp that replicates the style of the Nightingale lamp used by Florence Nightingale as she made her nightly rounds in the Barrack Hospital during the Crimean War. The Nightingale lamp is often used in nursing ceremonies today.

The duties of a floor nurse, as noted in the *History of Nursing, Duties of the Floor Nurse – 1887*, were somewhat different from those of today. "In addition to caring for your 50 patients," it said, "each nurse will follow these regulations:

1. Daily sweep and mop the floors of your ward, dust the patient's furniture and window sills.
2. Maintain an even temperature in your ward by bringing in a scuttle of coal for the day's business.
3. Light is important to observe the patient's condition. Therefore, each day fill the kerosene, clean chimneys, and trim wicks. Wash the windows once a week.
4. Any nurse who smokes, uses liquor in any form, gets her hair done at a beauty shop or frequents dance halls will give the director of nurses good reason to suspect her worth, intentions, and integrity.
5. The nurse who performs her labors faithfully… and without fault for… five years… will be given an increase of 5-cents a day."

NURSING ATTIRE OF 1962
Mrs. Thomas (Rosemarie) Ehrhardt, RN, St. Mary Mercy Hospital, is pictured (at left) in a collarless short-sleeved uniform with patch pockets. Adjacent to the Ehrhardt photo is a plaque bearing the name of St. Mary Mercy Advisory Board President Horace Singer Norton and a roster of board members listed up to the year 1947.
Reprinted by permission of the *Post-Tribune*, JUNE 19, 1962

NURSING ATTIRE OF 1962
In 1962, the *Post-Tribune* ran a story about nurses being able to choose their own attire. The Dior-inspired uniforms of that period were "a far cry from the early garb" of nurses, the article said. Shown here (at right) is Kay Huseman, RN, St. Mary Mercy Hospital in photo as it appeared in the *Post-Tribune* and her choice of three quarter-length sleeves and a collared uniform.
Reprinted by permission of the *Post-Tribune*, JUNE 19, 1962

Nursing Attire

Diamond-cut bodice fastenings, slightly full skirt and waistline piping are style features of the nurse photo shown in the center. Sketched (L-R) in typical nursing costumes of their era are a 17th century French nun; Florence Nightingale; an American nurse in the late 19th century; and a nurse's uniform from the 1920s.

Reprinted by permission of the *Post-Tribune*, June 19, 1962

The School of Nursing – The Teachers

IT'S BEEN *Said* IN 2009...

"The three year nursing program was always considered to be an excellent school in every way. There were physician instructors in the School of Nursing – Dr. Robert Martino was one of them and so was Dr. Raymond Carmody. They had a number of doctors who came in weekly, probably, for whatever class they were involved with. I suppose the Sisters were teaching in the beginning, years before I ever got there but during my time the Sisters were only there as directors – Sister Vitalis Witt, PHJC, Sister Cornelia Leible, PHJC, Sister Lourdes Meyer, PHJC – followed by Barbara Riblon and Mary Gulyassy."

Mary Ellen Donovan
SECRETARY TO THE DIRECTOR
ST. MARY'S MERCY SCHOOL OF NURSING
(BEGAN IN 1945 IN GARY)

IT'S BEEN *Said* IN 2009...

"I enjoyed and (still) treasure the three years of nursing education received at St. Mary's Mercy School of Nursing as we attended classes taught by faculty members from St. Joseph College in Rensselaer who came to our Gary nursing residence. As a class we were quite close and nurtured and supported one another. We were encouraged to 'think outside of the box' on many occasions and to administer holistic care before it was called holistic care! We had excellent nursing educators who mentored us in the classroom and in the hospital setting. We worked with live people!"

Rosemary Beckham Ofsaiof
ST. MARY'S MERCY SCHOOL OF NURSING
(CLASS OF 1961)

Father Joseph Smolar

"Our college credit courses were taught by the St. Joseph's professors, mostly priests and a few lay men. Their courses were anatomy, physiology, microbiology, chemistry, psychology, sociology, professional ethics, marriage in modern life and christian morality.

"By far our very favorite was Father Joe Smolar who taught us anatomy, physiology and microbiology. He not only was our teacher but became a good friend to all of us… He gave of himself to make sure we understood what he was trying to teach us. During our freshman year, he invited our class down to the Rensselaer campus for a tour and 'mixer dance' to meet the boys from 'St. Joe.' He also arranged a 'mixer dance' with the St. Joe boys from the Calumet Campus at the St. John the Baptist Panel Room in Whiting. It was there that I met and later married my husband, Tom."

Kay (Huseman) Marciniak, RN
ST. MARY MERCY SCHOOL OF NURSING
(CLASS OF 1961)

TESTING AND GRADUATION

The fee at the Indianapolis hotel was a mere $3.00 per night.
"There were about 13 of us in one room!" said Rosemarie Ehrhardt.

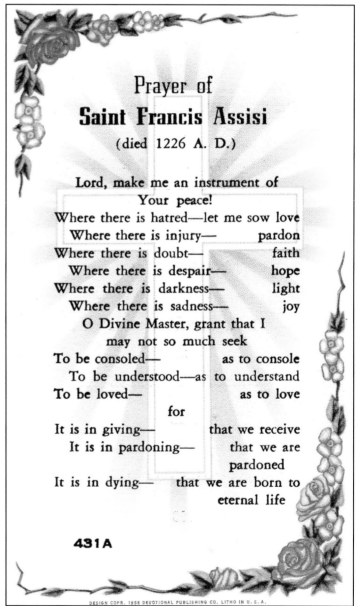

Prayer of Saint Francis Assisi
(died 1226 A. D.)

Lord, make me an instrument of
Your peace!
Where there is hatred—let me sow love
Where there is injury— pardon
Where there is doubt— faith
Where there is despair— hope
Where there is darkness— light
Where there is sadness— joy
O Divine Master, grant that I
may not so much seek
To be consoled— as to console
To be understood—as to understand
To be loved— as to love
for
It is in giving— that we receive
It is in pardoning— that we are
pardoned
It is in dying— that we are born to
eternal life

431A

This prayer of St. Francis of Assisi was the commencement prayer of the St. Mary Mercy Hospital School of Nursing.

(Left) Many graduation ceremonies for St. Mary Mercy's School of Nursing were held at Holy Angels Cathedral in Gary.
Holy Angels Cathedral Ektachrome by Wm. H. Harvey
CHJC, University of Notre Dame Archives

THE ALUMS

In 1976, the St. Mary Mercy Nurses Alumnae Association planned its annual benefit dinner dance to be held at St. Sava Hall in Gary. **SHOWN (L-R)** working on poster distribution are St. Mary Medical Center Assistant Administrator Mary Gulyassy; Bernie Kopcha, association secretary; Dorothy Miller, decorations; and Shirley Makivich (Urbanek), president.

Hobart Herald, NOVEMBER 1976

DID YOU KNOW?

At the annual alumnae dinner held at the Avalon Manor Banquet Center in Merrillville in June 2009, nursing classes from 1939-1968 were represented that evening.

1918 – MAKING HER WAY – SISTER WILLIBALDA HEIDT, PHJC

IT'S BEEN *Said* IN 2009...

"When I started in Gary in 1967 (the late) Sister Willibalda Heidt, PHJC, was still in charge. God have her soul. She was a very, very dedicated nun and a unique person. She had come from Germany in the early 1900s. The bishop of Fort Wayne realized that there were a lot of German immigrants and asked the bishop in Germany to send some German-speaking nuns to Northwest Indiana. She arrived in Fort Wayne and moved to St. Mary Hospital in the early 1920s.

"Sister Willibalda took her boards with the American Registry of Radiology Technologists and after she passed away the Sisters gave me her certificate from the American Society of Radiology Technologists (ASRT) – number five. At the time, to take an exam and be certified, a doctor from Michael Reese Hospital traveled from Chicago to Gary to examine her. She passed the exam and became one of the first Radiology Technologists.

"When Sister Willibalda was doing radiology, radiation protection was not known so these early radiology pioneers got exposed to excessive radiation. As a result, Sister Willibalda developed X-ray radiation burns on her fingers and in the late 1960s (the late) Dr. Ed Zucker grafted the ulcers on her fingers."

Heratch Doumanian, MD., RADIOLOGIST, RETIRED
MERCY HOSPITAL
(BEGAN IN 1967 IN GARY)

"Sister Willibalda was born and raised in Germany as a young child… She came to this country (and) she spoke great German. My grandmother, Elsie Salzman, spoke German. The Salzmans lived across the street so in order for my grandmother to keep up their language, she would come across to the hospital. If you went up to the cystoscopy room, you would see Sister Willibalda and my grandmother sitting there talking German to each other."

Bruce Lovell, X-RAY TECHNOLOGIST
MERCY HOSPITAL
(BEGAN IN 1963 IN GARY)

"Sister Willibalda was in charge of X-ray and took care of me when I wasn't feeling well one day. She insisted I have a chest X-ray which showed pneumonia. She was very vigilant when I was hospitalized at Mercy for five or six days."

Raymond Carmody, M.D., OPHTHALMOLOGIST, RETIRED
MERCY HOSPITAL
(BEGAN IN 1935 IN GARY)
NOTE: AT THIS WRITING IN 2009, DR. CARMODY IS 101 YEARS OF AGE.
HE RETIRED IN 2001 AT AGE 93 AFTER 70 YEARS OF PRACTICE.

"Sister Willibalda was a pearl and she treated me as her son. She was very kind and a very conscientious lady. She was becoming Parkinsonian with small foot steps and shaking of her hands. She had to take off at noon to go and rest and came back to do all the billing by hand with (the late) Mary Vranka. At the time, the two of them were running the department with Ann Mumford and Peggy Smith.

"Our load was in the range of 30-35 patients a day. It was a complicated system. I got involved and I tried to simplify as much as I could but it was still done by hand and Sister made sure that every single patient was billed and everything was accounted for."

Heratch Doumanian, M.D., RADIOLOGIST, RETIRED
MERCY HOSPITAL
(BEGAN IN 1967 IN GARY)

IN HER HONOR

This previously folded newspaper clipping displays a plaque that renamed the Radiology Department in honor of Sister Willibalda Heidt, PHJC, who began working in the department during the days of World War I and remained until her retirement in December 1980.

Pictured at the dedication ceremony (L-R) are Sister Catherine (Thelen); Heratch O. Doumanian, M.D., John Dandridge, Jr., administrator; and Reverend Joseph Herod, hospital chaplain.

Reprinted by permission of the *Post-Tribune*, DECEMBER 1, 1982

The 1920s

Hospital/Community Happenings
1927 – 1952 – The Junior League of St. Mary's Mercy Hospital

IT'S BEEN *Said* IN 2009...

"The Mercy Hospital Junior League was started by a group of young women in the late 1920s. They generally helped the hospital in the Obstetrics Department with many donations – i.e. a light over a birthing bed. There were about 30 in the group and we met in members' homes. The Junior League is still active and the last number of years it has made large stuffed red heart pillows and also little yellow Snoopy dog things for kids."

Margaret Dalby, LONGTIME MEMBER OF THE JUNIOR LEAGUE AND ST. MARY MEDICAL CENTER AUXILIARY

DID YOU KNOW?

1927 – The Junior League of St. Mary's Mercy Hospital was founded.

1952 – The Junior League sponsored the organization of the Mercy Hospital Junior Guild whose charter members were daughters and daughters-in-law of league members.

1953 – The Junior League also sponsored the formation of St. Mary's Mercy Hospital Women's Auxiliary. Approximately 400 women attended a Mercy Hospital gathering on May 18, 1953 to bring together volunteer workers from all parts of Gary to assist the hospital. The auxiliary is still in existence today.

(See "1953 – Auxiliary Beginning" for more information.)

```
HISTORY OF ST. MARY'S MERCY HOSPITAL

1927          Junior League          1953
                   of
              Gary, Indiana


           CHARTER MEMBERS

     Mrs. Clarence W. Bader

     Mrs. Dean K. Courtright

     Mrs. Carl W. Dillon

     Mrs. Andrew B. Elliott

     Mrs. William Glover

     Mrs. T. Mearl Kitchen

     Mrs. Harold Lower

     Mrs. Harold S. Phipps

     Mrs. J. Norman Quinlan

     Mrs. Henry H. Tuerff

     Mrs. William H. Irvin
```

Founded in 1927, the St. Mary's Mercy Hospital Junior League included 11 charter members. This list is reproduced from the league's 25-year history dating from 1927 – 1953.

The Junior League of Mercy Hospital was organized in 1927 with stipulations that membership was limited to 33 people with qualifications that included "Character, Intelligence, and General Uprightness." Monthly meetings were held in members' homes with the exception of September when the Sister Superior acted as hostess. Hostesses, the report further said, "serve a dessert or salad at one o'clock after which the business meeting is held. The remainder of the afternoon is spent sewing for the Maternity Department of the hospital."

The league's first project was to furnish a room on the maternity floor and in its early years also provided equipment for the hospital nursery: Dr. Apt Breast Pump; Dr. DeLee Foot Print Machine; Scialytic Surgical Operating Light; Ohio Nasal Catheter Oxygen Therapy Machine; and an E & J Resuscitating Machine used to revive asphyxiated infants born with retarded respiration.

Initially, funds were raised through membership dues, special assessments, bake sales and three public card parties. The league assisted the Red Cross and the children's department in the tuberculosis sanitorium until 1931 when it voted to dedicate all efforts toward the hospital. At holiday time, baskets of food amounting to five dollars each were given to needy families in Gary. During World War II, the league managed the defense stamp booth and served dinners at the Service Men's Center in the Y.M.C.A.

Marking Time...

1922
- Insulin, which regulates the use of sugar, was isolated and used for the treatment of diabetes by Frederick Banting and Herbert Best.

1923
- A whooping cough (pertussis) vaccine was developed.

1927
- Charles Lindbergh completed the first solo nonstop transatlantic flight (May 21st)
- Philip Drinker and Louis Shaw designed the first "iron lung" for polio patients.

"When we started there were about 14 or 15 of us all belonging to the same organization. We formed the auxiliary and we used to do things for the hospital. The hospitals need support and we just thought it was a good cause. We met every month and we had fund-raisers. Our annual style show was a big deal. I modeled once but we used to have a very nice store in Gary called Hudson's and they put on the style show for us most of the time.

"I also did work inside the hospital and so did several of the other girls.

"I was involved mainly because my husband, Dr. Leo Cooper, was involved with Mercy Hospital. The auxiliary was always known as the auxiliary and the guild was probably mostly daughters of auxiliary members. It was separate. We also had a Junior League that worked for the hospital but it wasn't really connected to the auxiliary."

Arlene Cooper, LONGTIME AUXILIARY MEMBER

THE JUNIOR GUILD

In 1952, the Junior League sponsored the formation of the Mercy Hospital Junior Guild which was to function as a separate organization. Charter members, comprised of daughters and daughters-in-law of league members, included Mrs. Robert O'Malley, Mrs. Samuel Phipps, Mrs. John Hanlan Tuerff, Mrs. Thomas Hayes, Mrs. Charles Bader, Mrs. A. J. Hayes, Mrs. James Culveyhouse, Mrs. Robert Pyle, and Mrs. Gerald Tuerff.

In December, 1952, the Junior League marked its 25th anniversary of volunteer service. Soon to follow would be St. Mary's Mercy Hospital Women's Auxiliary, a strong organization that remains in existence.

(See "1953 – Auxiliary Beginnings")

When the Mercy Hospital Junior League marked its 25th anniversary at the home of Mrs. Thomas Senese, special guest at the Silver Anniversary Tea was Emma J. Karr, head of the hospital's Pediatric Department. Miss Karr was in charge of the department when the league was first organized in 1927. **SHOWN HERE (L-R)** are Mrs. Harold Lower; Mrs. William J. Glover, who was first president of the group; Emma J. Karr; League President Mrs. Harold Phipps; and Mrs. J. Norman Quinlan (SEATED).

Reprinted by permission of the *Post-Tribune* DECEMBER, 1952

The 1930s
HOSPITAL/COMMUNITY HAPPENINGS

POLIO

DID YOU KNOW?

In 1947, the National Foundation for Infantile Paralysis reported that polio attacked thousands of people annually – 75% of them under 20 years of age – leaving half of them crippled for life.

IT'S BEEN *Said* IN 2009...

"While I was in training, we had the polio outbreak in Gary. I had two family members stricken with polio – one with bulbar who wound up as a paraplegic. As students, we went out into the community and helped give injections of the polio vaccine at the Health Department."

Evelyn Charbonneau Ryan, RN
INFECTION CONTROL, RETIRED
MERCY HOSPITAL
(BEGAN IN 1957 IN GARY)

Marking Time...

1930
- Unemployment reached 4.5 million; Congress authorized $116 million for additional public works, and President Hoover established a Committee on Unemployment Relief.

1933
- Franklin Delano Roosevelt was inaugurated as president (March 4) and proclaimed in his inaugural address, "The only thing we have to fear is fear itself."

1934
- The nation's most wanted criminal, John Dillinger, was shot and killed by FBI agents in Chicago, Illinois; sweetheart criminals Bonnie Parker and Clyde Barrow were killed by Texas Rangers.

1935
- The Social Security Act was established, creating a national retirement benefits program.

1936
- President Franklin Roosevelt was re-elected president, defeating Alfred M. Landon in a landslide.
- Howard Florey and Ernst Chain isolated pure penicillin from penicillium mold.

A SPECIAL GROUP

IT'S BEEN *Said* IN 2009...

"One group of general practitioners bears special mention as they were interns at Mercy and later practiced in the area. They are Drs. John Gallinatti, Andrew Russo, and John O. Carter (who is still on the staff at St. Mary's). They were excellent physicians and were essential in helping to arrange with the medical staff at Mercy a special internship for their classmate, Ronald Doneff. Dr. Doneff had severe polio as a senior medical student and required a respirator for a long period. Utilizing a wheelchair and oxygen, he served a year internship on my service. He became an outstanding dermatologist in the area and was an inspiration to all of us."

John T. Scully, MD., INTERNIST, RETIRED
MERCY HOSPITAL | (BEGAN IN 1955 IN GARY)

RAYMOND CARMODY, M.D. – RECALLING A 70-YEAR PRACTICE

Raymond Carmody, M.D. - Graduation photo
Loyola University School of Medicine, 1931

Raymond Carmody, M.D. in a recent photo.
He was 101 years of age in 2009.

IT'S BEEN *Said* IN 2010...

"Dr. Carmody was really one of the most outstanding physicians and a very good friend. We used to get a room with two beds at conferences that were held in Chicago or New Orleans or Florida and he used to say to me, 'Jose, you are snoring too much. I am going to take my pillow and blanket and sleep in the bathtub (laughs).'"

Jose H. Roig, MD.
OPHTHALMOLOGIST, RETIRED
MERCY HOSPITAL
(BEGAN IN 1967 IN GARY)

1935

IT'S BEEN *Said* IN 2009...

"When I finished my internship and residency from Cook County in 1935, Dr. Julius Chevigny and Dr. Keckich were practicing in Gary. When Dr. Keckich passed away from pneumonia, I joined Dr. Chevigny.

"When I first arrived in Gary, I roomed with Gene Swartz at the Dalton apartments. Gene was the deputy auditor of Lake County at the time and later became mayor of Gary. Gene married after a few years and Dr. Joseph Carbone, a pediatrician, and Dr. James Reynolds, a urologist, came to Gary from Cook County Hospital. They both needed a place so we all shared one apartment. Times were very hard and the $75.00 rent was split three ways which helped all of us. The $75.00 included maid service too.

"In those days, we received $2.00 for an office call and $10.00 for a house call. One day, I did 10 tonsillectomies for $10.00 each. There was no insurance or Medicare. People took the streetcar to work every day.

"There was no cafeteria in the hospital so we ate at a small restaurant across the street. Dr. Carbone was Italian and cooked for us on the weekends. He was an excellent cook."

Raymond Carmody, MD., OPHTHALMOLOGIST, RETIRED
MERCY HOSPITAL
(BEGAN IN 1935 IN GARY)
NOTE: AT THIS WRITING IN 2009, DR. CARMODY IS 101 YEARS OF AGE.
HE RETIRED IN 2001 AT AGE 93 AFTER 70 YEARS OF PRACTICE.

"The so-called cures that people believed in were pretty unusual. It was not uncommon for patients to come into the office with asafetida around their necks, garlic cloves in their shoes, or lemons on their heads to ward off a cold. The street cars were full of the smell of garlic because of this.

"One time, a patient came to see me because he had a running ear. I noticed there was a foreign body in the ear also. He said he had tried a cure that someone had told him about which involved grinding up a litter of newborn mice and then adding some oil. He had placed them in his bad ear.

"A gangster (gambling was wide open in Gary then) came in with his girlfriend who had an ear infection. Penicillin had just come out so I proceeded to give her an injection in the buttocks. He let me know in no uncertain terms that 'a shot in the buttocks could not help an ear!'

"I had to do a mastoid operation on a kitchen table because a boy had come down with measles and would not be allowed in the hospital for fear of an epidemic."

Raymond Carmody, MD., OPHTHALMOLOGIST, RETIRED
MERCY HOSPITAL
(BEGAN IN 1935 IN GARY)
NOTE: AT THIS WRITING IN 2009, DR. CARMODY IS 101 YEARS OF AGE.
HE RETIRED IN 2001 AT AGE 93 AFTER 70 YEARS OF PRACTICE.

"You did the best you could (in those days) since there were no antibiotics or emergency rooms. You worked long hours because you had to. Surgery was often unbearable because there was no air conditioning. A nurse would have to wipe your brows constantly so you wouldn't drip into the field.

"For the first 10 years of my practice I did eye, ear, nose and throat. Most of my house calls were ear problems. I had to lance an ear quite frequently. I always remembered that Friday night would be busy because so many people ate fish and would get a fish bone caught in their throat and it had to be removed. It was not unusual to try and stop a nosebleed either. To make house calls, you went down back alleys, up back stairs at all times of the night. One day, I dropped over at the pediatrician's office to say hello since they were on the same floor of the Gary National Bank Building. Dr. Thomas Senese was complaining about having to make 15 house calls. Dr. Joseph Carbone promptly told him, 'That's nothing. I made 22!'"

Raymond Carmody, MD., OPHTHALMOLOGIST, RETIRED
MERCY HOSPITAL
(BEGAN IN 1935 IN GARY)
NOTE: AT THIS WRITING IN 2009, DR. CARMODY IS 101 YEARS OF AGE. HE RETIRED IN 2001 AT AGE 93 AFTER 70 YEARS OF PRACTICE.

ADVANCES IN MEDICINE

"From the time I began in ophthalmology, there was a tremendous advance in technology especially in eye procedures with cataract surgery. I remember when I used to work with Dr. Ray Carmody, we used to put patients in the hospital the day before surgery. We used to give them glycerine by mouth so that the vitreous would not come out. We used to cut the eye at almost 190 degrees with half the eye open to remove the cataract. Back then, we were still using a technique called intra-capsular cataract extraction where the whole lens of the eyeball was removed. In the 1970s, with the use of a microscopic instrument, a new technique called phacoemulsification was developed with the introduction of the intra-occular lens implant. I did thousands of cataract surgeries. I retired in 2007/2008."

Jose H. Roig, MD., OPHTHALMOLOGIST, RETIRED | MERCY HOSPITAL | (BEGAN IN 1967 IN GARY)

ALSO REMEMBERING THE EARLY DAYS...

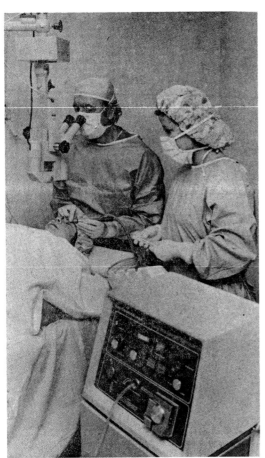

Jose H. Roig, M.D., ophthalmologist at St. Mary Medical Center in Hobart, demonstrates a new cataract removal technique with a phaco-emulsifier that shatters the cataract through the use of sound waves. Surgical Technologist Pam Cortese served as a mock patient as Surgical Technologist Nina Anteveski looked on.

Reprinted by permission of the *Post-Tribune* DECEMBER, 1980

IT'S BEEN *Said* IN 2009...

"In 1944, my husband had pneumonia and he was in a private room for about five days. He was quite ill and there were no antibiotics. I talked to a lady in X-ray and she took him down to X-ray where they had coils they put on his chest. That was before penicillin and they did it because his lungs were pretty congested. The intern had told me he might not live but he recovered and that was the technique at that time.

"It seems to me that the bill for five days in a private room was $100.00. I took him home by ambulance. He was on bed rest for several weeks."

Margaret Hart Swisher, AUXILIARY MEMBER, FORMER RN
GRADUATE OF ST. MARY'S MERCY SCHOOL OF NURSING, 1943

The 1930s
ENVIRONMENTAL SERVICES

Marking Time...

1940
- *President Franklin Roosevelt was re-elected for a record third term.*

1941
- *Japanese forces attacked Pearl Harbor, Hawaii, on December 7, killing approximately 3,000 soldiers and sinking four battleships.*

1943
- *Selman Waksman discovered streptomycin and coined the term antibiotic.*

1949
- *2,720 deaths occurred from polio and 42,173 cases were reported.*

In 1977, the Housekeeping Department, dubbed "proud professionals," published a cookbook, *Our Favorite Recipes*, as a fund raiser at St. Mary Medical Center.

One new type of uniform for housekeeping personnel was shown in this 1976 photo. Pictured (L-R) are Mary Knox, Melissa Jackson, Guka Sormaz and Mary Teamer.

Acts of Mercy, March, 1976

"My husband, Charles, was working in the laundry when I began and that is how we met. In the early days, we folded bath towels and patient gowns by hand. We put soap and bleach into the machines by hand. Now everything is computerized."

Dorothy Lawver, TEAM LEADER LINEN
MERCY HOSPITAL
(BEGAN IN 1970 IN GARY)

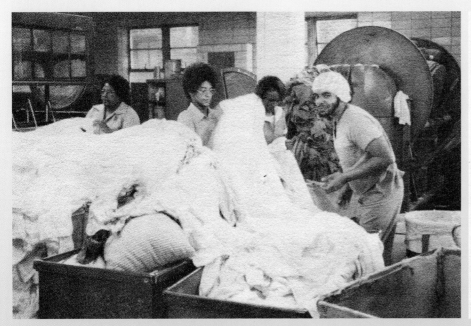

Shown (l-r) here are Mary Harris, Carolyn Lewis, Flora Burrell and Ernest Biddings as they separated dried laundry.

Acts & Facts, APRIL, 1977

Charles Lawver dumped cleaned linens into bins that were transported to the dryers.

Acts & Facts, APRIL, 1977

LENDING A HAND

"In the 1970s and 1980s, I worked in the Laundry Department at St. Mary's in Gary with the Lawvers – Dorothy, a supervisor, and Charles, a co-worker. I remember one time when my car – a blue Chevy Chevette – was stuck in the ice and snow and both of them helped me get it out. I am still grateful for their help.

"The people in this department were quite friendly. At the end of each day when it was time to leave, the team would say, 'laku noc,' which means 'good night' in Serbian."

Dennis Williams, FOOD SERVICE WORKER
ST. MARY MEDICAL CENTER
(BEGAN IN 1974 IN GARY)

Environmental Services – the Staff

Environmental Services staff photo – 2009

Back row, standing (l-r): Mariano Guajardo, Albert Ventura, and Rose Mola

Second from back, standing (l-r): Lorraine Thomas (short hair and glasses), Juanita Johnson, Manager Gale Hacker (hands on shoulders of person in front of her), Elfrida Komarnicki, and Tom Post

Third row (l-r): Tamara Dean (butterfly top), and Sandra Crook (patchwork top, half-kneeling)

Front row kneeling (l-r): Shauna Thompson, Joan Tschopp, Supervisor Debbie Lopez, and Debbie Deering

Environmental Services Maintenance Worker II, Jim White

Groundskeeper Don Decheske

Support Services Director Randy Norris

Linen Department staff photo – 2009
Shown here (l-r) are: Dorothy Lawver, Don Ellis, and Wayne Holmes

The Clean Team

With Beginnings in Gary • THEN AND NOW

ENVIRONMENTAL SERVICES, GROUNDS, LINEN...

Contributed by Randy Norris
Director of Support Services, Safety Officer

When I began my career at St. Mary Medical Center in August 1996, the Housekeeping Department was contracted to a management company. Most of the housekeepers reported directly to nursing. Changes were imminent, however, and I was able to reinstate housekeeping under my department umbrella. The "old" tower was very small and difficult to clean. Patients had to share a bathroom and shower. There was definitely room for improvement and when the New West Tower was built and opened in 2004, things changed tremendously. We were able to add staff members and started our Operational Excellence program. The housekeeping staff is now intertwined with nursing and feels much more of a part of patient care. The morale has increased significantly and by using our AIDET (Acknowledge, Introduce, Duration, Explain, and Thank) tools – a positive reinforcement program that incorporates some of the most positive, consistent scores in the hospital have been achieved. Our satisfaction scores for "cleaning of patient rooms" average 91% and the scores for "courtesy of person cleaning" average 90%.

Notably, our Environmental Services employees go well beyond their job responsibilities to be helpful. In 2006, a visitor was choking in the cafeteria. Housekeeper Tawny Pavese jumped out of her chair, quickly performed the Heimlich Maneuver, and dislodged the food from the visitor's throat. In 2008, one of our housekeepers, Zaklina Trajceski, was working in the Emergency Department and was asked to help a patient inside. When she arrived at the car, she realized the patient was in very bad shape and called for help. According to Trevor Loftis, M.D., her quick action helped save the man's life. Also, in 2008, one of our housekeepers, Christine Tellez and another employee, Glen Schultz, LPN, nursing float pool, were on their way home from work when they witnessed a car slide off the road into a nearby pond. Both stopped to help the elderly gentleman trapped in the car. Christine grabbed a blanket, they both went down the embankment, and helped give the man aid until the ambulance arrived.

It is a privilege to recognize the growth of the Environmental Services Department and the staff members who each day represent a generous spirit and work ethic – both on and off the job. They exemplify the best of all that St. Mary Medical Center offers its patients and families.

> "THE ROAD TO DAILY HAPPINESS IS NOT HARD TO FIND. IT'S WHAT WE DO FOR OTHERS THAT BRINGS US PEACE OF MIND."
>
> ~ UNKNOWN

Waterfall Cafe'

FOOD AND NUTRITION STAFF PHOTO - 2009

FRONT ROW (L-R): Bobbi Homola, Carolyn Johnson, Carol Riley, Debbie Boceski, Delores Clotman, and Esther Johnson

MIDDLE ROW (L-R): Delia Soto, Joyce Williams, Food Service Director Len Ayers, Louise Denham, Donald Waters, Linda Lundy, Sue Trajcevski, and Dennis Martin

BACK ROW (L-R): Melissa Moyer, Michele Ballard, Roxanne Ban, Thomas Mahan, Hugo Garcia, Darryl Anthony, Darren Hopkins, Kellie Goodwin, Sonya Williams, Vicki Brasovan, Marla Harford, Sandra D. Smith, Margie Carter, Darlene Kozyra, Jeremy Alexander, Dennis Williams, and Ryan Smith

NOT PICTURED: Allen Cathey, Claudia Dixon, Tawana Dugan, Kelly Green, Don Hall, Robbin Hood, Terrance Hughes, Pat Kemp, Honna Kozik, Norma Molinaro, Willie Petty, Judy Pipchok, Sara Sekula, Kathleen Wichlinski, Pam Woodward, Kim Youngkin, and Karen Zanolla

A GRATEFUL PATIENT WROTE THIS AT THE BOTTOM OF A MENU...

Hats Off to the Chefs!! Food is great. Thanks for your special touch! Have a great day.

ANONYMOUS

In 2006, for the second consecutive year, Len Ayers, Jr., director of food and nutrition services at St. Mary Medical Center, was named the Best Institutional Chef by the Guild of the Urban League of Northwest Indiana. He also won first place for the guild's 2006 Macho Cuisine Cook-Off with his recipe for roasted turkey breast medallions with bourbon sauce and rice pilaf. He also won first place in a second category for the 2006 Best Secret Recipe with the same entry for which he was named Best Institutional Chef.

Reprinted by permission of the *Post-Tribune*, DECEMBER 28, 2006

IT'S BEEN *Said* IN 2009... ~~~~~~~~~~~~~~~

"There's a big difference in our cafeteria now. Oh my goodness! A lot of times we have seven or eight entrees. People are coming from all over the area to eat.

My mom's neighbors come to the Waterfall Cafe every single day around 11:00 am. They say they love the people in the cafeteria and everybody here has grown to care about them. They love that food. They are older and she appreciates all the selections that they have here. She doesn't have to cook all those special things that her husband like to eat."

Pamala Woodward, DIETARY CLERK
ST. MARY MEDICAL CENTER
(BEGAN IN 1976 IN HOBART)

When I began working for St. Mary Medical Center in Hobart in 1998, patients were housed in the old hospital and all the rooms were semi-private. The conference rooms for all special functions and meetings were located on the second floor. The hospital census averaged approximately 100-125 beds. The cafeteria, under the direction of Len Ayers, had seating for 50 – 75 people. It included one four-well steam table, one beverage refrigerator, one five-foot portable salad bar, and one cash register. Two entrées, starch, vegetable, soup, and desserts were served.

A major renovation in 2004 was the addition of the New Patient Tower with all private beds. Food and Nutrition Services also saw improvements at that time with enhanced patient food service meals. The cafeteria was renovated and expanded food selections were incorporated into the menu from our new Waterfall Café with a seating capacity of 150 – 175 people. We also added seating for another 56 people on the outdoor patio adjacent to the cafeteria.

Patients (as of 2008) can now order from the cafeteria menu as well as the patient menu which includes a new selection of grilled items and choices from the new international station. Also featured is an exhibition station. A production chef, Ryan Smith, was brought on board in 2004 to enhance the meal preparation for the patients and also in the café. A room service menu for patients in the Labor and Delivery Unit was also added. The Waterfall Café was named for the wall-length waterfall that is the cafeteria's centerpiece along with a tropical fish aquarium. The international selections feature Japanese, French, Latin, American, Italian, and Indian cuisine. Other selections include a salad bar, deli and soup stations, a 10-well hot food line, and grill selections. Approximately 1,622 meals are prepared daily of which 835 account for patient meals. The department has grown from 38 to approximately 45 full-time employees. Eight employees have more than 30 years with the hospital, eight have more than 20 years, and eight have more than 10 years – proof positive of a friendly, professional working environment.

St. Mary Medical Center's Food and Nutrition Department has been featured in several local newspaper articles and *Food Management and Food Service Director* national magazines. In 2005 and 2006, Len Ayers was named the Macho Chef of the Year for Institutions, and was awarded the Best Secret Recipe in 2006 by the Urban League Guild of Northwest Indiana. He also was selected as the 2008 Future Horizons Award winner by the National Healthcare Foodservice Management Association. All this is quite a leap from the old cafeteria and department as we once knew it.

DID YOU KNOW?

In September 1977, the kitchens of St. Mary's Gary and Hobart hospitals began working with a computerized system that increased processing time for patient menus and reduced the margin for error in assembling patient trays. Previously, diet clerks had little time to spend with patients. The new system allowed dietary personnel to visit with patients and answer nutrition questions.

Hobart Gazette, SEPTEMBER 7, 1978

Shown *(at left)* in the 1940s and early 1950s
are workers in St. Mary Mercy Hospital's cafeteria.
CHJC, University of Notre Dame Archives

Carlos Otero, assistant director in Gary, and Ellen Watson,
supervisor in Gary, are shown at a 1978 St. Mary Medical
Center picnic.

Sandra Smith, a cook, prepares salads for the
Mercy Hospital salad bar in March, 1989.

IT'S BEEN *Said* IN 2009...

ANOTHER HELPING

"If we had anything left over from the cafeteria in Gary, one of the Sisters who was my boss would always save the food for the homeless to pick up in an area next to the Emergency Room."

Claudia Dixon, FOOD SERVICE SUPERVISOR
MERCY HOSPITAL
(BEGAN IN 1973 IN GARY)

IT'S BEEN *Said* IN 2009...

ANOTHER HELPING

"Practically every single day in the back of the hospital they had benches lined up all the way around in kind of a U-shape. (The) unemployed people who came there were fed by Sister Marca of the kitchen. I suppose it was mostly for the noon day meal.

"She had been on her feet for many, many years and her legs bothered her so she was given an electric scooter. That area in the back was also for delivery trucks so Sister learned to get around them pretty well – and she could get around the hospital too.

"The people in Gary, in general, did not know all the things the hospital did and could do for them. They just did it every day. I'm sure there were a lot of indigent people who went to the hospital and could not pay for anything. We didn't have an insurance situation at that time."

Mary Ellen Donovan, SECRETARY TO THE DIRECTOR
ST. MARY'S MERCY SCHOOL OF NURSING | (BEGAN IN 1945 IN GARY)

"Back in the 1970s and '80s in Gary, you went upstairs and read all the menus to the patients. We had more time to spend with them back then.

"We had one patient who was 27 and was dying with some kind of liver disease. She wanted me to take pictures of her, her husband and her three kids. It really touches you. She said, 'Pam, can you please take our last picture? I know I won't be around long.' I told her I wouldn't mind at all and her husband and kids got in bed with her and I took the picture. She was gone in two days. But, you know what? It was a lasting memory for them and for me."

Pamala Woodward, DIETARY CLERK
ST. MARY MEDICAL CENTER
(BEGAN IN 1976 IN HOBART)

"My mother, Vasilka Hristovska – known as Vi – probably started at St. Mary's in Gary in 1968 as a Kitchen Aide. We were there at the same time until they sold the hospital and she retired.

"I mostly remember that the portions of food were a lot bigger. At lunch time, they used to fry the whole fish with the head on it. It was bigger than the plate and they served it that way. With one serving of Cornish hens, they would give you the whole Cornish hen.

"You could order special grills for breakfast or lunch – 'How do you want your eggs done?' – and hamburgers and fried foods on the grill. They would cook it right in front of you. That's a little different from today."

Lily Karamacoska, ADMINISTRATIVE ASSISTANT, CLINICAL ANCILLARY SERVICES
COMMUNITY HOSPITAL
(BEGAN IN 1976 IN GARY)

"Sister Marca (chief cook and supervisor) was in charge of the kitchen and did a fine job. She was very strict and very demanding about keeping things clean. She had a very kind face and smile. When she grew toward retirement age, they brought her a scooter. I don't know if it was because of her hip or her knee but she couldn't get around the hospital very well. Somehow she got a three-wheeled scooter that was electrically powered to go down the hall and in and out."

Bruce Lovell, X-RAY TECHNOLOGIST
MERCY HOSPITAL
(BEGAN IN 1963 IN GARY)

"Hobart opened in April of 1973. I started May 26, 1973, in the kitchen. I was 16 years old and a student at Hobart High School. My aunt, Lorena Peters, worked at the Gary hospital for many years and suggested that I apply for a job. I remember the day I came in, the dress I wore, and the excitement of working in a brand new hospital. I was scared but it was wonderful. I worked there for 2 ½ years. Mr. Robert White was the department head at that time. I worked as a tray aide, on the tray line, in the dish room, in the cafeteria and sometimes had to work as a cook's assistant.

"The day after I graduated from high school, I began in medical records. Alice Nedoff was my department head. She was a one-of-a-kind woman – so knowledgeable. She was very intriguing – always had stories to tell – and was a wonderful boss. I worked in there for 29 years and was a coder for a good 20 years."

Joy James, CANCER REGISTRY TECHNICIAN
MERCY HOSPITAL | (BEGAN IN 1973 IN HOBART)

"Prior to my employment here I can remember one time I got sick so my mom rushed me to St. Mary's. Sister Wilma came around and she said, 'How are you doing young lady?' I told her I was doing much better. She made me feel real comfortable and I said, 'I need a job.' She said, 'You have to wait until you get out of here and you come back and see me.' She left me her card and I was thinking, 'Right, she is not going to hire me.' The next day I was discharged and… sure enough, she was there. She said, 'I remember you, Claudestine.' She asked if I was a hard worker. I told her, 'Around the house my work is very good. My mom groomed six kids well.' She said she was going to give me a try and not to let her down. I promised I wouldn't. She is the one who hired me and I have kept my commitment to her to this day."

In 2009 Claudia Dixon was recognized as Employee of the Year.

Claudia Dixon, FOOD SERVICE SUPERVISOR
MERCY HOSPITAL
(BEGAN IN 1973 IN GARY)

"I started off at St. Mary in Gary as a food service worker… I had a very good director, Judith Hack, who told me that I had to go back to school. I went to college for a year and a half and then I got pregnant and she said, 'You need to do a year in Ivy Tech and I want to promote you to supervisor.' I thought that was too much for me but she said she wanted me to further my education to move up in the organization… I'm here today because of her. I am very proud."

Claudia Dixon, FOOD SERVICE SUPERVISOR
MERCY HOSPITAL
(BEGAN IN 1973 IN GARY)

2009 Employee of the Year award given to Claudia Dixon

Shown here in 1993 is Food Service Worker Allen Cathey preparing food items for Meals on Wheels. St. Mary Medical Center in Hobart was responsible for the Meals on Wheels program.

"Be alert to give service. What counts most in life is what we do for others."
~ UNKNOWN

Food Service Manager Agnes Frazee (left) is shown at the 1978 management holiday party with Judy Hack, director of dietetics, Gary and Hobart.

The new tray system, Dinex, is displayed in 1977 by Food and Nutrition staff members. Shown (L-R) are: Jane Laughead, supervisor; Cindy Kolodziej, RD; Bobbi Homola, RD; Agnes Frazee, food service manager; and Nada Samardzija, cafeteria supervisor.

IT'S BEEN *Said* IN 2009...

"I think a good healthcare employee is one who comes into a hospital environment with some knowledge of healthy habits or understands the need to become aware of healthy behaviors in order to provide the best level of healthcare to the patient and the family.

"Since the closing of St. Mary's in 1995 and as I currently work in the health education area, I speak with other community healthcare agencies. I am often reminded that St. Mary's in Gary had the best food of all area healthcare institutions and was more like a 'family' than any other area healthcare institution.

"I certainly enjoyed my 21 years as an employee of St. Mary's and it is my hope that the legacy of 'family and good food' will continue to embody the symbol of a good healthcare system."

Rosie Thomas, FORMER DIRECTOR COMMUNITY AFFAIRS
MERCY HOSPITAL
(BEGAN IN 1973 IN GARY)

"Far and away the best prize that life offers is the chance to work hard at work worth doing."

~ THEODORE ROOSEVELT

CLINICAL DIETETICS

Contributed by Bobbi Homola, MPA, RD, CD
Regional Clinical Manager

Nutrition is a key element of quality, cost-effective health care. The focus of clinical dietetics in the old days… at least back to the '70s was on visiting patients, ensuring they were eating properly, and following their diets. We would educate them on their diets, hold classes for them, and assist them with meal planning and adjusting to their new lifestyle.

Patients in the hospital now are much sicker than they were 30-40 years ago. A lot of things have changed since then. Reimbursement, DRGs, lack of insurance, patients delaying treatment for whatever reason, etc. Regulatory agencies also recognized the impact good nutrition has on patients, requiring hospitals to screen patients with the purpose of identifying individuals who are malnourished or at nutritional risk. We know that compared to well-nourished patients, poorly nourished patients have higher morbidity, mortality and complication rates; longer hospital stays and higher average hospital costs. Today our focus is much more "clinical" in nature - defined by a variety of criteria – biochemical data, lab values, anthropometric data, food/nutrition history, procedures, diagnosis, etc. – before we even see the patient. Registered dietitians are faced with the ethical and legal issues in nutrition, hydration and feeding. Patients are more likely to be partners in their care today. Because nutrient deficiencies or excesses often exist before admission, our job as nutrition advocates gets tougher with the shorter length of stays, limiting the window of opportunity with each patient. Providing Medical Nutrition Therapy for a variety of disease states within that small window is difficult. Medicare reimbursement is now available for registered dietitians, providing Medical Nutrition Therapy for the treatment of diabetes and kidney disease on an out-patient basis, as dietitians are now Medicare providers.

All charting, back in the day, was on paper. There was always a fight for the chart, especially in the morning, with physicians making rounds, ward clerks taking off new orders that the physician just wrote, nurses charting, patients off the floor (with their charts) for a test. Charting is now done electronically and as the nation moves towards an electronic health record, dietitians are using Standardized Language for the Nutrition Care Process using International Dietetics & Nutrition Terminology.

Menus were pre-printed. We had color coded menus for about 4-5 different diets. If a patient needed a diet that was restricted even further than what was available, we would use the menu that came the closest and then "modify it" to meet their needs. We would scratch things off the menu that they couldn't have, and try to write something else in its place. When a patient had multiple restrictions, the menu was almost unreadable with all the items scratched off. Electronic food service systems now allow us the opportunity to make all of these changes BEFORE the menu is ever printed and placed before a patient. Now a patient never sees what he CANNOT have!

IT'S BEEN *Said* IN 2009…

"I had a gestational diabetic; she was having a baby at St. Mary Medical Center in Hobart and was having a really hard time with the diet. Her mother was a diabetic. Her mother didn't ever follow her diet so her daughter didn't think she needed to either but when you're having a baby, you realize you're responsible for somebody else's life. She brought her husband there for support and I told them it was a good healthy way for all of them to eat.

"I saw her not too long ago and she has had another healthy child since then. She is doing very well and credits that with the diet. She didn't have to go on insulin and that was her goal."

Bobbi Homola, MPA, RD, CD, REGIONAL CLINICAL MANAGER
ST. MARY MEDICAL CENTER
(BEGAN IN 1976 IN HOBART)

Alice Engle Nedoff
"A Touch of History – Generally Speaking"

by Alice Engle Nedoff, Registered Record Administrator (RRA)

Special to *"For the Record,"* a publication committed to enhancing
the Health Information profession, DECEMBER 14, 1992

In April, Pam Wear, RRA, spoke to the Indiana Health Information Management Association about the computer-based medical record. While listening to the innovative discussion, it occurred to me that I had been in the field of medical records for 50 years. How this profession has changed!

We have changed from a Record Room to a Medical Record Department, from shorthand to machine dictation, from manual typewriters to word processors, from alphabetical indexing of diseases and operations to numerical coding. Now we are discussing the change from paper to computerized database.

Release of information has changed, too. Fifty years ago we didn't have copy machines so releasing information would have been an overwhelming process, but we had only a few requests per year from insurance companies and lawsuits were rare. This area, however, holds my most significant memory.

We were in the midst of World War II when a pilot crashed eight miles east of Gary, IN. He was pulled from the wreckage yelling, "Save the bombsight, save the bombsight!" He was admitted to St. Mary Mercy Hospital in Gary, still ranting and raving about the bombsight. The young lieutenant soon recovered from his concussion and visited the Medical Record Department daily for several days.

Finally, a representative from the United States Army Air Force came to pick him up. This officer asked our director, Sister Maxelenda, for the lieutenant's record. She told him he couldn't have it.

"Sister, the officer stated, "I am a colonel in the United States Army Air Force, and I demand the medical record."

Sister stood up to her full 5-foot-1-inch height, put her hand on her hip, and with a defiant gleam in her eye, said, "Sir, concerning matters in this Medical Record Department, I am the GENERAL!"

Many years later, we learned that the bombsight that had so concerned the lieutenant had been designed for use in dropping the atomic bomb. We had no idea that we had touched history nor that the incident was top-secret, but I suppose the two officers knew the medical record would be safe with the Sister General as its protector.

Alice Engle Nedoff's employment began at St. Mary Mercy Hospital in 1942.

Meeting the Air Force

THE FIRST PAYCHECK

"This is my first paycheck from 1980. Stenographers with no experience made $5.00 an hour in August of 1980. I received a cost of living raise (54-cents) as noted next to my name. I thought the hospital made a mistake since I had only worked there four or five weeks and received such a large increase. I turned my paycheck into Human Resources back then as I thought it was an error.

"Today stenographers are called transcriptionists. Their starting wage is $13.01 with no experience and with experience can move up to $24.40 per hour."

Jo Toigo, RHIT, CCS
Director, Health Information Management
St. Mary Medical Center
(began in 1980 in Gary)

LOOKING BACK...

As part of a Medical Record Week promotion in the mid-1980s, photos were taken of various staff members in the Medical Records Department.

Shown here is Accredited Record Technician (A.R.T.) Jayne Dillon at her desk on 5West. A.R.T.s were put on the units when the Diagnosis Related Groups (DRGs) were coming out and were able to work more closely with the physicians. Jayne worked at the Gary location from 1982-1990 and at the Hobart location from 1990-1994.

A.R.T. Nancy Higgins is shown at her desk in Gary's Medical Record Department. She was employed at the Gary location from 1982-1990

A.R.T. Victoria Morena is shown here in the mid-1980s with the ICD-9 Coding Books that consisted of three separate volumes. Now they are a one-volume book or are available through computer programs – no text needed!

A.R.T. Rochelle Strickland-Taylor is shown here working on Release of Information.

HEALTH INFORMATION MANAGEMENT
STAFF PHOTO – 2009
<u>BACK ROW (L-R):</u> Sandy Plummer,
Karleen Sutkowski, Carol Hibbard,
Mary Constandars, Debbie Husek,
Helen Urban, Sofia Cornejo, Stacy Smith,
and Karri Borders
<u>MIDDLE ROW (L-R):</u> JoAnna Harrington,
Jennifer Puckett, Kathy Dominguez,
Barb McVicker, Sylvia Cervantes,
Christine Hodorowicz, Teresa Simmons,
and Kathy Maroules
<u>FRONT ROW (L-R):</u> Director Jo Toigo,
Jackie Boozer, Beckie Havens,
Charice Fergerson, and Laura Gawlinski
<u>NOT PICTURED:</u> Margie Stratton,
Michelle Greco, Karen Rieck,
and Denise Marsh

With Beginnings in Gary • THEN AND NOW

HEALTH INFORMATION MANAGEMENT DEPARTMENT...

Contributed by Jo Toigo, RHIT, CCS, Director

The Health Information Management Department will, to the majority of the public and senior health professionals, always be thought of as the Medical Records Department. The primary use of the medical record is a communication tool for continued health care, quality review of the appropriateness of care, financial reimbursement so that payments can be made to the care provider(s), legal protection for patients and health care providers, education for health care professionals, research, statistics and public health awareness.

As the department has evolved, gone are the days when employees of medical records were referred to as medical librarians. Even though the professional name of the department changed many years ago, the hospital hallways display posted signage with both department titles – Health Information Management and Medical Records. In the past, Medical Record departments were located in the basement due to the weight of the paper records and weight limits on higher floors. The medical record was exclusively handwritten and was considered a repository of information. Doctors were expected to be inquisitive by examining one's body inside and out and recording all its imperfections. Physicians were trained to peer into your life, past and present, and ask sensitive and uncomfortable questions. The doctor-patient relationship was meant to be confidential and solely for the benefit of the patient. Doctors, after all, through the Hippocratic Oath, had pledged their patients' confidentiality. Medical records were rarely accessed except for follow-up patient care. Rules and regulations have always existed concerning access to health information but back then only one person at a time could access information given that it was a paper document.

A few decades ago, healthcare was almost exclusively rendered in hospitals, physician offices and nursing homes. For many years, patients were admitted to the hospital but were not necessarily ill. Physicians could admit their patients for annual physical examinations or other diagnostic work ups and a stay in the hospital was routinely several days in length regardless of the problem. Patients, rarely if ever, looked at their medical records. In fact, most were unaware of the extent of the documentation that was compiled on their behalf. If a patient wanted access to the medical record, the physician authorized the review which is contrary to today. Criterion for release of information was on a need-to-know basis. With a proper release-of-information request, the medical record was reviewed by the Health Information Management professional who confirmed the diagnosis, the procedure and the admission/discharge dates.

Virtually all patients currently admitted to the hospital are extremely ill. Patients value their medical record and its privacy. They routinely get copies of their clinical documentation and are increasingly internet-savvy as informed consumers exploring such topics as clinical information, patient rights, pharmaceutical information, and hospital quality/safety reports.

Basic medical-record keeping moved from typewriters and manual patient index cards as the nation embraced a national organization for standardization of record-keeping services.

Duplicating equipment was introduced into the release-of-information process, radically changing the brief abstract of a medical record to full-page copy documents. Lofty goals from the government also led to a cost-containment payment system, Diagnosis Related Groups (DRGs), and the Medical Records Department moved out of the basement and into the board room 25 years ago.

In 2007, St. Mary Medical Center initiated the Electronic Medical Record as our hospital embraced the goals endorsed by our two recent U.S. Presidents. Consequently every job in the hospital involved with patient record entry changed. Suddenly relevant information was equally accessible to everyone involved in good health care. Remote coding/abstracting responsibilities were an electronic solution to Health Information Management professionals. Whereas previously it could take 30 minutes to find a paper record, today's electronic solutions take 30 seconds. The health information system at St. Mary Medical Center is computerized, interactive and contains timely, dynamic documentation that supports patient care. The specificity of the information is key to providing good health care and the HIM Department is the information hub of the health care system. The pledge of confidentiality however is now challenged by a world where computers rule and health information is simultaneously available based on proper computer access. Ethical decision-making always requires choice and the right choice requires courage. This is today's reality in relation to health informatics.

Although limited technology belongs to our early history, Health Information Management has kept pace with timely advances. Proud of a great work ethic among our employees and meaningful relationships over time, St. Mary Medical Center fosters a family environment with a hospital-wide team approach – a team approach that is present in the best healthcare system in Northwest Indiana and beyond – Community Healthcare System.

Past HIM Directors:

(Dates unknown)	Sister Maxelenda Preiss, PHJC, RRL
"	Sister Johannetta Bergman, PHJC, RRL
"	Therese O'Connor
1973 – 1988	Alice Nedoff, BA, RHIA
1988 – 2002	Donna Dubois-Wilson, MSA, RHIA
May 2002 to present	Jo Toigo, RHIT, CCS

Record Keepers Timeline - "In sickness and in health":

1912 – Club of Record Clerks met at Massachusetts General Hospital to study clinical records.

1928 – American College of Surgeons invited record clerks to their annual meeting. Association of Record Librarians of Northern America founded.

1938 – Association name was changed to American Association of Medical Record.

1960 – Membership reached nearly 4,500.

1969 – House of Delegates voted to change the association's name to the American Medical Record Association.

1978 – AMRA membership reached 23,000.

1988 – AMRA celebrated its 60th anniversary. Medical Record Week was created.

1991 – Association changed its name to American Health Information Management Association (AHIMA).

1992 – Society for Clinical Coding (CCS) was established.

1999 – The Chicago office moved to 223 North Michigan Avenue.

2003 – AHIMA celebrated its 75th anniversary. Health Insurance Portability and Accountability Act (HIPAA) regarding privacy took the forefront in public awareness. (HIPAA was originally enacted in 1996.)

Source: AHIMA's *Body of Knowledge* (BoK)

We are the Caretakers of the Caretakers

"Consciously or unconsciously, everyone of us does render some service or another. If we cultivate the habit of doing this service deliberately, our desire for service will steadily grow stronger, and it will make not only for our own happiness, but that of the world at large."
~ Mahatma Gandhi

HUMAN RESOURCES STAFF PHOTO – 2009
SEATED: Ellen Page, HR specialist; STANDING (L-R): Director Yvonne Hoff; Linda Adler, recruiter; Kim Van Eerd, Personnel Assistant; Debra Harvoth, HR specialist

With Beginnings in Gary • THEN AND NOW

HUMAN RESOURCES DEPARTMENT...

Contributed by Yvonne Hoff
Director

In the early days of the Human Resources Department at Mercy Hospital in Gary, there were no computers, no fax machines and the intranet was not even a thought. Everything we did took so much time... from selecting candidates, interviewing, and checking references to the actual employment process because we did everything in pen and pencil with carbon paper!

Today, we handle more than 2,500 resumes a year, more than 500 interviews, and 200 new hires. Obviously this volume can only be accomplished because we have become more efficient through better technology. We hope to eventually become even more stream-lined and environmentally friendly in a completely paperless world.

The Human Resources Department's role has definitely changed. "Then" our main focus was to hire and maintain benefits for our employees. "Now" Human Resources is an integral part of quality, management development and strategic planning. Recruitment and retention are important to maintaining the quality and continuity of care for the hospital. Now, more than ever, we are looking for better ways to retain our employees and identify candidates who will help us continue on our path of operational excellence at St. Mary Medical Center.

IT'S BEEN *Said* IN 2009...

"When I was hired at St. Mary's Gary in 1985, I distinctly remember Rosie Thomas who worked in the Personnel Department. She was a personnel assistant and processed new hires and so forth. She had been at St. Mary for a long time and she took me under her wing and trained me in many areas of the department. I can say that she is the one who molded me into the person I am today. I remember her telling me to just do my best. She really made a big impact on me."

Debra Jenkins
REGIONAL ASSISTANT OF MISSION EFFECTIVENESS
ST. MARY MEDICAL CENTER
(BEGAN IN 1985 IN GARY)

Pharmacy in the early days

In the medicine cabinet

"We had a medicine cabinet in the chart room where we charted. None of the medicine was made up, even morphine. We had to take the pills and put them in sterile water and shake it up. We would then take it to the patient and give it. Nothing was in tubes like nowadays where everything is all made up for them. We had a class they called materia medica which taught us what to do. The cupboard for the medication was locked, especially with morphine. The Sister had the keys and she would open it. You would take that medication and read the directions three times before you mixed it and when you went to the patient you read it again to make sure you had the right one."

Helen Petrovich, RN
Mercy Hospital
(began in 1934 in Gary)

This photo, said to be dated in the late 1940s, appeared in a booklet called "*Your Career in Nursing.*" Shown at left in the pharmacy is Sister Coelestine Deininger, PHJC, who was both a pharmacist and pharmacy director. On the right is Pharmacist Helen Krupinski.

"Sister was a great record keeper of everything that occurred in the pharmacy," said Mary Ellen Donovan, former secretary to the director of St. Mary's Mercy Hospital School of Nursing. "All meds were dispensed from there."

Photo source: Donaldson, Indiana Archives

It's been *Said* in 2009...

"I started in August of 1977 in Gary. I came from St. Joseph's Pharmacy on the corner of Tyler in Gary. When Joseph, the pharmacist, would run out of pharmaceutical drugs, I would go to St. Mary's pharmacy to get what he needed and I thought, 'I wish I could work there.' Mr. Bud Guba was the pharmacist in the Gary hospital then.

"Unfortunately, St. Joseph's Pharmacy burned down in October of 1976. I started as an outpatient filing clerk in the (hospital) business office under Mary Ann Danko, I think."

Lucy Rodriguez
Cash Control Clerk, Patient Accounting
St. Mary Medical Center
(began in 1977 in Gary)

It's been *Said* in 2009...

"At St. Mary's in Gary, the first clinical pharmacist started working there around the early 1980s and that's when the pharmacy program began there. Her name was Theresa Prosser and she was a PharmD, a pharmacist doctorate, who made sure she was referred to as doctor. There were very few PharmDs back then."

Lily Karamacoska
Administrative Assistant
Clinical Ancillary Services, Community Hospital
(began in 1976 in Gary)

(Left): Sister Catherine Thelen, PHJC, a graduate of St. Louis University College of Pharmacy, continued her work part-time at St. Mary Medical Center.
Word-Gathering, Spring, 1981

(Right): St. Mary Medical Center
To Serve with Love brochure, 1984

THE PHARMACY OF TODAY

Shown in 2009 is the recently remodeled IV room used for preparing IV fluids for patients.

In 2009 is recent technology in use in the pharmacy including the tube station for sending medications to the nursing units and an Omnicell unit for secure storage of medications.

PHARMACY DEPARTMENT STAFF PHOTO - 2009
FRONT ROW (L-R): Melodie Suvajac, Dyan Perry, Jessica Coros, Jerry Brokemond, Heather Lopez, and Director Michelle Meyer
BACK ROW (L-R): Debbie Evans, Dawn Biller, Andy Kasianchuk, Mary Jokerst, Greg Mays, and Tia Sparks
NOT PICTURED: John Laskowski, Bill Borys, Emmeline Benavides, Dawn McIntyre, Kinesha Bailey, Evita Howard, Betsy Flores, Janet Stricklin, Barbara Haviza, Murray Jones, Diane Stevens, Melissa Shoback, JC Rositas, and Joyce Smith

With Beginnings in Gary • THEN AND NOW

PHARMACY DEPARTMENT...

Contributed by Michelle Meyer, RPH, Director

When St. Mary Medical Center first opened in Hobart, pharmacy services were far different than they are today. One major difference was that the pharmacy had no computer system. All medications for patients were recorded into a handwritten patient profile and kept in a binder in the department. Everything was handwritten or typed on an old-fashioned typewriter, including labels for IV infusions. Medications were all hand-delivered to the nursing units for administration to the patient. The pharmacist made all tube feedings (products similar to Ensure, etc.) in a blender in the department. At that time, alcohol such as beer and whiskey was actually considered a treatment and kept with other locked medications.

Today, the practice of pharmacy is more diverse. Much of the manual tasks have been eliminated with technology allowing the pharmacist to be more active in the care of our patients. Computers assist with maintaining patient medication profiles and printing labels for medications when needed. Medications are available on nursing units via big medication cabinets that allow the nurse access to medications for his/her patients when needed. These cabinets allow us to provide timely patient care in a safe and effective manner. We also have tubes similar to the drive-up at a bank to send medications more quickly to the nursing units for our patients. This expedient technology allows the pharmacist more time to monitor certain medications and teach staff and patients certain disease states. In the very near future this will allow pharmacists to be available on the nursing units for better service.

Finally, actual alcohol is no longer considered a pharmaceutical treatment so the days of dispensing whiskey and beer are far behind us!

RESPIRATORY CARE

RESPIRATORY THERAPY DEPARTMENT STAFF PHOTO – 2009

<u>BACK ROW (L-R):</u> Tom Coates, Alice Hale, Debbie Brink, Melissa Albin, Greg Burris, Julie Arnold, Tina Wilson, Nada Pavlovski, and Patty Gutowski

<u>MIDDLE ROW (L-R):</u> Kelly Barrasas, Marie Ruiz, Julie Konja, Manager William Willer, Dee Bedella, Joann Borns, Marilynn Chavez, and Nancy Howton

<u>FRONT ROW (L-R):</u> Elizabeth Copak, Krista Galloway, Jackie Highsmith, and Tina Cowan

NEURODIAGNOSTICS

NEURODIAGNOSTICS DEPARTMENT STAFF PHOTO – 2009

<u>BACK ROW (L-R):</u> Manager William Willer and Milos Damjanovic

<u>FRONT ROW (L-R):</u> Shirley Brown and Dianne Spencer

SLEEP LAB

SLEEP LAB STAFF PHOTO – 2009

<u>PICTURED (L-R):</u> Dee Bedella, Nick Johnson and Carrie Rozwara

"While I was in Gary, one of the big things we started was Dr. Kamen's Inhalation Therapy Department. Our main purpose was when the patients had surgery to make sure that they did not become congested, that they would cough up and breathe. We taught them proper breathing mechanisms or if they knew when they had a problem the doctors ordered treatments. I would teach the girls to get their patients to cough up everything so we were very active in keeping them up and walking and moving so that we could prevent any pneumonia. It was a big help, then, when we had that for the surgical patients."

Sister Philomene Pawlik, PHJC, R.N, RETIRED
DONALDSON, INDIANA
(BEGAN AT MERCY HOSPITAL IN 1955)

Shown in this 2003 photo is Cecil Noel who, thanks to the success of his pulmonary rehabilitation exercises at St. Mary Medical Center, was symptom-free and could play golf again.

Vim & Vigor, SPRING 2003

CAN'T SLEEP?

Emilio Soria, M.D., St. Mary Medical Center's Sleep Diagnostics
Vim & Vigor, SPRING, 2007

An article in the spring 2007 issue of *Vim & Vigor Magazine* discussed sleep disorders and what to do about them.

"The good news is most sleep disorders are treatable once patients take the first step to have a sleep study performed," said Emilio Soria, M.D. "Today's advanced medical equipment is designed for comfort during evaluations. There are no needles involved... no pain. We use music and meditation CDs to help create a relaxed environment."

With Beginnings in Gary. THEN AND NOW

RESPIRATORY CARE SERVICES...
RESPIRATORY CARE/NEUROLOGY/SLEEP LAB
Contributed by William Willer, Manager

Breathing is something most people take for granted... that is, until it becomes something that is hard or nearly impossible to do on a daily basis.

At St. Mary Medical Center, we strive to provide skilled respiratory therapy throughout the hospital. Respiratory Care Practitioners are often the first health care professionals called to the scene when patients are experiencing respiratory complications.

We have specific concentrations in Acute Care, Emergency Room, Pulmonary Rehabilitation, and Pulmonary Function testing. Our therapists are trained in the current modalities and therapies as well as advanced and cutting-edge forms of ventilation for critical patients. We currently have one of the most credentialed respiratory departments in the region.

Respiratory Care Practitioners (RCPs) specialize in the assessment and treatment of respiratory and cardiovascular pathologies. These include chronic lung problems, such as asthma, bronchitis, emphysema, COPD, and more acute multi-systemic problems stemming from other pathological conditions such as heart attacks, stroke, or trauma as well as complications at birth. RCPs are specialists in airway management, mechanical ventilation, blood acid/base balance, and critical care medicine. RCPs work closely with other medical disciplines including physicians, nurses, speech therapists and physical therapists.

The 1970s saw the growth of Inhalation Therapy, not only at Saint Mary Medical Center but throughout the nation. With the changes and advancements in the profession, the department's name was subsequently changed to the Respiratory Care Services Department. There was a time when respiratory therapists were on-the-job trained technicians with little formal education. Their main function was to ensure safe oxygen use, to administer intermittent positive pressure breathing (IPPB) treatments, to perform cardiopulmonary resuscitation (CPR), and to operate negative pressure (iron lung) ventilators.

Over the years, inhalation therapists have evolved into being college and university trained clinicians. With the advent of positive pressure mechanical ventilators and the more widespread hospital provision of neonatal and pediatric care, the more sophisticated respiratory therapy skills and procedures have become. They include (but are not limited to): managing mechanical ventilation (invasive and non-invasive), intubation and placement of other airways, arterial line insertion, cardiac catheter advancement, tracheostomy recannulation, nasotracheal suction, drawing and interpreting arterial blood gases, pulmonary waveform analysis, inhaled medication delivery, oxygen delivery (via nasal cannula and various mask devices), managing a variety of aerosol therapy devices, and performing pulmonary function tests.

The department established new guidelines on patient care, recruited registered therapists, acquired new state-of-the-art equipment, and worked very closely with physicians and house staff to provide comprehensive quality patient care.

We began an affiliation with Indiana Vocational Tech as a primary student clinical practice site for the Associate Degree Program in Respiratory Care, which continues to the present. In 2002, we added an Indiana University Associate Degree Program. This affiliation keeps us current and helps us recruit well-prepared therapists into an ever-changing profession and environment.

Many physicians have had a strong influence on our department throughout the years but none more important than Jack Kamen, M.D., who not only strongly supported us but also played a key role in the development of staff into an effective, cohesive team. Next, Charles Rebesco, M.D., introduced us to, challenged us to maximize our talents, and guided us through new technology for more than the two decades.

Today the department provides a full range of services from critical/trauma care to diagnostic tests like pulmonary lung function tests and metabolic monitoring. A recent advancement in the department includes the implementation of Patient Driven Protocols which are respiratory plans of care that promote high quality, state-of-the-art, and cost efficient therapy. The department continues to assist with patient discharges and provides pulmonary rehabilitation education programs to promote wellness.

Post-Tribune

1065 Broadway, Gary, Indiana 46402   (219) 881-3000

April 29, 1986

Dr. Jack M. Kamen
440 Tippecanoe
Gary, Indiana 46402

Dear Dr. Kamen:

Congratulations!

You have been selected as a winner in the Health and Medicine category of The Post-Tribune's 1986 Edgar L. Mills Community Service Awards program. The announcement is being made in the Post-Tribune Sunday, May 4...

Sincerely,

Terence O'Rourke
Managing Editor

TOR:lk

Enclosure

DID YOU KNOW?

Jack Kamen, M.D., was selected as *The Post-Tribune's* 1986 winner of the Edgar L. Mills Community Service Award in the Health and Medicine category. He was notified of his recognition in a letter from the newspaper's Managing Editor, Terence O'Rourke. Among his achievements, he was listed as medical director of Pulmonary Services, Intensive Care, the Pain Control Clinic and Anesthesiology, as well as working to inaugurate a new Cancer Pain Control Center that was destined to open in the Hobart hospital.

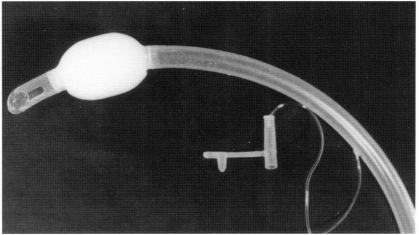

ENDOTRACHEAL CATHETER
This device is inserted into the windpipe (trachea) via the mouth or nose. It is commonly used by the anesthetist or anesthesiologist during surgery and is also often utilized in the Intensive Care Unit to assist or maintain breathing.

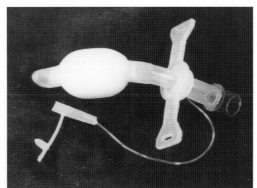

TRACHEOTOMY CATHETER
This catheter is inserted into the windpipe (trachea) via a small surgical incision made in the neck and functions similarly to the endotracheal catheter. Either device may be attached to a ventilator that assists or controls a patient's breathing.

IT'S BEEN *Said* IN 2009...

"My granddaughter, Hillary Friedman, was almost breathless with excitement. 'Grandpa, they're using your tracheotomy tubes!' she said.

"This was mid-2009 and she had recently been hired by Riley Children's Hospital in Indianapolis to work as a nurse in their transplant unit. During her orientation week she was introduced to the Respiratory Care Unit where an instructor demonstrated the various breathing devices utilized in the care of patients with respiratory problems. 'And this,' she said, holding up a catheter that is introduced into patients' tracheae (wind-pipes), 'is what we use for our sickest children.' 'And Grandpa,' Hillary said, 'it was your tube!'

"To start at the beginning: It is sometimes necessary to augment a patient's breathing by introducing a catheter ('tube') into his/her trachea or windpipe via the mouth or nose (endotracheal tube) or through a small incision made in the neck (tracheotomy tube). This catheter (or 'tube') is then often connected to a respirator that provides any necessary breathing assistance. For the respirator to work efficiently, an air-tight seal must be affected between the tube lying within the trachea and the trachea itself. In the past, a donut-shaped balloon ('cuff') that encircled the tube was inflated to make this seal.

"Therein lay the problem. Occasionally the cuff could be inadvertently over-inflated resulting in damage to the delicate tissues of the windpipe which in turn could cause a constriction or other severe, and at times, permanent damage. This led to the invention of a cuff filled with polyurethane foam that would self-expand only until it touched the trachea. Over-inflation was thereby nearly impossible.

"Dr. Carolyn Wilkinson, a colleague from Northwestern University and the co-developer, and I did all the experimental work at St. Mary Medical Center in Gary, Indiana, which was published in a well-recognized anesthesiology journal. Dr. Seymour Shapiro, a surgeon working at St. Mary's, was so taken by this device that he quit his practice and with Charles Bivona, a representative of a medical device manufacturer, established the Bivona Corporation to produce these catheters. It still exists in Gary and continues to supply these tubes for use throughout the world."

Jack M. Kamen, MD DIRECTOR OF I.C.U., DIRECTOR OF ST. MARY MEDICAL CENTER PAIN CENTER
CHIEF OF DEPARTMENT OF ANESTHESIOLOGY, DIRECTOR OF RESPIRATORY CARE, DIRECTOR OF MEDICAL EDUCATION, RETIRED
MERCY HOSPITAL
(BEGAN IN 1952 AT ST. CATHERINE HOSPITAL)

"We had a 16 year-old patient who was severely injured when she was thrown from a car and then struck by two other vehicles. Among other severe injuries she suffered a severed esophagus. A prominent Chicago hospital proposed a transplant to bridge the injured region, using her large bowel for the purpose. This probably would have caused her significant permanent discomfort.

"Coincidentally, about that time, I read of a specialist at Massachusetts General Hospital who specialized in esophageal repair. I discussed her pathology with him and after evaluating her studies, he agreed to attempt a repair without using a bowel transplant.

"Transporting the patient proved to be a problem because of a large post-injury air-filled cyst that developed in her lung. Flying in a commercial airliner would result in a significant expansion of the cyst because of the low pressurization, with resultant respiratory distress. An ambulance jet plane was therefore employed and by flying at a low altitude, the trip was accomplished without incident. I was accompanied by one of our stellar ICU nurses, Myrna Sison.

"When the patient was ready for discharge, after a successful repair, I was informed by their Physiology Department that she was capable of flying back by commercial jet. Although I disagreed, they prevailed and she boarded an American Airlines plane. A call from the airline in mid-flight, asking for advice because she was 'turning blue,' confirmed my fears. It was recommended that oxygen be started immediately, and to either land as soon as possible or descend to a lower altitude. The pilot opted for the latter.

"The patient is now happily married, has three children, and lives and works in Valparaiso."

Jack M. Kamen, MD. DIRECTOR OF I.C.U., DIRECTOR OF ST. MARY MEDICAL CENTER PAIN CENTER
CHIEF OF DEPARTMENT OF ANESTHESIOLOGY, DIRECTOR OF RESPIRATORY CARE, DIRECTOR OF MEDICAL EDUCATION, RETIRED
MERCY HOSPITAL
(BEGAN IN 1952 AT ST. CATHERINE HOSPITAL)

THE 1940S – TWINS GALORE!

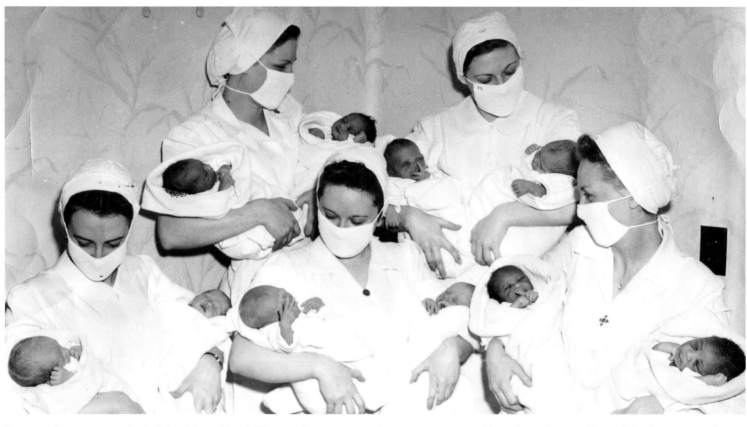

Five sets of twins were in the St. Mary Mercy (Gary) Obstetrics Department at the same time, presumably in the mid-1940s. Three of the five nurses in the photo are known to be Kay Comerford (bottom left), Mildred ("Tootie") (Mulhern) McTigue (bottom middle), and Kathryn Mikulich (top left).

Reprinted by permission of the *Post-Tribune*, 1945-1948

Emerging Changes in Healthcare

What They Remembered

IT'S BEEN *Said* IN 2009...

"I can remember as a little girl going with my mother who worked as a nurse and we would drive in the back to pick up her paycheck – in the back of the hospital that ultimately became the whole new wing. It just changed so dramatically. In fact, I was born and raised and grew up for the first couple years a block away from the hospital. I lived on Third and Tyler."

Judy Candiano, REVENUE CYCLE CONTROL SUPERVISOR, PATIENT ACCOUNTING
MERCY HOSPITAL
(BEGAN IN 1969 IN GARY)

IT'S BEEN *Said* IN 2009...

"There have been massive changes in medicine since I began. The biggest change, at least in general practice and family practice, has been the availability. We were constantly available at that time and I would probably make fifteen house calls a week.

"We didn't have the Emergency Room access that they have now and frankly, I don't think people came to hospitals as much as they do now. I don't think they required as many tests. There weren't maybe that many back then. So the Emergency Room in Gary was not very busy actually.

"We did not have available a lot of the things they have now. We didn't have ultrasound. We had basic X-rays and blood work, of course, but we weren't doing angiograms and things like that. We had some antibiotics and of course penicillin was the number one thing we had at that time."

Dr. John O. Carter, MD., FAMILY PRACTICE
LAKE GEORGE MEDICAL CENTER
(BEGAN AT MERCY HOSPITAL AS AN INTERN IN 1956)

Mercy Hospital Expansion

On May 5, 1944, the approval of a $61,800 FWA (Federal Works Administration) grant to finance the bulk of a $113,000 projected addition to Mercy Hospital was announced by Congressman Ray J. Madden "who helped expedite the hospital's application at the Washington end," the *Post-Tribune* reported. The new facilities would be used to house and train members of its war-expanded nursing and training staff. The addition of the fifth floor to the original hospital structure was completed to provide housing and classrooms for approximately 50 nursing trainees. The *Post-Tribune* further stated that Mercy Hospital's total outlay for the nursing corps facility would boost to well over $725,000 the aggregate volume of federal and local funds expended by the two Gary hospitals to keep pace with the overload imposed by the war.

"The secret of success is to do the common things uncommonly well." - JOHN D. ROCKEFELLER

The 1950s
Hospital/Community Happenings
Lake George Medical Center

"Lake George Medical Center is a family practice that has doctors available most of the time – all of the time by phone or emergencies. Dr. Richard Stookey is here with me as well as my two sons, Mark and John E. Carter. My sons both decided they wanted to go into medicine. I didn't influence them one way or the other, at least knowingly I didn't."

Dr. John O. Carter, MD., FAMILY PRACTICE
LAKE GEORGE MEDICAL CENTER
(BEGAN AT MERCY HOSPITAL AS AN INTERN IN 1956)

"Oh I can remember in 1957, 1958, 1959, even in the early 1960s when I was in practice, our office calls were just $3.00 and you could make a house call for $5.00 or $10.00 dollars.

"I spent a lot of time in the car so sometimes I would go home and get my wife and kids and they would ride with me to some of the house calls so I could see them."

Dr. John O. Carter, MD., FAMILY PRACTICE
LAKE GEORGE MEDICAL CENTER
(BEGAN AT MERCY HOSPITAL AS AN INTERN IN 1956)

SISTERS MILBURG AND THERESE
Sister Milburg, PHJC, who came to St. Mary Mercy Hospital as Mother Superior in 1951, returned to the Poor Handmaids of Jesus Christ convent in Donaldson, Indiana, before reassignment to her next post. Her successor as hospital administrator, or Mother Superior as they were known, was Sister Therese, PHJC.

Marking Time...

1950
- *A minimum wage of 75 cents per hour was set by the Fair Labor Standards Act.*

1952
- *A polio epidemic swept the U.S. killing more than 40,000 people.*

1954
- *The television series, The Tonight Show, premiered on NBC.*
- *Hosts included Steve Allen (1954-57); Jack Paar (1957-62); Johnny Carson (1962-92); Jay Leno (1992-).*

THE GARY POST-TRIBUNE:
Wednesday, February 23, 1955   **21**

Mercy Chief To Leave Post Here

Sister Mary Milburg, Mercy Hospital sister superior since 1951, will leave Gary tomorrow for reassignment.

She will return to the Poor Handmaids of Jesus Christ convent at Donaldson for assignment to her next post.

She came to Gary Sept. 4, 1951 as successor to Sister Mary Alphonsine.

Sister Mary Milburg served **Sister Milburg** as superior at hospitals in Fort Wayne, Chicago and in Wisconsin. She is a graduate nurse and director of all hospitals of the order in the community.

Name of her successor here was not announced by convent officials at Donaldson.

Name New Chief for Mercy

Sister M. Therese has been appointed mother superior of Mercy Hospital.

She succeeds Sister M. Milburg who left Gary this week for assignment at the Poor Handmaids of Jesus Christ convent at Donaldson.

The new mother superior has previously served at St. Ann's Hospital, Chicago. For the past six years she has been provincial mother of the Donaldson convent.

Sister M. Cornelia, director of Mercy Hospital's school of nursing for the past 3½ years, has been named assistant superintendent of the hospital.

Sister M. Lourdes, director of the department of education, succeeds Sister M. Cornelia as head of the nursing school.

Reprinted by permission of the *Post-Tribune,* FEBRUARY 1955

DID YOU KNOW?

IT'S BEEN *Said* IN 2009...

IN THE 1950S – KIDS TO WORK

"I was born in 1951 at Mercy Hospital in Gary. All five of my siblings were born there. When we were kids, my mom, Elvira Bravo, worked steady midnights for many years as a nurse's aide in different areas.

"Around 1955 or 1956, they were allowed to take their kids to work. My mom would dress us up in our pajamas and we would… stay on the fifth floor which was the pediatrics floor. They would… wake us up and serve us breakfast and the doctor would come in with one of the little doctor kits for us. The people who worked midnights took turns bringing their kids in. I think they made arrangements with their supervisors.

"We were already tired (because) we didn't leave home until 10:30 p.m. and our bedtime was usually 8:00 or 9:00 p.m.… They gave us juice and a nurse would come in and tell us a story… They got us up by 6:30 a.m. because the night shift got off at 7 a.m.

"She worked in Gary for 42 or 43 years. When I came to work I discovered a lot of people that my mom basically worked with or trained."

Jesse Bravo, FORMER TELECOMMUNICATIONS TECHNICIAN
ST. MARY MEDICAL CENTER
(BEGAN IN 1992 IN GARY)

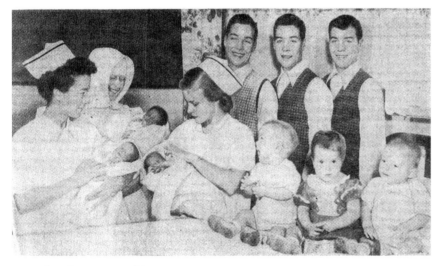

1953 – AND BABIES MAKE THREE

In 1953, the Chicago Sun-Times featured a photo showing three sets of triplets at Mercy Hospital in Gary. Sister Inez Wilmering, PHJC, is shown holding newborn Robert Sur near his brothers, Peter and Thomas. They were visited by three-year-old triplets Michael, Jeannine and Todd Rogers (who share the same birthday with the Sur trio) and 17-year-old triplets Richard, Robert and Ralph Jeffrey.

Chicago Sun-Times, OCTOBER 1, 1953

IT'S BEEN *Said* IN 2009...

IN THE 1950S – TRIPLE DELIGHT

"… I went to the dentist one time. The girl who worked in the dentist's office said she had a friend who was going to have triplets. I happened to be having my OB experience at that time so I got to be in there for the delivery of the triplets. It was a big thrill to be there. I still have a picture of that. We got our picture in the Chicago paper.

"At that time, we wore the old habits. For nursing Sisters, they were white. So my picture in the newspaper is in my old habit where we were all closed in."

Sister Inez Wilmering, PHJC
RETIRED
DONALDSON, INDIANA
(BEGAN AT MERCY HOSPITAL IN 1952)

Gary... the City and Era that Was

Mercy Hospital was important to the city of Gary and also served the communities of Crown Point, Griffith, Hobart and Lowell.

In the 1930s, those who sought medical care were also attracted to a beautiful, bustling city where visitors and citizens alike could walk for miles and feel comfortable in their surroundings. They might have greeted passersby before hopping on a five-cent street car ride to Twelfth and Garfield from Tolleston.

For several decades thereafter, the downtown area – with Broadway as its nucleus – was the place to shop for clothing, shoes, and bridal dresses during busy lunch times or after work. Doctors maintained offices in the bank building at Fifth and Broadway, known to be the busiest intersection in Northwest Indiana. The State and Palace theaters drew regular crowds. Parents walked children to the parks. The steel mills were active and employed those who had emigrated there to earn an honest wage.

Some of the interns lived across the street from the hospital in a furnished apartment building. Physicians, approximately 35 of them at one time, lived on the popular west side of the city, all within a three-block area near the hospital.

IT'S BEEN *Said* IN 2009...

"I used to live at Birch Avenue in Gary – close to Wirt High School – from 1964 – 1974. My wife and I were married at the St. Mary church in Miller and had our wedding reception at the famous Gary Hotel on Broadway which at that time was the equivalent of State Street in Chicago during Christmas with regard to lighting, decorations, and shopping."

Rodolfo L. Jao, M.D., FIDSA
INTERNAL MEDICINE/INTERNIST
SPECIALTY IN INFECTIOUS DISEASES
MERCY HOSPITAL
(BEGAN IN 1973 IN GARY)

For the Love of Mercy

IT'S BEEN *Said* IN 2009...

"I loved Gary. I lived in the convent on Pierce Street for two years with Sister Bertram Boeving, (PHJC), Sister Frances Royer, (PHJC), Sister Florence Kuhn (PHJC), and Sister Stephen Brueggeman, (PHJC). It was the bishop's old house – beautiful house with three or four fireplaces in it. It was in the middle of a lot of oppression with neighborhood windows boarded up and broken glass in nearby places. There is another group of missionary Sisters living there now and they work at the hospital in Hammond."

Sister Mary O'Hara, OP, CHAPLAIN
ST. MARY MEDICAL CENTER
(BEGAN IN 1989 IN GARY)

IT'S BEEN *Said* IN 2009...

"The hospital in Gary at the time had a very good reputation for hospitality, for being clean and knowing what they were doing. There were people there who were 'people people' – they had no differentiation of age, color or religion. It was just the community hospital and a very, very good place to visit."

Sister Michelle Dermody, PHJC
RETIRED, DONALDSON, INDIANA

A Look at the Racial Situation
Gary in the 1930s

"(The African-Americans) called me 'Sunshine.' In those days, you did not mix the blacks and whites. They were separated. There were some beds in one great big room. It was the Depression so they did not have private rooms. They just shoved them in there and I would go in there and talk to them. Black and white – they could be on the same floor but never together. Later, they had a double bed in every room and it would be two blacks or two whites."

Helen Petrovich, RN
MERCY HOSPITAL
(BEGAN IN 1934 IN GARY)
(NOTE: HELEN PETROVICH WAS 95 YEARS OLD AT THE TIME OF HER INTERVIEW.)

"The first day I walked into my office in 1935, the waiting room was segregated. I was so upset that I ended it that first day."

Raymond Carmody, MD.
OPHTHALMOLOGIST, RETIRED
MERCY HOSPITAL
(BEGAN IN 1935 IN GARY)
NOTE: AT THIS WRITING IN 2009, DR. CARMODY IS 101 YEARS OF AGE.
HE RETIRED IN 2001 AT AGE 93 AFTER 70 YEARS OF PRACTICE.

"For many years black doctors were not accepted on the staff at St. Mary's. They could not admit patients to any floor. They were only given certain floors. When I came in, some of the white doctors would not serve in Gary. They were all going south to Merrillville and Crown Point. There was a tremendous shortage of doctors."

Vijay Dave, MD., CARDIOLOGIST
MERCY HOSPITAL
(BEGAN IN 1977 IN GARY)

MERCY TAKING NEGRO MEDICS' APPLICATIONS

HOSPITALS—MERCY

1-30-42

Negro physicians may now make application for admission to practice medicine and surgery at Mercy hospital, the medical staff raising no objections at a meeting last night to the recent action of the hospital board opening the institution to Negro members of the medical profession. No action by the staff was called for inasmuch as the board had decided the question.

Similar action has been recommended to the board of directors of Methodist hospital by its medical staff. The Methodist board is expected to approve the recommendation at its next meeting Oct. 1.

First published February 30, 1947
Courtesy of Gary Public Library
Reprinted by permission of the
Gary Post-Tribune, Jubilee Edition, MAY 20, 1956

GARY IN THE 1940S
1947 – BENJAMIN F. GRANT, M.D.

In 1947, the medical staff accepted the application for staff privileges by Benjamin F. Grant, M.D., the hospital's first black physician. This was a major step in the desegregation process. Prior to that there were written and unwritten policies in place that reflected not only the hospital but national trends as well.

Benjamin F. Grant, M.D.

IT'S BEEN *Said* IN 2009...

"Benjamin Grant was a black guy – the first leader. He has raised more money for the NAACP than anybody in the whole country. If he was alive, he would have been 100 years old. He was the first one to break the color barrier. He paved the way for a lot of minority patients and doctors.

"Dr. A. S. Williams was a most open-minded, honest, black physician. He was bright. Anybody and everybody who met him was his friend and not his enemy. He brought together whites and blacks like Martin Luther King did. He is the reason why we had at least ten doctors. Dr. Michael Linton, Dr. Bernadette Aghaji, Dr. Bill Washington, Dr. Steve Simpson are all the new young doctors brought to St. Mary Medical Center by Dr. A.S. Williams when he was opposed by all his colleagues. He was good cement. He believed in Gary and in community."

Vijay Dave, M.D., CARDIOLOGIST
MERCY HOSPITAL
(BEGAN IN 1977 IN GARY)

GARY IN THE 1950S

By the mid-1950s, Gary had 16 African-American physicians, 13 of whom were on staff at Mercy and Methodist hospitals.

BLACK STUDENTS ADMITTED TO NURSING SCHOOL

IT'S BEEN *Said* IN 2009...

"I went into nurses training at St. Mary Mercy for three years – from 1952 – 1955. Sister Lourdes (Meyer), PHJC, was the first instructor when I got there and became director of nursing after I was there for a while. I think we must have had about 40 and our class had the first black girl as a student and we had the first married woman. We had classes in the daytime – first (as) a "probie" (probationary student) where… through the program… students got their caps around December. They were all so proud."

Sister Inez Wilmering, PHJC, RETIRED
DONALDSON, INDIANA
(BEGAN AT MERCY HOSPITAL IN 1952)

In 1952, the first black students were admitted to St. Mary's Mercy School of Nursing. Several years later, on August 21, 1955, Miss Janice Coefield became the first African-American in Lake County to receive her diploma there. An anonymous account of that time, recorded at the Motherhouse in the Donaldson, Indiana archives said: "Race no longer, but sound character, necessary scholarship, and an intensive desire to help suffering humanity are the prerequisites of the student entering Saint Mary's Mercy Hospital School of Nursing."

"In the early 1950s – 1953, 1954 – there were five blacks in my nursing class. Some of the nurses had come from Valparaiso and some surrounding towns so they had never seen blacks. At first, you don't know what to expect but then we all became good friends. We would help one another because a lot of times when they put us on the nursing unit, the RNs would be prejudiced and would give the blacks the hardest patients. The whites would come and help us because we might be on the floor for three or four hours in the morning and then we had to get to class in time so you had to finish up your work. I think we all learned how to work efficiently and fast within that time frame and the room had to be perfect. You had to do whatever patient they gave you and clean up the room. Otherwise, she would call you back to clean it up.

"We didn't miss class because, being the five black ones there, we had a standard we had to maintain basically. The other four black classmates were Carol Smith, Christel Williams, Lucinthia Murray, and Mary Jones."

Flora Dean Meeks, R.N, RADIOLOGY, RETIRED
MERCY HOSPITAL
(BEGAN IN 1960)

"People today may not have experienced the racial situation as it was in 1959 when I began working on 2South. We were not permitted to put different races in the same room together. One of the first questions the admitting office would ask when they called was the color of the patient. We had to move patients around so there would be two people of the same race in the same room. In the 1960s, I remember there were pickets at the Gary hospital on Tyler Street with signs about the racial situation."

Shirley Makivich Urbanek, R.N, RETIRED
ST. MARY MERCY HOSPITAL
(BEGAN IN 1959 IN GARY)

GARY IN THE 1960S
1963 – HOSPITAL INTEGRATION TALKS HIT STALEMATE

HOSPITAL INTEGRATION TALKS HIT STALEMATE

In 1963, a qualification in a general policy statement by Gary's Methodist Hospital representatives brought a stalemate in negotiations with the Civil Rights Committee. Meetings, held at Mercy Hospital, involved both Gary hospitals.

CHJC, University of Notre Dame Archives

St. Mary Mercy Hospital of Gary, in the finest Judaic-Christian tradition, has a policy of care and aid to all who come to its doors; following its moral and ethical principles, there shall be no discrimination or segregation and no restriction because of race, creed, color, national origin or ancestry, in any area of its institutional life.

Signed at Gary, Indiana, this 29th day of July, 1963.

ST. MARY MERCY HOSPITAL

By: *Sister M. Cornelia*
    Administrator

Witnesses:

Mrs. Jeanette Strong
Laurence Anderson Jr.
Rev. H. H. Thomas

Representatives of the Combined
Civil Rights Organizations

Mercy Hospital Policy of Care Statement (ABOVE) – JULY, 1963
CHJC, University of Notre Dame Archives

IT'S BEEN *Said* IN 2009...

"It's just hard for people today who have only been around Northwest Indiana or Lake County for 20 or 25 years to even begin to comprehend the change that took place in Gary from the '50s to the '70s. It was just unbelievable. It was a whole combination of things. Yeah, I would say that the hospital communities, Mercy and Methodist as well, hung in pretty well through all the turmoil. There were some tensions and there was some divisiveness but people really rallied around the mission of taking care of people and those organizations were the most obvious examples of what everybody hoped could happen in terms of a rational form of integration in the community."

John Birdzell
FORMER PRESIDENT OF LAKESHORE HEALTH SYSTEM
(BEGAN IN 1985 WITH ANCILLA SYSTEMS INCORPORATED)

The 1963 stalemate over hospital integration talks occurred over the following statement: "Non-discrimination and elimination of segregation based on race, creed, color, ancestry or national origin, with cognizance of the personal rights of all patients." At issue was the clause, "with cognizance of the personal rights of all patients."

ST. MARY MERCY HOSPITAL
540 TYLER STREET
GARY - INDIANA

July 25, 1963

Dear Mother Symphoria:

Just a few lines to say we are still working hard and trying very hard to be the kind of daughters you want us to be. We had a prompto Lay Advisory Board Meeting this noon at the request of Mr. Charles Daugherty, who has been our good samaritan in representing us at these N.A.A.C.P. Council Meetings, and also sat with us at our meeting with this group Tuesday, which lasted approximately three hours.

We presented our hospital admittance policy, also the statement which our good Bishop drew up for us.

The Bishop was gone on his retreat at this time, but will be back late this evening. He, however, was very much concerned and interested to know how the Meeting turned out.

At our Lay Board Meeting this noon, it was the consensus of the members that we meet with them on Monday as previously scheduled, and merely make a statement that they were all given our Policy and the Joint Statement of the Bishop and myself, and say these are the policies we abide and operate by, and if they have any complaints of discriminating practice by personnel responsible to or employed by us in the future, to bring it to our attention - we would certainly look into the matter and correct it.

Now for some equipment which we need very urgently --
1.' 12 linen carts for the laundry to distribute the linens to the floors - this will be on the same services as St. Elizabeth's and St. Catherine's. The cost will be approximately $2598.00

2. One of our O.R. tables is completely out. Need a replacement -- approximately $2500.00

Enclosed you will find a return card for your convenience, also, the last newspaper clippings.

With kindest greetings to you dear Mother Symphoria, and to Mother Theodolinda, and all the Sisters.

As ever in the Sacred Hearts of Jesus and Mary,

Very sincerely yours,

Sister M. Cornelia
Sister M. Cornelia

In July 1963, (ABOVE) St. Mary Mercy Hospital Administrator Sister Cornelia Leible, PHJC, wrote to Mother Symphoria, PHJC, to keep her apprised of ongoing NAACP Council meetings. CHJC, University of Notre Dame Archives

THE MERCY HOSPITAL CHRONICLES

As previously mentioned, for many years the Poor Handmaids of Jesus Christ kept careful records – anonymously hand-written by several of the Sisters – pertaining to the history of their hospitals. From October 15, 1956 on, all Chronicles were typewritten. Excerpts of their accounts, gratefully obtained from the University of Notre Dame Archives, continue throughout this book, including the following series of entries pertaining to the racial situation in the early 1960s.

FROM THE PHJC CHRONICLES – 1963

July 4, 1963 – NAACP agitation begins. Accusations of discrimination and disintegration hurled. Meetings with the Lay Advisory Board, with the Executive Committee, with the Right Reverend Bishop, and Mr. Daugherty to meet the problems. All concurred that the Negro has full attention to his rights and needs at St. Mary Mercy. The right to place patients for the best patient care is to be adhered to, and consideration of the human rights of a person are to be taken into consideration in placing patients. Emergency bed shortage is one of the criteria.

July 18 – Picketing began at Methodist Hospital… to be initiated at Mercy Hospital the following week.

July 23 – Sister Cornelia (Leible), PHJC; Sister Johannetta (Bergman), PHJC; Mr. Paul Bellendorf, and Mr. Charles Daugherty met with eleven members of the NAACP regarding the problem of integration and discrimination. Little information given and no conclusion after a three-hour meeting, since no agenda had been given by the Community Council as requested by Mercy Hospital. During the following days, both Gary hospitals were blasted by the NAACP. Methodist Hospital was picketed daily.

July 25 – An impromptu meeting of the Lay Advisory Board as to the course to be followed in the problem of segregation and discrimination.

July 29 – A second meeting with the NAACP. The meeting opened at 7:15 p.m.. Sister Cornelia (Leible), PHJC; Sister Johannetta (Bergman), PHJC; Mr. Bellendorf, Richard Purcell, M.D., of the staff, and Mr. Charles Daugherty (as the hospital attorney) were present. The meeting was carried on in a friendly manner and concessions were made. An agreement on policy was signed. Then reporters, photographers had a party!

July 31 – The last day of a troublesome month. Integration on a cautious basis of patients – very few and no rebuttals.

There were rumblings throughout Gary of the Negro situations but all seemed in order at St. Mary Mercy Hospital. Integration mildly and cautiously done. The General Staff meeting on August 1 passed without any arguments over the issue. The misgivings on the part of some of the Mercy doctors were quieted with explanation of the policy that Mercy would hold to.

CHJC, University of Notre Dame Archives

"Look back, to slavery, to suffrage, to integration and one thing is clear. Fashions in bigotry come and go. The right thing lasts." ~ANNA QUINDLEN

"Being racially separated on the hospital floors was just the way things were done. Until they started the sit-ins in Gary, they tried to integrate Marquette Park, and then Froebel High School and that is when it began to change in the hospitals.

"Dr. Benjamin Grant was probably an instigator at the time because he demanded that his patients get the same care and treatment as the white patients. Dr. Kenneth Washington did too.

"Most of the rooms were double so if you put a black patient in with a white patient, she didn't want to be in that room and would ask to be moved. It was probably two or three years before it became fully integrated with people just accepting it… but it didn't happen overnight. Dr. Hershel Bornstein was white but he had lots of black patients and he would insist that his patients be treated equally. He was a general practitioner."

Flora Dean Meeks, RN, RADIOLOGY, RETIRED
MERCY HOSPITAL
(BEGAN IN 1960 IN GARY)

"The School of Nursing continued as long as the enrollment was up. We had a total of 905 students who graduated from there. Then, unfortunately, things changed for Gary and the number of people coming into Gary changed. As Gary went, so did the enrollment. That was well before 1968 and that's when they decided, I guess, that it wasn't going to be feasible to continue with the school."

Mary Ellen Donovan
SECRETARY TO THE DIRECTOR
ST. MARY'S MERCY SCHOOL OF NURSING
(BEGAN IN 1945 IN GARY)

"Mercy Hospital was the first integrated medical staff in the state of Indiana. (The demise of Gary) was caused by the "white flight" and (Richard) Hatcher's being elected mayor."

Robert S. Martino, MD.
ORTHOPEDIC SURGEON
MERCY HOSPITAL
(BEGAN IN 1965 IN GARY)

"Gary, unfortunately, went through some troubled times in the late 1960s and 1970s and made the business community feel unwanted. It drove the business out of there. St. Mary's Hospital felt the effect and the Ancilla Sisters were concerned about putting improvements in the hospital."

Robert J. Welsh
FORMER ST. MARY MEDICAL CENTER, ST. CATHERINE HOSPITAL BOARD MEMBER
ST. MARY MEDICAL CENTER CHAIRMAN OF THE BOARD (1997 – 2001)
CFNI BOARD MEMBER

"In 1968, there were lots of racial tensions. It was the time of Civil Rights Movement and Martin Luther King. It was turmoil and it was tough. I never had any prejudices. To me, every human was a human. This black/white situation was not known in my home country, so when I came to the U.S. discrimination was something new and very strange to me."

Srbislav Brasovan, MD., OBSTETRICIAN/GYNECOLOGIST
Mercy Hospital
(BEGAN IN 1968 IN GARY)

GARY IN THE 1970S

Racial barriers, evident in the community and across the nation for many years – were found not only in the hospitals but also in schools, businesses and neighborhoods. Gary, once a thriving city, fell victim to "white flight" and socioeconomic change. Stores closed in the downtown area, drug problems surfaced, tension and violence increased, and students' academic achievement declined. "For sale" signs persisted in affluent residential areas.

Still, there were those within Mercy Hospital who valued lifelong friendships with co-workers regardless of race, color or creed and say their Mercy years – as a family – were among the best.

GARY IN THE 1980S

CONTINUING MEDICAL EDUCATION...

Contributed by Vijay Dave, M.D.,
Medical Director
and Susan Miller, MLIS
Regional Director of Medical Education

Vijay Dave, M.D., long known for his dedication to continuing medical education, is honored with this bust displayed at St. Mary Medical Center in Hobart, located right outside the auditorium. It was dedicated to him in 2004.

Vijay Dave, M.D., confers with students as part of the Continuing Medical Education program

IT'S BEEN *Said* IN 2009... ∼∼∼∼∼∼∼

"Mayor (Richard J.) Daley gave me an award because I used to be very active in Chicago. It was for Outstanding Indian Citizen. I started the first Indian newspaper in Chicago in 1973. It was called *Chingari* which means 'when you light the fire and have a spark.'"

Vijay Dave, M.D., CARDIOLOGIST
MERCY HOSPITAL
(BEGAN IN 1977 IN GARY)

Cardiologist Vijay Dave, M.D., is shown here with his prestigious Sagamore of the Wabash award from the governor of Indiana (left) and a humanitarian award from his native country of India (right).

Vim & Vigor, WINTER 2004

Susan Miller, MLIS
Regional Director of
Medical Education

St. Mary Medical Center's Continuing Medical Education program began in the 1950s at the facility in Gary Indiana, then known as St. Mary Mercy Hospital. With the newly established pathology residency, a need for medical education was identified. Using the *New England Journal of Medicine* case presentations as a model, the Clinical Pathological Conferences (CPC) were started by Earl Mason, Ph.D., M.D., and his associates. The CPCs were offered monthly. Soon thereafter, John Scully, M.D., and Jack Kamen, M.D., recognizing that the advances in intensive care medicine required continuing medical education, initiated the Morbidity and Mortality conferences. These conferences were used to educate both physicians and nurses working in the Intensive Care Unit, pioneering the "team approach."

The Medical Education program formalized and Jacob Pruitt, M.D., served as the director of Medical Education through 1980. In 1981, Vijay Dave, M.D., accepted the position as director of Medical Education and remains so today.

The CME Program grew as the membership of the medical staff increased. Dr. Dave expanded the program to include a Summer Extern program and Summer Shadowing program. Originating in 1988 and 1990, respectively, these programs were started in collaboration with the Indiana University School of Medicine – Northwest Campus. The Summer Extern program accepts medical students, while the Summer Shadowing program is geared toward pre-med college students interested in pursuing a career in medicine. Medical staff members and clinical staff directors serve as preceptors for the rotating students. Since the program's inception, hundreds of the summer externs have become physicians serving our local communities.

In addition, many international students, at various stages of their training from first year and beyond, have received exposure to the practice of American medicine by rotating with several medical staff members. We have hosted students from several countries including Egypt, India, Pakistan, Syria, Thailand, and Vietnam.

Based on need, grand rounds, visiting professors, CPCs, and cancer conferences make up the continuing medical education activities. These activities are planned to support and meet the needs of the physicians, keeping them on the cutting edge of medical practice, thereby providing the most favorable outcomes possible for the patients and maintaining high-quality care.

IT'S BEEN *Said* IN 2009...

"We used to have Dr. Jacob Pruitt here. He was the director of Medical Education but when he submitted his resignation they called me and said I didn't have a choice. Mary Gulyassy said effective immediately I was the director of Medical Education… and for five years I didn't get any money.

"I organized our student program and it has become big. One student came from California and by word of mouth students came from Vietnam, China, Czechoslovakia, Macedonia, Austria and believe it or not, Iraq. They came, obviously, from India. I am from India. It is very rewarding. I have been director of Medical Education for almost 30 years.

"I would say 20 is the average number of students at one time. I give a lecture and say, 'This is a real hospital. Your job during this next eight weeks is to see what a real hospital is. This is what America is. Harvard, Yale, or Stanford is really small in number but St. Mary or Methodist hospitals are real hospitals that provide real care to Americans.' I tell them this is a hospital setting where they can see what it is like and see what the hospital has to offer them. Then, they can see if medicine is for them.

"Of all, what I love is director of Medical Education. It keeps me young. I have exposure to all this. Thanks to the administration, I have had full, full, support."

Vijay Dave, M.D., CARDIOLOGIST
MERCY HOSPITAL
(BEGAN IN 1977 IN GARY)

IT'S BEEN *Said* IN 2009...

"The number one person who has supported me with (the student program in) Continuing Medical Education is Milton Triana. I don't think I have ever met such a human being. He has such dignity and is an honest man. He is a competent person and a sincere man. So many people have higher titles and higher pay but nobody comes close to Milt Triana. Milt Triana had a book where he wrote down the issues. Most of the time, all the issues were addressed – not resolved but addressed by the end of the day.
"Number two is Barb Blejski who is downstairs. This lady is so competent. In other institutions it would require three-plus people to do what Barb does.
"Susan Miller is another person for whom I have a lot of respect.
"Janice Ryba has helped me too. I will give you an example. Every three or four years hospitals get accreditation from the Indiana State Medical Association. They come in and check your program. We are the only hospital in Northwest Indiana that got a special recommendation for six years. There are very few hospitals in the entire state that get this. That is why we can give medical education credit. We were thrilled!"

Vijay Dave, M.D., CARDIOLOGIST
MERCY HOSPITAL
(BEGAN IN 1977 IN GARY)

MORE EDUCATION – ON THE FACULTY

"The one real object of education is to have man in the condition of continually asking questions."
~ BISHOP MANDELL CREIGHTON

IT'S BEEN *Said* IN 2010...

"Going into medicine was like a calling. I just felt I wanted to be in medicine and I wanted to be a surgeon. I retired in April 1988.

"My mission, besides surgery, was teaching at Indiana Medical School at the Northwest Center. I knew anatomy from surgery, of course, and I taught it for 14 years. Joe Koscielniak was one of my students – a good one. I was an adjunct professor and I became Clinical Associate Professor of Surgery, Emeritus. Indiana Medical School has become the second largest medical school in the country."

William J. Glover, MD., GENERAL SURGEON, RETIRED
MERCY HOSPITAL
(BEGAN IN APPROXIMATELY 1947 IN GARY)

IT'S BEEN *Said* IN 2009...

"The School of Nursing was GREAT. There was more hands-on training. Now it's more books and computers. I taught nursing students while a resident at Chicago Wesley Hospital (now Northwestern Memorial Hospital) and Cook County Hospital and when I came to Gary I did the same – plus I got a teaching appointment at the medical school at Indiana University Northwest in anatomy and orthopedics.

"Teaching medical students was and is stimulating. They would make rounds, scrub in for surgery, and help with anatomy labs. It has changed because now only residents can scrub and assist in surgery. The students from I.U.N. could suture by the end of their first years."

Robert S. Martino, MD., ORTHOPEDIC SURGEON
MERCY HOSPITAL
(BEGAN IN 1965 IN GARY)

IT'S BEEN *Said* IN 2009...

"I taught OB/GYN at the University of Indiana for many years – Northwest campus. My favorite part was introductory lectures. I am a passionate collector of old OB/GYN books and I have quite a few oldies in very good condition. I usually would take a hundred year old OB/GYN text book of *Modern Obstetrics and Gynecology* and I would read a chapter to the students. They would laugh their heads off. I would tell them, 'Now remember, 100 years from now your children's children will be sitting in those chairs right there and somebody is going to read to them your text book and they will be rolling.' Nowadays, we do not really know how it was yesterday unless we were there. Whatever was there wasn't bad for their time. We could not change it... We are the best for today."

Srbislav Brasovan, MD., OBSTETRICIAN/GYNECOLOGIST
Mercy Hospital
(began in Gary in 1968)

IT'S BEEN *Said* IN 2009...

"Because of the tremendous number of patients with diabetes, it affected so many areas of other diseases. In addition, I had a faculty appointment for many years as Clinical Associate Professor of Medicine – Indiana University School of Medicine – and it happened that one of the primary areas I taught was diabetes. As a result, I always had a tremendous interest in it."

John T. Scully, MD., INTERNIST, RETIRED
MERCY HOSPITAL
(BEGAN IN 1955 IN GARY)

IT'S BEEN *Said* IN 2009...

THE GLOBAL PICTURE

"Healthcare not only preserves life, it can improve life a great deal – especially today with rehabilitation activities that are going on. People are living much longer than they did when I came into the business and one reason is the hospitals are doing a much better job. People's lifestyles change.

"What I learn in teaching international healthcare is that we're far behind the rest of the world in that regard. We have probably the best healthcare in the world and the worst healthcare system in the world. The mechanism by which it is delivered is absolutely disgraceful and it's amazing that we put out such a great product. We have the worst infant mortality, the worst life expectancy among developed countries and those are two pretty important matters. We're ranked 17th in life expectancy and 21st in infant mortality among developed countries – something like that. We get a little better every year but so does the rest of the world."

Bill Schenck, PRESIDENT, BOARD OF DIRECTORS, ST. MARY MEDICAL CENTER SINCE 2001
BOARD MEMBER, COMMUNITY FOUNDATION OF NORTHWEST INDIANA, INC.

IT'S BEEN *Said* IN 2009...

"I am on the faculty at Indiana as a voluntary faculty member. One year, we actually had 12 medical students who rotated through our office and it was a lot of fun to have some seniors banter back and forth saying, 'Okay we are going to do this case, this is the procedure, go look it up, go read about it, go learn the anatomy and then as we are doing it we are going to play 20 questions.' Way back when I was a medical student, I got to assemble a hip prosthesis. All the important steps were done (by the surgeon) but I got to put it together and I got to put it in."

Joe Koscielniak, MD., ORTHOPEDIC SURGEON
MERCY HOSPITAL (EXTERN)
(BEGAN IN 1984 IN HOBART)

In an Emergency

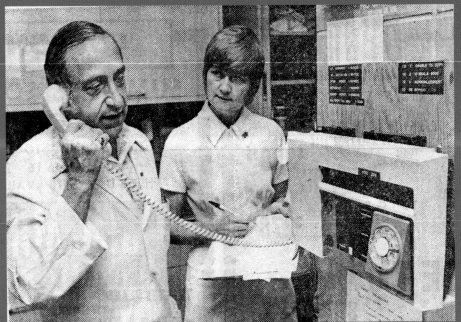

Daniel D. Thomas, M.D., a Gary Mercy Hospital Emergency Room physician, used the hospital's new radio system in 1974 to speak with a Gary Fire Department ambulance crew bringing in an accident victim. Barbara Rothermel, Mercy Hospital Emergency Room head nurse, recorded vital information so staff members would be ready when the patient arrived. Two-way radio bases were installed at the Gary and Hobart hospitals as part of the Indiana Hospital Emergency Radio Network (IHERN).
Reprinted by permission of the *Post-Tribune*, June 8, 1974

Gary

A major new emergency treatment center opened at St. Mary Medical Center in Gary in 1988. Shown here is Medical Director of the Emergency Room, Cornelius Arnold, M.D. The 9,247 square-foot facility included two trauma rooms for emergency surgery; two psychiatry holding rooms; and a consultation/waiting area. A new entrance to the center enabled quick access from Fifth Avenue.
Reprinted by permission of *The Times*,
February 24, 1988

IT'S BEEN *Said* IN 2009...

"At one point in the history of St. Mary Medical Center, I was chairperson of the board. We usually met in the Gary facility. It was the time when we were beginning to build the new Emergency Room and pediatrics in the Gary facility. I was fairly young at the time and remember signing the papers for the bond issue. One of the affidavits I had to sign was that I was experienced and capable of making these large financial decisions. I was sure I was going to jail since I was just a young Sister but it all worked out."

Sister Nora Hahn, PHJC., Provincial
Donaldson, Indiana

With Beginnings in Gary • THEN AND NOW

EMERGENCY DEPARTMENT...

Contributed by Paula Rousis, RN, Nurse Manager

HOBART EMERGENCY DEPARTMENT EXPANSION – 2009

Shown here is a rendering of the St. Mary Medical Center Emergency Department expansion. The groundbreaking was held in October 2009 with plans to build an addition along the west face of the Outpatient/Emergency area and total renovation of the existing Emergency Department. When complete, the new area will have two trauma rooms, two triage rooms, 12 general treatment rooms including a private obstetrics room with separate bathroom, and eight "fast-track" rooms to treat patients with minor injuries. At this writing the $12.5 million project is scheduled for completion by fall 2010.

When I first started working at St. Mary Medical Center Emergency Room in Hobart in 2003, we were treating approximately 55 patients a day. The department has not truly been remodeled since the 1970s. As the technology increased, the hospital continued to improve and provide quality care and updated equipment; however, there was no increase in the size of the department. There are still curtains dividing the available rooms and every possible piece of wall, hall, and space is used to render the top quality care for which we are known.

In the past eight years, there has been a large turnover of staff and few senior staff members remain. The Emergency Room recently lost its charge nurse, Linda Breitzke, who was an integral part of the Emergency Department for the past 30 years. Without her, it is difficult to provide an extensive history of our department.

BREAKING GROUND

Shown here at the Emergency Department groundbreaking ceremony in 2009 are (l-r); Brian Snedecor, mayor, city of Hobart; Paula Rousis, RN, nurse manager; Bishop Dale Melczek; Frankie Fesko, chairman, CFNI Board of Directors; William Schenck, president, St. Mary Medical Center Board of Directors; John Gorski, then chief operating officer, Community Foundation of Northwest Indiana, Inc.; Janice L. Ryba, hospital CEO and administrator; and John Mulligan, M.D. chairman, Emergency Department

Speaking for the current staff, however, we restarted the Emergency Department in 2005. When this departmental change occurred, processes and paperwork changed and most of the staff at that time left the hospital. The remaining staff was left to begin anew. A new physician group was in place with new staff members who had varied amounts of experience from a vast number of emergency departments. With much work and commitment, our emergency room has turned into a department that is well recognized and visited by many surrounding communities. As new staff members join our team, they are amazed at how we are able to provide services to the number of patients we have in our tiny department. It is a challenge every day to use every available corner of our Emergency Department to treat our patients. Staff members often laugh at the newest idea we create to meet this challenge.

We have developed an Emergency Medical Services (EMS) program, become a provider hospital for multiple pre-hospital services, and have grown significantly in our patient volume. We now have many patients who drive past other area hospitals to visit our Emergency Department to be admitted to St. Mary Medical Center. We have become the front door of the hospital and welcome all who need our assistance. As an added measure of quality care, we initiate discharge calls to all of our patients who have been treated and released. This allows us to answer any questions they may have and offer assistance or instructions for any follow-up care.

The hospital is renovating and expanding our Emergency Department to create more space and access for more patients. A groundbreaking for this purpose was held in October 2009. The Emergency Department team now includes a consistent medical staff, nursing staff, registration staff and housekeeping staff. We are "on the bus" and continue to improve our skills and achieve very good patient outcomes.

IN GARY

IT'S BEEN *Said* IN 2009...

"I was working in the Emergency Room when Louis "Buddy" Hutchen was fatally shot in 1948. He was in the 'rackets' and the murder has never been solved. He was a very large man and the police brought him in on a cart in a black overcoat and a hat on his face. He had been shot with 13 machine gun bullets and he was dead on arrival."

Vivian Fugate Springer
RN, RETIRED
MERCY HOSPITAL
(BEGAN IN 1948 IN GARY)

"Methodist was only six blocks away so the two hospitals were very close. We had Gary policemen who were security guards in the Emergency Room so we got to know them pretty well. If they ever heard over the radio that our hospital or Methodist had a problem, they would show up in force to make sure that everything was okay."

Karen Gerke, RN
DIRECTOR OF SURGERY
ST. MARY MEDICAL CENTER
(BEGAN IN 1972 IN GARY)

"I started out working in the Emergency Room when I first graduated. I worked there for 10 years. The surgeries took a long time then. The chest was opened wide and gall bladders had big incisions across the right side. There was a lot of clamping and a lot of bleeding and a lot of recovery time. Now you go in, get small incisions and go home that same day."

Phyllis Mattingly Coil, RN
FORMER STAFF NURSE
EMERGENCY ROOM
MERCY HOSPITAL
(BEGAN IN 1952 IN GARY)

In Gary (continued)

"From 1973 –1975, I worked in the Emergency Room and drug wars were very prevalent. We would see patients coming in with drug overdoses and they would have the syringes still in their arms. I was a farm girl. I had never seen any of these kinds of things. Barbara Rothermel was the head nurse in Emergency. There were about six patient bays and a trauma room. We got a lot of gunshot wounds and a lot of stabbings. A motorcycle gang came in once and dropped off one of their friends who was a trauma case. When we went out from work that night after the 3-11 p.m. shift, they were all over the parking lot just waiting to see how he was doing. It was a huge group of 50 or 60 motorcycle people and, if I remember correctly, he made it."

Karen Gerke, R N, Director of Surgery
St. Mary Medical Center
(began in 1972 in Gary)

"I remember one note I received from a girl who had been battered. I took her aside and talked to her. I did that often with (patients like that)... I told her she could change her life and turn it around. I told her she was a young girl. I said I didn't get married until I was older. When I was around 26, I finished my education and became a nurse... I told her she could do it, and she did it, too. She made it a point to come back later. She told me I saved her life. I carried the note with me for so very long."

Kathy Carrico, R N, Lead Nursing Supervisor
St. Mary Medical Center
(began in 1982 in Gary)

In Hobart

A family member writes in the mid-1970s...

On behalf of the members of our family... let me take this opportunity to thank Dr. (John) Gallinatti and the fine crew in the Hobart hospital Emergency Room. My wife's mother is much better and undergoing a series of tests. Please convey our feelings to the ladies on duty in Receiving, the two splendid nurses for their interest and professionalism, and the gentlemen (Red Coats) who assisted us in a variety of ways.

C. L. K.

A patient writes in 2009...

My brother and I would like to thank the staff in the Emergency Room and 2W for the care bestowed on our mother... Mom was brought into the Emergency Room after suffering a stroke. She was treated quickly and efficiently. No question or concern that we might have had ever went unanswered.

After leaving Intensive Care, Mom was moved to 2W. My brother and I both live in Illinois and were not able to get to the hospital daily so there were a lot of phone calls. The nursing staff always answered our questions and never made us feel like we were a bother... There are staff members we would especially like to thank from 2W – Bonnye, Nancy, and Justin.

Over the last few years, my dad was in and out of hospitals in Northwest Indiana and Chicago. I have had a chance to see different nursing staffs in action. By far the treatment of the patient and the family at St. Mary's was the most outstanding. We thank you so much.

Sincerely,
Nina

"In 1968 or 1969, a father and his two sons were bow and arrow hunting some place outside Indiana. They had some beers and they put some arrows on the ground looking up. One of the boys decided to pick up a can of beer and one of the arrows went all the way through his right eye. It cut the eye and the lid in two and they went immediately to the Emergency Room of Mercy Hospital. I was called in and told the family, 'I don't know if I can save the right eye but I think the left eye will be okay.' I remember the father begging to have one of his eyes transplanted to his son. The bad eye was immediately removed because it was not only affecting the orbital area but also the way to the brain. We stopped the bleeding and I told the father that one eye would in time serve his son perfectly well. I put a prosthesis in one eye. It looked pretty good and the family was happy."

Jose H. Roig, MD., OPHTHALMOLOGIST, RETIRED
MERCY HOSPITAL | (BEGAN IN 1967 IN GARY)

"I remember my mother wanting to come out here (to Hobart) to work but she lived in Gary. My father was pushing her to come out here and work. I remember they called it Kellar's Clinic.

"Dr. Phil Kellar is a great friend of mine now. I didn't know him well then. I guess he was a big backer of the hospital. He had a huge practice in Hobart and was a very, very popular doctor. From what I understood – because I wasn't here then, he had a lot to do with the hospital coming into being.

"I later worked with him. He was an Emergency Room doctor. He was a spectacular man. In fact, he was one of the first Emergency Room specialists in this area. He was an excellent diagnostic technician. Everybody just adored working with him. I was very sad to see him go."

Kathy Carrico, R.N, LEAD NURSING SUPERVISOR
ST. MARY MEDICAL CENTER
(BEGAN IN 1982 IN GARY)

"In my position, in any situation we lead. We are pioneers. I can tell you a story of a patient driving a car on I-94 who was in a car accident. The patient came to the Emergency Room with chest pain and an EKG showed a heart attack and a left leg was fractured and bleeding. The ER physician called me. I could have refused to come because the patient was bleeding. How can I do an angioplasty on a patient who is bleeding? When you do an angioplasty, you have to give a blood thinner so I came and did an angiogram of the leg and it showed there was no arterial rupture or laceration. So I did angioplasty of the heart and then let the patient recover and sent the patient to have surgery of the leg. The patient is alive and walking.

"The way we managed this case is not ever written in any textbook. It was nothing we saw before. It became an example of care for all cardiologists in the U.S. and the world how to handle the problem when the patient comes with heart attack and bleeding. I gave many lectures in China, Europe, and the U.S. and have written about this case so it became the standard of care for patients with heart attack and bleeding."

Thach Nguyen, MD., CARDIOLOGIST
ST. MARY MEDICAL CENTER
(BEGAN IN 1987 IN HOBART)

"With the pediatric traumas that come in - because I got hit by a car when I was a kid - I really feel a connections to the children and doing my best to either stabilize them and get them ready for transfer or take care of them and fix their broken bones and make them as comfortable as possible. I'm happy to see when kids get better right away. We can fix them pretty quickly pretty in the Emergency Department and get them running around again."

Robert Boby, EMERGENCY MEDICAL SERVICES COORDINATOR
ST. MARY MEDICAL CENTER
(BEGAN IN 2003 IN HOBART)

Changes in Emergency Care

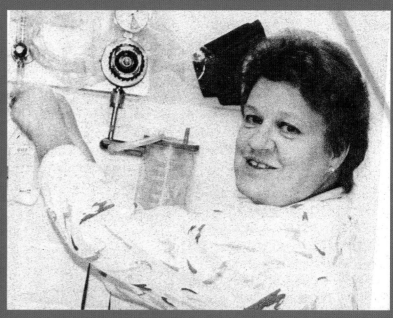

In 1974 Gary Mercy Hospital's cardiovascular surgical team inspected a $10,000 computerized pump, a lifesaving device to be used in emergency care of heart attack victims. Shown (L-R) are Veera Porapaiboon, M.D., Felipe Chua, M.D., and Kosin Thupvong, M.D.
Reprinted by permission of the *Post-Tribune*, FEBRUARY 8, 1974

Emergency Room Staff Nurse Victoria Sohovich, RN   Photo – 1990

IT'S BEEN *Said* IN 2009...

"I worked in the Emergency Room for many years and experienced many changes in patient care – beginning with physicians being on-call for ER care to physicians always being present as full-time scheduled employees in ER. (By contrast), they were able to initiate care immediately on the patients – i.e., starting IVs, having standing orders for certain types of cases, ordering lab work, X-rays and EKGs. We developed a higher degree of nursing skills and I enjoyed the variety and challenge each day presented."

Vickie Sohovich, RN
EMERGENCY ROOM STAFF NURSE
MERCY HOSPITAL
(BEGAN IN 1953 IN GARY)

Emergency Medical Services

IT'S BEEN *Said* IN 2009...

"In the late 1970s, all hospitals in Lake County met to discuss the feasibility of sponsoring an Emergency Medical Services System. This new concept would include education, training and medical direction of Emergency Medical Technicians (EMTs) and Paramedics. The commitment would include staff, physician and financial resources.

"The goal was to deliver care to the patient even before he/she entered the Emergency Room. It was an expensive and very daunting commitment with no guarantee of success. There were a few models of EMS beginnings in the country but many people at that time were not convinced that this idea would be successful.

"It was finally the Methodist Hospital in Gary that agreed to sponsor the program. It was a herculean endeavor, and as municipalities began to purchase ambulances, the hospital trained the personnel needed to man them. Through the years, several other hospitals began programs and in the early 2000s, St. Mary Medical Center agreed to sponsor a very successful Illinois service, Superior Ambulance, which had decided to expand into the Indiana area. Several other services began to request sponsorship and thus began our successful EMS program."

Deborah Krejci, RN
MANAGER, SYSTEM AND REGULATORY MANAGEMENT
ST. MARY MEDICAL CENTER | (BEGAN IN 1977 IN HOBART)

A Dedication

In May 1997, a new Emergency Medical Services room was dedicated at St. Mary Medical Center to the memory of the late Herlof "Ted" Hansen from the Hobart Fire Department and Frank Gilbert of the Portage EMS. Hansen died while fighting a fire in 1995 and Gilbert was seriously injured in an auto accident while caring for a patient. Shown here in the new EMS room among Hobart fire personnel is Marge Hansen (in the middle), mother of the late Ted Hansen.

Hobart Gazette, MAY 29, 1997

With years of persistence, St. Mary Medical Center became the sponsoring hospital in 2010 for the Hobart Fire Department Emergency Medical Services (EMS) division. Ambulances previously dispatched from the Hobart Fire Department transported patients to Methodist Hospitals in Gary. The new system was implemented in the fall of 2009 and the agreement was reached through EMS Coordinator Robert Boby and his team. Pictured (l-r) are Bob Lamprecht, EMS director for the Hobart Fire Department; Paula Rousis, RN, nurse manager, St. Mary Medical Center Emergency Department; Robert Boby, St. Mary Medical Center EMS coordinator; John Mulligan, M.D., EMS medical director; Janice L. Ryba, hospital CEO and administrator; Hobart Mayor Brian Snedecor; Bill Mc-Corkle, Hobart Fire Department chief; and Brian Taylor, Hobart Fire Department assistant chief.

Evolving Full-time Coverage

IT'S BEEN *Said* IN 2009…

"Emergency rooms were commonly called accident rooms because they did not fulfill all of the things that they do now. This was in 1955 and for some years thereafter before it switched over and was called an Emergency Room.

"It was interesting that there was no staffing by a physician at that time, that each doctor was responsible for his own patient. Then we effected a rotation whereby one doctor would be on call and present in the Emergency Room for 24 hours so everyone rotated. Later, around the late 1960s or early 1970s, full-time coverage with Emergency Room physicians became available."

John T. Scully, M.D., INTERNIST, RETIRED
MERCY HOSPITAL
(BEGAN IN 1955 IN GARY)

EMERGENCY CARE – A SPECIALTY

"There was no cardiologist on in 1977 but the director of ICU, Dr. John T. Scully, was a brilliant internist with a cardiology background. Almost all patients with cardiac problems were seen by him. The treatment for heart attacks was at least two weeks of complete rest in the ICU... no television, phone or anything that might excite the patient.

"The specialty of emergency medicine didn't exist, but the medical director of the Emergency Department, Dr. Phillip Kellar, was another brilliant diagnostician. His background, family practice, was one of the busiest practices in town. I remember being told one June that all the graduates of that year's Hobart High School class had been delivered by him 18 years prior.

"For many years, the medical staff in the ER (called Emergency Room until the 1990s when it was called the Emergency Department) consisted of physicians of various backgrounds who worked extra hours after their "day job" as surgeon, family practitioner, etc. I remember being told about a very popular physician who would not allow nurses to take blood pressures, as that was a skill that was too important to hand off to a nurse.

"The specialty of 'emergency medicine' began to take hold in Hobart in the 1980s. Around that time, the hospital hired a group of 'emergency certified physicians' from Illinois to staff both the Hobart and Gary facilities. This was truly an original concept for us and the first in a long chain of subcontracted groups of emergency specialists.

"A large percentage of the nurses who worked in Hobart had transferred from the Gary facility when Hobart was built. Most of them had been schooled by either the Mercy or Methodist nursing program, as universities did not offer this kind of education during their training. Marge Beckham was the head nurse and Vicki Sohovich was the assistant – if not in title, certainly in duties. There was a strong camaraderie between those nurses trained in hospitals – an experience we can only imagine.

"It was a very different world in nursing, too, in 1977. Our director of nursing was extremely fond of nursing caps, and the dress code had just been updated to allow nurses to wear pants. Still, most wore dresses and white hose and were very traditional in both dress and behavior.

"At the time, it seemed like the world of medicine and nursing changed at a much slower pace. Some concepts surfaced now and then that we knew would never fly – concepts like DRGs, case management, 12-hour shifts, triage, and paramedics. When people in town were sick in 1977, they would... call the operator who would notify the funeral home to pick them up and bring them to the hospital; '911' hadn't been invented yet."

Deborah Krejci, R.N, MANAGER, SYSTEM AND REGULATORY MANAGEMENT
ST. MARY MEDICAL CENTER
(BEGAN IN 1977 IN HOBART)

IN MEMORIAM – LINDA BREITZKE

"My very first friend at St. Mary Medical Center was Linda Breitzke, RN, whose first nursing job as a graduate was in the Obstetrics Department (OB) (later called Labor, Delivery, Recovery and Postpartum, or LDRP) at St Mary's in Hobart. After approximately a year, she transferred to the Emergency Department where we met when I was hired as a new graduate in 1977. Linda was an amazing girl whom one might call the 'Poster Child for Emergency Nursing.' She was bright, funny, empathetic, a lifelong learner, a natural teacher and could tell a joke like nobody else. Patients would ask for her by name as they knew they would always get great care. She had unshakable ethics and was always the person you would go to for a short, straight answer to a long and complicated question. Her husband Greg, and sons Greg and Matt, were the love of her life. When her younger son made the finals on 'American Idol' in 2009, the entire town was glued to the television and rooting with her. Linda passed away only a few months later – leaving behind a positive, indelible footprint for all those whose paths she crossed."

Deborah Krejci, RN, Manager, System and Regulatory Management
St. Mary Medical Center
(began in 1977 in Hobart)

FROM THE *PHJC Chronicles* – NOVEMBER 23, 1958

The joint Infection Control committees of St. Mary Mercy Hospital and Methodist Hospital meet to discuss infection control. Interesting and active meeting held. Dinner served.

CHJC, University of Notre Dame Archives

Evelyn Ryan's nephew, Ian Ameling, created this personal logo for Evelyn when she worked in Infection Control. It is called "Bee on the Watch" for good infection control practices.

While the date of a formalized Infection Control Department at St. Mary Mercy Hospital in Gary is uncertain, treatment of infection has long been a part of total patient care.

Although no formal program was in effect, nurses and physicians were always keenly aware of not wanting infections in patients, especially on the surgical unit. When an infection occurred, patients were treated with antibiotics in the hospital until the infection was gone.

When St. Mary Medical Center was built, the position of Infection Control coordinator was shared between the Gary and Hobart campuses by Charlie Simmons, RN. As antibiotic use increased, the bugs causing the infections changed, and more importance was placed on having an Infection Control program.

Evelyn Charbonneau Ryan (1957 graduate of St. Mary's Mercy Hospital School of Nursing) recalls the steadily increasing importance placed on the identification and treatment of infections but does not recall any specific specialty or committee focusing on the issues at that time. Evelyn was hired as an Infection Control nurse in April of 1992 but her part-time position became full-time due to increased demands from the Indiana State Board of Health (ISBOH) and from The Joint Commission.

In 2010, the Infection Control coordinator job was filled by Alicia Snedecor, RN. As with healthcare in general, prevention was steadily assuming a large (or even larger) role than treatment in the infection control arena. In fact, many hospital-acquired infections, now considered preventable, have found their way to the headlines of medical literature. As third party payors refuse to reimburse for these conditions, the role of infection prevention has come to the forefront and has become a specialty in both medicine and nursing.

Much has changed over the decades in this specialty:
- Historically, use of antibiotics was standard treatment for colds, flu and many other maladies. Now we know that the unnecessary use of these medications has contributed to the evolution of resistant super bugs that challenge even the strongest antibiotics available.
- In the 1970s, it was considered unprofessional and even insulting to wear gloves while caring for patients. Now hand washing and wearing gloves are mandatory for the protection of both the patient and the staff.
- In 2008, Infection Control changed its name to Infection Prevention. A multidisciplinary committee chaired by Rodolfo Jao, M.D., and Denise Weaver, M.D., meets monthly to review infections and discuss important topics in infection control. Infection Prevention is a full-time specialty with a professional organization and numerous professional periodicals.
- All hospitals now have an Infection Control program. With inevitable change and increased awareness, administrators, board members and healthcare facilities are supporting the importance of infection reduction and its resultant impact on financial and patient care.

"One of the major functions of infection control is to monitor appropriate usage of antibiotics. The multiple drug-resistant microorganisms (MDRO) are major problems in therapeutics and infection control – namely, Methicillin Resistant Staphylococcus Aureus (MRSA), Vancomycin Resistant Enterococci (VRE), Extended Spectrum Beta-lactamase (ESBL) forming E-coli and Klebsiella pneumoniae, and Multiple Drug Resistant Pseudomonas species, M. Tuberculosis, etc."

Rodolfo L. Jao, MD, FIDSA, INTERNAL MEDICINE/INTERNIST
SPECIALTY IN INFECTIOUS DISEASES
MERCY HOSPITAL
(BEGAN IN 1973 IN GARY)

KEEPING WATCH ON INFECTION

"Sometimes I look back and I can't believe how much medicine has changed, how different everything is, and how far medicine has advanced. We are now keeping people alive who would have died in 1965 when I began my career.

"Hand washing was a major thing in Gary. Dr. A. Jahns, an orthopedic surgeon, worked on getting the little Handy Wipes that were placed on the patients' trays so they could at least wash their hands…"

Judy Elieff, DIABETES EDUCATOR, RETIRED
MERCY HOSPITAL | (BEGAN IN 1965 IN GARY)

Introduction of Antibiotics for Clinical Usage - USA

1930-1940	1941-1950	1951-1960
Sulfa Drug	Pen + Streptomycin	Erythromycin
Penicillins	Streptomycin	Polymyxin - B
Tyrothricin	Bacitracin	Vancomycin
Griseofulvin	Choloramphenicol	Kanamycin
	Tetracyclines	Septra/Bactrim

1961-1970	1971-1980	1981-1990
Lincomycin	Amkacin	Aztreonam
Gentamicin/Tobramycin	Mezlocillin	Quinolones
Ampicillin	Pipracillin	Ciprofloxacin
Cefalosporins	Ticarcillin	Cefotaxime
Newer Penicillins - Oxacillin/Nafcillin	Clindamycin	Mupirocin
		Ampicillin/ Sulbactam (Unasyn)

1991-2000	2001-2005	2006-2010
Azithromycin	Synerzid	Daptomycin
Clarithromycin	Linezolid	Tigecycline
Levofloxacin	Ertapenem	Doripenem
Imipenem	Meropenem	Telavancin
Ceftriaxone		
Ticarcillin+Tazobactam (Zosyn)		-
Fluconazole		

INTRODUCTION OF ANTIBIOTICS

"There are many write-ups in the paper about MRSA, or Methicillin-Resistant Staphylococcus Aureus. That was a bug you did not hear about when I was in training – staph infections, yes, but not the drug resistance.

"My last 10 years in infection control were the era of the resistant drugs. The late 1990s and early 2000s were the era of the super bugs."

Evelyn Charbonneau Ryan, RN
INFECTION CONTROL, RETIRED
MERCY HOSPITAL
(BEGAN IN 1957 IN GARY)

During the time of St. Mary Medical Center's existence, there have been numerous introductions of antibiotics for clinical usage in the United States. Shown here are the history and dates of different antimicrobial agents introduced for clinical usage from the period of 1930-1940 to 2006-2010. Major progress in antibiotic research occurred during the 1950s, 1960s, 1970s, and the 1980s. From 2007 through 2010, however, only two or three antibiotics were approved by the Food and Drug Administration (FDA) for clinical use.   Submitted by Rodolfo L. Jao, M.D., FIDSA

MATERIALS MANAGEMENT

SUPPLY PROCESSING DEPARTMENT

"We closed in November 1995, but some of us had to stay on until December. I was in Supply Processing Distribution (SPD) the whole time. We used to call it Central Service. We supplied the hospital with all of the supplies – fluids and surgical trays and dressings and linen packs for surgery.

"At first some of our supplies weren't made up. We'd have to put gauze in sterilized pans and then sterilize the gauze, pour the solution over and then put them in a container. They used the gauze for burn victims who spent most of their time in intensive care and later on the fourth floor in intermediate care.

"Over time, we began to get (pre-packaged) disposable instruments that had already been sterilized."

Laverne Colbert
SUPERVISOR, SUPPLY PROCESSING DISTRIBUTION, RETIRED
MERCY HOSPITAL
(BEGAN IN 1972 IN GARY)

PRINT SHOP

"I can remember down by the mailroom, they used to have Bill Rathbaun. He was the printer. We didn't have copiers. You gave him the job and he did it. You put your order in and you came back in a day or two to pick it up."

Mary Constandars
HEALTH INFORMATION ANALYST
ST. MARY MEDICAL CENTER
(BEGAN IN 1975 IN GARY)

With Beginnings in Gary. THEN AND NOW

MATERIALS MANAGEMENT...

Contributed by Marcia Keilman, Buyer
Community Healthcare System

It has been said that the Materials Management Department started out with just a couple of ladies in the storeroom area in the hospital – well before the 1970s, although the date is uncertain.

I was hired by St. Mary Mercy Hospital in May, 1970, as a clerk-typist in the Purchasing Department. The warehouse, print shop and purchasing offices were all located in a building on Fifth Avenue across the alley from the hospital. The building used to be a car dealer showroom with a second floor. Our offices were in the front of the building. We had to type each purchase order on multiple carbon copy forms and then mail the purchase order to the vendors. Inventory control was handled by one person using the Kardex system. A card for each item was stored in the warehouse.

MATERIALS MANAGEMENT DEPARTMENT STAFF PHOTO – 2009
SHOWN (L-R, CLOCKWISE) are: Marcia Keilman, Nancy Moran, Virginia Pastar, Diana Bohling, Mike Homrich, Charles McLaughlin, Sharry Plonczynski, Bryant Levant, John Utesch, Michelle Larson, Mary Benoit, Pam Moore, Irma Santiago, Doris Lawson, and Cathy Nelson

"The storeroom was on the ground level and when the Rob O'Connor Lincoln-Mercury building moved, the hospital bought it and moved the storeroom over there. The guy in charge at that time was named Pauley and they called it 'Pauley's Palace.' It was right across the alley from the hospital but it's all torn down now and is a parking lot."

Jim Wade, ENGINEERING MANAGER
MERCY HOSPITAL
(BEGAN IN 1960 IN GARY)

Note: At this writing in 2009, Jim Wade has worked at the Gary and Hobart hospital sites for 49 years and is the oldest active employee at St. Mary Medical Center.

In November 1976, the old warehouse on Fifth Avenue in Gary, adjacent to the boiler room, was razed. The entire area was to be leveled and turned into 45 additional parking spaces for the Gary hospital. Warehouse employees had previously moved supplies and stored equipment into a new warehouse location closer to the hospital.

Acts of Mercy, NOVEMBER 1976

After several years, the purchasing office was moved to Kasper Hall (a building next to the hospital on the first floor), which also housed the library, and the Education and Human Resources departments. Kasper Hall also was the home of the Sisters who lived on the third and fourth floors. We kept up with the trends by updating our ways of ordering and processing purchase orders.

Our department handled the ordering of equipment/supplies for the Hobart hospital when the facility was under construction. St. Mary Medical Center and St. Catherine Hospital merged various departments including the Materials Management Department. When the Gary hospital was sold in 1992, the purchasing offices moved to St. Catherine Hospital. The warehouse was relocated to another building on West Fifth Avenue. Supplies were delivered to Hobart by a hospital-owned truck until a storeroom was established at Hobart and deliveries could be shipped directly to Hobart by the vendors.

Materials Management was under the direction of at least eight different directors including Service Master from 1970 through 2003. St. Mary Medical Center in Hobart did not have a Purchasing Department on-site until the late 1990s.

When Community Healthcare System purchased the two hospitals, our department was incorporated with that of Community Hospital. We are now one department located in Munster and handle the purchasing for the three hospitals in addition to off-site locations.

With Beginnings in Gary • THEN AND NOW

STOREROOM/RECEIVING DEPARTMENT...

Contributed by Carol Reeves
Storeroom/Receiving Manager

STOREROOM STAFF PHOTO – 2009
FRONT ROW (L-R): Toni Reed and Susan Nowak SECOND ROW (L-R): Damon Bruce, Cindy Whalen,
Laverne Stidman, Sue Magee and Derek Long THIRD ROW (L-R): Manager Carol Reeves, and Edmond Hunter

Hospitals, always in need of supplies, have evolved from a somewhat rudimentary system of purchasing and storage to the sophisticated, computerized operation that exists today.

The Storeroom/Receiving Department is an integral part of the Materials Management Department. Not originally known by that name, it has changed dramatically since the early years. Gary's Mercy Hospital of the late 1970s, for example, had bulk supplies that were kept in a warehouse located nearby on West Fifth Avenue. A staff of six people handled case after case of bedpans, toilet paper, crutches, eye packs and much more.

At one time, there were more than 25 staff members and several supervisors at the downtown Gary facility. Apart from the warehouse, the hospital's in-house department was eventually called Supply Processing Dispatch (SPD). In 1972, staff members recall, large oxygen tanks had to be delivered to the toxicology lab above the boiler room. They were carried up three flights of stairs because there was no elevator or transporting equipment.

When St. Mary Medical Center opened its Hobart site in 1973, supplies were sent to Hobart from Gary – usually five or six skids daily – and once in Hobart, the storeroom would break down the deliveries within the hospital. Supplies were distributed by two staff members taking cart-filled supplies to eight different units. Once they returned with empty carts, supplies were repeatedly loaded and delivered until the units had what they needed.

The Gary campus often received three deliveries daily – smaller, more frequent amounts because of its close proximity to the warehouse.

In 2001 when Community Healthcare System was formed as a three-hospital system, the three storerooms remained independent. In 2005 when linen was included in St. Mary's departmental responsibilities, it was no longer known as Supply Processing Dispatch (SPD). It is now simply called "Storeroom."

The Storeroom staff has decreased in size to seven material handlers, one team lead, and one department manager. The linen room is now an independent department that operates through Environmental Services. The mail is no longer sealed and stamped in the storeroom but is done by an outside service, Online Data System.

With increased efficiency, the material handlers individually go to the units and take inventory and enter their data into the system so that a list can be generated to select the supplies and deliver them back to the unit. The storeroom services over 80 departments including off-campus facilities.

The Storeroom/Receiving Department will keep pace with the successful growth of St. Mary Medical Center, proud to be a participant in one of Hobart's finest assets.

IT'S BEEN *Said* IN 2009…

"Ed Hunter was over the storeroom when I was hired in Gary. We made a lot of bulk deliveries. Most of the supplies in the storeroom are stocked on the units and it is not necessary to deliver in bulk. This makes keeping inventory of supplies much more efficient. Everything is on shelves now and has easier access than when it was in bulk racking. We have a smaller crew that distributes the supplies and most of the bulk supplies are ordered through the ePro system."

Derek Long, MATERIAL HANDLER, MATERIALS MANAGEMENT
ST. MARY MEDICAL CENTER | (BEGAN IN 1977 IN GARY)

ORGANIZED SUPPLIES

TUBE STATION

Tube stations were originally installed in June 2003 for the Emergency Department, ICU, OB/SPD, surgery, laboratory and pharmacy. It originated from a nursing division request to then hospital CEO Milt Triana who agreed with its importance and functionality. When the New Patient Tower opened in 2004, tube stations were added to the patient floors and the Infusion Unit. The system, fast and efficient for patient care, provides a traceable chain of custody for medicine and specimens.

Sources: Former St. Mary Medical Center CEO Milt Triana (began in 1969) and Maintenance Worker IV, Ralph Watkins, (began in 1982)

IN THE LIBRARY

There were two Mercy Hospital libraries in place that dated back before the mid-1940s – one was for the nursing/hospital staff, located in the School of Nursing building, and the other one was for the medical staff, located near the Medical Records Department within the hospital.

(Left) In a 1992 *Post-Tribune* feature story, Medical Librarian Cindy Macko is shown at work in the library at Mercy Hospital in Gary.

The St. Mary Medical Center library in Hobart is shown as it currently appears (2008 photo).

(Above) In 1968, with hospital expansion, the new Mercy Hospital library was located in Kasper Hall at Sixth and Polk avenues. Standing (l-r) are Librarian Lois Pence and Mary Gulyassy, director of the new Department of Education. Seated (l-r) are Mrs. J. T. Boteler, clerk; Sister Clarence Caspermeyer, PHJC; and Sister Natalia Bleise, PHJC.
Reprinted by permission of the *Post-Tribune*, 1968

In its early years, the first so-called library at St. Mary Medical Center in Hobart was a bookcase filled with medical textbooks located in the doctors' lounge where it was overseen by the administration secretary. The library services that were based at the St. Mary Medical Center – Gary facility, however, were an important resource and were also available to the Hobart staff by the Gary librarian and library assistant.

HONORING JOSEPH E. KOPCHA, M.D.

The St. Mary Medical Center library is shown here in 1986 following its dedication in memory of Joseph E. Kopcha, M.D.

Times photo by John Bojda

Doctor remembered

The medical library at St. Mary Medical Center in Hobart was named in honor of the late Dr. Joseph Kopcha today. The honor was bestowed upon Kopcha for his years of service to the hospital and work within the medical profession. His widow, Bernice, and Dr. Jay Scharoff, medical director, pull a volume from the shelves of the library.

Reprinted by permission of *The Times*, JANUARY 21, 1987

The reference library at the Hobart site, located nearby administration, opened as a full-service, staffed library in 1981 and has been relocated numerous times. It was moved to an adjacent room in 1986 to provide additional space for the medical staff lounge and was dedicated in memory of Joseph E. Kopcha, M.D. The library moved twice after that – in 1993 to an area one floor above that had previously been used for storage. It was reconfigured and moved again in 1998 to an adjacent conference area to allow for development of the Acute Rehabilitation Unit where it presently remains. Current Librarian Cindy Macko provided services at the Gary St. Mary's Hospital/Medical Staff Library from 1976-1993 while serving Hobart St. Mary from 1985 to the present. Library Assistant Jane Brown began her employment at the Gary library and staffed the library in Hobart from 1981-1985.

Information search methods, retrieval, and delivery have changed considerably over the years. Literature searches were originally conducted using a print index, and interlibrary loans were obtained via typed and mailed request forms or telephone contact. The use of computer technology, fax machines, and scanners now allow for database and Internet searches, automated (interlibrary loan) document request and retrieval, transmission of requested material via e-mail, and an overall faster turnaround time. Library walk-in traffic and telephone requests have expanded to fax and e-mail requests, and online database search services are available to staff via the hospital Intranet. The library continues to be staffed by a part-time degreed medical librarian who maintains a small print collection of current books and journal titles but now also provides a one-stop shopping library of services on the Intranet. This includes information on the library and its services, search request form availability, free health information links, online information service databases, and online access to selected journals in the library's collection. The librarian continues to look for ways to expand and upgrade information service offerings for the benefit of medical and hospital staff.

The location, size, and configuration of the library have changed several times over the years, information provision services have expanded, and staffing patterns have changed. One thing has not changed – commitment to the provision of information that supports the hospital's mission and staff needs in continuing education, research, and quality patient care.

The Medical Staff – To Be a Physician

"The field of medicine has meant, well, my life. I'm still studying. I am still trying to teach even as I am outside that area and the most important thing I did was to motivate other people... I sort of feel like I have done my job. My efforts couldn't have been more sincere than they were."

Earl J. Mason, Ph.D., M.D., FORMER DIRECTOR OF THE LABORATORY, RETIRED
MERCY HOSPITAL
(BEGAN IN 1965 IN GARY)

"No one has had a greater love affair with medicine than myself and no one has been happier in this field than I was for all the many years that I practiced. I was very content in internal medicine and subsequently, with all the changes in medicine, I was director for many years of an Intensive Care Unit."

John T. Scully, M.D., INTERNIST, RETIRED
MERCY HOSPITAL
(BEGAN IN 1955 IN GARY)

"Next to my wife, Shirley, and my children Suzy, David, Daniel and Joyce, the field of medicine meant everything to me. It was a joy that dominated my life. Additionally, if you have a mate who is in synch with you, you then have a perfect existence.

"I couldn't wait to get to work and I loved to solve medical problems. My late son-in-law, also a physician, said that he would willingly pay to practice medicine. I know exactly how he felt."

Jack M. Kamen, MD, DIRECTOR OF I.C.U., DIRECTOR OF ST. MARY MEDICAL CENTER PAIN CENTER
CHIEF OF DEPARTMENT OF ANESTHESIOLOGY, DIRECTOR OF RESPIRATORY CARE, DIRECTOR OF MEDICAL EDUCATION, RETIRED
MERCY HOSPITAL
(BEGAN IN 1952 AT ST. CATHERINE HOSPITAL)

"I still make house calls for a lot of my regular patients ... who cannot come in."

Vijay Dave, M.D., CARDIOLOGIST | MERCY HOSPITAL | (BEGAN IN 1977 IN GARY)

"For me medicine is more than a profession. It sort of becomes what you are. The idea that every day you get to help somebody is a big reason to get out of bed. I can't imagine doing something else. After 23 years as a physician, every day is interesting. Every day is a new challenge and it's great!

"Neurology is a field that is still in its infancy in some ways. The brain is still sort of the biggest mystery in the universe as far as we can tell – certainly the most complicated. It may be that we will never be able to completely understand it.

"The brain is where we live. Everything else is support structures in a way – not to take anything from the heart or the lungs or the liver or skin or any other organ, but if you got new skin or you got a new heart or new set of lungs, you're still you. If your brain could exist in another person's body, that's where <u>you</u> are and that's the difference."

Mark Simaga, MD, NEUROLOGIST | ST. MARY MEDICAL CENTER | (BEGAN IN 1997 IN HOBART)

At Issue – Death and Dying
The Thoughts of Several Physicians

IT'S BEEN *Said* IN 2009...

"When I was training and went to school, if we lost a patient we felt we had failed. Nowadays, given what we know and how we apply it, I think we can better deal with the situation. I look at it that if I have done everything I possibly can do to try to get (a patient) through, I do not think it is a failure. At that point in time it is more of just the fact that it was his time to go. There is a power that is higher than any one of us that says it is his time. Physicians as a whole can deal with patients' families a lot better – probably in a more humane way – but there is always room for improvement."

Joe Koscielniak, MD, ORTHOPEDIC SURGEON
MERCY HOSPITAL (EXTERN)
(BEGAN IN 1984 IN HOBART)

IT'S BEEN *Said* IN 2009...

"I think the acquisition has supported what was previously in place in terms of the emotional and the pastoral support of the patients. I think there are things in place to try to give more universal support to the death and dying of a patient through education and written information but it just hasn't come to fruition yet…

"Everything is, 'Make me live longer.' 'Make me look younger.' Everything is defined for prevention. When it comes to the dying process, people don't realize that it is a unique situation to heal, to communicate. It is taboo in our culture to talk about it. No one can ever die. The medical legal system supports that whenever someone dies it's a mistake – there are no accidents. Everything we do is to try to divert our attention away from the actual act of dying and it's crazy, I mean it's totally crazy...

"I think physicians have trouble facing death. I think sometimes we view it as a failure. Sometimes when the end is near, we just sign off or we exit but I think it's important to talk to a patient and the family and reassure them that you are not leaving. Our job also includes their comfort that they made the best decisions they could at a very difficult time. Then, as a physician, you've done your best job. Those are probably my most gratifying moments."

Jack Ziegler, MD, CARDIOLOGIST
ST. MARY MEDICAL CENTER
(BEGAN IN 1982 IN HOBART)

IT'S BEEN *Said* IN 2009...

"(Regarding end-of-life patient care and how physicians embrace it), many practitioners were trained to handle a patient's acute hospital episode and were not focused as much on addressing the quality of that patient's life in the end and what that means. With many patients living much longer, that trend has now caused many physicians to start learning more about end-of-life issues. We have a number of physicians at St. Mary Medical Center, like Drs. Ziegler and Devanathan, who prepare families for difficult end-of-life decisions. On the hospital side, we certainly try to make many resources available, especially regarding hospice care, so we can help those families transition to the appropriate level of care."

Janice L. Ryba, CEO AND ADMINISTRATOR
ST. MARY MEDICAL CENTER
(BEGAN IN 1984 AT COMMUNITY HOSPITAL)

DID YOU KNOW?

In 1979, a small committee of the Catholic Charities Board of Directors, consisting of Sister Wilma Boeving, PHJC; Albert Costello, M.D.; and Father Joseph Semancik explored the possibility of creating the first hospice program in Northwest Indiana. The organization flourished and today is known as Hospice of the Calumet Area.

MEDICAL STAFF SERVICES...

Contributed by Barbara Blejski, CPMSM, Director

MEDICAL STAFF DEPARTMENT PHOTO – 2009
STANDING (L-R): Joy Sternal and Director Barb Blejski
SITTING (L-R): Jennifer Constant and Lupka Marinceski

IT'S BEEN *Said* IN 2009...

"I didn't work in Gary but when I started working in Hobart in 1994 all of the physicians were on both staffs. Some physicians continued to practice at the Gary facility while others practiced at both hospitals. My fear of starting a new job at another facility after 18 years was unfounded because the physicians and staff welcomed me and I continue to make new friends.

"One of the biggest challenges we have in healthcare today is to ensure we are following the requirements set forth by regulatory agencies."

Barbara Blejski, CPMSM, DIRECTOR, MEDICAL STAFF SERVICES
ST. MARY MEDICAL CENTER
(BEGAN IN 1994 IN HOBART)

The Medical Staff Services Department began at St. Mary Mercy Hospital in Gary many years ago and remained there even after St. Mary Medical Center was built in Hobart. Any medical staff issues were funneled through Administration. When the Gary facility was sold, the Medical Staff Services Department was transferred to St. Mary Medical Center in Hobart in approximately 1992.

The responsibilities of this department have changed over the years. In the early days, the physician would simply complete an application and a few references were verified. Today, when a physician completes an application, references are received from all facilities where the physician has trained or practiced since medical school. Among other requirements are the physician's valid license and proof of malpractice insurance coverage. The medical staff office is responsible for assuring that there is a process of assessing and validating the qualifications of a licensed independent practitioner to provide health care services. This helps in ensuring high quality patient care by protecting the public from incompetent physicians. The medical staff develops minimum requirements for medical staff membership, as well as assessing and validating a clinician's qualifications against established criteria. Training and experience requirements are determined to authorize that a practitioner has the competency to carry out each procedure or method of treatment. The qualifications of applicants are evaluated using the appropriate criteria to approve or deny requested privileges.

In the past, personnel in the medical staff office were categorized as secretaries. With increased responsibilities and expansion of the department, however, my job title has evolved from administrative secretary to medical staff secretary to medical staff coordinator to director of medical staff services. Due to the responsibilities added and based on experience, we are certified professionals who verify that the medical staff complies with standards approved by The Joint Commission, Indiana State Board of Health, and The Center for Medicare and Medicaid.

St. Mary Medical Center takes pride in doing its very best for all those who enter the hospital's doors – physicians, patients, patient families, staff members, and volunteers. The Medical Staff Services Department is an integral part of delivering more than a century of quality care.

General Surgeons

General surgeons, according to John T. Scully, M.D., were William Glover, M.D.; Robert Milos, M.D.; Robert N. Bills, M.D.; Robert J. Bills, M.D.; (son of Robert N.,) and Walter Robinson, M.D.

Acknowledging the General Practitioners

It's been *Said* in 2009...

"The general practitioners were an integral force at Mercy. They were the forerunners in medicine before family practitioners came into being. Most of the doctors (around the 1930s and 1940s and for years after that) had offices in the Gary National Bank building or in downtown Gary. The Gary contingent included the following physicians:

Walter Behn, M.D.
Adolph Goldstone, M.D.
Joseph Goldstone, M.D.
Henry Lebioda, M.D.
Joseph Ornelas, M.D.
Joseph Sala, M.D.

Walter Sala, M.D.
George Slama, M.D.
John Slama, M.D.
Preston Vye, M.D.
Charles W. Yarrington, M.D."

John T. Scully, M.D., Internist, retired
Mercy Hospital
(began in 1955 in Gary)

It's been *Said* in 2009...

"One group of general practitioners bears special mention as they were interns at Mercy and later practiced in the area. They are Drs. John Gallinatti, Andrew Russo, and John Carter (who is still on the staff at St. Mary's). They were excellent physicians and were essential in helping to arrange with the medical staff at Mercy a special internship for their classmate, Ronald Doneff. Dr. Doneff had severe polio as a senior medical student and required a respirator for a long period. Utilizing a wheelchair and oxygen, he served a year internship on my service. He became an outstanding dermatologist in the area and was an inspiration to all of us."

John T. Scully, M.D., Internist, retired
Mercy Hospital
(began in 1955 in Gary)

Recognizing the Family Practitioner

It's been *Said* in 2009...

"When I got there in 1967, there were very few specialists, very few internists. Dr. John Scully and Dr. Ernest Mirich were the ones on the market. Most of them were family practitioners who were very busy and depended a lot on the radiologists. I remember giving lots of advice to the family practitioners. I looked forward to communicating with the practitioners because it was a two-way street. I would learn the clinical aspect from them and they would learn from my imaging skills."

Heratch Doumanian, M.D.
Radiologist, retired
Mercy Hospital
(began in 1967 in Gary)

It's been *Said* in 2009...

"The general practitioner literally had to be a jack of all trades. He worked long hours, saw large numbers of patients, and shouldered most of the patient/doctor responsibility. He even did minor surgeries himself. The GP was appreciated and respected by the entire town. People would always tip their hats out of respect for doctors back then.

"The nurses were wonderful. They worked very long hours and were so helpful to the doctors and patients. The nurses were very diverse in nationality as many had fled from other countries because of the war."

Raymond Carmody, M.D.
Ophthalmologist, retired
Mercy Hospital | (began in 1935 in Gary)
Note: At this writing in 2009, Dr. Carmody is 101 years of age. He retired in 2001 at age 93 after 70 years of practice.

Recognizing the First Ophthalmologist

It's been *Said* in 2009...

Robert Young, M.D.

"We came to Gary in 1951 and lived there for 18 years, until 1969. My husband, Bob Young, an ophthalmologist and eye surgeon, was on the staff at Mercy Hospital for about 20 years. We came here because he was the only ophthalmologist in Gary at the time. The other doctors were all ear, nose, and throat.

"My husband's first office was located on Seventh and Broadway and then there was an opening at Fifth and Broadway (in) the Gary National Bank. That was an exciting building. No doctors had offices in the hospital and there wasn't a medical office building or anything like that."

Ruth Young, wife of Ophthalmologist Robert Young, M.D.

A Look at the Laboratory

Pictured here are lab photos from Mercy Hospital in Gary – 1924. Calumet Regional Archives, Indiana University Northwest

Suikay Ku, medical technologist, is shown here in a 1988 lab photo. Milt Triana, then regional director of laboratories, said the lab is one of the most highly used patient care departments at St. Mary Medical Center. The speed and accuracy of results can sometimes mean the difference between life and death.

Summary, June 1988

IT'S BEEN *Said* IN 2009...

"Dr. Earl Mason was the medical director of the laboratory in Gary and Hobart. He was a brilliant man with high standards. He always wanted everything to be state-of-the-art and always wanted us to be the first in technology or in any testing procedure. He always strived to be in the forefront of medicine. The lab was known to be the 'Mayo Clinic of Northwest Indiana' during his time."

Elizabeth Yee, Vice President, Clinical Ancillary Services
Community Hospital | (began in 1977 in Gary)

Earl J. Mason, Ph.D., M.D.
Reprinted by permission
of the *Post-Tribune*,
July 12, 1965

Mercy Hospital Administrator Sister Cornelia Leible, PHJC, and Earl J. Mason, M.D., review their letter of accreditation from the College of American Pathologists.
Reprinted by permission of the *Post-Tribune*, JUNE 20, 1966

In 1976, the medical laboratory at St. Mary Medical Center, under the direction of Earl J. Mason, Ph.D, M.D., was awarded an "outstanding" accreditation rating by the College of American Pathologists (CAP). The organization was comprised of more than 6,500 pathologist physicians in the United States whose accreditation program was known to be one of the premier medical peer evaluation systems in the world. Accreditation was designated to medical laboratories able to meet CAP's rigid standards.

Testing the new Radiometer Micro Tonometer purchased at Mercy Hospital are the Chemistry Department's Section Chief Technologist Robert A. Davis (seated) and head of the laboratory, Earl J. Mason, Ph.D., M.D. The life-saving device – used to measure the balance in the blood between acids and alkalis – was the only one of its kind in the area in 1968.
Reprinted by permission of the
Post-Tribune, NOVEMBER 8, 1968

With Beginnings in Gary • THEN AND NOW

LABORATORY DEPARTMENT...

Contributed by Anthony "Tony" Costello, Ph.D,
Site Director

IT'S BEEN *Said* IN 2010...

"Laboratories wanted highly skilled trained technologists in Illinois and Indiana plus we had an arrangement that the tuition was relatively small providing the students agreed to stay for a period of time in St. Mary Medical Center's Laboratory if they were asked. This enabled St. Mary Medical Center to quickly have a very high skilled group of technologists and become the leading laboratory in all of Northwest Indiana for some of the special tests and skilled tests that were important in bringing the most important diagnoses to the attention of the doctors.

"Elizabeth Yee was one of the first students that we had in our school and she stayed for several years in our laboratory. She was particularly interested in microbiology... but as you know, she has continued to excel in her specialty and also in administration."

Earl J. Mason, Ph.D., MD.
FORMER DIRECTOR OF THE LABORATORY, RETIRED
MERCY HOSPITAL
(BEGAN IN 1965 IN GARY)

When I began at Mercy Hospital in Gary as a clinical chemist in 1976, you bought raw reagents, made everything up yourself, and would mix the reagents to do the tests – tests like enzymes, LDH, glucose – they were all more or less manual. Then a little automation came in and the instrument would take the raw chemicals and mix them with the sample to do the test (auto analyzers). Another step was taken after that with the ACA Dupont – it looked like a plastic case with pouches that have pills or powder or liquid in them. The instrument would crunch them, they would fall into the reaction chamber and you would get the reaction going. Today, the instrument does it all. In fact, it even samples the specimen, it centrifuges, and it puts it on the instrument. There have been tremendous changes.

Today, we are doing more and more with less and less. It's not that you are making a person do so much more; it's that one person CAN do so much more because of the improvement in technology. When I came to St. Mary in 1976, the two laboratories had close to 200 full-time employees (FTEs). Today, all three of our laboratories (of Community Healthcare System) don't have that many full-time employees. It's the down-sizing. The technology has changed such that in the old days we wanted to get one SMA (Simultaneous Multiple Analyzer). It's an instrument that did 12 tests. It's a panel – like our basic metabolic panel (bmp) today. These tests give you an indication of body's function and where you stand. In those days we used to have three instruments to do those tests. Today we not only do those 12 tests but many more tests on one instrument. In the old days, we had three technologists doing these 12 tests. Today one person does all that and more.

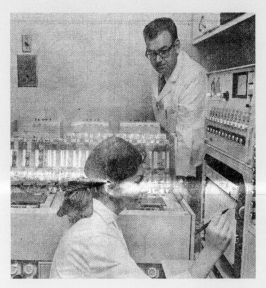

Michael Caplis, M.D., director of Mercy Hospital's Bio-Chemistry Department, is shown here as Technician Donna Zielazny (seated) charts the results of a test being run through the Sequential Multichannel Authoanalyzer 12/60. It was one of the newest in the field in 1969, capable of performing 12 chemistry tests per 60 seconds or a total of 720 separate tests in one hour.
Reprinted by permission of the
Post-Tribune, NOVEMBER 23, 1969

There are sections (hematology and histology) which are manual but automation is coming to these sections as well.

Processing of tissue in histology used to take 24 hours but now we have a processor that does it the same day. It's a microwave so eventually – and it's already happening – we'll have results that afternoon for specimens sent that morning. If you're a woman who has a breast biopsy and you're concerned that you might have cancer and it needs treatment, you don't want to agonize over a 72-hour period to wait for that answer. The results certainly bring peace of mind if it's negative or if it's positive, you can say, 'Okay, let's get something done.'

In 1987, the laboratories were swapped. That is when we brought the main lab to Hobart and took the stat lab to Gary (A stat lab only does testing that is needed on site; all other tests were sent to the main lab). This was done to increase the size of the Emergency Room in Gary. To do that, with the lab right next to emergency, we needed to shrink the lab and the stat lab takes up less space than the main lab.

The lab was regionalized when John Birdzell became the CEO of Lakeshore Health System. All three labs of Lakeshore Health System were pulled together – those of St. Catherine Hospital, and St. Mary Medical Center of Gary and Hobart. We are proud to be dedicated participants in an important field of hospital healthcare operations. All those who enter our St. Mary Medical Center doors come to us for professional care. They deserve the best and we are here to see that they receive it.

IT'S BEEN *Said* IN 2009...

"Many laboratory employees remember the March 1998 spring storm that trapped the staff in the hospital. The Physician Office Building was just completed but not yet in use. The staff used the building as a place to rest so they could relieve the staff on duty. During the night, the fire alarm went off in the building to add to the confusion and drama of the storm."

Lynne Wennmacher
SENIOR TECHNOLOGIST | ST. MARY MEDICAL CENTER | (BEGAN IN 1991 IN HOBART)

IN REMEMBRANCE – TERRY ABRIOL

IT'S BEEN *Said* IN 2009...

"Terry Abriol was a very good and hard-working hematology senior technologist in the 1980s at the Hobart laboratory. She was scheduled to work the day after Thanksgiving Day. That day, we happened to have very icy conditions and Terry lost control of her car and went off the road by the bridge on 61st Avenue about a mile from the hospital. Terry was killed. Her death was a shock and a very sad time for everyone in the laboratory."

Jackie Juskevice
LEAD RECORDS CLERK | MERCY HOSPITAL | (began in 1966 in Gary)

IN REMEMBRANCE – SANDY GALLAGHER

IT'S BEEN *Said* IN 2009...

"Sandy Gallagher was a phlebotomist at St. Mary Medical Center in Hobart. Every Christmas she and her husband, Dave, a maintenance worker at St. Mary Medical Center, would dress up as Mr. and Mrs. Santa Claus. They visited all the patients who had to spend Christmas in the hospital. The patients were very appreciative of their thoughtfulness. Unfortunately Sandy developed a brain tumor and passed away. It was also a very sad time for the laboratory staff."

Anthony "Tony" Costello, Ph.D.
SITE DIRECTOR | ST. MARY MEDICAL CENTER | (began in 1976 in Gary)

MEDICAL TECHNOLOGY

"I was interested in conducting the necessary activity for establishing a School of Medical Technology so it was organized under my direction and it started with a small number of students – actually three to five (students) back in 1968 – and then it slowly increased in activity and scope and was fully accredited by the Medical Society for Clinical Pathologists as a bona fide school. Jean Halowaty was the first supervisor of the School of Medical Technology under me. Eventually, we were approved for 15 students and altogether we graduated in the range of approximately 250 medical technologists."

Earl J. Mason, Ph.D., M.D.
FORMER DIRECTOR OF THE LABORATORY, RETIRED | MERCY HOSPITAL | (BEGAN IN 1965 IN GARY)

"I thank the Lord every day that I came here. We had a medical technology school here so a lot of those young ladies up there working for me now were trained 30 years ago. We kid that we're all getting old together. They're all very interested in doing a good job, are all very dedicated to the patients, and want to make sure that when the patients come here, they're getting the best we have."

Anthony "Tony" Costello, Ph.D.
SITE DIRECTOR
ST. MARY MEDICAL CENTER
(BEGAN IN 1976 IN GARY)

Shown in this 1967 photo are members of the professional staff at the School of Medical Technology as they attend a meeting conducted by Earl Mason, Ph.D., M.D. (far right), director of the school and chief pathologist at Mercy Hospital. From left are Roger Wait, chief technologist at Mercy andinstructors' consultant; Donald Love, school coordinator; Ted Cabrera, M.D., associate director of the school; and Alex Slonicki, M.D., director of clinical biochemistry at Mercy Hospital.

Reprinted by permission of the *Post-Tribune*, MAY 14, 1967

"As a student, I recall that every medical technology student dreaded going into St. Mary Medical Center on Tuesdays since it was the standing schedule for oral examination day with two Ph.D.s in biochemistry. It was expected that the students would know the material inside and out."

Tina S. Ngo, MPA, MT (ASCP), SM
REGIONAL DIRECTOR, LABORATORY
ST. MARY MEDICAL CENTER
(BEGAN IN 1981 IN GARY)

DID YOU KNOW?

The School of Medical Technology was operated through the laboratory at St. Mary Medical Center in Gary. The school was later moved to St. Mary Medical Center in Hobart. It provided a fourth-year student program which included 32 semester hours of education that were recognized by affiliated universities and colleges as the senior year of college. It was for students who had completed three years of prerequisite education and appropriate course work at the university or college level so that the student would graduate with a Bachelor of Science Degree in Medical Technology.

Sue Demitroulas, former director of the School of Medical Technology, offered this account of the premier school that trained many students until it closed in 1994.

"Most hospitals did not have a (School of Medical Technology). In the local area only, St. Margaret Hospital and St. Mary Medical Center maintained medical technology programs. At that time, most schools were hospital-based. Today, they are usually university-based.

"There were only six or seven in the state. Schools were expensive and required a commitment of the hospital, the lab director, and the entire lab staff who did much of the teaching. Jean Halowaty was the first director of the program, followed by Rita Blastick, and then myself. The program director's job was to handle the administrative duties and maintain accreditation standards. A national accrediting agency set the standards. We were required to have a well-established curriculum and validate our teaching and testing methods to insure that graduating students met the criteria for graduation and become registered. Student prerequisites required that all students had completed their junior year of college which included at least 27 chemistry hours and 27 biology hours. Prerequisites are more extensive today.

"Michael Caplis, Ph.D., and Anthony "Tony" Costello, Ph.D., taught chemistry which was perhaps our most difficult course. Accreditation was very comprehensive. We had to use all six levels of education to test the students – comprehensive skills and their problem solving skills, etc., and we had to prove that we actually did that on our exams.

"We were affiliated with a lot of universities – (among them) Calumet College of St. Joseph, St. Joseph's College in Rensselaer, Purdue University Calumet, Purdue West Lafayette, Valparaiso University, St. Mary of Notre Dame, Ball State, Indiana State, and Indiana University.

"The average class size was 9-13 students. They were small because there was a lot of one-on-one education. The students were very motivated. Like most science majors, they were academically strong. The program graduated excellent medical technologists. In fact, many of the graduates are currently employed at all three Community Healthcare System hospitals. Program graduates appreciated the opportunity to receive a quality education and recognized that working at CHS provided a wide variety of employment opportunities, so they chose to stay even though they have opportunities to work anywhere. Some of the graduates moved into management positions and several of the graduates returned to universities to obtained M.D. (Doctor of Medicine) degrees."

"They closed the School of Medical Technology when I left the lab in 1994."

In 1980 Earl Mason, Ph.D, M.D., director of Laboratories and Nuclear Medicine at St. Mary Medical Center, was appointed adjunct professor of biology at Purdue University Calumet. Sue Demitroulas, MT (ASCP), education coordinator of the hospital's School of Medical Technology, was appointed assistant adjunct professor of biology.

PATIENT ACCESS DEPARTMENT
STAFF PHOTO – 2009
SEATED (L-R): CEO and Administrator Janice Ryba; Director Kelly Grata; Supervisor Registration Jamie Henry; Vice President Finance and Chief Financial Officer Mary Sudicky.
THREE PEOPLE STANDING IN MIDDLE ROW (L-R): Eleanor Florence, Nneka Simmons, and Minerva Yanez
BACK ROW STANDING (L-R): LaCresha Cooper, Carol Curotto, Sherry Maypray, Quinton Foreman, Sandie Childs, Diane Cruse, Karen Cruz Payne and Dianna Winborn.

With Beginnings in Gary • THEN AND NOW

PATIENT ACCESS DEPARTMENT...

Contributed by Kelly J. Grata, Director

IT'S BEEN *Said* IN 2009...

"Insurance payments and procedures were very different years ago. A patient would come in on a Friday to have a routine kidney X-ray done on a Monday... and he/she stayed. When I was in training, we used to get patients for gallbladder surgery and they were in the hospital for 10 days. Now it is outpatient surgery."

Shirley Makivich Urbanek, R.N., RETIRED
ST. MARY MERCY HOSPITAL
(BEGAN IN 1959 IN GARY)

IN EARLIER DAYS...
Georgina Martinez, Admitting Department, 1984

The Patient Access Department, also known as admitting or registration, impacts every patient who comes to St. Mary Medical Center. Our patients' experiences begin when we register them for outpatient, inpatient, ambulatory or emergency services. We serve the main hospital as well as the outlying clinics of Winfield Physical Therapy, Outpatient Rehabilitation, Imaging Center, and the Portage Outpatient facility. Although the registration process is completed by our department, it is vital for us to work closely with the Health Information Management and Patient Financial Services to insure an accurate billing outcome.

We operate a 24-hour department, seven days a week. Our number-one goal is patient satisfaction. Courteous and friendly service combined with speed and accuracy of collecting and inputting patient demographics and insurance information are the keys to our success. The average registration process is less than five minutes.

Through the years our employees have experienced many changes from computer technology, staffing, Health Information Systems (HIS), and management. When the system is down, we type patient information on a blank intake form, manually assign an account number and make copies of documents. Once the system is running again, we re-enter the information into the Health Information Systems and scan the documents.

In 1978, there were seven registrars in the Patient Access Department and to date we have 29. Three of our 29 employees have more than 30 years of service with St. Mary Medical Center.

We have transitioned into new Health Information Services and an insurance verification system, implemented scanning of patient documents collected at the time of registration, developed a work flow for bed-side registration in the Emergency Department, and implemented a quality software program that is designed to catch errors during the registration process.

Throughout the Patient Access Department, we all recognize that teamwork is a key element and we cross-train our employees within each area of registration to include the Emergency Department, admitting, and outpatient areas.

The role in the Patient Access Department keeps changing, determined by the complexity of the healthcare industry. With pride in our past and pride in our continued success, our focus remains with ongoing staff education and our slogan, "Just Do It Once."

IT'S BEEN *Said* IN 2009...

"I started at the Gary Campus in 1973 and moved to the Hobart campus later that year. That was the first year that women were allowed to wear slacks to work at St. Mary's. The registration process was completed on typewriters, no physician order was needed for outpatient testing, and there was no insurance verification. The patient's word was the verification. Today, we have online insurance verification that displays patient benefits and eligibility in approximately 30 seconds."

Sandie Childs
REGISTRATION REPRESENTATIVE
ST. MARY MEDICAL CENTER
(BEGAN IN 1973 IN GARY)

DID YOU KNOW?

ADVANCE DIRECTIVES
Advance directives are documents that indicate your choices for future healthcare if you become incapacitated and unable to communicate. There are two kinds: living wills that describe your preferences for life-sustaining treatment, and durable powers of attorney for healthcare that designate someone else to make healthcare decisions for you if you cannot do so. Hospitals are required by law to ask patients if they have an advance directive and give them an opportunity to make one if they wish. The St. Mary Medical Center discusses advance directives with patients upon their admission.

Neighborly Care, SPRING, 1992

IT'S BEEN *Said* IN 2009...

"Our job is a lot easier than it used to be. Computers and scanners have made our job almost paperless. Until we implemented scanning in 2006, we had one dedicated employee making three copies of the Emergency Room charts. I recall having six supervisors and three Health Information Systems."

Jackie Pratt
REGISTRATION REPRESENTATIVE
ST. MARY MEDICAL CENTER
(BEGAN IN 1978 IN HOBART)

IT'S BEEN *Said* IN 2009...

"Working at St. Mary Medical Center was a great inspiration to me. We were a family. I enjoyed working in the admitting office. I learned a lot of medical things that I didn't know about and it taught me a lot.

"When we moved over to the north entrance in 1972, we started using computers. It was quite an experience as I didn't know what world I was entering. I gained a lot of knowledge and it expedited time."

Mary L. Turner
FORMER ADMITTING CLERK, RETIRED
MERCY HOSPITAL
(BEGAN IN 1965 IN GARY)

IT'S BEEN *Said* IN 2009...

"When I first started, I typed the surgery schedule on a typewriter. My first manager was Rhonda Williams who is now manager of Patient Financial Services. I have seen many employees come and go, including long term employees Louise Guernsey, Sally Gonzalez, Judy Smith, and Dorothy Bailey. These ladies have since retired and their personalities, knowledge, and expertise are greatly missed. They taught me so much and I hope I can have the same positive impact on others as these ladies did on me."

Jamie Henry
REGISTRATION SUPERVISOR
ST. MARY MEDICAL CENTER
(BEGAN IN 1998 IN HOBART)

PATIENT FINANCIAL SERVICES
STAFF PHOTO – 2009
FRONT ROW (L-R): Regional Director Karen Schneider, Cate Fedorchak, Mary Allen, Michelle Applewhite, Juliette Warren, Jugoslava Stanisavljevic, and Faye Philips

SECOND ROW (L-R): Dina Anton (standing), Kenyette Ishmon, Vidhya Devanathan, Adrienne Williams, Marie Davis-Mack, Patricia Booyer, Jean Luedtke, and Katherine Keslin

BACK ROW (L-R): Barbara Stone, Minerva Acevedo, Imelda Kemp, Tim Ferguson, Linda Thompson, Keyona Cartwright, Tina Kietzman, Carol Jackson, Lisa Ward, Cassandra Neal, Gayle Brumley, Judy Candiano, Linda Woodley, and Monita Puckett

NOT PICTURED: Deanita Anguiano, Marylynn Arana, Barbara Bane, Kim Barrix, Christine Bell, Karen Benish, Justine Biesczat, Megan Boender, Paulette Bonds, Dawn Bradley, Susan Brennan, Karen Brum, Kimberly Buehler, Stacey Camacho, Scott Corriere, Crystal Dattulo, Ruthie Davis, Marie DeBiase, Hue-Ella Deggans, Linda Dishman, Theresa Dobkowski, Lilliana Doughty, Shawn Esquivel, Jacqueline Flores, Patricia Franklin, Joan Glinski, Linda Govea, Margaret Govert, Monica Grudzien, Christa Hacker, Cherun Hampton, Tracy Heintz, Diane Hill, Sheri Hooks, Jowanna Ivy, Lolita Jones, Lynn Karzas, Catherine Kowalczyk, Char Kullerstrand, Marla Lopez, Julie McCarthy, Qwinellia Norwood, Kathleen O'Neill, Elizabeth Puentes-Cortez, Marcella Ramirez, Linda Reece, Roy Robles, Lucy Rodriguez, Debbie Sado, Nancy Sivak, Renita Sneed, Cathy Soczyk, Diane Solis, Lisa Sotak, Angela Sulewski, Carla Szarkowicz, Rosemary Valdes, Melody Vinyard, Jessica Wells, Kathleen Wells, Julie Wilkens, Brenda Wilkerson, Rhonda J. Williams, and Rhonda M. Williams

With Beginnings in Gary • THEN AND NOW

PATIENT FINANCIAL SERVICES DEPARTMENT...

Contributed by Karen Schneider, Regional Director

The Patient Financial Services Department's role is to collect payment for services provided by the hospital. Our responsibilities include insurance verification, billing, collections, cashiers, financial counseling, and clerical support. Through the years, we have undergone many changes to our name, location and business processes. Originally we were known as The Business Office, then Patient Accounts, and now Patient Financial Services. In the healthcare industry, our business process is called the revenue cycle to more accurately depict the integral working relationship we must maintain among many hospital departments such as registration, Health Information Management, Case Management and others to insure that bills get paid as healthcare processes and requirements become more complex.

The Patient Accounts office was originally located at St. Mary Medical Center in Gary, Indiana where the billing was done for both hospitals. Back then billing and collections were done in separate areas. The Collection Department was on the first floor across from administration and the Billing Department was located in the basement of the St. Mary Gary location. In the early 1980s, a separate business office opened at the St. Mary Hobart location. The office was on the first floor in an office behind registration which is the current location of nursing administration. In 1990, the Lakeshore Healthcare business office was opened to handle billing and collections for St. Mary Hobart, St. Mary Gary, and St. Catherine Hospital. The office was located offsite on Tenth Street in the old Prudential building in Hobart. In August 2004, Patient Accounts became a regional office for our three-hospital health system, several years after the formation of Community Healthcare System. We then opened office space on the second floor of the Community Diagnostic Center at 10020 Donald S. Powers Drive in Munster, Indiana, and remain there in 2009. Our financial counselors are still located at the main hospital building.

How we handle our business practices has changed radically over the years. We started out as a manual paper-processing center and have evolved into a high-tech computerized operation. Our role keeps changing, driven by increasing complexity of the healthcare financing system in the United States. In the old days, charges were tallied on ledger cards and manually filed in a special, color-coded folder by patient name in file cabinets. Insurance companies were billed using hand-typed claim forms. Each insurance company had a different form and a different requirement for billing.

Early on, a business office employee used an adding machine, a typewriter, telephone, and pen and paper. In the 1970s, we started using NCR machines and ledger cards. In the 1980s, we modernized with Cathode Ray Tubes (or CRTs) and microfiche to handle patient calls and questions. We had to work with information that was a week old. Today, computer access allows immediate, real-time information exchange. Daily tools include head sets, scanners, fax machines and e-mail. Billing is done electronically. Payments are received as electronic funds transfers. Complex software programs assist us with data entry, bill auditing, record tracking, archiving, and data retrieval.

Some things never change. Teamwork has always been a key element in Patient Financial Services. We need to understand many facets of our organization in order to provide the best customer service and successfully collect accounts. Each person must build upon the work of another to successfully get a bill paid.

SHOWN (L-R): Elizabeth Redford, Cristina Soto, Irene Pacheco, and Rhonda J. Williams

IT'S BEEN *Said* IN 2009...

"I came in just on the cusp of computers. The only thing I think we did was send data to the corporate office in Chicago at St. Ann's. When St. Ann's closed, they moved it to St. Elizabeth's Hospital in Chicago. At one point in time that's where they also printed out the payroll and if the payroll was behind, we sometimes had to drive up to Chicago to pick up the paychecks and bring them back so everybody would get paid on time. Isn't that amazing?"

Judy Candiano
REVENUE CYCLE CONTROL SUPERVISOR
MERCY HOSPITAL
(BEGAN IN 1969 IN GARY)

IT'S BEEN *Said* IN 2009...

LISTEN AND LEARN

"If you take the time to listen and put yourself in the patient's situation, I truly believe problems can be resolved. In the back of my head, I have always thought of St. Mary's. We did our work, but we also became a family. I mean if you had a problem you could share it with co-workers or the priests and nuns based at the hospital. We always had time for each other and I think that is what made St. Mary Medical Center in those days what it is today."

Joni Bucko
FINANCIAL COUNSELOR, RETIRED
ST. MARY MEDICAL CENTER | (BEGAN IN 1975 IN GARY)

IT'S BEEN *Said* IN 2009...

"When I became a biller in the late 1970s or early 1980s, the billings were kept in boxes and boxes and boxes in the billing room or under our desks! As a new biller, I was... very concerned about billing these out quickly so we could receive payment. I remember being told, 'Even if the claims are not billed out, Medicare still sends us a weekly average check based on a complicated accounting process.'

"Today if you do not bill Medicare or are behind in billings you are not paid an average weekly payment and you will not receive reimbursement."

Monita Puckett, REVENUE CYCLE ANALYST
ST. MARY MEDICAL CENTER | (BEGAN IN 1976 IN GARY)

IT'S BEEN *Said* IN 2009...

"I started at St. Catherine's in 1973 as a Medicare biller but I took time off and went back to St. Catherine's in 1982. In 1990, the Patient Accounting Department combined with St. Mary's and our office was located in Hobart from 1990 to 2004 until we moved to the Munster location. So I've been here steadily since 1983.

"We've got a beautiful office building now. Our office building in Hobart – offsite down the street – was rapidly falling apart but that was our second home. I'm here to do what I'm supposed to do, but there were a lot of good times when the Saints were the Saints. We were family. You could walk down the hallway and feel feelings for other people. Here... it's new relationships all the time.

"I appreciate Community Healthcare System now and I'm thankful for my job and I'm grateful that St. Mary's did tide me over – take care of me. I've just got a lot of good memories."

Gayle Brumley
TELEPHONE ANALYST
ST. MARY MEDICAL CENTER
(BEGAN IN 1982 AT ST. CATHERINE HOSPITAL)

PLANT OPERATIONS

IT'S BEEN *Said* IN 2009...

"(With the boiler system) there were some coal stokers and we had to get in there and clean all the ashes and soot out of them. We did an annual inspection. The first gas boiler wasn't used any more and they put a new boiler in its place.

"They had a coal bin along the whole area and they had to make a fuel oil tank. The company that was putting the boiler in didn't want to get the license from the city of Gary to have union workers come in. They wanted to use their own people because they were from Illinois. One Sunday, this company brought tons of welders, brought the steel in, and made this big oil tank inside a coal chute (or bin). They started it early in the morning and finished it that day. Monday morning, the city inspectors came in and looked at it. There was nothing they could do because it was done on a Sunday and you didn't have to have permits (for that day) back then and it stayed. It was pretty interesting."

Jim Wade
ENGINEERING MANAGER
MERCY HOSPITAL
(BEGAN IN 1960 IN GARY)
Note: At this writing in 2009, Jim Wade has worked at the Gary and Hobart hospital sites for 49 years and is the oldest active employee at St. Mary Medical Center.

IT'S BEEN *Said* IN 2009...

TOXICOLOGY/GUN LAB

"There were several things housed here in the St. Mary Gary Boiler Plant Building – the boiler room, and of course it had the tower to the chimney for the boilers. It housed some of the overnight technicians. They stayed there when they worked midnights and that was their area. For some of them it was their place of residence.

"Later it was redesigned to accommodate toxicology and the gun lab on the top floor. There were some interesting things that were part of the lab. The gun lab was personally interesting to me. The Gary Police Department would bring their confiscated weapons as evidence for analysis to determine if a bullet came from that particular weapon. It was well known throughout the area as one of the best toxicology and gun lab centers."

Ismael "Izzy" Alicea
MAINTENANCE WORKER III
ST. MARY MEDICAL CENTER
(BEGAN IN 1979 IN GARY)

BOILER PLANT BUILDING

IT'S BEEN *Said* IN 2010...

TOXICOLOGY

"Dr. Michael Caplis, a Ph.D. in chemistry from Purdue University, quickly established the second best toxicology laboratory in the United States. From the time of about 1968 or 1969 until 1975 or 1976, the laboratory could identify the drugs found on people who were arrested for illegal drug use. They could be identified within a matter of one or two days and the person who was guilty could be prosecuted with evidence. Otherwise, it took weeks to send the samples to Indianapolis to be identified. By that time, many of the suspects were allowed to go free and then escape.

"This sort of community assistance was extremely important to the police and rapidly became a county-wide effort to keep this laboratory going and to use it as much as possible for prosecution of illegal drug use."

Earl J. Mason,, Ph.D., M.D.
FORMER DIRECTOR OF THE LABORATORY, RETIRED
MERCY HOSPITAL
(BEGAN IN 1965 IN GARY)

THE BOILER HOUSE OF MERCY HOSPITAL IN THE EARLY 1950s
"They converted the old coal-stoker boilers into a combination of gas and oil. All the hospital rooms were heated by steam with the old-type radiators in each room. A lot of people can't imagine what it was like back then."

Jim Wade, Engineering Manager

PLANT OPERATIONS/MAINTENANCE
STAFF PHOTO – 2009
BACK ROW (L-R): Patrick Montesdeoca,
Ismael "Izzy" Alicea, and Mike Vician
– all of Maintenance; and Lee Pacheco –
Plant Operations
FRONT ROW (L-R):
Mark Tonevich and Gary Coppinger – both
of Maintenance

With Beginnings in Gary • THEN AND NOW

PLANT OPERATIONS...

Contributed by Ismael "Izzy" Alicea, Maintenance Worker III

Shown here in March 1982 is part of the maintenance
crew standing behind a snow plow on the grounds of
St. Mary Medical Center.
FRONT ROW (L-R): Dave Gallagher, John Spence, Merle Morlan,
Jim Wade and Bill Holtz
BACK ROW (L-R): Ron McGee and Dave Barenie

IT'S BEEN *Said* IN 2009...

"In the physical plant, the cleanliness, the services that are provided are
just as good as I've ever seen and being in a small community and a small
hospital, these are things that you just wouldn't expect."

Mark Simaga, M.D., NEUROLOGIST
ST. MARY MEDICAL CENTER
(BEGAN IN 1997 IN HOBART)

A lot has changed in the last thirty years from what was once known
as "maintenance" and is now referred to as Engineering Services or Plant
Operations. Changes within the department have coincided with changes
within healthcare. Today, just as state-of-the-art technology is usually
associated with departments such as radiology, surgery or emergency
services, the department of Plant Operations has also taken advantage of
state-of-the-art software.

In the past, maintenance work requests were transacted through a simple
phone call to the shops or by a hand-written note. Preventive maintenance
work orders were logged on a ledger maintained by an employee. By contrast,
today's software allows engineering services to collectively track the number of
work orders completed in a given month, show which departments requested
the highest number of orders, and verify which maintenance technician
completed the work order. The software allows managers to follow, by task
codes, what type of work requires the greatest amount of time. The manager
then has greater control of his/her departmental labor hours.

In the early days at Mercy Hospital, our heating was limited to a switch that turned on a valve that allowed steam to flow and provide heat – our version of modern technology at that time! Today, we manage our heating and cooling through energy management systems. Computerized software allows an assigned technician to see exactly what is taking place at the Air Handling Unit even if the unit is off site. The technician can see fan operation, discharge temperatures, room temperature or the setting on a thermostat in a specific room. All this can be done by logging on to any desktop or laptop-based program.

The majority of maintenance staff members were promoted through other departments within the facility. Although promotions within the facility are desired, higher skill level requirements call for an evaluation of trade experience.

Mentoring was prominent in the early years. Most new maintenance staff affiliates were trained by long-term employees within the department. As a new member at St. Mary Medical Center, you were generally assigned to a co-worker who held seniority by age and experience. A hospital's daily success, or operational excellence, requires interactive knowledge from one department to another.

In 1995, St. Mary made provisions to move its entire Engineering Services operation to the Hobart campus due to pending negotiations to conclude services at the Gary campus.

In both Gary and Hobart, the Plant Operations Department has long been an important component of St. Mary Medical Center and our staff continues to serve patients and staff members with efficiency and pride.

IT'S BEEN *Said* IN 2009...

"I remember my mentor at St. Mary Medical Center, Bud Christoff, who labeled me as 'kid.' He would point his left index finger with a minor twist and say, 'Come on kid, you can do it!!' The day my father passed away, Bud was the first person I called and I said, 'Bud, I lost my dad so you will need to play the part of Dad for me.' This man took that statement to heart and regarded me as a son. My mentor and co-worker will never be forgotten. I tell that story to express the family-style atmosphere at St. Mary Medical Center. I am glad to say that tradition still remains."

Ismael "Izzy" Alicea
MAINTENANCE WORKER III | ST. MARY MEDICAL CENTER | (BEGAN IN 1979 IN GARY)

"IZZY'S" BONUS

Ismael "Izzy" Alicea (right) explains to Administrator Paul R. Kaiser how spending a few dollars will save thousands in the laundry. Izzy's idea earned him a $300 bonus.
Acts & Facts, December, 1980

Typically, the hospital's circuit board needed to be replaced 10 or 15 times annually. Through some investigation, however, Ismael "Izzy" Alicea discovered that it was one or two small components on the circuit board that were faulty and were valued between 59-cents and $2.50. The parts, available at most electronic supply stores, could be easily replaced in an hour by employees of the hospital's bio-medical electronics staff. Through the Employee Suggestion Program begun in 1976, Izzy reduced the cost of doing the hospital's wash and was awarded a $300 bonus by then Administrator Paul R. Kaiser.

SWITCHBOARD DEPARTMENT - MERCY HOSPITAL

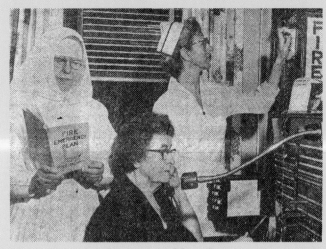

MERCY EMPLOYEES PREPARED TO MEET FIRE EMERGENCY – OPERATIONS CENTER
The hospital switchboard is the nerve center of Mercy Hospital's communication system. **SHOWN (L-R)** in this 1959 photo are Hospital Administrator Sister Cornelia Leible, PHJC, as she checks the hospital's printed emergency manual. Mrs. Helen Hopkins, nursing aide instructor, RN, inspects the fire alarm. Seated is Switchboard Operator Miss Agnes Ryan.
Reprinted by permission of the *Post-Tribune*, NOVEMBER 22, 1959

Sister Catherine Pavlovich, PHJC, (standing) speaks to a long-time employee about the convenience of the new telecommunications equipment.

Word-Gathering, SPRING, 1981

With Beginnings in Gary • THEN AND NOW

COMMUNICATION SERVICES...

Contributed by Sherry Martin
Regional Manager Telecommunications

COMMUNICATION SERVICES
STAFF PHOTO – 2009
FRONT ROW (L-R): Regional Manager Sherry Martin; Patricia Young; Alice Williams; and Helen Cooley
BACK ROW (L-R): Ed Fralinger and Donna Garcia
NOT PICTURED: Rose McDougall and Judy Nowak.

When the hospitals merged in 2001, the switchboard at St. Mary Medical Center was under the guidance of Sister Mary Ellen Goeller, PHJC, in the Pastoral Care Department. As the departments across the system were reorganized and responsibilities were shifted, I was offered the opportunity in 2004 by David Nellans, the vice president of Engineering and Support Services, to begin traveling to all three hospitals to standardize operations and policies and procedures.

I was pleased to find that all three hospitals had operators answering the phones instead of using a recording. I feel that automated answering devices are inappropriate especially since so many of our customers are the elderly, or they just don't feel good or they are dealing with emotional situations. We try to… figure out the best way to handle their requests.

When I first started coming over here to Hobart, I noticed immediately how friendly the people were. Everybody says hello to you in the hallways. They made me feel very welcome.

Shown (l-r) in this 1988 photo at St. Mary Medical Center in Hobart are Lead Operator Ruth Hall who worked days, Midnight Operator Helen Cooley, and Alice Williams who worked days and other fill-in shifts.

Shown here is the switchboard room at the Hobart facility as it looked in the mid-1980s. There were two people who worked the day shift, one person on the 3-11:00 p.m. shift, and one person on the midnight shift.

This is the switchboard room today. Displayed are two operator stations with finger-tip information available and a number of alarms on the wall. The schedule usually includes three day-time operators, two evening operators and one for the midnight shift.

The Auxiliary – Its Formation and Growth
1953 – Auxiliary Beginnings

In May 1953, the St. Mary's Mercy Hospital Women's Auxiliary was formed at a Mercy Hospital tea hosted by the Junior League. Under the leadership of Junior League President Mrs. Harold Phipps, 400 interested women attended the gathering in Gary to learn about volunteer opportunities for Mercy Hospital. By September of 1953, the newly-formed auxiliary was assisting with all hospital departments, including operating a gift cart.

In 1953, new officers of the Mercy Hospital Auxiliary were installed in the hospital auditorium by Sister Milburg, PHJC, hospital administrator.
Seated (l-r): Mrs. Sam H. Cohn, treasurer; Mrs. J. J. McKenna, president; and Mrs. J. A. Cargone, vice president.
Standing (l-r): Mrs. David Root, corresponding secretary; Mrs. Dean I. Gross, third vice president; and Mrs. Charles H. Glueck, second vice president. **Not pictured:** Mrs. J. R. Walsh, recording secretary.

Reprinted by permission of the *Post-Tribune*, 1953

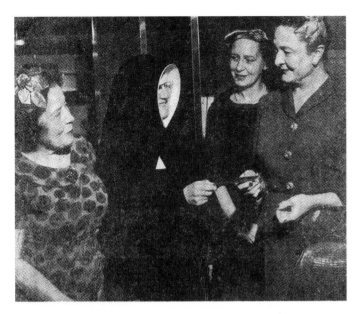

Pictured here in the 1950s is Mother Therese, PHJC, (second from left) accepting an auxiliary donation for $7,800 from (l-r) Mrs. R. G. Ebert, Mrs. Sam Schwartzberg, and Mrs. Michael Madden.

Reprinted by permission of the *Post-Tribune* (date unknown)

One of the earliest photos available of the St. Mary Mercy Hospital Auxiliary, taken in May, 1953, shows Mrs. E. H. Heilstedt, left, social chairman of the auxiliary as she discusses the annual spring brunch and style show held at the Gary Country Club. Mrs. E. Courtney Sorrells (right) was program chairman for the brunch. Mrs. M. W. Madden (center) was co-chairman of the annual Holly Bazaar, one of the auxiliary's major fund raising events. (The Holly Bazaar raised more than $6,300 in 1957, and in all its years of existence has raised thousands of dollars for the hospital.)

Reprinted by permission of the *Post-Tribune*, MAY, 1953

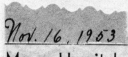

Mercy Hospital Auxiliary Board Hears Reports

Members of Chi Chapter, Pi Sigma Phi Sorority, donated $75 to be used to purchase equipment for the pediatrics section of Mercy Hospital. Members of the board of the Mercy Hospital Woman's Auxiliary, meeting yesterday at the hospital, learned of the donation which will provide books, puzzles, magic slates and other games for the children's ward.

Mrs. Dean I. Gross, sewing chairman, reported that 292 articles had been completed for the hospital and seven pair of drapes for the nurses home.

The general meeting of the auxiliary Jan. 18 will include a postal grab bag, announced Mrs. Thomas J. Senese, ways and means chairman. A report was given by Mrs. Samuel Brady, chairman of the floor work and surgical supplies committee. The committee members read to the patients, feed them, arrange flowers for the rooms and assist in any way on any floor. They also make surgical dressings as they are needed.

Mrs. Richard J. Wilder, clerical and printing chairman, and Mrs. Charles Belcher, pediatrics section chairman, asked for volunteers for their respective committees.

The next regular board meeting has been changed to Dec. 1

Dec. 1, 1953

Women Sew, Give to Gary Hospitals

To Decorate Building for Christmas

The first project of the Women's auxiliary of St. Mary's Mercy Hospital will be to furnish and equip the sewing room in the new laundry addition to the hospital. Members of the board meeting yesterday afternoon at the hospital, voted on the new auxiliary name and the project.

There is a sewing room on each floor of the hospital at present but the new laundry which will be completed in the near future, will be adequate for all hospital sewing. The auxiliary's project will include purchase of new furniture and new sewing machines.

Of the 525 members of the newly formed auxiliary, 186 are working at the hospital each week. Mrs. Charles Glueck, chairman of the gift shop, has arranged a meeting of all shop and gift cart volunteers for Dec. 19. The gift shop has been in operation for a little over a month.

Mrs. Samuel Brady, floor work committee chairman, announced that her committee will decorate Christmas trees on all floors of the hospital except in the pediatrics ward. Members of Gamma Gamma Chapter of Beta Sigma Phi Sorority have arranged a special party for the pediatrics ward for Dec. 20. The chapter will provide decorations, a decorated tree, gifts and refreshments.

Even in its infancy the auxiliary was involved in sewing, an auxiliary activity that remains prevalent today. A first auxiliary project was to furnish and equip the sewing room in the Gary hospital's new laundry addition. Prior to the addition, there was a sewing room on each floor of the hospital.

Reprinted by permission of the *Post-Tribune*, DECEMBER 1, 1953

Mercy Auxiliary Roster Nears 500, Seeks Recruits

A membership committee was appointed at a meeting of the executive board of the Woman's Auxiliary of the Mercy Hospital Monday in the Rose Room of the hospital.

Mrs. Joseph A. Carbone, chairman of the committee, announced the membership now stands at 457, and an effort will be made to recruit new members. Those appointed to the committee are Mrs. Michael Madden, Mrs. Ellsworth Strang Jr., Mrs. Sidney Pachter, Mrs. Clifford Streigal, Mrs. John Reed of Hobart, Mrs. P. K. Hunsicker, Mrs. David Root of Crown Point, Mrs. John Mirro of Lowell, Mrs. Robert Winslow, Mrs. R. F. Carmody of Chesterton, Mrs. Fred Schutz, Mrs. Theodore Lorenty, Mrs. Daniel Thomas, Mrs. Fred Collins, Mrs. John Vohr and Mrs. J. M. Mather of East Gary.

The sewing committee chairman, Mrs. Dean I. Gross, appointed seven members to assist her. Each will have charge of a certain area of the city. They are Mrs. Charles Atkins, West Side; Mrs. Norman Quinlan, Glen Park; Mrs. James Cassidy, Ogden Dunes; Mrs. Streigal, South; Mrs. O. A. Clark, hospital; Mrs. Charles Weislogel, Miller, and Mrs. A. P. Craig, Ambassador Hotel.

Mrs. R. R. Danek announced that she and Mrs. Samuel Brady will meet next week to plan an adult care department.

Board members were requested by the president, Mrs. J. J. McKenna, to attend the Indiana Hospital Auxiliary Association meeting Nov. 6 at Indianapolis. She also announced that a gift

service cart was started at the hospital this month and was greatly appreciated by the patients and visitors.

Mrs. Charles Belcher, chairman of pediatrics, told the group that volunteers are needed to serve in the pediatrics ward. Mrs. John B. Radigan donated a table and chairs to be used by the older children. Flannel boards also have been added to the ward.

In 1953, the auxiliary boasted more than 450 members. A *Post-Tribune* article reflected committee activities. Reprinted by permission of the *Post-Tribune*, OCTOBER 19, 1953

Mrs. J. J. McKenna (right), president of the Women's Auxiliary of St. Mary's Mercy Hospital, presents a charter designating membership in the American Hospital Association to Sister Milburg, PHJC, hospital administrator. At left is Mrs. Cyril L. Hale of Chicago, a hospital board member who was guest speaker at the auxiliary's second meeting.

Membership involved three broad areas – service within the hospital, fund raising, and public relations – for the auxiliary to work to improve hospital service to patient and community. Volunteers were required to wear a bright cherry red pinafore.

Reprinted by permission of the *Post-Tribune*, JANUARY 18, 1954

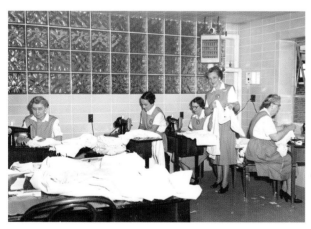

Shown in the newly opened sewing room at Mercy Hospital are members of the women's auxiliary as they repair the hospital's torn linen. Working (l-r) are Mrs. Joseph Gallas, Mrs. Courtney Sorrells, Mrs. Martha Davis, Sewing Committee Chairman Mrs. Dean I. Gross, and Mrs. Raymond Dwyer.

Reprinted by permission of the *Post-Tribune*, 1954

CHRISTMAS IN MAY

Mrs. Leo Cooper (seated left) and Mrs. Orville Tittle, (right) co-chaired a style show at a "Christmas in May" auxiliary fund-raising event in 1959 and modeled apparel from the show. Also modeling were Mrs. Bertram Jensen (standing left) and Mrs. Donald Davies (standing right).

Reprinted by permission of the *Post-Tribune*, MAY, 1959

A Mercy Hospital open house was held in honor of National Hospital Week so those touring the facility could view activities and hear them explained by the faculty.

The Women's Auxiliary sponsored a tea. Shown here (l-r) are visitors Marilyn Valo and Irene Damaskon; Auxiliary President Mrs. J. J. McKenna; Pediatric Clinical Instructor Sue Claussen; and auxiliary member Mrs. Leo Cooper.

St. Mary Medical Center
Auxiliary Archives

In June 1955, St. Mary Mercy Hospital purchased the Crystal Apartments in Gary as a residence for four new interns. Auxiliary members were asked to provide such items as rugs, lamps, draperies, and pictures and ample donations were received to furnish each of the four-room apartments. Shown (l-r) in an intern's apartment with furnishings are Mrs. W. Hoffman, Mrs. Thomas J. Senese and Mrs. F. J. Kelley.

St. Mary Medical Center
Auxiliary Archives

Auxiliary – the 1960s

Assistant Hospital Administrator Paul Bellendorf received more than $6,000 from St. Mary Mercy Hospital's Women's Auxiliary – $500 from service cart sales and approximately $5,600 from Holly Bazaar sales. Shown (l-r) are Mrs. Frank Fleck; Mrs. Bertram Jensen; Holly Bazaar Co-chairman Mrs. Thad Menzie, outgoing auxiliary President Mrs. Orville Tittle, and Holly Bazaar Co-chairman Mrs. Robert Dering.

Reprinted by permission of the *Post-Tribune*, 1962

Hundreds of patrons were tempted by items from the "Sugar 'n Spice" sale for the holidays. Shown (l-r) are women's auxiliary members with homemade sweets in hand: Mrs. Matt Erdelec, Mrs. Ted Calenberg, Mrs. Joseph Cudlo, and Mrs. Richard Reeves.

St. Mary Medical Center Auxiliary Archives

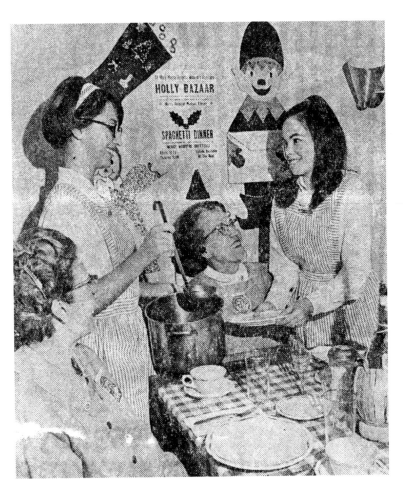

Candy Striper volunteers Rosi Saska (standing left) and Marybeth Lucas (standing right) are shown as waitresses for a Holly Bazaar spaghetti dinner in 1968. Seated (l-r) are Mrs. Rosa Vye, novelty chairman, and Mrs. Frank Fleck, finance chairman.
Reprinted by permission of the *Post-Tribune*, NOVEMBER 8, 1968

Sister Georgine (Schleper), PHJC, (second from right), chairman of Mercy Hospital's Candy Striper program, is shown in 1967 placing a headband on Odete Boynes honoring her for 75 hours of Candy Striper service. Also standing (l-r) are Mrs. Kenneth Enderlin, co-chairman of the honorary Candy Striper party; Candy Striper Brenda Nelson; and Mrs. Dale Howells, also a party co-chairman.
Reprinted by permission of the *Post-Tribune*, DECEMBER 14, 1967

CANDY STRIPERS

High school students interested in volunteering may find themselves in hospitals where – sometimes with the recommendation of high school counselors – they are invited to participate. With a desire to pursue careers in health-related fields or to obtain a first-hand look at the inner-workings of a hospital, the junior volunteers have been prevalent for many years. Office filing, making beds, talking with patients, or working in an X-ray Department exemplify many of the volunteer activities.

In 1991, among the three hospitals of Lakeshore Health System, there were approximately 60 volunteers, three of whom were males. Today (in 2010), the volunteer students – no longer referred to as Candy Stripers – gain educational experience and hospital insight through a variety of activities directed by Sister Mary Ellen Goeller, PHJC, Regional Director of Mission Integration.

Teenage volunteers Heather Alford (left) and Linda Nowcaradan are shown in this 1991 St. Mary Medical Center photo.
Reprinted by permission of the *Post-Tribune*, JULY 14, 1991

IT'S BEEN *Said* IN 2009...

"We went to Catholic grade school. I remember the Sisters very well because some of them worked at the hospital. My mom worked in Gary for 42 or 43 years and knew the nurses so we would go to the nurses' home right next to the hospital and have lunch or take them out to lunch.

"On weekends, a lot of high school kids would get on the bus and go from Glen Park to Fifth Avenue, get a transfer, and go work at the hospital as Candy Stripers. My sister Tina was a Candy Striper. The hospital was a very good employer."

Jesse Bravo
FORMER TELECOMMUNICATIONS TECHNICIAN
ST. MARY MEDICAL CENTER
(BEGAN IN 1992 IN GARY)

FASHION SHOWS OF THE '60S AND '70S

At a 1969 luncheon/fashion show sponsored by the St. Mary Mercy Hospital Women's Auxiliary at the Gary Country Club, Mrs. John Scully modeled one of the latest trends – a pants suit. Typically, the annual sold-out luncheons were a time to present checks for monies raised, present new officers, and appreciate the volunteerism of many.

Newspaper source unknown, 1969

Shown here as they plan for the St. Mary Medical Center Auxiliary's annual fashion show and luncheon are (l-r) Lillian Kubiak, decorations chairwoman, with Marian Smith and Ann Sicula. The 1975 theme was "Ides of March," the day of Julius Caesar's murder.

St. Mary Medical Center Auxiliary Archives

AUXILIARY – THE 1970S
CELEBRATING 20 YEARS IN 1973

On the occasion of the Hobart hospital auxiliary's 20th anniversary in 1973, Administrator Paul Bellendorf and Department of Education Director Mary Gulyassy said in a letter to the auxilians:

(Your 20th anniversary) recalls two decades of close association and friendship with women distinguished by a loyalty of purpose and vitality of action not easily found in any other hospital. The same spirit that motivated the founders remains undiminished today. The proven worth of the auxiliary has long been established.

In 1973, the Mercy Hospital Auxiliary held its installation of new officers. Shown (l-r) are: Mrs. Robert Rothacker, recording secretary; Mrs. Dewey Leever, corresponding secretary; Mrs. Eugene Swartz, second vice-president; Mrs. Paul Heuring, incoming president – receiving the gavel from outgoing President Mrs. James Wassall; Mrs. Frank Saikley, state president; Mrs. Edward Marlatt and Mrs. William Ridgely, treasurer.

Hobart Herald, JANUARY 17, 1973

A $75,000 GIFT

Mrs. James Wassall, president of the St. Mary Mercy Hospital Women's Auxiliary, presented a check for $7,500 to Hospital Administrator Paul Bellendorf. The initial payment went toward the auxiliary's $75,000 gift toward the Hobart hospital's construction. Payments of equal amounts were pledged from the auxiliary twice a year for five years.

Acts of Mercy publication,
FEBRUARY, 1972

IT'S BEEN *Said* IN 2009...

"When the Hobart auxiliary was first getting organized, we went to Gary for our meetings before the Hobart hospital was built. We were trying to recruit members in 1972 and 1973. The Gary group used to meet in their cafeteria area and it was very formal with all the silver teapots and coffee. Everything was very proper so that was pretty neat. Eventually, we had our own meeting place here. The awards luncheons would always be combined."

Mary Jaroscak
37-YEAR AUXILIARY MEMBER, HISTORIAN | ST. MARY MEDICAL CENTER | (BEGAN IN 1972)

IT'S BEEN *Said* IN 2009...

"We had a superb Pink Ladies' Auxiliary. Their presence and involvement were a great asset to both Gary and Hobart hospitals."

Sister Wilma Boeving, PHJC, ASSOCIATE ADMINISTRATOR, RETIRED
MERCY HOSPITAL | (BEGAN IN 1967 IN GARY)

The Red Coats are here

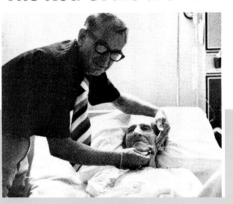

Red Coats Volunteer Delbert Clifft shaves male patients as his contribution to the sick. Clifft did so in ICU and CCU for a number of years as part of the Red Coats group of volunteer services.

Acts of Mercy, Vol. 9, No. 6
– JUNE, 1973

IT'S BEEN *Said* IN 2009...

"We always had the (male) Red Coats and they had their own separate group. There used to be approximately 30 of them. Andy Liposcak was instrumental in taking care of all of the Red Coats and Harold Babcock who just passed away was in charge of them for years. We decided that we were just like one group so we mixed them all together – the Red Coats and the Pink Ladies. The guys are still called Red Coats but we all meet together and do everything together.

"Mr. Paul Heuring donated a car the first two or three years so we had these big car raffles. A bunch of us would take the car and go to different grocery stores on Saturdays and sell raffle tickets. It did well back in the 1970s."

Sister Wilma Boeving, PHJC, ASSOCIATE ADMINISTRATOR, RETIRED
MERCY HOSPITAL | (BEGAN IN 1967 IN GARY)

COUPONS FOR EQUIPMENT

Before construction began in 1971 on Mercy Hospital Southeast in Hobart, the hospital auxiliary began a Betty Crocker coupon collection campaign that garnered a lot of dough, allowing for the eventual purchase of an electrocardiograph machine for the coronary unit. By the time the hospital opened in 1973, auxiliary members had collected approximately 340,000 coupons, or approximately half of the required 600,000 total number needed to obtain the machine. Because the equipment was needed for immediate use, the company allowed the auxiliary credit on coupons already collected toward the cost of the equipment. Chairman of the drive, Alice Messina, coordinated the collection of 533,000 coupons by February 1974 and the shortage of $685 was made up in cash contributions.

THE HOLLY BAZAAR IN GARY

it's been *Said* in 2009... ~~~~~~~~~~~~~~~~~~~~~

"The auxiliary started in 1972 in Hobart and in 1953 in Gary. We met at Augustana Lutheran Church in the basement for our sewing until the hospital added a building in Hobart and the Sewing Group moved to the second floor. There used to be approximately 50 women. Now we're down to 12 but we have two bazaars every year – a spring bazaar and Holly Bazaar where we sell handmade things and some of the same items are sold in the gift shop – knitting, crocheting, embroidery – a little bit of everything. Some of the early volunteers also went to Gary where they hemmed sheets and pillowcases and made baby layettes for the newborns there. Now a few women knit baby hats for each baby born in Hobart – on average 20 hats a week. When we started doing that it was estimated at 'probably 75 a year' and now we're up to 80 a month!"

Carol Piscione, Auxiliary Member
St. Mary Medical Center

Alice Messina, chairman of the Betty Crocker Coupon collection, is shown here in 1973 reading letters that accompanied coupons sent by people from throughout the United States. By collecting nearly 600,000 coupons, the hospital auxiliary was able to obtain a heart monitor for the coronary unit of the Hobart hospital. The auxilians were recognized for their determination and success. Reprinted by permission of the *Post-Tribune*, April 29, 1973

Mary Catherine Yast, 5 ½ years old, daughter of Dr. and Mrs. Charles Yast, admires a doll bed, one of many children's toys displayed at the fifth annual Holly Bazaar of St. Mary Mercy Hospital's Women's Auxiliary. Also shown are bazaar co-chairmen Mrs. R. G. Ebert (left) and Mrs. M. W. Madden.
Source unknown

Mother Therese, PHJC, administrator of St. Mary Mercy Hospital, accepts a check for $7,900 from Women's Auxiliary members Mrs. C.T. Vorwald (left) and Mrs. Charles Daugherty. The donation represented proceeds from the annual Holly Bazaar and was to complete payment for improvements made to the hospital bakery.
Reprinted by permission of the *Post-Tribune*, 1961

Members of the St. Mary Mercy Hospital Auxiliary tried out a new sewing machine that was to be used at weekly workshops in preparation for the auxiliary's annual Holly Bazaar.
STANDING (L-R): Mrs. Frieda Carlson, bazaar chairman; Mrs. Frank Fleck; and Mrs. William DeGau, auxiliary treasurer. Seated at the machine is Mrs. Thomas Powell.
Hobart Herald, April 4, 1973

Phyllis Diller Contributes to Holly Bazaar Items

Phyllis Diller, famed star of stage and television, is among the women who have contributed handmade items to the renowned Holly Bazaar given annually by the women of the St. Mary Mercy Hospital Auxiliary.

This year the bazaar will be held in two parts, the first at St. Bridget's Church, Front and Center Streets in Hobart Indiana, on November 12, from 9 a.m. to 6 p.m.; and the second phase to be held at St. Mary Mercy Hospital, 6th Avenue and Tyler Street, Gary, on November 13 from 10 a.m. to 4 p.m.

Miss Diller sent an example of her fine white crocheted lace to Mrs. Eugene Wineinger of Hobart Township a member of the auxiliary, who got the idea from a friend who had received am item requested for a benefit.

The Holly Bazaar will feature a host of beautiful and clever and handmade items on which the ladies of the auxiliary have been working, diligently, for many months.

Sparkling Christmas ornaments, stockings, card holders, mantel decorations, table and tree skirts, and runners are among the holiday items offered.

Christmas shoppers will be able to choose from a variety of lovely gifts for all ages. In addition, there will be a bake sale, a trash and treasure booth, and a complete Sunday dinner, at Hobart only, served from noon to 6.

The dinner complete with a complimentary glass of Chianti wine, all of the spaghetti one can eat served with both meat sauce and meat balls, a tossed salad, French bread and spumoni with coffee tea or milk will be served from noon to 6.

On November 13, Monday the second phase will be held at Gary Mercy Hospital, on the lower level of the new wing. Some new and different items will be offered.

All proceeds from the bazaar, and the sale of tickets for the red Ford Pinto will go to the new hospital in Hobart. St. Mary Mercy Southeast. The winner of the Pinto will be drawn on November 13 in Gary. The winner need not be present.

Everyone is urged to attend the Holly Bazaar, one of the most popular in the area, to select some of the outstanding offerings for Christmas and in this way contribute to a worthy cause. The new Hobart hospital is expected to open its doors on February 1, 1973.

(RIGHT) Famed comedian Phyllis Dillar sent an example of fine white crocheted lace as part of the 1972 fund-raising Holly Bazaar given by the women of the St. Mary Mercy Hospital Auxiliary.

Photo source unknown

THE HOLLY BAZAAR IN HOBART

Heuring Motors in Hobart donated a Pinto to the Mercy Hospital Auxiliary which was raffled off as part of the group's Holly Bazaar. Paul Heuring handed the keys to auxiliary member Mrs. Ray Nemtuda (seated). Also pictured (l-r) are Mrs. Don Jaroscak and Mrs. Tom Steininger. Proceeds from the raffle and bazaar were donated to the new Mercy-Methodist hospitals.

St. Mary Medical Center Auxiliary Archives

IT'S BEEN *Said* IN 2009...

"In 1972 when we were trying to get new members for the Hobart hospital, the Gary Sewing Group implemented its first activity to help Hobart prepare for its first Holiday Bazaar. It was always a big fund-raiser. They started with a spaghetti dinner and years later turned it into a chicken noodle dinner that was held at St. Bridget Church Crescent Room in Hobart."

Mary Jaroscak, 37-YEAR AUXILIARY MEMBER, HISTORIAN ST. MARY MEDICAL CENTER (BEGAN IN 1972)

1976 – AUXILIARY DONATES $100,000

In 1976, Administrator Paul R. Kaiser sent a congratulatory letter to the auxiliary thanking them for their $100,000 donation. In part he said,

The St. Mary Medical Center Auxiliary has performed so many acts of kindness for the hospital… over the years that it becomes increasingly difficult to express our feeling of gratitude in words that really reflect our respect and indebtedness to each of you.

1977 – AUXILIARY DONATES $150,000

Upon receiving $150,000 from the St. Mary Medical Center Auxiliary, Hospital Administrator Paul Kaiser (left) is shown with Auxiliary President Mrs. Vera Johnson and Auxiliary Treasurer Mrs. Evangeline Retson as he gives them a list of how the donation would be allocated. It would be spent on such things as an X-ray machine, an update of the Intermediate Care Unit, and a pulmonary function machine.

St. Mary Medical Center Auxiliary Archives

THE AUXILIARY – CELEBRATING 25 YEARS IN 1978

In recognition of 25 years of volunteer service by the St. Mary Medical Center Auxiliary, a celebratory Silver Anniversary luncheon was held at Wicker Park Social Center in Highland in May 1978. In addition to a generous cash contribution, volunteers donated more than 58,000 hours of service for that year. At the time, there were 315 auxilians who raised money from such projects as the gift shop, bazaars, sales, and a TV set rental program.

Twenty-five years later, the auxiliary's focus was revisited. Formed in 1953, it was established through members of the Mercy Hospital Junior League. Its purpose was threefold: 1) to give volunteer service to patients in the hospital so that professional staff members could devote more time to their duties; 2) to have members promote knowledge of the hospital's general services and overall program to the public; and 3) to raise funds to provide some of the necessary "extras" not covered by the hospital budget.

1978 – AUXILIARY DONATES $160,000 TO GARY AND HOBART HOSPITALS

The 1978 donation amounted to $160,000 for a number of fund-raising projects at the Gary and Hobart hospital campuses. Gary Hospital Administrator Paul R. Kaiser noted the purchase of electric beds for the Gary hospital's Orthopedic Ward; the relocation and remodeling of the Gary Intensive Care Unit; and the purchase of the "Scintiview," a pre-programmed, microprocessor expandable image control system.

AN AUXILIARY GIFT

A gift from the hospital auxiliary, 25 new electric patient beds arrived at St. Mary Mercy Hospital in Gary in 1978. They were installed on the orthopedic floor, 2South, to provide greater patient comfort.

Acts and Facts, St. Mary Medical Center publication
Gary and Hobart, SEPTEMBER, 1978

Auxiliary – the 1980s
1984 – Record Donation

In 1984, the auxiliary set a record with a $240,000 donation to St. Mary Medical Center.

And more...
In 1986, John Bisaha, associate executive director of the hospital, accepted a check for $105,000 from St. Mary Medical Center Auxiliary Finance Chairman Bertina Carlson.

Acts & Facts, February 1986

Children and adults had an opportunity to ride Viola, an Asian elephant, when the circus came to town in 1999. The Hobart event, held on the grounds of St. Mary Medical Center, was a fundraiser sponsored by the hospital auxiliary.
Hobart Gazette, September 10, 1999

The St. Mary Medical Center Auxiliary donated $85,000 to the hospital in 2004. Shown admiring the check are (l-r) Dan Potosky, Rae Marie Tomkiewicz, Cheryl Alderson, Jack Ziegler, M.D., and Marsha King.

St. Mary Medical Center Auxiliary Archives

Auxiliary – the 1990s

In 1995, the St. Mary Medical Center Auxiliary donated $120,000 to the hospital. The funds were earmarked for the new women's center. The medical staff also provided $5,000 for the new facility.

Shown here in the 1990s (in the middle) is Toni Shropshire who was vice president of Customer Service and Community Relations as she accepted an auxiliary donation for $200,000 from (l-r) Helen Matsey, Mary Jaroscak, Barbara Dubach, and Gerrie Simpson.
Reprinted by permission of the *Post-Tribune*, 1993

In September 1999, the auxiliary sponsored the Kelly Miller Circus on the grounds of St. Mary Medical Center. Crowds packed the show "under the big-top" and were treated to rides on an Asian elephant named Viola who weighed approximately 9,800 pounds.

The auxiliary also presented a check for $120,000 again in 1999. "I can't say enough about the good work they do," said Dick Sierra, executive director of the St. Mary Medical Center Foundation.

Auxiliary – 2000 and Beyond

For the year 2000, the auxiliary presented St. Mary Medical Center with a donation of $157,000. Shown here (l-r) are Sister Mary Ellen Goeller, PHJC; Teresa Mears; Hospital Administrator Milt Triana, and Lois Miller.

St. Mary Medical Center Auxiliary Archives
February 2001

Charter Members

<u>Shown (l-r):</u> Teresa Koehler, Ann Maxwell, Lenore Moehl, Alice Forsythe, Marge Neier, Catherine Schultz, Carol Piscione, Mary Jaroscak, Betty Bartholomew, Lillian Husek, and Kay Hersh. <u>Not pictured:</u> Jean Fasel, shown in photo

In 2009, The Scholarship Garden fund-raising campaign brought in more than $3,500 to help support the Auxiliary Scholarship Fund. A past recipient, Marcia Irby, (middle) Emergency Department technician, said at the ceremony: "I'm a single mother who was trying to work and go to school at the same time. The scholarship I received allowed me to spend a little more time with my son. It really made a difference." Shown with Marcia are (left) Lois Miller and (right) Janice Ryba, CEO and administrator.

Jean Fasel
Charter member

St. Mary Medical Center – Auxiliary Board Members - 2009

<u>Pictured in top row (l-r):</u> Carol Piscione, Pauli Burelli, Kay Roos, Mary Ellen Penovich, John Burton (President), Carol Szklarski, Chuck Kuznicki, Jan Raymond, Linda Young, and Kay Hersh
<u>Middle row (l-r):</u> Lois Miller, Jackie Modglin, Mary Adams, Phyllis Kuznicki, Mary Pogo, and Sister Mary Ellen Goeller, PHJC
<u>Front row (l-r):</u> Marcella Tharp, Martha Miller, and Victoria Thompson
<u>Not pictured:</u> Dorothy Fabian, Jo Hay, Donna Lajic, and Richard Smith

The St. Mary Medical Center Auxiliary made an $82,000 donation to the Hobart hospital in 2010. Pictured (l-r) are Chief Operating Officer of Community Healthcare System John Gorski; Auxiliary Treasurer Martha Miller; Auxiliary President John Burton; CEO and Administrator Janice L. Ryba; and Vice President, Clinical Ancillary Services Elizabeth Yee.

St. Mary Medical Center Auxiliary Archives

IT'S BEEN *Said* IN 2009...

"I ran the gift shop for a good many years. I was here every day of the week working and (going on) buying trips to Chicago and elsewhere. I said that was half the fun of it. In fact, Sister Mary Ellen (Goeller) also liked to go with me. Those days were very satisfying as I got to meet so many workers who are still good friends. Volunteering makes your life better in every way."

Betty Jo Bracken, LONGTIME AUXILIARY MEMBER

IT'S BEEN *Said* IN 2009...

"The hospital seems to appreciate us a whole lot and this year we were able to donate $100,000. Years ago, with Gary, we were always close to $200,000 and then it went down to $80,000, in that range. At one point the Gary gift shop was like a shopping center because there were no stores left in Gary and people went to the hospital gift shop for their gifts.

"Then Gary closed up and now it's one hospital. We have new members getting involved and more ideas and more fund-raisers. This past year was exceptional. The membership, under the leadership of President John Burton, stays right around 250 with orientation for new members held monthly. The gift shop seems to be doing well especially now that we take credit cards."

Mary Jaroscak, 37-YEAR AUXILIARY MEMBER, HISTORIAN
ST. MARY MEDICAL CENTER
(BEGAN IN 1972)

IT'S BEEN *Said* IN 2009...

"Sister Mary Ellen Goeller has a lot to do with the volunteers. I think she is very appreciative of the volunteers and she is dedicated to us. She is not frivolous. If you're doing a good job, she tells you but if you do something wrong, she tells you in a very kindly way and not in front of somebody else."

Margaret Hart Swisher, AUXILIARY MEMBER, FORMER RN
GRADUATE OF ST. MARY'S MERCY SCHOOL OF NURSING, 1943

"I'm blessed to work with the volunteers whose actions send messages of peace and love in small things; just like Mother Teresa said, '…we do small things with great love'. The Volunteer Services Office is filled with hospitality and friendship. It serves as the crossroads for all volunteers as they begin their daily tasks and customer service to St. Mary Medical Center patients and visitors."

Grace Veliz, DEPARTMENT ASSISTANT, VOLUNTEERS
ST. MARY MEDICAL CENTER
(BEGAN IN 1997 IN HOBART)

ST. MARY MEDICAL CENTER AUXILIARY
Past Presidents

1953-55	Mrs. J. J. McKenna
1955-57	Mrs. Charles L. Belcher
1957-59	Mrs. R. P. Barnett
1959-61	Mrs. Sam Schwartzberg
1961-63	Mrs. Orville Tittle
1963-65	Mrs. Robert Winslow
1965-67	Mrs. Jack Snyder
1967-69	Mrs. Bertram Jensen
1969-71	Mrs. Edward Fleming
1971-73	Mrs. James A. Wassall
1973-75	Mrs. Paul Heuring
1975-77	Mrs. Carl Lazzaro
1977-79	Mrs. Vera Johnson
1979-81	Mrs. Stanley Smith
1981-83	Mrs. Louise Meyette
1983-85	Mrs. Helen Wehner
1985-87	Mrs. Velma Lonner
1987-89	Patricia Palansky
1989-91	Judy Doan
1991-93	Barbara Dubach
1993-95	Helen Matsey
1995-97	Mary Dristas
1997-99	Lois Miller
1999-2001	Lois Miller (Acting)
2001-03	Lois Miller
2003-05	Daniel Potosky
2005-07	Janice Raymond (January 2005 thru December 31, 2007)
2007-08*	Janice Raymond (January 2007 thru June 30, 2008)
2008-10	John Burton (July 1, 2008 thru June 30, 2010)

* We had to change the term of office due to the Hospital fiscal year and Board appointments.

1956

HOSPITAL/COMMUNITY HAPPENINGS

1956 – MERCY HOSPITAL'S GOLDEN JUBILEE

Published in the *Post-Tribune* in 1956 as part of Gary's 50th Golden Jubilee celebration was the Golden Jubilee emblem.
Courtesy of Gary Public Library
Reprinted by permission of the *Gary Post-Tribune*, MAY 20, 1956

GROWING WITH GARY

This description of Gary was editorialized in the *Post-Tribune* as part of the city's Golden Jubilee: "What is there to explain the fact that Gary, a community undreamed of 51 years ago, is today hailed by leading retail authorities as one of the 'hottest' cities in America?

"True, this de facto twentieth century metropolis has long since attained the physical stature of Indiana's second city, with an urban population nudging 160,000.

"But isn't it a fact that its proximity to Chicago, with its great opulence of competitive attractions, tends to blunt, in a serious degree, Gary's prospects as a city of business opportunity?

"Well, conceding that the allures of the great colossus to the west do lead to the siphoning off of indeterminate sums of consumer dollars which otherwise might be expected to land in local tills, the answer seems to be that Gary is doing very well indeed, despite this handicap of happenstance, and that it certainly bids fair to do even better in the years ahead."
Reprinted by permission of the *Gary Post Tribune*, MAY 20, 1956

IT'S BEEN *Said* IN 2009...

"The city of Gary and the city of Hammond were always competitive. I was raised in Hammond... but downtown Gary was a great place to shop – secure and comfortable. There was no fear. There were no boarded up places. At Bishop Noll, we had kids who came in from Gary on the South Shore. We thought that was pretty cool – to come to school on a train. We used to take a bus or a train to visit our high school friends. The bus cost you a nickel. Gary was a fun place to go."

Sister Michelle Dermody, PHJC, RETIRED | DONALDSON, INDIANA

Marking Time...

1955
- *The external defibrillator was introduced in hospitals and later became a standard item of equipment aboard ambulances.*
- *First bone marrow transplants were performed in humans.*
- *A polio vaccine developed by Dr. Jonas Salk was successfully tested in 44 states.*

1958
- *Cardio Pulmonary Resuscitation was discovered.*
- *John Enders developed a vaccine against measles.*

1959
- *Penicillin was synthesized in the laboratory.*

Growing with Mercy Hospital

"Mercy Hospital, as it is familiarly called, goes bravely on its way to serve God and man."

Reprinted by permission of the *Post-Tribune*, FEBRUARY 1956

This photo from a local newspaper shows St. Mary Mercy Hospital as it appeared in 1956. An addition (at left) is shown under construction and when completed would bring the hospital's total capacity to 335 beds – 203 for adults, 68 for children and 64 bassinets.

Newspaper source unknown

The Sisters of Saint Mary Mercy Hospital

cordially invite you to attend

The Solemn Ceremony

Commemorating Fifty Years of Dedicated Service

By The Ancilla Domini Sisters

on Tuesday, the twentieth of August

nineteen hundred and sixty-three

at 10:30 a.m.

Hospital Chapel

540 Tyler Street

Gary, Indiana

Pontifical High Mass

Most Reverend Andrew G. Grutka   Celebrant

Saint Mary Mercy Hospital – Commemorating 50 Years of Dedicated Service
CHJC, University of Notre Dame Archives

As part of the Gary hospital's Golden Jubilee Week from June 10-16, 1956, Mercy Hospital Personnel Director, Marian J. Danek, wrote of the hospital's growth, changes, and accomplishments in its first 50 years. Following are excerpts as published in the *Post-Tribune*.

"There is a vast difference between the four frame residences that (originally) served as a hospital at Sixth and Carolina and the spacious, well ventilated, brightly lighted and completely equipped home of today. Classrooms, study halls and recreation rooms have been provided to give the students opportunity to seek perfection in their courses.

"Four graduates of St. Mary Mercy (Nursing) School gave their services to their country during World War I. The first year after the war found nursing conditions rather chaotic, owing to the devastating effects of the influenza epidemic and the usual post bellum conditions."

CHJC, University of Notre Dame Archives

HALF CENTURY OF SERVICE
Admiring the 50th anniversary symbol at a noon banquet at Mercy Hospital are (l-r): the Reverend J. Ambrose Newton, hospital chairman; Bishop Andrew G. Grutka of the Gary Diocese; and Hospital Administrator Sister Cornelia Leible, PHJC. The banquet, attended by approximately 170 people, was one of three separate events at the hospital as the Ancilla Domini Sisters commemorated 50 years of service at Mercy. Bishop Grutka officiated at a Pontifical High Mass prior to the banquet and was one of the banquet speakers along with Representative Ray J. Madden, D-Gary, and Gary Mayor John Visclosky.

CHJC, University of Notre Dame Archives

FROM THE PHJC CHRONICLES – OCTOBER 15, 1956

Beginning today there will be charges for Recovery Room services:

Routine – $5.00 for minors and children

Majors – $10.00

Special – $15.00 for those requiring special care

CHJC, University of Notre Dame Archives

A booklet published a few years after the 50th anniversary of St. Mary Mercy Hospital in Gary indicated hospital statistics of that time:

Patient Day Cost was $39.29

Highest Room Charge was $27.00

Average Daily Census was 278

Average Length of Stay was 6 days

A hospital staff of 590 employees consisted of 52 Administrative people, 139 Dietary, Household and Property, and 390 Professional Care of Patients. There were also 63 Student Nurses and 100 Student Practical Nurses.

THE GOLDEN JUBILEE DOLLS

When St. Mary Medical Center - Gary was sold in 1993, eleven Barbie dolls and one Allen doll (Ken's friend) were found packed away in a box on the top shelf of a closet in Kasper Hall. Each doll was dressed in the uniform appropriate for his/her position and area of work during the 1950s and 1960s. Although documentation is uncertain, it is said that the dolls were dressed and displayed as an exhibit at St. Mary Medical Center in celebration of the city of Gary's 50th anniversary celebration in 1956. "The doll wearing the blue top and blue cap signifies how unit secretaries dressed; yes, unit secretaries wore caps! The doll wearing pink stripes was, of course, a Candy Striper. When the Sisters worked their shifts as nurses they wore all white habits – also signifying their role as nurses. Otherwise the habits they usually wore were the colors of their order – perhaps black and white, brown and ivory, or navy blue and white."

Mary Jo Fisher, Director, Education Department

St. Mary Medical Center

(began in 1993 as Regional Educator – Gary, Hobart and East Chicago hospitals)

Changes in Office Nursing from 1956 Forward

Martha Nichols in 1956

Martha Nichols, RN, head nurse at Lake George Medical Center, began in Physician Practice in 1956. She offers here the significant comparisons of office nursing... then and now.

"I have been a nurse at Lake George Medical Center for over 52 years and have seen many changes in office nursing. When I started, the charge for an office call was $3.00 and an antibiotic injection was included if needed. My starting salary was $3.50 per hour so salaries as well as charges have greatly increased.

"Nurses were female and wore a crisp white uniform with a cap. Now they can wear almost anything and the cap is a thing of the past. Men now play an equal role in nursing.

"Nothing was disposable. We washed and sterilized gloves. The needles, glass syringes and all instruments were sterilized and reused. Gone are the days of mercury thermometers and mercury sphygmomanometers.

"Family practice doctors were called general practitioners and did everything including delivering babies, setting broken bones, and performing minor surgery. Now everything is specialized and patients are referred to a specialist.

"Doctors and sometimes the nurse made house calls. Now we have Home Health Nurses.

"We worked long hours – six days a week, evenings, and two hours on Sunday afternoon to accommodate the sick. We would see walk-in patients in the morning and take appointments in the afternoon and evening. Now everyone has to have an appointment and sometimes it is a few days before they can be seen.

"There was no hospital in Hobart and since we had evening hours we were often used as an Emergency Room. No one was turned away as we did not have to worry about being a provider for the insurance company. Actually there were only a few medical insurance companies. Blue Cross/Blue Shield was the most popular. Now there are many insurance companies that dictate the care of the patient.

"Office records were on 5" x 7" cards and very little documentation was done. Now the charts are much larger to accommodate the documentation of EVERYTHING.

"X-rays done in the office were read by the doctor since there was no radiologist available.

"There were no ultrasounds, CT scans or MRIs and blood tests were limited. Modern technology has aided the doctors in making diagnoses but has also raised the cost of healthcare.

"The fear of a lawsuit is more prevalent now making the doctor order some tests that might not be medically necessary but are needed to protect the doctor.

"Carbon paper and the mimeograph machine have been updated to a copy machine.

"The speed of obtaining information has been improved by the use of the fax machine and computers.

"The doctor has a choice of so many drugs that were not available years ago and now we have generic for some drugs that lower the cost of medicines.

"The health benefits now are so much greater than when I started."

1956 – CONSIDERING A HOBART HOSPITAL

"In the 1950s in Hobart, coming down on Highway 51, Mr. (John) Sapper would come out and wave to everybody to stop their cars while he had the cows going to the west pasture. Then in the evening, you would be stopped because he was taking the cows back home to the west pasture and barns. That was lots of fun.

"There was nothing there. They talked for many years about what they were going to build across the street here. We just never thought it was ever going to happen. Now look. The town just grew and grew. It is a very good area."

Helen Urban, HEALTH INFORMATION ANALYST
ST. MARY MEDICAL CENTER
(BEGAN IN 1976 IN HOBART)

"As a former mayor I served as a member of the board of the hospital. I was one of the volunteers who helped Paul Heuring collect signatures in support of the hospital. We were each given a packet and we would contact friends. We were told this was going to be a 100-bed unit and more or less an auxiliary hospital.

"When the hospital first opened, we were very excited about Labor and Delivery and the Emergency Room. If you went into labor and had some place to go immediately instead of driving six or seven miles, that was the big thing. There was no stigma on Gary. It was just the idea that we would have something very close."

Margaret Kuchta, MAYOR OF HOBART, 1988-1992
ST. MARY MEDICAL CENTER VOLUNTEER
LONGTIME HOBART RESIDENT, COMMUNITY ADVOCATE

Although the Hobart hospital wouldn't become a reality until 1973, local leaders began working as early as the 1950s on a hospital that was needed for the fast-growing south Lake County area.

In August, 1956, Paul Heuring, chairman of the Hobart Chamber of Commerce Hospital Community Committee, reported at a chamber luncheon about preliminary discussions for a hospital in Hobart. He had previously met with Secretary of the Lake County Medical Association John Twyman, Herman Pflughoeft, and C. R. Bjorklund, M.D. Martha O'Malley, M.D., head of the hospital division of the State of Indiana, had suggested to Twyman that a two-part state survey would be helpful whereby: 1) doctors and hospitals would fill out lengthy questionnaires relative to facilities and conditions and 2) business and civic organizations would be contacted for a study of size, kind and location for a hospital. This information would then be submitted to Dr. O'Malley for a final decision.

Hobart, at that time, was 14th on a list of approximately 50 cities in Indiana that had applied for consideration. A city approved for a hospital, it was said, could obtain one-third of the cost from the federal government after pledges or bonds for the other two-thirds were shown.

A local newspaper article (source unknown) said the matter of a hospital in the area had been "kicked around" for several years but additional information was needed to determine if surrounding towns would be interested in the project, especially given the crowded conditions of existing hospitals and the dire need for another facility.

"For years they talked about a hospital (in Hobart) and I think Mr. Paul Heuring kept fighting for it and somehow it all finally came about. Mrs. Dorothy Heuring was active with the Gary auxiliary group back then."

Mary Jaroscak
37-YEAR AUXILIARY MEMBER, HISTORIAN
MERCY HOSPITAL
(BEGAN IN 1972)

Marking Time...

1963
* On November 22, on a trip to Dallas, Texas, President John Fitzgerald Kennedy was assassinated. Vice President Lyndon Baines Johnson was immediately sworn in as president.

1965
* The Medicare and Medicaid programs were signed into law by President Lyndon B. Johnson as amendments to Social Security legislation (July 30).

1967
* The Chicago Blizzard of 1967 dumped a record 23 inches in Chicago and suburbs.

HOSPITAL/COMMUNITY HAPPENINGS

IT'S BEEN *Said* IN 2009...

"The Hobart Chamber of Commerce formed a committee called the Hospital Community Committee to try to get a hospital in Hobart sometime in the early 1960s. We really needed a closer hospital because when there was a real emergency it was a long way to the Gary hospital. The hospital fund-raising project was a long, long haul. Paul Heuring was chairman. I believe it became a separate committee from the Chamber at one point.

"Hobart has a lot to offer. We have an excellent school system. We have the uniqueness of a downtown with a lake in the middle of it. Our City Improvement Committee likes to think we have a great gathering at the band shell. When people come back in the summertime after they have moved away, they come on Thursday nights because they know they'll see their old neighbors or friends. That's kind of nice.

"(Additionally), a hospital is something that is needed as a foundation of a good community. The hospital has always been so cooperative with Hobart – with the City Improvement Committee, with city officials, and the Chamber of Commerce. It is just part of the family now. I think that was the missing part in Hobart at one point."

Virginia Curtis, LONGTIME HOBART COMMUNITY ADVOCATE/HISTORIAN

FROM THE PHJC CHRONICLES – JUNE 22, 1962

Sister Cornelia (Leible), PHJC, Sister Johannetta (Bergman), PHJC, Mr. Paul Bellendorf, and Mr. Joe Radigan went to the Motherhouse to discuss problems relating to the Booz-Allen recommendation, the acquisition of property for the new satellite. Forty acres were purchased at the corner of Route 51 and 61st Avenue. In order to be able to control the environment in the future, an adjoining tract was placed in trust.

CHJC, University of Notre Dame Archives

1962 – A LETTER FROM THE PROVINCIAL SUPERIOR

CONVENT ANCILLA DOMINI SISTERS

Donaldson, Indiana

Office of:
Provincial Superior

J. M. J.
November 19, 1962

Sister M. Cornelia
Administrator
St. Mary Mercy Hospital
Gary, Indiana

Dear Sister Cornelia,

Due to the apparent urgency and rapid development of additional hospital facilities in your immediate area and county, we find that it is now necessary for you to advise your Lay Advisory Board of the program intended by the Ancilla Domini Sisters for St. Mary Mercy Hospital and the area that it serves.

You are instructed to act in behalf of the Ancilla Domini Sisters at St. Mary Mercy Hospital towards the implementation of the following directives:

1. Bring the present hospital facility to a capacity necessary to adequately serve the patients in that area. This new addition should include not only bed capacity of approximately an additional 50 - 70 beds, but should also make provision for adequate X-Ray, Laboratory, Central Supply, Surgeries, Dietary, Recovery Room, Storage Facilities. Your new facilities should include a department of physical therapy, a gift shop and snack bar, and the remodeling of the present nursery to meet the standards as set down by the Indiana State Board of Health. Renovation of your current emergency room facilities are of paramount importance. Allocation of new beds for medical or surgical patients can be determined upon the conclusion of the Booz-Allen study.

2. Plan the construction of a 150 bed general, short stay, hospital with provisions for additional expansion in the Merrilliville-Hobart area. This construction to be undertaken by the year 1967. This plan has always met with the approval of the Bishop, and will certainly meet the needs of the people in that area. (In the past we have not felt the necessity or advisability to make our plans of this new hospital known, but feel that the Booz-Allen survey and study will need this information for consideration in our total program. It is our hope that the Booz-Allen consulting firm will work closely with you in the implementation of this program for the harmonious satisfaction of all.)

3. Future plans will also include the construction of a nurses' home and a college, which eventually would also lend itself to a degree program in nursing education.

Upon receiving the recommendations from the Booz-Allen firm you are authorized to retain an architect to start preliminary plans for the construction of a new hospital in the above-mentioned area.

We immediately recommend and authorize you to appoint a committee from the Mercy Hospital Lay Advisory Board to acquire an adequate hospital site for the construction of this new hospital. We have allocated the funds for the acquisition of this site and will assume that this matter will receive your prompt attention. Please keep this information confidential until after the acquisition of the new hospital site has been satisfactorily executed, for our experience has been that if information of this sort is made public, potential sites immediately increase in cost.

Other particulars of our intentions in your area are known to you, and may be discussed with your Lay Advisory Board and with Booz-Allen so that a solidification of our total program may be understood by these fine gentlemen.

Let me take this opportunity to advise you that Mother General will be in your area about the first of the year, and assume that preparations for her welcome and visit are underway. Am sure that your fine Lay Board would enjoy meeting Mother General, and hope that you can make arrangements accordingly.

May God assist you during this time of great decision and please ask your Sisters to remember us in their prayers.

In November 1962, St. Mary Mercy Hospital Administrator Sister Cornelia Leible, PHJC, received a letter from Mother Symphoria, PHJC, who was Provincial Superior at the time. Sister Cornelia was instructed to contact the Lay Advisory Board with upcoming plans. The plan was to increase the capacity of Mercy Hospital in Gary with the construction of a 150-bed general, short-stay hospital in the Merrillville-Hobart area. The letter is reproduced here. Lay Advisory Board members were Mr. Raymond Daly, Mr. Charles E. Daugherty, Judge Fred Egan, Mr. John Radigan, Mr. Joseph Radigan, Mr. Jack Taylor, and Mr. Eugene Swartz. Assistant hospital administrator was Paul C. Bellendorf.

CHJC, University of Notre Dame Archives

542820   **Warranty Deed**

This Indenture Witnesseth, That   BESS M. HAYWARD, an unmarried person,

STATE OF INDIANA SS.NO.
LAKE COUNTY
FILED FOR RECORD

1964 FEB 5   PM   BOOK **1257** PAGE **45**

of   Lake RAY BUTZ, RECORDER, in the State of   Indiana

Convey and Warrant to   ST. MARY MERCY HOSPITAL of GARY, INC.

of   Lake   County, in the State of . Indiana   , for and in consideration

of One Dollar and other good and valuable considerations --------- Dollars,
the receipt whereof is hereby acknowledged, the following described *Real Estate* in
Lake   County in the State of Indiana, to-wit:

DULY ENTERED
FOR TAXATION
FEB 26 1964

The Northeast Quarter of the Southeast Quarter of
Section 6, Township 35 North, Range 7 West of the
2nd P.M., in Lake County, Indiana.

The Grantee herein accepts this conveyance subject to the
following exceptions:

AUDITOR LAKE COUNTY

1.   Taxes for the year 1963 payable in 1964 and subsequent
thereto.

2.   Restrictions and limitations, if any, contained in original plat
and prior deeds.

3.   Easements of record, zoning ordinances, laws and amendments
thereto.

In Witness Whereof, The said   BESS M. HAYWARD, an unmarried person,

has hereunto set her   hand   and seal , this   31st   day of   January   1964.

Bess M. Hayward (Seal) _____ (Seal)

_____ (Seal) _____ (Seal)

_____ (Seal) _____ (Seal)

This instrument prepared by: Charles E. Daugherty, Attorney at Law, Gary National
Bank Building, Gary, Indiana.

STATE OF INDIANA, _____ Lake _____ COUNTY, SS:

Before me, the undersigned, a Notary Public, in and for said County and State, this _____ 31st
day of _____ January _____, A.D., 19 _64_, personally appeared the within named _____

_____ Bess M. Hayward, an unmarried person, _____

_____ Grantor _____ in the above conveyance, and acknowledged
the execution of the same to be _____ her _____ voluntary act and deed, for the uses and purposes herein mentioned.

IN WITNESS WHEREOF, I have hereunto subscribed my name and affixed my official seal.
My Commission expires Dec. 20, 1967   Albert F. Harrigan   Notary Public

Albert F. Harrigan

Shown here (at left) is the Warranty Deed in which Bess M. Hayward's land is transferred to St. Mary Mercy Hospital of Gary, Inc. in 1964.

BESS M. HAYWARD

1886-1976

It is said that Bess M. Hayward sold her farm in the 1960s for a fraction of its value so that the Hobart hospital committee could move forward with its plans. The farm, located at 61st and Route 51, is where St. Mary Medical Center stands today.

IT'S BEEN *Said* IN 2010... ~

"Beth Kaminski was the administrator of the hospital then and we had known Beth for many years. When the hospital was completed they hung an honorary picture and plaque about Bess Hayward and her family in the downstairs hospital hallway."

Bob Bailey
FORMER LONGTIME
HOBART BUSINESSMAN
NEPHEW-IN-LAW OF
BESS M. HAYWARD

Leaders struggled with a lot of planning and fund-raising until a breakthrough occurred (as reported in the 1993 Ancilla Systems Annual Report) when Bess M. Hayward, daughter of early Hobart settlers, permitted the system to acquire 85 acres of land near her home. Bess Hayward's father, George Hayward, was the founder of the Hayward Land Company which consisted of several farms in the Hobart area.

DID YOU KNOW?

They always said Bess's dad, "old George Hayward," used to grow corn and grain in order to feed more pigs and cows so that he had enough money to buy more land to grow grain to feed more cows and pigs. They had a farm at the corner of 53rd and Mississippi Street and I-65 ran through it and divided it.

IT'S BEEN *Said* IN 2010…

"While Bess, the last Hayward descendant, was blessed by what her family before her created, she also had her own strong sense of giving to her community. This is evidenced by the land where the hospital now stands as an important center of Hobart.

"An early committee began a search to find a suitable site for the hospital that was close enough to the then population of Hobart, had excellent road connections, and would be located where all of Hobart and the surrounding towns could benefit from such an institution. They discussed their vision with Bess Hayward since an excellent site that met all criteria was her land at the northwest corner of Rt. 51 and 61st.

"While this property was still productive farm land and might have been sold to another farmer or to one of the housing developers who had already begun to look for parcels for subdivisions that were not as well located, Aunt Bess gave her word that she would not sell to others until the hospital committee could present a proposal. Truth be told, Bess sold this farm for the hospital at a fraction of what others might have offered had they heard the farm was being considered for sale.

"Further, even her family wondered why she considered selling this main parcel across from her house. She replied that she had other farm land, enough money in the bank, and Hobart needed a hospital more than she needed this property. This is the Bess Hayward we loved."

Bob Bailey
FORMER LONGTIME HOBART BUSINESSMAN
NEPHEW-IN-LAW OF BESS M. HAYWARD

IT'S BEEN *Said* IN 2009…

"Bess M. Hayward is descended by the Sykes, Dorman, and Bailey families – all longtime Hobart residents. My wife Sarah was a Dorman and her mother Edith was a Sykes who married J. C. Dorman. The Sykes and Hayward families were double cousins. A brother and a sister married a brother and a sister. All our families are old Hobart families, but especially the Haywards and Sykes. There were a number of land grant farms in the family and we still manage one that goes back to 1855.

"Bess never married and lived with her sister and husband, Emily and William Elkins, in the large white home on the east side of Route 51 across from the hospital. The house, which still stands, was on a spacious parcel and the south lawn is where Karp's Feed Store is currently located. Later in life Bess sold the home and moved closer to Lake George. Independent her whole life, Bess was the first woman in Lake County to receive a driver's license.

"In the early days, the houses going down Route 51 weren't built and the Dorman side of the family had a golf course down there. Across from the golf course was where a number of doctors resided along with a man by the name of A. B. Keller who was the Treasurer of International Harvester Company. With the growth of Hobart, the hospital helped anchor some of the advancement of the city coming south on Route 51. St. Mary Medical Center isn't going anywhere. It has been a big addition."

Bob Bailey
FORMER LONGTIME HOBART BUSINESSMAN
NEPHEW-IN-LAW OF BESS M. HAYWARD

Exemplifying the Land and Its People

"I live right across the street from the hospital here. The Bracken family owned land all the way up to the ditch. We owned clear back to County K and up to Tenth Street. It was sold off piece by piece. Bess Hayward owned land here and on past ours and lived in the big white house closer to hospital. She was an only child and she was at the Brackens' a lot. She was a nice lady… She helped procure the land for the hospital. The Dormans are her cousins and they used to own as much as we did along South Lake Park and also did a lot toward the hospital.

"My husband, Howard Edward Bracken, III, loved that farm and loved to farm it. The hospital was ready to open when I moved out here and it was all vacant land – no retail shops, nothing. The farmers changed their fields every year because of the soil but eventually development came along with the hospital.

"To raise money, they had dinners. This was a little before my time but… it was nothing to whip up a dinner for 12 people. Everybody had a big dining room and a big kitchen, naturally. If anybody got sick… they took care of each other. It was nice to have a hospital nearby in case we needed it.

"How wonderful to have an A-rated hospital in Hobart, all due to many peoples' hard work."

Betty Jo Bracken
LONGTIME AUXILIARY MEMBER

SPOKEN LIKE A NATIVE
"I'm 86 years old and have had a lot of experiences. I… love Hobart. I'm not a native but we have lived here 59 years and I feel like this is my home.

"Crown Point and Hobart were settled about the same time, in the early 1800s, I believe. The government had opened up these lands to people who had served in the French-Indian Wars and the people were allowed to buy tracts of 640 acres at 25 cents an acre. They bought them directly from the government and the government had purchased the land from the Indians. I believe there were five or six Pottawatomie Indian tribes here.

"Up until 1940, we only had 5,000 people and then the 1950 census showed we had 10,000 people. Since then it has grown and the people have come in waves. In the early 1950s, quite a few people emigrated from Gary and… people had come back from the war. Today the population of Hobart is about 28,000."

Margaret Kuchta, MAYOR OF HOBART, 1988-1992
ST. MARY MEDICAL CENTER VOLUNTEER
LONGTIME HOBART RESIDENT, COMMUNITY ADVOCATE

Hobart was already growing in the 1960s, but the hospital was destined to make a positive impact when it opened in 1973. Farming in nearby areas remains evident.

Today, in 2010, fields of soy beans, a product of the last several years, can be found along 61st Avenue. People raised such things as oats, wheat and corn and at this writing the Sykes farm at 61st and Colorado has 200 acres of corn. With crop rotation, it may become 200 acres of beans in the following year.

In the early 1900s, there were no tractors and combines. The combines were steam combines. Teams of horses and single share plows helped manage the fields and farmers endured back-breaking work. Today farms are plowed and harvested with a big diesel tractor (with all the attachments) that in one pass can accomplish what it would have taken early farmers 30 passes to complete.

NEW HOBART HOSPITAL PLAN ANNOUNCED – MAY 12, 1965

200 Beds in Hobart
Nun Order Hospital Plan Told

HOBART—Plans were officially disclosed today for the new $6 to $9 million, 200-bed hospital to be constructed here.

Its name will be Queen of Peace Hospital.

NEW HOBART HOSPITAL PLAN IS ANNOUNCED

An article in the *Post-Tribune* in the spring of 1965 announced plans for a new 200-bed hospital in Hobart, Indiana. The name of the hospital, the *Post-Tribune* said, was to be Queen of Peace Hospital.

Reprinted by permission of the *Post-Tribune*, MAY 12, 1965
CHJC, University of Notre Dame Archives

This 1965 photo, with the gavel in the lower right corner, was most likely taken at Hobart City Hall. Hospital planners are: Top row (l-r) Richard Black, manager, Gary National Bank, Hobart Branch; Mrs. O'olah Evans, city clerk-treasurer; L. J. "Red" Titus, mayor, city of Hobart; Reverend John Schaeffer, pastor, St. Bridgets Church, Hobart; Paul Heuring, Heuring Motors, Hobart; John Mahoney, president, Hobart Chamber of Commerce; "Pete" Harrigan, Harrigan Real Estate, Hobart; and William Herbert, First Federal, Hobart. Seated (l-r): Sister Milburg, PHJC, director of hospitals, Ancilla Domini Sisters; Sister Cornelia Leible, PHJC, administrator, St. Mary Mercy Hospital.

1965 – QUEEN OF PEACE

When it was thought that the new hospital in Hobart would be called Queen of Peace, Miss Myra Hunter, director of public relations for Saint Mary Mercy Hospital, wrote to the Queen of Peace Hospital in New Prague, Minnesota in search of a reproduction of the Blessed Mother under the title of "Queen of Peace." Although the title never materialized, this page and the following page include correspondence in the spring of 1965 with discussion of the image of the Queen of Peace.

Prior to the opening of St. Mary Medical Center in 1973, for a time the hospital was to be called Queen of Peace. The billboard that stood on the corner of the hospital lot – then surrounded by open corn fields – reflected that title.
Photo courtesy of Virginia Curtis, former editor of *Hobart Herald*

April 14, 1965

Sister Mary Margaret, O.S.B.
Administrator
Queen of Peace Hospital
New Prague, Minnesota

Dear Sister Mary Margaret,

We have been searching for a reproduction of Our Blessed Mother under the title "Queen of Peace" and so far have been unsuccessful.

Since your hospital is under her patronage using this title, we wonder if you might be of assistance to us.

If you have any publication, letterhead or any printed material which would show us how Mary appears as "Queen of Peace" we would be most grateful to receive it.

Thank you for your assistance!

Most gratefully,

Miss Myra Hunter
Director, Public Relations

Hunter sent a letter of inquiry in April, 1965 to Sister Mary Margaret, O.S.B., administrator of Queen of Peace Hospital in New Prague, Minnesota
CHJC, University of Notre Dame Archives

April 22, 1965

Miss Myra Hunter
Director Public Relations
Saint Mary Mercy Hospital
540 Tyler Street
Gary, Indiana

Dear Miss Hunter,

I received your letter in regard to a reproduction of
Our Blessed Mother under the title of "Queen of Peace"
and I regret that we do not have any publication,
letterhead or any material which would be suitable or
would meet your needs.

A year or so ago I did write to a Monastery in the East,
I believe it was a Benedictine Monastery but they did
not have any brochures or material that would be suitable.
I checked the file and am unable to locate the name of
the Monastery. Possibly the Catholic Directory would be
of some help to you. I do know that there is a hospital
in California as "Our Lady of Peace."

If you do find something suitable, would you please send
me a sample or any information you may have on "Queen of
Peace?"

Thank you so much.

Sincerely yours,

Sister Mary Margaret, OSB
Administrator

Sister Mary Margaret, O.S.B., responded a week later.
CHJC, University of Notre Dame Archives

April 22, 1965

Dear Mother Symphoria:

Will you please look this over and give us your opinion and
return to us at once. We prefer the picture of the small statue
but with her hands like the drawing without the crown. This is
the only picture we have and would like it back with your personal opinion. Thank you.

Sister M. Cornelia

Dear Sister Cornelia,

It would seem to me that if you use the title QUEEN then the
crown would be almost a necessity. It would not necessarily have to
be the crown as you have it but a coronet of some kind as queens
naturally wear indicating that they are queens.

I suppose a crown or no crown would be a personal thing.

I like the drawing as you have it.

Veyy kind greetings.

Mother M. Symphoria, P.H.J.C.

Maybe the hands could be extended to WELCOME the sick similar
as in the statue that they have in a chapel at Dernbach"!!!!!

Saint Mary Mercy Hospital Administrator Sister Cornelia conferred with
Mother Provincial, Mother M. Symphoria, PHJC, of Donaldson, Indiana,
in April of 1965 about the image of the Queen of Peace.
CHJC, University of Notre Dame Archives

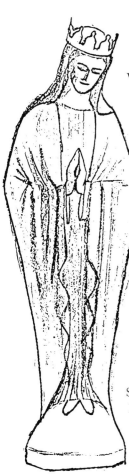

A *Post-Tribune* article of May 12, 1965 said, "Plans were officially disclosed today for the new $6 to $9 million, 200-bed hospital, to be constructed (in Hobart). Its name will be Queen of Peace Hospital." The announcement, which coincided with National Hospital Day, was made by Sister Milburg, director of hospitals for the PHJC Sisters.

The hospital was to be situated in the northwest quadrant of 61st Avenue and Indiana 51 on the south edge of Hobart. The building was to be on 85 acres already owned by the Poor Handmaids of Jesus Christ.

During that same time:

- No immediate plans had been made for a fund drive but officials said it would be necessary.
- It was estimated that construction would take two years.
- Plans for the 200-bed hospital included provisions for a 100-bed increase.
- An estimated 700 new hospital positions would become available with a payroll of $2 million annually.
- Simultaneously, Methodist Hospital announced plans for a 120-bed in Lake County.
- Indiana's State Board of Health, in 1963 and 1964 reports, stated that Lake County was in need of more than 1,000 new and replacement hospital beds.

"Queen of Peace Hospital will in no way replace the present St. Mary Mercy Hospital in Gary," Bishop Andrew Grutka of the Gary Diocese said in the *Post-Tribune* publicity. "We have been assured the current plans for modernization of St. Mary Mercy Hospital will continue so that both might provide the best facilities and highest quality of care."

Saint Mary Mercy Hospital Administrator Sister Cornelia Leible, PHJC, conferred with Mother Provincial, Mother Symphoria, PHJC, of Donaldson, Indiana, in April of 1965 about the image of the Queen of Peace.
CHJC, University of Notre Dame Archives

THE POOR HANDMAIDS OF JESUS CHRIST-CELEBRATING 50 YEARS

In August 1963, the Poor Handmaids of Jesus Christ celebrated their half-century of presence at Gary's well-known Catholic-supported hospital that had rendered care for approximately 469,000 patients and the births of 76,500 babies since 1913. The peak year for births totaled 4,001 infants in 1956.

One of the Sisters spoke of the modern conveniences they had in contrast to the pioneer Sisters who endured extreme poverty, hardships, and poor working conditions when the hospital was first established – grateful that perseverance had led them to decades of success.

FROM THE PHJC CHRONICLES – AUGUST 20, 1963

It was the Commemoration of the Fifty Years of service of the Poor Handmaids of Jesus Christ in Gary. The day was anticipated because of the return to Rome of our Bishop Andrew Grutka.

The festivity consisted of a Solemn Pontifical High Mass offered by the bishop. The Capuchin Choir from Saint Mary's Seminary, Crown Point, sang. Invited guests: The priests of the Gary Deanery, about 60 in number; the mayor and other notables of Gary; the honorable Congressman Ray Madden, the Lay Advisory Board; the Medical Executive Board; the former presidents of Saint Mary Mercy Medical Staff; the administrators and assistants of the Lake County hospitals; two Poor Handmaids Sisters from the missions in neighboring areas; PHJC Sisters from the out of town areas.

CHJC, University of
Notre Dame Archives

THE GARY CLINIC

IT'S BEEN *Said* IN 2010...

"There were about 30 doctors who opened the Gary Clinic in 1965. It was an outpatient clinic with all the capabilities of an X-ray Department, Emergency Room, offices for different specialties. It was already open when I came there in 1967. It was very popular and it was located in an ideal place at 61st and Broadway. It was a great idea for many patients who came from Crown Point, Schererville, Lowell – they came from all over and they didn't need to go all the way to Gary, Indiana.

"We saw patients who didn't have the means to cover their medical insurance, people who were unemployed.

"The clinic didn't close for a long time. In fact, one of the general surgeons and a group of physicians in our group decided to open one of the first nursing homes located in Gary. The person who started it was a very good, outstanding General Surgeon, Dr. Seymour Shapiro."

Jose H. Roig, M.D., OPHTHALMOLOGIST, RETIRED
MERCY HOSPITAL
(BEGAN IN 1967 IN GARY)

IT'S BEEN *Said* IN 2010...

"When I was in practice, I started with Dr. Oscar Almquist. We got along great because I'm part Swedish and he was Swedish. Then, the Ross Clinic opened and I was one of the founding members of the Ross Clinic. At one time, we had 31 doctors at that clinic. It served the people in Merrillville, of course, and the surrounding areas of Gary and Hobart. We had an Emergency Room and a laboratory and X-ray. It was really a tremendous thing at the time."

William J. Glover, M.D., GENERAL SURGEON, RETIRED
MERCY HOSPITAL
(BEGAN IN APPROXIMATELY 1947 IN GARY)

With Beginnnigs in Gary
Imaging Services in Doumanian's Day

It's been *Said* in 2009...

"We had a lot of doctors who gave talks on cancer and different things. In fact, one doctor, Dr. (Santiago) Lopez, gave a talk on cancer and during that time I contracted cancer. I was very knowledgeable about him and he was a dynamic doctor.

"I felt secure because I could always ask Dr. Heratch Doumanian for a referral for my daughter because she was born with scoliosis. Dr. Aram Semerdijan was a help then. My supervisor, Dr. Richard Marks, was excellent too. They all came to my rescue when I needed them."

Jamesetta Meadows, Stenographer, Retired
Mercy Hospital
(began in 1967 in Gary)

It's been *Said* in 2009...

"After I finished medical school at the American University of Beirut, I wanted to have a specialty that covered all of medicine and I realized radiology was one of them – you have to know everything from head down to toe… New technology kept me busy, active, and it was very challenging."

Heratch Doumanian, M.D., Radiologist, retired
Mercy Hospital
(began in 1967 in Gary)

> "Dr. Doumanian in radiology – quite brilliant, well liked, well respected."
>
> *Mike Adler*
> Former Director of Public Relations
> Mercy Hospital
> (began in 1977, Gary and Hobart)

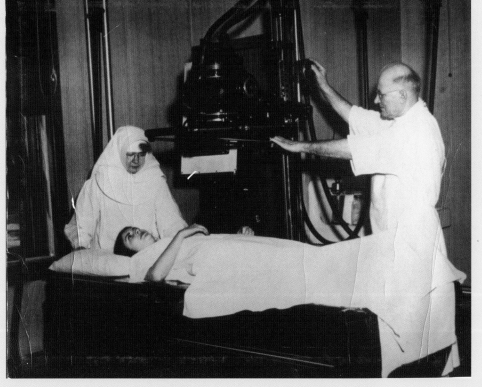

This photo, published in the *Post-Tribune* in 1982 said in its caption: "Pioneer radiologic technologists, Sister Willibalda Heidt, PHJC, left, and Joseph Meich, technologist at right, worked with 'modern' X-ray equipment in the early 1940s. Today, such equipment may be found only in museums and has been replaced with sophisticated high technology, much of it utilizing computers."

Retired Radiologist Heratch Doumanian, M.D. said, "This is an old General Electric machine of the 1930s that was still in operation in 1967."
Reprinted by permission of the
Post-Tribune, 1982

"Joe Meich had a very interesting history. During the first World War, he was a medic in the German army and before the war he worked with Wilhelm Conrad Roentgen (1845-1923) in his lab so he had first-class knowledge of Dr. Roentgen, the inventor of radiology."

Heratch Doumanian, M.D., RADIOLOGIST, RETIRED
MERCY HOSPITAL
(BEGAN IN 1967 IN GARY)

"The unique part of this time was a man by the name of Mr. Joe Meich. Mr. Meich lived across the street from the hospital and he was my neighbor down on Tyler Street for as long as I could remember. Mr. Meich explained to us that as a youngster he used to turn the crank on the generator that would generate electricity while Wilhelm Conrad Roentgen was working on the development of X-ray. He was a very kind man – probably 70 years old at the time and was still working."

Bruce Lovell, X-RAY TECHNOLOGIST | MERCY HOSPITAL | (BEGAN IN 1963 IN GARY)

DID YOU KNOW?

German physicist Wilhelm Conrad Roentgen (1845 – 1923) discovered X-rays in 1895 but did not understand at first what they were. In science and math, X refers to an unknown. By the end of the decade hospitals had put X-rays to use, taking pictures (called radiographs) of bones and internal organs and tissues to help diagnose illnesses and injuries. Using the new technology, doctors could "see" the insides of a patient. In 1901, Roentgen received the first Nobel Prize in physics for his discovery of X-rays.

"I remember in 1963 when I was a student in radiology, I attended an educational meeting at the Gary campus and we were touring their department. Somehow, I ended up in the basement where I was shown some old chest X-ray images on sheets of glass. I had read about images being taken on glass plates but had never seen any. They had hundreds of them stored there. X-ray film had been in use for years already."

David Padilla, DIRECTOR, CARDIOLOGY SERVICES NON-INVASIVE
ST. CATHERINE HOSPITAL
(BEGAN AT MERCY HOSPITAL IN THE EARLY 1970S)

"The office clerks are the same. We don't have stenography now because they are separate from us. Back then, we had our own three stenographers but two were always here always at one time. One was Rose Camacho and another was Jamesetta Meadows. From what I understand, Ms. Meadows was a fast typist. One day when she threw that carriage it just went completely off the typewriter and that story was told often. Jamesetta Meadows was a transcriptionist from Gary and then she came to Hobart to type before she retired."

Beverly Armenta, COORDINATOR, RADIOLOGY SUPPORT
MERCY HOSPITAL
(BEGAN IN 1972 IN GARY)

"… We were very active in angiography. Methodist did not do any so we used to get all the referrals. At our peak early in the 1970s, we did over 350 procedures in that lab every year.

"We began doing cardiac catheterization in a converted fluoroscopy room in the X-ray Department. The first cardiac catheterization, coronary heart was done in that lab in the early 1970s."

Heratch Doumanian, M.D., RADIOLOGIST, RETIRED
MERCY HOSPITAL
(BEGAN IN 1967 IN GARY)

This 1969 radiology photo shows Rosa Camacho (standing) next to the cardvayer filing system where patient information was typed on cards. Elaine Karpus is seated by a push-button keys typewriter.

"Dennis Gumbert was a great boss. He was the one who asked me to come here with him from Gary because he was being moved over here from Gary."

Beverly Armenta, COORDINATOR RADIOLOGY SUPPORT
MERCY HOSPITAL
(BEGAN IN 1972 IN GARY)

THAT FAMILY FEELING

"We were… a big family because a lot of the people (had) worked… in Gary for a good while. We had a little aide there, Mary Vranka. She worked across the street at Holy Angels Cathedral. She cleaned the church and she always set up the altar for the priest. She was very religious and she cooked for the nuns in the convent. She also was a radiology technologist. We don't know if she ever really got her certificate or she was just trained. She called all the females Susie. She was the nicest little lady. She worked for hours on end. We didn't have computers at the time, mind you, so we were still typing on the typewriters with the carriages. She logged a lot of statistics of the department by hand, and she was very respected by everybody in the hospital. She is deceased now."

Beverly Armenta, COORDINATOR RADIOLOGY SUPPORT
MERCY HOSPITAL
(BEGAN IN 1972 IN GARY)

"X-ray was very primitive in comparison to what it is now. The first big change I saw was the process of developing our X-rays. We used to have dryers large enough to line up the X-rays on hangers down the hall where they would dry. There was a dark room technician by the name of Sylvia Pavlos.

"(Very dramatic in our) productivity around the late 1960s was the introduction of an automatic film processor, the X-o-mat. It was by Kodak and consisted of a developer, fixer, and drying process. You would put the film in inside the dark room and it came out on the other end as developed, processed film. ("We named the X-o-mat Heidi. One of the gals knew that Heidi was Sister Willibalda's name from home.)

Bruce Lovell

"Everything is computerized now. It wasn't like that in those days. We had to measure each X-ray patient with a caliper. We had a technique chart… You had to sit down, even if you had to take your shoes off to do the math.

"The techniques were changing so you had to really be on your toes. It was… a professional setting. The radiologist in the 1960s was Dr. Vincent Galante… there with a sub-associate by the name of Dr. Robert Miller."

Bruce Lovell, X-RAY TECHNOLOGIST | MERCY HOSPITAL | (BEGAN IN 1963 IN GARY)

DID YOU KNOW?

In 1981, St. Mary Medical Center purchased an $850,000 computerized tomographic (CT) Scanner that was housed - and pampered in - a 45-foot long, eight-foot high semi-trailer to be used between the two St. Mary hospitals in Gary and Hobart. Hospital officials believed it would provide patients with the latest diagnostic equipment and would save the hospitals $800,000 by not having to purchase a second permanently — installed scanner.

THE MOBILE SCANNER

The St. Mary Medical Center mobile CT scanner weighed 48,000 pounds. A sophisticated suspension system prevented the equipment from being damaged during 13-mile trips between the Gary and Hobart hospitals.
Hobart Gazette, JUNE, 1981

THE MILLIONTH SCAN

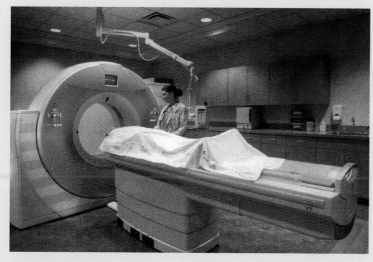

Shown here is the Siemens SOMATOM Definition™ AS Scanner, a 64-slice CT system considered to be the fastest, most adaptive technology currently available. It enables staff members at both Community Hospital and St. Mary Medical Center to perform virtually any type of CT examination imaginable. It also features one of the industry's largest gantry openings that provides a wide open space for examinations and the ability to accommodate a variety of body types.

Vim & Vigor, FALL 2009

Pictured here scanning a patient's head in 1995 is CT Technician Dawn Wood performing the one-millionth scan of the GE Medical Systems CT scanner. St. Mary Medical Center spokesman Dennis Gumbert described the machine as "special" – designed to take head-to-toe pictures of the inside of patients' bodies.
Reprinted by permission of the *Post-Tribune,* JUNE 22, 1995

• THEN AND NOW

IMAGING SERVICES... CONTINUING IN HOBART

Contributed by Debra Phillips, Supervisor

IT'S BEEN *Said* IN 2009...

A WORD FROM THE NEUROLOGIST

"In neurology, there have been huge improvements in the last 20 years and it comes from advancements with imaging and electrodiagnostics. We can do things we never could do before and we can make decisions now based on solid information.

"It's still wonderful that as a neurologist I can pretty much go into a room with a flashlight and a pin and a hammer and usually figure out to within a quarter of an inch where the problem is in the nervous system but to have the backup, to have a real solid way of knowing that you're right or wrong makes a huge difference.

"We have the transcranial ultrasound. We have wonderful ultrasonographers and now we've just recently started with the ability to do 24-hour longterm EEGs in the Intensive Care Unit where lots of people end up having subclinical seizures that we never knew about before. Now we can find those things. These are all things that are sort of coming along as well as some of the biggest centers you'll ever see."

Mark Simaga, M.D., NEUROLOGIST
ST. MARY MEDICAL CENTER
(BEGAN IN 1997 IN HOBART)

The Imaging Department at St Mary's in Hobart has been an ever-changing area. When we first opened in the early 1970s, we were a three-room department with three people who worked days and had a call system for midnights. We were located on the first floor where the surgery department is now. Since then, we have moved and redesigned the work area multiple times. Today (in 2009), we are a department of more than 60 imaging employees in all areas of expertise with nine diagnostic rooms just at our Hobart location that include X-ray, CAT scan, ultrasound and MRI. We also have expanded our services into Portage and Winfield at hospital-owned clinics.

We also have a beautiful new Women's Center next door (just off 61st Avenue in the Center for Imaging and Radiation Oncology) that gives same-day results. In the past, a patient would go to a tiny room at the end of the X-ray hallway, have her mammogram and wait for the doctor to call with results — sometimes days or even until her next appointment if everything was negative.

Of course back then there was no CT or MRI – just diagnostic X-ray in which we set manual techniques and ran film through wet processors. On an average day, two radiologists would do all the exams and read films. This could easily include various angiograms of the neck and/or legs. Except for a heart catheterization performed in the catheterization lab, all other specials were performed right in the X-ray Department Special Procedure Room.

As imaging advanced in the early 1980s, we acquired our first CT scanner and the Diagnostic Outpatient Center began doing our MRI examinations. Our patients went next door to our Center for Imaging and Radiation Oncology (CIRO) by ambulance until May 2009 when we completed the new special imaging wing of which we are so proud.

For more than 30 years, we have seen the computer replace our Cardex, the PACS (digital computer picture archiving) replace our hard films as well as a tremendous amount of paperwork with almost a paperless workflow now. We all feel blessed to have been a part of this amazing growth and to be able to serve the patients in our community.

SHOWN (L-R) at the Imaging Building Grand Opening/Ribbon Cutting event are Pete Dyba, director, Imaging Services; Mike Marocchi, supervisor, Special Imaging; Jayesh Thakrar, M.D., chairman of Radiology; and Janice L. Ryba, St. Mary Medical Center CEO and administrator. The opening of the new center included the most advanced CT, MRI and ultrasound technology available.

IT'S BEEN *Said* IN 2009...

"In our imaging area, we serviced a patient who had been driven to the hospital by a family member for service with an approximate timeline of when that service would be completed. It was completed sooner than expected. The patient was quite ill, didn't feel well, and was waiting for a ride home. Our staff member drove the patient home so she would be in a more comfortable environment."

Janice L. Ryba
CEO AND ADMINISTRATOR
ST. MARY MEDICAL CENTER
(BEGAN IN 1984 AT COMMUNITY HOSPITAL)

"Promise only what you can deliver. Then deliver more than you promise."

~ UNKNOWN

TRANSCRIPTION DEPARTMENT STAFF PHOTO – 2009
BACK ROW (L-R): Shelly Swert, Shannon Liesch, Amy Mangold,
Lori O'Neal, Joseph Danton, and Supervisor Jil Cannon
SEATED (L-R): Diane Reed, Rosa Camacho, and Anka Karna

With Beginnings in Gary • THEN AND NOW

TRANSCRIPTION DEPARTMENT...

*Contributed by LeeAnn Shea, Regional Manager
and Jil Cannon, Supervisor*

The Transcription Department, which dates back to St. Mary Mercy Hospital in Gary sometime before the mid-1960s, is responsible for transcribing reports dictated by the physicians. Historically, it has been part of the Medical Records cost center with supervisors serving in management roles.

In 2001, however, when Community Healthcare System was formed to include three hospitals under one organization, the Transcription Department became its own cost center with its own independent management team. Since then, employees of the Transcription Department have reported to directors with Kim Seitzinger serving as the first regional manager of the department.

Electric typewriters were used in the early days – comprised of a small, letter-imprinted ball that bounced around as you typed. Dictation was received from the physicians via hard-wired dictation stations on the nursing units and in Medical Records.

In the mid-1970s, a new dictation system included large tapes that recorded directly into the Transcription Department. Doctors began to dictate from outside the hospital.

In 1978, we finally went "high-tech" when the first word processors were delivered to the department. For the first time, we were able to return to our previous typed reports, make minor modifications, and reprint the report. Previously, one change from a physician meant the entire report had to be retyped.

In 1985, in an effort to centralize transcription, all but one of the transcriptionists was moved from the Gary facility to Hobart. Recordings at that time were completed on small cassette tapes and the majority of them were sent to Hobart to be typed. In 1986, transcriptionists were hired for the Gary facility and separate departments were once again established at both facilities.

The year 1992 brought a second effort to centralize and transcriptionists from St. Mary Medical Center in Hobart and St. Catherine Hospital in East Chicago were all located with the transcriptionists in Gary. Ramona Fissinger was the transcription supervisor at that time.

In 1993, the hospital was sold to Northwest Family Hospital and St. Catherine Hospital and St. Mary Medical Center transcriptionists were moved back to Hobart on the 4th floor of the Medical Arts Building. Jinny Davis was the transcription supervisor from 1993 to 1994 and Jil Cannon has been transcription supervisor since 1995. Finally, in 1998, the St. Catherine Hospital transcriptionists were moved back to East Chicago and the Transcription Department established two separate locations.

With the implementation of Meditech in 1996, we were able to print the reports directly to the floor, and it was the transcriptionist's responsibility to know where to send the final report. We no longer had to physically take reports to the nursing units and place them on the charts every few hours. The implementation of the Fusion Text/Dolbey system in 2006 increased the automation of our reports and included the ability to fax reports to physicians.

We have slowly acquired transcribing responsibilities for other areas within the hospital – the lab in 1996 and radiology in 1997.

Imagine! We now have physicians who can dictate from anywhere in the world as long as they have access to a phone. In March 2010, we established eScription in our department. This application is known as back-end speech recognition where the dictating physician does not need to do anything differently but the transcriptionist is presented with the text that the computer interprets from the dictation, thereby changing our role from transcriptionist to editor.

The Transcription Department is proud to be a conduit of communication in the all-important field of healthcare. Our job is one of great challenge, great change, and also great rewards.

Seated in the Hobart Health Information Management Department in 1989 is Jil Cannon, shown doing transcription on the department's first computer, a word processor that used five-inch floppy discs to function.

IT'S BEEN *Said* IN 2009...

"History and physicals were and always will be the priority of any Transcription Department. It was no different in the early 1970s, especially when it came to the pre-operative history and physical reports early in the morning. The Transcription Department opened at 7:00 a.m. and Cheryl Anderson and I worked that shift together every day for over 13 years in Gary. Margaret Hazinski was the supervisor and Mrs. Alice Nedoff was the director of Medical Records during those years."

Jil Cannon, SUPERVISOR
TRANSCRIPTION DEPARTMENT
MERCY HOSPITAL | (BEGAN IN 1973 IN GARY)

"Start by doing what's necessary; then do what's impossible; and suddenly you are doing the impossible."
~ST. FRANCIS OF ASSISI

1967 – Paul C. Bellendorf – First Lay CEO of Mercy Hospital

Paul C. Bellendorf became the first lay CEO of Mercy Hospital in 1967. He would serve in that capacity until 1973. He is shown here with his predecessor, Sister Cornelia Leible, PHJC, as they discuss the duties of his appointment.

Reprinted by permission of the *Post-Tribune*, June 11, 1967

It's been *Said* in 2009...

"Paul Bellendorf was a real gem. He had such a warm heart and he did so much for them. I remember him very well. He was one of the best administrators."

Sister Sharon Schaefer, PHJC, RN, retired
Donaldson, Indiana
(Worked at Mercy Hospital, Gary, in the 1960s)

It's been *Said* in 2010...

"I was born in Gary. I was there the day Hobart opened because I lived in Hobart. There were a lot of people around – press coverage – and… an open house at the hospital. Paul Bellendorf was the chief executive then – and very attentive. Anybody could walk into his office and he would say, 'Come right in.' He was a very gracious man. I knew him very well."

William J. Glover, MD., General Surgeon, retired
Mercy Hospital
(began in approximately 1947 in Gary)

It's been *Said* in 2009...

"When I arrived at Mercy Hospital in 1967 as assistant administrator, Sister Cornelia (Leible), PHJC, was leaving. She was the administrator and the superior at the time. Mr. Paul Bellendorf was her associate administrator and he became the first lay administrator in our PHJC hospitals. Mother Theodolinda, PHJC, was assigned as our superior and Sister Odillia, PHJC, was appointed to the assistant administrator position."

Sister Wilma Boeving, PHJC
Associate Administrator, retired
Mercy Hospital
(began in 1967 in Gary)

When it Snowed

"There was a tremendous snow storm in 1967. At that… time we still lived on the west side of Gary and the two hospitals were separated by six blocks. No one could get to the hospital other than plowing physically through the snow and it lasted for days. I remember that I had four (grade-school-aged) children and they all managed to make their way to Mercy Hospital to help feed the patients. Maybe that was the first time they developed an interest. One became a nurse and two are doctors. The other one is a defense attorney in health issues."

John T. Scully, MD.
INTERNIST, RETIRED
MERCY HOSPITAL
(BEGAN IN 1955 IN GARY)

"We had such committed students (in the School of Medical Technology) and they were so conscientious. They were really committed to helping out. If there was a snow storm and somebody couldn't get in, they would volunteer to work a couple of hours, which they didn't have to do. They were really wonderful young people. I have to say that they're lifelong friends."

Sue Demitroulas
BUSINESS ANALYST, IT DEPARTMENT
MERCY HOSPITAL
(BEGAN IN 1967 IN GARY)

1967 – Joining the Hospital Staff
PHJC Sisters Theodolinda Rauf and Wilma Boeving

Mercy Bee

St. Mary Mercy Hospital - 540 Tyler Street, Gary, Indiana

| Volume 111 | July - 1967 | Number 6 |

Sisters Assigned to Mercy

SISTER M. THEODOLINDA ASSIGNED AS RELIGIOUS SUPERIOR OF SISTERS

SISTER M. WILMA NAMED ADMINISTRATIVE ASSISTANT

On Wednesday, June 22, Sister Theodolinda, P.H.J.C., joined the Mercy staff as Religious Superior for the Sisters assigned to the hospital.

Monday, June 26th brought the second of our recent additions to St. Mary Mercy, in the person of Sister Mary Wilma. Sister Wilma has been assigned to St. Mary Mercy as Administrative Assistant to Mr. Bellendorf, Administrator.

Mercy Bee, JULY, 1967

1968

Hospital/Community Happenings

It's been *Said* in 2009...

"Having the hospital in Hobart means they don't have to go to downtown Gary. That sounds cold but that's the truth. That was the reason why the people here in Hobart wanted this hospital for so long.

"It was as though all of a sudden there was a big bundle of decay put in the city of Gary and the storefronts were empty. The dress shops were gone, the bridal shops were gone, and we didn't have Gordon's Department Store or Sears or Goldblatt's. The other thing I recall about Gary had to do with the mills. When we worked midnights and the mills were active, the sky was always so lit up and if there was a strike the sky was so dark. The strikes had a definite impact on patients and the amount of patients that came in. Insurance didn't pay; people didn't come in."

Shirley Makivich Urbanek, R.N., RETIRED
St. Mary Mercy Hospital
(began in 1959 in Gary)

1968 – Breaking Ground for Mercy's New Hospital Wing

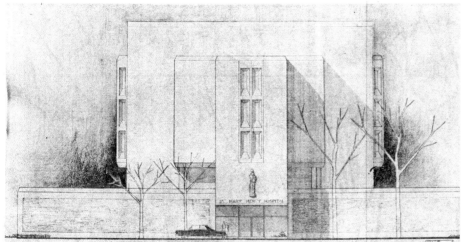

This rendering shows the 180-foot expanse of the front of the Mercy Hospital expansion. When completed, it was said to "rank among the nation's most complete and modern." The front faced the west on a driveway from Sixth Avenue leading to a parking lot along Fillmore Street. The new five-floor, air-conditioned building extended 200 feet to a connection with the existing building that faced Tyler Street. The upper floors provided for approximately 135 additional beds, bringing the hospital's medical-surgical bed capacity to approximately 440. The lobby and foyer housed the admitting office and a gift shop. There also was a new chapel, expanded surgery, Emergency Department, laboratory, recovery room and ancillary facilities. Plans were prepared by the Gary architectural firm of Hall-Kane Associates.

On Thursday, August 15, 1968, a groundbreaking ceremony was held at Mercy Hospital for the new wing that would be completed in 1972. Gold-painted shovels were used to dig up the first spadefuls of dirt. Lay Advisory President Charles E. Daugherty said: "This groundbreaking is the first phase in a program to which the board is committed – to remodel and expand Mercy's existing facilities and in the spring of 1970 to break ground for another hospital in the Hobart area."
Shown at the ceremony are (l-r): Lay Advisory President Charles Daugherty, Gary Mayor Richard Hatcher, Bishop Andrew G. Grutka, John T. Scully, M.D., Sister Cornelia Leible, PHJC, and
Sister Joann Schafer, PHJC.
From the Donaldson, Indiana Archives

Marking Time...

1968
- Gamma knife was used in patients.
- On April 4 Martin Luther King Jr. was assassinated in Memphis, Tennessee, inciting riots in many cities.

1969
- Richard M. Nixon was inaugurated as 37th President of the United States.
- On July 20 astronaut Neil Armstrong, commander of the Apollo 11 mission, became the first human to set foot on the moon.

- The Woodstock rock music festival was held near Bethel, New York (August 15-19).

DID YOU KNOW?

The entire roster of the Lay Advisory Board of St. Mary Mercy Hospital in 1968 included Charles E. Daugherty, Raymond E. Daly, Judge Fred A. Egan, Matthew Glogowski, Mrs. Ann Gregory, John Hill, George A. Jedanoff, Orval J. Kincaid, Matthew J. McAnary, Joseph P. Radigan, John Radigan, Sr., Jack T. Snyder, Eugene H. Swartz, and C. Darrow Tully.

Relay Bulletin, Association of Ancilla Domini Hospitals
CHJC, University of Notre Dame Archives

IT'S BEEN *Said* IN 2009...

"Our Lay Advisory Board, with Mr. Charles Daugherty as president, gave countless hours… Much thanks is due to them for their dedication to the Gary and Hobart programs."

Sister Wilma Boeving, PHJC
ASSOCIATE ADMINISTRATOR, RETIRED
MERCY HOSPITAL
(BEGAN IN 1967 IN GARY)

1968 – THE GARY CHAPEL

BEFORE THE CHAPEL WAS RAZED
Shown here is the St. Mary's Hospital chapel
– Gary, Indiana
CHJC, University of Notre Dame Archives

Interior of the chapel – St. Mary's Mercy Hospital
Calumet Regional Archives, IU Northwest

In early summer, 1968, to make way for the new hospital building, demolition began on the chapel, existing buildings, and houses on Fillmore Street.

In the summer of 1968, this area was once a four-apartment structure that stood on Fillmore Street north of West Sixth Avenue. A quick demolition rendered it ready for the multi-million dollar rebuilding and expansion program for Mercy Hospital.
Reprinted by permission of the *Post-Tribune*, MAY 5, 1968

This aerial photo shows the ruins of the Mercy Hospital chapel when it was razed to make room for the addition of new treatment facilities. The expansion and modernization was partially financed through funds from the Gary Joint Hospital Fund Drive.
Reprinted by permission of the *Post-Tribune*, JUNE 17, 1968

1968 – MERCY AND METHODIST HOSPITALS JOINT FUND DRIVE

J. C. Johnson (seated left), president of the Methodist Hospital Board of Trustees and Sister Cornelia, PHJC, Sister superior at Mercy Hospital, are pictured signing the agreement that would result in Gary's first joint hospital fund-raising effort. Standing with them (l-r) are Clarence Goris and Herschel Davis of the Methodist Hospital board and Charles Daugherty and Frederick Dudderar of the Mercy Hospital Lay Advisory Board.

St. Mary Medical Center Auxilliary Archives

Tell Hospital Bed Shortage

Patient Jam At Mercy, Methodist

The *Post-Tribune* headline of Friday, March 5, 1965 publicized a critical hospital bed shortage. The story further said, "Scores of seriously ill persons cannot be admitted to Gary's two hospitals because of an acute lack of hospital beds. One qualified source said the bed shortage is the worst he has ever known it to be at the two hospitals. Administrators at both hospitals stated that their facilities are jammed to capacity and waiting lists have been set up for future admissions. At Mercy Hospital, a few beds had to be temporarily placed in the hallway to await the discharge of someone from a hospital room."

Reprinted by permission of the *Post-Tribune*, MARCH 5, 1965
CHJC, University of Notre Dame Archives

IT'S BEEN *Said* IN 2009...

"The biggest medical issue in Gary was the incredible inadequacy of hospital beds in many areas. The unfortunate situation was that the funding of the two hospitals (Mercy and Methodist) was totally inadequate.

"Interestingly, the largest employer in the area was U.S. Steel. At that time, they had 35,000 employees and with a lot of hard work by many, many people we worked out a joint hospital fund drive, arranged strictly on the basis that we got matching funds with U.S. Steel.

"For many years, at least from the time that I got there in the mid-1950s, Mercy in Gary had a ward on the first floor – an open ward – that was kept for U.S. Steel. Rooms were always kept available for admissions for U.S. Steel accident cases. They always had these beds available. At no time did the hospital ever get any compensation from U.S. Steel.

"We got the Joint Fund Drive going with great difficulty... but we got good cooperation from U.S. Steel and both Gary hospitals got some badly needed beds."

John T. Scully, M.D., INTERNIST, RETIRED | MERCY HOSPITAL | (BEGAN IN 1955 IN GARY)

A *Post-Tribune* editorial of February 4, 1967 said the agreement of the boards of Methodist and Mercy hospitals to partner in a fund drive to meet the city's hospital needs "is probably the most important decision taken for Gary's future in several decades. The need was so obvious it cried for action."

"The sorest need," the editorial further said, "is to bring the two existent hospitals up to the standards a city of this size deserves both by expansion of beds and modernization of facilities."

Looking ahead, however, the total community could not ignore continued growth in the suburbs and both hospitals had announced plans to build satellite facilities in the future – Methodist in the Merrillville/Crown Point area and Mercy in the Hobart area.

IT'S BEEN *Said* IN 2009...

"After a very successful fund drive for Gary and the Hobart satellite hospital in 1968, the West Wing in Gary was added and the planning for the satellite hospital in Hobart went in high gear with a (very large) budget."

John T. Scully, M.D.
INTERNIST, RETIRED
MERCY HOSPITAL
(BEGAN IN 1955 IN GARY)

The Gary Joint Hospital Fund Drive that began in September of 1966 culminated with a total of $5,137,000 to be divided equally between Mercy and Methodist hospitals. The Mercy Hospital groundbreaking ceremony, held August 15, 1968, signified Mercy Hospital's intent to add 134,000 square feet of space to the hospital's general facility, according to Mercy Hospital Administrator Paul C. Bellendorf. The new five-story structure would house the majority of principle operations and provide 132 medical-surgical beds by 1970 if construction needs were met.

A St. Mary Mercy Hospital *Mercy Bee* publication of September, 1968, noted that three contracts had been awarded for the project: Calumet Construction Company of Hammond was low bidder at $569,000 for general construction; Dedelow, Inc., was low bidder at $64,525 for the plumbing contract; and Hyre Electric of Highland was low bidder at $10,000 for the electrical contract.

1968 – School of Nursing Closes at St. Mary Mercy

As chronicled in the Poor Handmaids of Jesus Christ *Relay Bulletin* in March of 1968, a notice appeared entitled, "Provincial Council approves closing of St. Mary Mercy School of Nursing."

Committee meetings resulted in the recommendation of the Corporate Board of Ancilla Domini Sisters to report at its meeting of March 2, 1968. Resolved: That Saint Mary Mercy Hospital, the president of the board of directors, administrator and superior of the Sisters be advised of the approval to close the school of nursing, and to work out an adequate solution for placing the students in the freshman and junior year.

The committee had reported to Mother Clarice that because of small enrollment, difficulty of obtaining faculty, difficulty of retaining graduates, and the availability of collegiate program in the area, St. Mary's Mercy School of Nursing would be closed with the graduation of the current class.

CHJC, University of Notre Dame Archives

Nuclear Medicine

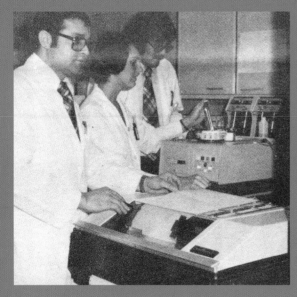

Computers programmed to perform certain blood tests on blood serum became an invaluable arm for technologists in the chemistry section of the medical laboratories. Shown here in 1976 is Domenico Lazzaro, M.D. (left), as he reads printouts. Cindy Brito, M.T. (ASCP), chief chemistry technologist in Gary and Robert Beyer, M.T., (ASCP) assistant supervisor in Hobart, load a deck of samples into the analyzer.

Acts of Mercy, August 1976

IT'S BEEN *Said* IN 2009...

"When we were developing and expanding our Nuclear Medicine Department at St. Mary's in Gary, we were working late hours to set up the new equipment – until nine or ten o'clock almost every night of the week. I was supervisor at the time and to break up the tension of working so late, technician Bob Graves and I decided to have wheelchair races from one end of the hallway where nuclear medicine was located all the way down to radiology at the opposite end. So he and I raced and then we would turn around and come all the way back. One evening, Sister Judian Breitenbach, PHJC, spotted us and pulled me aside. She told me rather sternly that the races were not to be conducted in the hospital even though no one was around. Then, about to smile, she asked me who won!

"Sister Judian (Breitenbach) and I have been longtime friends and I think the world of her. She is a great lady."

Milt Triana, Retired Hospital Administrator
St. Mary Medical Center
Special Projects Coordinator, Community Healthcare System
(began in 1969 in Gary)

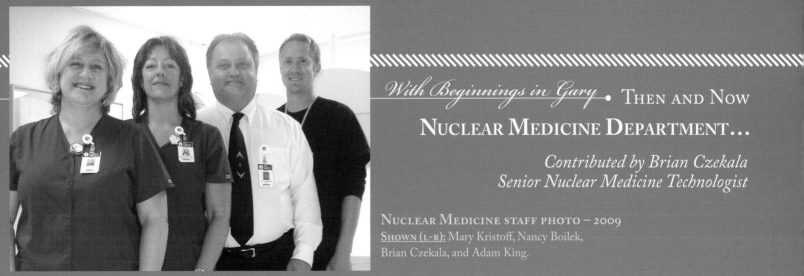

Contributed by Brian Czekala
Senior Nuclear Medicine Technologist

NUCLEAR MEDICINE STAFF PHOTO — 2009
SHOWN (L-R): Mary Kristoff, Nancy Boilek,
Brian Czekala, and Adam King.

St. Mary's Nuclear Medicine Department had its beginnings in Gary, Indiana prior to the evolution of the Hobart campus. The year was 1968 when the department was started by Director of Pathology Earl Mason, Ph.D., M.D., and Manager Milton Triana. The first type of imaging device developed for nuclear medicine was the rectilinear scanner and two of them were purchased for the department. There were only a few radiopharmaceuticals to choose from to evaluate pathological processes and images were produced on a piece of paper. The department volumes were small with only two or three procedures done per day although each procedure took two or three hours to perform.

In 1972 came the advent of the scintillation camera and Pelayo Cabrera, M.D., became the new medical director. A Siemens Searle camera was purchased which reduced imaging time, produced images on film which had exceptional resolution compared to the rectilinear images, and made imaging a simpler process for the technologist. Department volumes increased with the help of Milt Triana's marketing strategies. Dr. Cabrera produced a book that explained the value of nuclear medicine to the clinical outcomes of patients. It showed normal and abnormal lung, brain, thyroid, bone and liver images side-by-side with an explanation and display of the pathological processes. Dr. Cabrera also took nuclear medicine to "Grand Rounds" in an attempt to promote the modality. The department's efforts were successful as the business grew and evening hours were added.

The Nuclear Medicine Department at the Hobart campus was started in 1975 under the direction of Earl Mason, Ph.D., M.D., and Manager Mary Ann Swann. The first camera purchased was a single head Picker camera system. Later, the department added a bone density unit, which at that time was a procedure performed in nuclear medicine due to the images being produced by a gadolinium source and a computer that analyzed the data. In 1990, the department expanded under Ken Vanderhye who was named manager of both Nuclear Medicine departments at the Gary and Hobart campuses. A new camera system was purchased – a Siemens orbiter with a computer that enabled images to be processed. When Nuclear Medicine was remodeled in 1994, the department gained more square footage for the arrival of a new technology, multi-headed cameras, faster computers, and color images. Under the leadership of Amarjit Kochar, M.D., the Picker Prism 3000 was purchased. This was a triple-headed camera and the first of its kind in Northwest Indiana that provided the ability to produce SPECT imaging. In 1995, a dual-headed camera followed – a Picker Prism 2000 – and the department had grown to a three-camera operation.

In 1999, Jaime J. Cebedo, M.D., was named director of radiology when the department was switched from being under the auspices of pathology to that of radiology. In 2000, Brian Czekala became Senior Nuclear Medicine Technologist and saw the last single-headed camera leave the department to be replaced by the Philips Axis dual-headed system. All of the computer systems on each of the existing cameras were also upgraded with the newest software to analyze images. The arduous task of paperwork – tracking radiopharmaceuticals, radioactive sources, and patients – was simplified by acquiring a computer system, Syntrac, to make the task paperless. Then in 2005, the department became filmless and paperless with the purchase of the PACS system. The last piece of equipment added was the Siemens Symbia camera in 2008 with state-of-the-art technology and the ability to be upgraded to fusion SPECT/CT imaging. The system can image patients up to 500 pounds and perform every facet of nuclear medicine. Patients can even watch their favorite DVD while their scan is performed.

The Department of Nuclear Medicine has grown over the years from the archaic rectilinear imaging systems to the high technological age of multi-headed cameras with high-speed computer systems. The labor intensive jobs of filming and paper filing have been replaced by PACS systems. These changes have created a modality that has flourished with many new radiopharmaceuticals that can diagnose disease at the cellular level detecting small changes in the metabolism of the human body. Under the direction of the Medical Director of Radiology, Jayesh Thakrar, M.D., the newest addition in 2009 to the specialty will be a PET/CT system – a highly sensitive tool that is able to pinpoint the location of cancer in the body so the physician can make treatment recommendations. All this technology would be nothing without the dedicated technologists who greet our patients with a smile and warm words and provide them with excellent care.

IT'S BEEN *Said* IN 2009...

LOOKING INTO EDUCATION

"When I started in Gary in 1965, there was no Education Department. Around 1970, Mary Gulyassy was director of the nursing school. She is deceased now. She developed an Education Department. The School of Nursing had closed in 1968 and she took some of the instructors from there. They were all we had. We had Lois Murray who did more of the nursing education and Ruth Sutherland organized programs for some of the ancillary departments like medical records and the lab."

Judy Elieff, DIABETES EDUCATOR, RETIRED
MERCY HOSPITAL
(BEGAN IN 1965 IN GARY)

With Beginnings in Gary • THEN AND NOW

EDUCATION DEPARTMENT...

Contributed by Mary Jo Fisher, MS, APRN, BC,
Director
and Deborah Krejci
Manager, System and Regulatory Management

EDUCATION DEPARTMENT STAFF PHOTO – 2009
<u>PICTURED (L-R):</u> Lisa Poradzisz, diabetes instructor; Rosa Gregorczyk, RN Clinician; Director Mary Jo Fisher; and Etta Weatherspoon, RN, MS, clinician.

While the Department of Education started from the closing of the School of Nursing, Mary Gulyassy must have been a visionary to cover the hospital house-wide. In those days, educational departments were devoted to nurses and their needs.

Approximately 20 years ago, it was realized that all employees needed education as nurses were not the only professionals and hospitals could not afford to have educators in every department. The Department of Education became more far-reaching, serving all staff education needs.

IT'S BEEN *Said* IN 2009...

"Education is and has always been important in nursing. We are constantly learning because medicine is always changing! New drugs, old drugs that are used in different ways, new medical devices, and new patient care protocols are always being developed. We, as nurses, must keep up with the changes. Our Education Department provides us with the tools we need by providing written material, hands-on experience, and competency testing to make sure we know the who, what, when, where and why of our job."

Jen Somers, RN
CLINICAL NURSE LEADER, ICU/CCU
ST. MARY MEDICAL CENTER
(BEGAN IN 1991 IN HOBART)

MARY GULYASSY

"The director of the School of Nursing (in 1945), when I first started working in the nursing office, was Sister Vitalis (Witt), PHJC. They closed the nursing school in 1968. Then I was transferred to the Department of Education in Gary. It was headed by Mary Gulyassy who had been director of the School of Nursing and then went into the Department of Education. She was made director of the Education Department by Mercy Hospital Administrator Paul Bellendorf. She later became associate administrator of the hospital.

"After they formed the hospital in Hobart, she was associate administrator there and I was her secretary. I retired at the end of 1989."

Mary Ellen Donovan
SECRETARY TO THE DIRECTOR
ST. MARY'S MERCY SCHOOL OF NURSING
(BEGAN IN 1945 IN GARY)

"Mrs. Mary Gulyassy was an (associate) hospital administrator. She was a wonderful person who took an interest in all the employees. She would roam the hospital and come up and talk with people. She wasn't there to criticize. She was there to support you."

Jen Somers, R.N
CLINICAL NURSE LEADER, ICU/CCU
ST. MARY MEDICAL CENTER
(BEGAN IN 1991 IN HOBART)

Deborah Krejci, currently manager of system and regulatory management, took a position in staff education in 1989 under then Director Marianne Erdelac. Marianne was a graduate of one of the first graduating classes of Masters prepared Clinical Nurse Specialists. It was under her leadership that we became accredited to offer continuing education for nurses in Indiana. At that time, education services worked for both the Gary and Hobart facilities. We were the first sponsoring hospital of the American Heart Association for Advanced Cardiac Life Support courses and the first hospital to offer Pediatric Life Support in Northwest Indiana. She implemented a community First Aid course that was extremely popular with the community.

Marianne, a tireless worker, computerized all the policies for the hospital – as the only employed nurse at the time who knew how to use a computer – and elevated the caliber of nursing education at St. Mary Medical Center to a degree that had not been implemented previously. While Marianne eventually took a position in Colorado to be near family, a well established standard of excellence continues with the Education Department.

"Education is simply the soul of a society as it passes from one generation to another."

~ GILBERT KEITH CHESTERTON

HOSPITAL/COMMUNITY HAPPENINGS

Pictured here are the Ancilla Domini Sisters, sponsors of the new St. Mary Medical Center. Shown (l-r) are Sisters Martine Tenholder, Vivian Brand, Symphonia Mueller, Clarice Van Hoedt, Kathleen Quinn (in back), Antonita Altmix, Anna Marie Piontkowski, and Cornelia Leible.

Great Lakes Regional Bulletin, Hospital Building and Equipment (HBE) News, JANUARY, 1972

DID YOU KNOW?

In August 1971, an Employee Fund Drive, with a goal of $75,000, was launched for St. Mary Mercy Hospital Southeast in Hobart, Indiana.

SISTER AQUINATA THEILMANN, PHJC, RETIRES

Attending a 1971 testimonial dinner in honor of Sister Aquinata Theilmann's retirement from St. Mary Medical Center Gary/Hobart are members of the administrative staff: (l-r) Mr. Paul Bellendorf, administrator; Sister Wilma Boeving, PHJC, associate administrator; Mary Gulyassy, director of Department of Education; Sister Judian Breitenbach, PHJC, assistant administrator – nursing; unknown; Sister Aquinata Theilmann, PHJC; Mr. Jack Burton, director of planning and development; Mr. William E. Pauley, director of materials management; Betty Brinzo, administrative assistant; Mr. Dominic J. Bay, director of public relations; and Mr. Howard Jack, director of personnel.

St. Mary Medical Center Auxiliary Archives

Marking Time...1970

- *A powerful new immunosuppressive drug was discovered in a mold from a soil sample collected in Norway. This new drug, called cyclosporin A, eventually revolutionized transplant surgery.*

- *DNA fingerprinting was developed.*
- *Ultrasound technology became commercially available.*

How it happened in the 1970s

A GOOD MOVE

"Dr. Mayur Desai – he goes by Shreyas Desai – is on staff here at the hospital. We started an office together. We did not have money so we went to a place in Evanston and got some furniture. The furniture was not delivered but... I remember it was the 26th of September, 1977, at 11 o'clock and a patient came in. I said to him, 'Believe it or not, I am a doctor. I don't have my certification displayed but I am a doctor.' I told the patient we could schedule an appointment or I could take him to the Emergency Room where I could check him. By that time, a truck pulled in. They asked for Dr. Dave and Dr. Desai. Here was our furniture. Dr. Desai and I opened the boxes, put the examination table together, and examined him. That's a true story."

Vijay Dave, M.D., CARDIOLOGIST | MERCY HOSPITAL | (BEGAN IN 1977 IN GARY)

The Elevator

"In the late 1970s, the Gary hospital had an elevator operator who would close the elevator gate and get you to your floor. The elevator operation was a little tricky since you would need to adjust the level of the elevator with the floor before you could get off."

Charlotte Barber, LIS SPECIALIST
ST. MARY MEDICAL CENTER | (BEGAN IN 1977 IN GARY)

"We had an elevator on the first floor – a good old gate elevator with an elevator operator named Olga. I don't remember her last name. She would stop at all the floors and pull the gate open with a lever. When she wasn't there, we had to control it ourselves and we got used to that. Our department was right off the main hospital entrance on Tyler Street.

"When surgery built a new wing on the first floor, the prior surgery area on the fifth floor became storage for different departments. We used to go up there every day to get old files. They would actually leave the windows open because they had the air cut off from that part of the hospital because it was just for storage. I would look up and there would be a pigeon on one of the file cabinets. They would just be flying around."

Beverly Armenta, COORDINATOR
RADIOLOGY SUPPORT, RADIOLOGY
MERCY HOSPITAL
(BEGAN IN 1972 IN GARY)

1973 – Administration Changes at Mercy Hospital

Upon the resignation in 1973 of Paul Bellendorf who had served as hospital administrator for the Gary and Hobart Mercy hospitals, Paul R. Kaiser was appointed the new administrator of both hospital sites. The announcement, made by Board of Directors President, Sister Martine Tenholder, PHJC, also stated that Kaiser had been associated with the Ancilla Domini hospitals since 1954.

Acts of Mercy, Vol. 9, No. 6 – June, 1973

Acts of Mercy

Vol. 9, No. 6   ST. MARY MERCY HOSPITAL, Gary and Hobart,

Paul C. Bellendorf leaves Mercy for new challenges

Hospital welcomes Paul R. Kaiser as new Administrator

Board of Directors
President,
Sister Martine
Tenholder, PHJC
*Great Lakes Regional
Bulletin, Hospital
Building and Equipment
(HBE) News,* JANUARY, 1972

Paul C. Bellendorf

Paul R. Kaiser

TEAMING UP FOR SPORTS

CORPORATE OLYMPICS

IT'S BEEN *Said* IN 2009...

"Lakeshore Health System participated in the Corporate Olympics where the local hospitals in the area would compete. St. Mary Medical Center won second place in a dance we did in the late 1980s – maybe 1988. There were seven or eight of us and we were called the Lakeshore Jammers. Laverne Stidman, a St. Mary employee, was one of the dancers and was real upbeat and I just loved his enthusiasm."

Sharon Forszt, FORMER ADMINISTRATIVE ASSISTANT TO CEO
ST. MARY MEDICAL CENTER
(BEGAN IN 1975 AT ST. CATHERINE HOSPITAL)

IT'S BEEN *Said* IN 2009...

"One thing… that brought all the associates together was the Corporate Olympics back in the 1990s. It was a competitive event with area hospitals, and a happy time for everyone who competed in several sports. It was sponsored by the Wellness Council of Northwest Indiana. At that time, all three hospitals were under (the umbrella of) Lakeshore Health System. Our teams were comprised of associates from St. Mary in Gary and Hobart and St. Catherine in East Chicago. In the end, our team, Lakeshore, won first place in the participation walk and second place in cheerleading and the basketball shoot-out. Some of the areas of competition were swimming, basketball, running, biking, walking, volleyball and the T-shirt competitions."

Debra Jenkins, REGIONAL ASSISTANT OF MISSION EFFECTIVENESS
ST. MARY MEDICAL CENTER | (BEGAN IN 1985 IN GARY)

Hospital Athletes

"Our laboratory staff remembers the days when we had bowling leagues and softball teams. We had great times with employees from other departments and it also strengthened the team bond."

Jackie Juskevice LEAD RECORDS CLERK
MERCY HOSPITAL
(BEGAN IN 1966 IN GARY)

Exercising Friendships through Bowling

"We had a volleyball team for a while and Judy Carter and I started a bowling league. Each hospital had its own league and we bowled for years and we traveled with people who are still my friends today."

Judy Candiano, REVENUE CYCLE CONTROL SUPERVISOR, PATIENT ACCOUNTING
MERCY HOSPITAL
(BEGAN IN 1969 IN GARY)

Final Standings and Captains:

	Team		Captain
1.	Team	10	John Palm
2.	Team	1	Mike Taylor
3.	Team	5	Jim Wade
4.	Team	12	Jim Vargas
5.	Team	2	Dave Bavenie
6.	Team	8	Jerry Ribar
7.	Team	9	Priscilla Gates
8.	Team	3	Robert Sims
9.	Team	7	Tom Jettirs
10.	Team	4	Pat Woodfork
11.	Team	11	Sandy Quandt
12.	Team	6	Chuck Hartman
High average men			Jack Burton 174
High average women			Judy Carter 169

High Game — Men
1st	Emil Ciochina	245
2nd	Robert Sims	234
3rd	Jim Kursch	233

High Game — Women
1st	Priscilla Gates	225
2nd	Betty Mosely	214
3rd	Ethel Sims	199

High Series — Men
1st	Jack Burton	636
2nd	John Palm	595
3rd	Bill Gorman	564

High Series — Women
1st	Judy Carter	576
2nd	Mary Pajor	519
3rd	Sand Flores	495

The League

Among the St. Mary Mercy Mixed Bowling Leagues that existed for a number of years, the 1972-1973 season included an awards banquet at the Merrillville Holiday Inn. Posted here are team results and captains. Officers for the 1973-1974 season were Jack Burton, president; Carl Sharp, vice president; and John Palm, treasurer. *Acts of Mercy*, Vol. 9, No. 6 – June, 1973

"One of the events that made working at the hospital very memorable and from which many friendships developed was the hospital bowling league that Pat Nescak and I organized. We had personnel from various departments participating, including several doctors. To this day some are my best friends who now participate in a golf outing each year – namely Pat Nescak, Jennie Purcell, Colette Lewandowski, Peggy Kamysz, Marie Czarnecki and Annie Soto."

Vickie Sohovich, RN
EMERGENCY ROOM STAFF NURSE
MERCY HOSPITAL
(BEGAN IN 1953 IN GARY)

In 1975, at the Ancilla Domini Hospitals' two-day bowling tournament in Des Plaines, Illinois, Millie Samardzija and Betty Mosley placed first in the doubles competition. In regular team events, St. Mary Gary placed fourth and St. Mary Hobart placed seventh. In the singles competition Walter Sala, M.D., placed third.

1975
FRONT ROW (L-R): Gary hospital bowling team members
Emil Ciochina and Danny Briscocho
BACK ROW (L-R): Hattie Rose, Betty Mosley, and Alice Gildon

1975
FRONT ROW (L-R): Hobart hospital team members
Walter Sala, M.D., and Arnie Cieslak
BACK ROW (L-R): Vickie Sohovich, Mrs. Arnie Cieslak
(spectator), Judy Candiano, and Millie Samardzija.

Pictured (l-r) are Irene Pacheco and
Norma Pierce, bowling enthusiasts,
participated in the 1981 State Bowling
Tournament in South Bend and won.

1981
St. Mary Medical Center bowling team members included Norma Pierce, Annie Soto,
Irene Pacheco, Nancy Shackleford and Pat Nescak. (Other team members included
Marie Czarnecki, Kathy Dubach and Monita Puckett.)

BASKETBALL

IT'S BEEN *Said* IN 2009...

"One time in 1985, we had a basketball game between St. Mary Gary and St. Mary Hobart at Griffith High School. Any employee could play. I don't know who organized it, but it was fun competition."

Lucy Rodriguez
CASH CONTROL CLERK, PATIENT ACCOUNTING
ST. MARY MEDICAL CENTER
(BEGAN IN 1977 IN GARY)

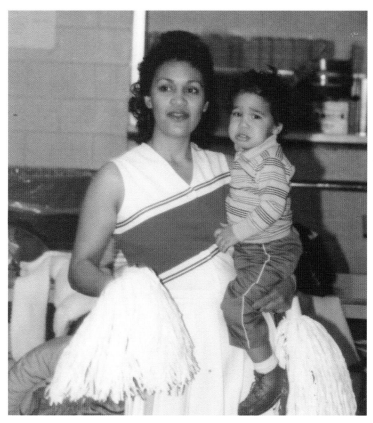

Pictured here, in 1985, is Lucy Rodriguez with her two-year-old son, Jonathan Rodriguez. A one-time basketball game between St. Mary-Gary and St. Mary-Hobart was initiated by the employees. St. Mary-Gary won.

Nancy Van Horn (top row, second from left) organized a group of volunteer cheerleaders for the Gary-Hobart hospital basketball game in 1985.

Shelley Richter, ward clerk, (holding the ball) led the Hourly Women's Basketball Team (SMMC – Hobart) to victory and the title of Female Hospital Basketball Champions in 1980.

In 1980, The Hourly Men's Basketball Team (SMMC – Gary) earned the title of Male Hospital Basketball Champions and declared, "We're #1."

Tennis Anyone?

"For 25 years, beginning in the late 1970s, I was in charge of the annual Inter-Hospital Tennis Tournament among members of the Medical Staff of St. Mary Medical Center (Mercy Hospital), the Methodist Hospitals, and St. Anthony Hospital... I enjoyed organizing this sports activity not only because of the camaraderie and sportsmanship issue but also because the administrators and/or CEOs of the hospitals were able to participate and sponsor this annual event. It was nice to see the CEO and administrator playing together, competing with each other in a friendly manner. I remember playing with Paul Kaiser, John Dandridge, (Jr.), John Betjeman, Joseph Mark, Larry Mangold, Tony Durso and the giving of awards by Beth Kaminski and Milt Triana."

Rodolfo L. Jao, M.D., FIDSA
INTERNAL MEDICINE/INTERNIST
SPECIALTY IN INFECTIOUS DISEASES
MERCY HOSPITAL
(BEGAN IN 1973 IN GARY)

Visiting the tennis courts while attending a continuing medical education conference in Scottsdale, Arizona in the 1990s were (L-R) Rodolfo Jao, M.D., Mrs. Atassi, Joseph Mark, and Bassem Atassi, M.D.

Winners of the first tennis tournament held in 1978 were:
FRONT ROW (L-R): Robert J. Bills, M.D.; T. Huang, M.D.; Rodolfo Jao, M.D.; Robert Wylie, M.D.; M. Veluz, M.D.
BACK ROW (L-R): Paul and Avril Kaiser; Mrs. Veluz; Mrs. Robert Wylie; Dr. and Mrs. Paul Yocum, Jr.

Also attending a continuing medical education conference in Scottsdale, Arizona in the 1990s were (l-r) Karen Burniston, Beth Kaminski, John Birdzell and Rob Bergin.

IDs, Recognition and Pins – In Mercy Hospital's Day

Shown here are employee indentification cards from the early days. Deleted from the cards are social security numbers but notably, in the early days, social security numbers were printed on each card.

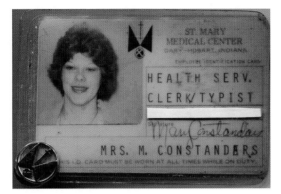

Mary Constandars

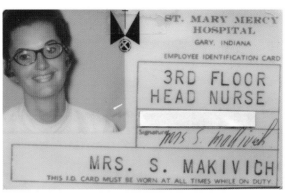

Shirley Makivich Urbanek

Jo Puchowski Toigo

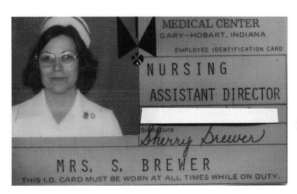

Sherry Brewer

It's been *Said* in 2009...

"I married right before I started at St. Mary's so I was Puchowski then. I hired in for a five-week internship in transcription. Margaret Hazinski, supervisor of medical records, told me their stenographer, which is what they were called then, was moving out of state and there would be a position available. Sure enough, she called in a couple of weeks.

"Margaret Hazinski reported to Mrs. Alice Nedoff. I am a loyalist to St. Mary's. It started with Mrs. Nedoff and the people who mentored me raised me professionally. Mrs. Nedoff was a business woman... One of her phrases that I remember her telling me is, 'Jo, if you don't use your head, you're gonna use your feet. You've got to be prepared and think it through.' She was always right. She would say down-to-earth things like, 'When you girls go to meetings, you should at least have clear nail polish on. You want to represent yourself well when you're in a group. There's nothing wrong with that. It's inexpensive and quick.' She took it to that level of caring about us. She was very loyal to the company and made us feel the same way, even to this day. I learned a lot."

Jo Toigo, RHIT, CCS
Director, Health Information Management
St. Mary Medical Center
(began in 1980 in Gary)

Recognition
Shown here is a recognition pin given to a hospital employee for completing five years of employment. The pin was issued in 1979.

"I CARE"
The "I CARE" pin was distributed among employees at St. Mary Medical Center in Gary around the late 1980s. It signified the special care that employees administered to patients.

SECURITY DEPARTMENT STAFF PHOTO – 2009
<u>TOP ROW (L-R):</u> Walter Thomas, Stephen Duran, Dain Allande, Theodore Robinson, Robert Zimmerman, and Brian Rodriguez.
<u>BOTTOM ROW (L-R):</u> Cynthia Pate, Ted Walsh, Aaron Milevsky, Christina Lohman, Robert Smith, and Emilio Rodriguez.

With Beginnings in Gary • THEN AND NOW

SECURITY DEPARTMENT...

Contributed by Edward Fralinger
former Security Officer

Shown here in 1976, Paul Piazza (seated), security section shift supervisor at St. Mary Hospital in Gary, keeps a close watch on six closed-circuit television monitors hooked up to several indoor/outdoor cameras on the hospital grounds. Andrew Skinta, (standing) hospital security chief, said the system helped "nip several potential incidents in the bud."
Reprinted by permission of the *Post-Tribune,* SEPTEMBER 22, 1976

The Security Department was established in 1970 by Andrew Skinta who was a retired police captain from the Gary police department. In January of 1971, Ed Fralinger joined Andy Skinta and Walter Lowe in Gary until Andy received permission from Mr. Paul Bellendorf to increase the number of security officers to six. Over time, the security force was expanded further. Then in 1973, St. Mary opened its satellite hospital in Hobart. In July 1990, security was restructured and until 2006 was provided by security agencies under contract with St. Mary Medical Center in Gary and Hobart. On July 1, 2006, St. Mary Medical Center hired its own staff of security officers. Since that time, the security has been in-house, continuously changing to meet the needs of the hospital.

Security is a challenge in a large facility like the Hobart hospital. St. Mary Medical Center has approximately 250,000 people pass through its doors annually. Employees enter the hospital at several entrances and must wear regulatory employee badges.

Although it is relatively new, the in-house Security Department has more officers who are available for better physical coverage of the facility. The hospital has one of the most state-of-the-art camera systems in the county. The new system helps cover other areas of the hospital and also helps local law enforcement. Two vehicles now patrol the hospital grounds and parking lots. Notably, with a significant decrease in the number of officer turn-overs, the overall efficiency of the Security Department has improved. Patients and loved ones come to the hospital in a time of need. We are proud to be here to help the process run more smoothly, efficiently and safely.

Knowing Your Hospital Codes

Hospitals maintain a list of safety codes, often voiced on the intercom system to signal in-house needs.

"They put a camera up on the outside of the building sometime in the early 1970s. I think we had one on top of the old north end and if you zoomed in you could see the steel mills. You could scan and see the north parking lot and the east parking lot which used to be old houses until they were destroyed. Eventually, they put a place for dialysis on the corner of Sixth and Tyler."

Ed Fralinger
COMMUNICATIONS OPERATOR
MERCY HOSPITAL, (FORMER SECURITY OFFICER)
(BEGAN IN 1971 IN GARY)

"Ten years from now, I actually think the hospital will be bigger. Who knows? We may even get more floors. We're packed and you can hear the code purple all the time (for more beds needed). I know we have new hospitals going up out east of us in Valparaiso and Chesterton, but I think we're going to be bigger and better."

Dee Bedella
COORDINATOR, SLEEP LAB/COMMUNITY LIAISON
ST. MARY MEDICAL CENTER
(BEGAN IN 1988 IN HOBART)

"The Sisters had a small convent in Kasper Hall. My office was on the first floor of Kasper Hall and to get to the elevator where the convent was located on the third and fourth floors, you had to pass my office. So I got to know the Sisters very well; there were only about eight or nine of them in all.

"You know there were codes; code red is fire and code yellow was something else. Sister Wilma (Boeving, PHJC) was known as a code black when she came up on the floor. She is a very, very friendly and wonderful individual but boy, if you break protocol, watch out. As associate administrator, she also had a great number of technical departments like laboratory, radiology and others reporting to her. One of the reasons the hospital was excellent in its patient care delivery was because Sister Wilma was persnickety. I say that as a compliment. She wanted things done according to the standards of (The Joint Commission). She was well liked, very well respected and for those who stepped out of line, she was probably feared."

Mike Adler
FORMER DIRECTOR OF PUBLIC RELATIONS
MERCY HOSPITAL
(BEGAN IN 1977, GARY AND HOBART)

"Never stop serving your customers. They'll love you for it."

~UNKNOWN

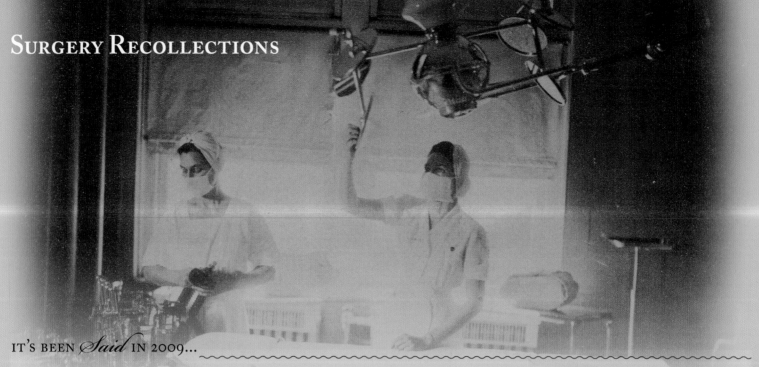

Surgery Recollections

By Coincidence

"One story that I thought was kind of interesting was one that Dr. Kamen and I were involved in many years ago. Both of us were in the Intensive Care Unit at Mercy in Gary and we saw this patient together in consultation and immediately made a diagnosis of a ruptured aneurysm in the aorta, which is a grave problem. We took the patient up on the rickety elevator and neglected to inform the nursing director of surgery that we were coming up. Let's say she was distressed – yelling and screaming – and we said, 'Margaret, things will be fine.' We then went into one of the operating rooms where another patient was sitting on the edge of the operating table and he was waiting for an anesthesiologist to come in.

"We said, 'We're sorry, sir, but we really need this area.' and he said, 'Well by all means.' We went ahead and fortunately the surgery was successful which it usually is not. We got the nursing director calmed down and exactly two weeks later to the day, we had the exact same experience with the same diagnosis and the same need in an afternoon with the same nurse yelling at us. And when we got up to the surgery, we went into this room and there he was – the same person – sitting on the edge of the table!

"He said, 'Oh no, not you two again,' and immediately got off the table and said, 'I'm not going to have this operation – it must mean something.' I always remember it because one would never expect such a coincidence."

John T. Scully, M.D.
Internist, retired
Mercy Hospital
(began in 1955 in Gary)

A patient writes in the mid-1970s...

I want to thank all of the nurses, aides, housekeeping people and everyone I came in contact with during my hospital stay in Gary. Everyone seemed so concerned about me and that made me feel better. When I returned from surgery, I was very sick but the nurses were always there when I needed them and the aides too. I am not Catholic but the chaplain and the visiting Sister stopped by often… and gave me words of encouragement. Thanks again for your kindness during my illness and God bless you all.

- M.U.

"Some of the most significant Operating Room changes I saw over time dealt with anesthesia and its safety, the length of some surgical procedures that were shortened by new instrumentation, and the way in which cataract surgery was originally done with the patient's head immobilized and kept immobilized for several days post-operatively. Now the cataract procedure is done as outpatient surgery."

Marguerite Bendt, RN
Operating Room Supervisor, retired
Mercy Hospital | (began in 1946 in Gary)

"In the hospital Operating Room, nurses like Phyllis Mattingly Coil and Mae Bell were exceptional and nurtured us as we developed our confidence. They taught us to anticipate needs and taught us perfect surgical techniques. Cost effectiveness was an issue back then. We sharpened needles and re-used them. We cleaned rubber gloves, sterilized them and used them again."

Rosemary Beckham Ofsaiof
ST. MARY'S MERCY SCHOOL OF NURSING
(CLASS OF 1961)

Robert Martino, M.D., (center) stands in the new Mercy Hospital surgical suite Operating Room in 1972 with a nurse and Anesthesia Aide Paul Routes on the occasion of the first procedure performed there – a lumbar disc surgery.

"My first day at work, I was supposed to go through an orientation... (but) I didn't have a nurse preceptor. We were so short-handed that the head nurse, Darlene Lee, and I were the only two nurses on this unit. It was a Genitourinary (GU) floor with Dr. Samuel Richter, Dr. James Reynolds and Dr. John Brincko. Wednesday was their day and we had so many surgeries that you would have your lunch out on the table because you weren't going to leave the floor.

"So the head nurse said, 'Well, I will be down here... and that is your unit down there. If you have any problems, call me.' I made it through that day and I did not call her one time... She had her own patients. I sent six people to surgery, brought them back, and recovered them. I made it through and I saw her at the end of my shift. That was my orientation. She asked me how it went and I said, 'Just fine.' I gave her my report. I didn't miss a thing. I missed no medicines – nothing. I attributed that, though, to the school of nursing because they taught us very well. They taught us how to organize. It has helped me through all my years."

Pat De Neal, RN
FORMER DIRECTOR OF NURSING
MERCY HOSPITAL
(BEGAN IN 1964 IN GARY)

Karen Gerke, RN
Director of Surgery

SURGICAL SERVICES STAFF PHOTO – 2010
SEATED: Kristen Schaller, RN
SECOND ROW (L-R): Maricela Aguirre, Stryker; Devin Stallworth, OR technician; Jennifer Bysiek, RN; and Debbie Creech, RN
THIRD ROW (L-R): Christine Frech, RN; Kelly Macielak, RN; Amber Hand, OR technician; Gail Dault, RN; Dianna Vargas, OR technician; and Sanadah Patterson, OR technician
FOURTH ROW (L-R): Michael Jewett, OR technician; Darlene Layhew, scheduler; Julie Chitwood, surgery aide; Lisa Wilcox, surgery case coordinator; Carol Burns, RN, charge nurse; and Peggy Jackson, anesthesia technician
FIFTH ROW (L-R): Sheila Waddle, CRNFA, manager; David Lopez, OR technician; Calvin Taylor, minor procedure/endoscopy technician; and James Williams, OR technician

A Look at the Staff

Endoscopy Department staff photo – 2009
Seated (l-r): Kristi Hamstra, RN; Maria McGrory, RN
Standing (l-r): Debbie Boren, minor procedure technician; Pam Taylor, charge nurse; and Jeanette Barbosa, RN

Pain Clinic staff photo – 2009
Shown (l-r): Melanie Ores, charge nurse; Ana Cream, department assistant; Teressa Hajduk, RN

Post Anesthesia Care Unit (PACU) staff photo – 2009
Standing (l-r): Susan Thornberry, RN; Shannon Gawlik, RN; Margaret Camacho, charge nurse; and Jeanne Walker, staff RN
Seated (l-r): Cherita Wright, unit secretary; Rhoda Wilder, RN; and Lillie Stanford, RN

Pre-Admitting staff photo – 2009
Seated: Sheerin Moss, RN
Standing (l-r): Mary Argenta, RN; Kim Ruschak, RN, and Shirley Clare, RN
Not pictured: Jan Stirn, RN

Same Day Surgery staff photo – 2009
Standing (l-r): Danielle Larson, unit assistant; Talonda Hollies, RN; Michelle Lynn, RN; and Mauro Perez, unit assistant
Seated (l-r): Meridee Randall, RN; Erica Glover, charge nurse

It's been *Said* in 2009...

"We used to do a lot of things because that's just the way we did things. If there was an infected case, you had to cover the anesthesia machine and all the cabinets and everything in the room with sheets and blanket. Sometimes surgeons would take off their caps and their shoe covers. We sopped the blankets in antiseptic solution at the doorways so you wouldn't carry the bug and germs out into the hallway. This was in Gary probably until the mid-1980s, early 1990s..."

Karen Gerke, RN
Director of Surgery
St. Mary Medical Center
(began in 1972 in Gary)

Surgeons' Lounge

The St. Mary Medical Center's Surgeons' Lounge was named in honor of John Reed, M.D. in 1989. Shown (l-r) are: Beth Kaminski; Father David Nowak; Robert Martino, M.D.; John Reed, M.D.; Judy Smith; Betty Peters; and Sister Bertram Boeving, PHJC. Seated at the table in the foreground are Dr. Reed's grandchildren.

With Beginnings in Gary • Then and Now
Surgical Services...

Contributed by Karen Hogan Gerke, RN
Director, Surgical Services
Rose Rasmusen Schmelter, RN, Staff Nurse, Surgery
Carol Bielak Burns, RN, Charge Nurse, Surgery
Pamela Piechocki Taylor, RN, Charge Nurse, ENDO

<u>St. Mary Mercy Hospital, Gary, 1970.</u> It is estimated that a formalized Central Sterilization didn't come into existence until the mid-1970s.

Earlier, the Surgery Department was on the fifth floor of the South Wing. There were five operating rooms, all with screened windows. Nurses scrubbed and circulated (there were few surgical technicians 40 years ago) and all the staff nurses and aides washed and sterilized instruments and trays at the end of the day for the next day's cases. There was no Sterile Processing Department or staff in those days. In fact, there were few instrument trays – just single instruments that each "scrub" pulled together to set up her room for each individual case. Pre-packaged suture packs did not exist; disposable supplies were not yet available, and cloth drapes were still in wide use. The nuns washed "lap" sponges that the nurses re-packaged, sterilized and re-used.

Sleep rooms for surgery staff and anesthesia staff were part of the department because the staff was required to stay in the hospital in case they needed to help with emergency surgery. This included staying in the hospital the entire weekend if you were on call.

The Post Anesthesia Care Unit (PACU – recovery room at the time) had three or four bays. The recovery room staff was not required to be on call, regularly worked the Monday through Friday day shift, and did not have to work holidays or weekends. Is it any wonder that there were never any openings in the recovery room? Once a nurse got there, she never left until she retired!

(left) Veera Porapaiboon, M.D.
Cardiovascular/Thoracic Surgeon

(right) Kosin Thupvong, M.D.
Cardiovascular/Thoracic Surgeon

IT'S BEEN *Said* IN 2009...

"Because of my training in cardiovascular radiology... I was quite proficient in angiography. I was surprised at how fast was the response from the staff for referring patients. The Gary Clinic became the Ross Clinic. It brought in two vascular surgeons – Dr. Veera Porapaiboon and Dr. Kosin Thupvong – so they began doing open heart surgeries.

"From the early 1970s until the early 1980s, we were quite active. All this time, cardiologists were coming to Northwest Indiana... and I worked very closely with them to make cardiac catheterization in Gary a success. With Dr. Porapaiboon and Dr. Thupvong, downtown Gary Mercy was quite active in cardiovascular surgery."

Heratch Doumanian, M.D.
RADIOLOGIST, RETIRED
MERCY HOSPITAL
(BEGAN IN 1967 IN GARY)

On July 21, 1972, the new Surgery Department on the main floor of the new West Wing opened. There were six operating rooms (no windows!) and two cystoscopy rooms. There was plentiful supply and equipment storage space and office space. PACU, down the hall from surgery, had seven patient bays. An elevator to the patient floors opened directly into the Operating Room on one side and PACU on the other side. A "dumbwaiter" system sent carts with dirty instruments directly down to the SPD/Sterile Processing area. It was a beautifully-designed Operating Room (OR) and a delightful environment for staff members.

In the early 1970s, the first open heart surgery was performed in downtown Gary by Fred Weidman, M.D. Physicians such as Dr. Weidman remained at the heart patient's side for the first 24 hours post-operatively until open heart surgery became more commonplace and a Cardiovascular Unit was opened in 1974.

Trauma victims were not unknown at the hospital. Surgery staff was frequently called in for gunshot, stab wounds and mill accidents. By this time, the call team could leave the hospital but had to return within 30 minutes if called back. This rule remains today (in 2009). If the patient went to the Intensive Care Unit (ICU) or Critical Care Unit (CCU) after surgery, the surgery staff had to push the patient up a ramp connecting the "old" part of the hospital (where those units were located) to the "new" part of the hospital where surgery was located. The staff would get a good running start and "puuuush" the cart up the ramp, glass IV bottles swinging and swaying and clanking against the IV poles, until the top of the ramp was reached and they continued down the hall to ICU or CCU. (The Emergency Room staff had other uses for the ramp; some involved wheelchair and cart races down the ramp on less busy nights.)

In 1977, Anesthesiologist Jack M. Kamen, M.D., opened the Pain Center which at the time was one of only four such clinics in the state. The recovery room staff helped with procedures in a room adjacent to the recovery room. Although Dr. Kamen is retired, the Pain Center has been a feature of St. Mary Medical Center in Hobart ever since, making it the longest running Pain Center in this area.

In 1993, the hospital was sold and became Northwest Family Hospital, thus continuing the mission – for a brief period of time – of providing the care to the under-privileged in Gary that was begun by the Ancilla Domini Sisters in 1913 at 540 Tyler Street.

St. Mary Mercy Hospital, Hobart, 1973. The new satellite hospital opened in Hobart. Surgery was located on the first floor and had three operating rooms, a cystoscopy room, and four recovery room bays. Pam Taylor remembers being told by Miss Marguerite Bendt, the surgery/recovery room manager, that Hobart was going to be "the country hospital doing small surgical procedures" and that the Gary facility was going to remain the "main hospital with the larger, more complex cases." If that was the plan in 1973, it really didn't work out that way! In September, 1974, the hospital legally changed its name, becoming St. Mary Medical Center Gary/Hobart.

In September, 1984, "surgery without hospitalization" opened in the space previously occupied by the obstetrics delivery room. Thus began the "outpatient surgery experience" at Hobart. Previously, almost all procedures had been done on an inpatient basis. Thereafter, same-day surgery patients would recover in the unit and go home late in the afternoon of their surgery day. Outpatient surgical procedures were never scheduled after 12:00 noon to make sure the patients would be ready to go home by late afternoon. The lead time to get an outpatient surgery on the schedule back then was three days. Things certainly have changed. Outpatient procedures are now done late into the evenings and can be added to the schedule the same day as surgery.

THE PAIN CENTER

As it became busier, surgery needed more operating rooms. In 1988, three additional operating rooms were opened, adding an open heart suite and two large orthopedic/neurosurgery rooms. Also added were a larger recovery room (PACU) and an eight-room, same-day surgery area complete with a small GI endoscopy room.

Due to the influx of outpatient procedures (fully 60% of all surgical procedures are performed as outpatients) a larger same-day surgery unit was opened on 2East in July 2006. Opened at the same time was a beautiful three-room GI Endoscopy and Minor Procedure Unit adjacent to 2East. Because the number of surgery cases increased, lithotripsy and pain procedures were moved to the minor procedure area, freeing up operating rooms for larger procedures. The unused same-day surgery space adjacent to surgery is now being used as the holding area for surgery – a wonderful use of this space.

As we continue to grow, we look forward to providing superior perioperative care to our patients and their families.

Jack M. Kamen, M.D., is shown in this 1978 photo looking over the facilities of the Pain Center at St. Mary Medical Center in Gary (aka Mercy Hospital). It was dedicated by the Reverend Henry Langhals, hospital chaplain, and Rabbi Raphael Ostrovsky, spiritual leader of Congregational Beth Israel of Hammond. The center, located since August 1977 in the post-operative unit of the hospital, established new offices to continue treating patients suffering from diverse pains caused by disease.

Reprinted by permission of the *Post-Tribune*, OCTOBER 26, 1978

IT'S BEEN *Said* IN 2009...

"St. Mary Medical Center had the first pain-control center in the region and was the first to use patient controlled analgesia. As implied, the patient exerted some control over the amounts of pain relievers that he/she was administered. It is now used almost routinely but back then in the '80s, it was a great 'novelty'."

Jack M. Kamen, M.D.
DIRECTOR OF I.C.U., DIRECTOR OF ST. MARY MEDICAL CENTER PAIN CENTER, CHIEF OF DEPARTMENT OF ANESTHESIOLOGY, DIRECTOR OF RESPIRATORY CARE, DIRECTOR OF MEDICAL EDUCATION, RETIRED MERCY HOSPITAL
(BEGAN IN 1952 AT ST. CATHERINE HOSPITAL)

IT'S BEEN *Said* IN 2009...

"I met Jack Kamen... he lived on Second and Cleveland Street in Gary with his wife, Shirley, and two sons. He was kind of the first pulmonary specialist that we had in those days. He commandeered and brought to this area from Chicago Rush a person by the name of Lynn Duvall who later became my wife. She was brought here in the mid-1970s to do open heart anesthesia. She is a certified registered nurse anesthetist (C.R.N.A.)."

"Dr. Kamen was an anesthesiologist at that time and probably one of the most giving doctors that I met in my career at Mercy Hospital. When a patient couldn't afford to buy medication or insurance would not cover it, Jack Kamen had a standing bill in the pharmacy. He would send a patient down and the medication was given to the patient. Dr. Kamen paid for it out of his own pocket... In the middle 1980s, he started a pain (center) procedure that is very dominant now. Many years ago, he was a pioneer for pain control in our area. He did epidurals and facet injections, but that was back in the times when it was not really in vogue. Some way, somehow, Dr. Kamen knew how to do those kinds of things."

Bruce Lovell
X-RAY TECHNOLOGIST
MERCY HOSPITAL | (BEGAN IN 1963 IN GARY)

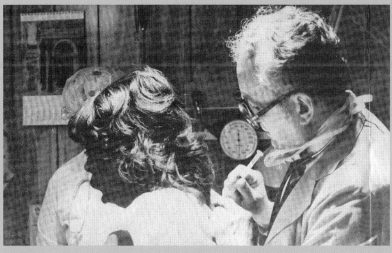

Jack M. Kamen, M.D., administers a trigger point injection to a patient.
Summary, APRIL 1988

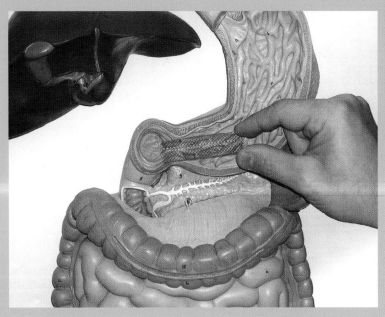

Peter Marvelis, M.D.
Gastroenterologist

John Mirro, M.D.
Gastroenterologist

This diagram shows where the enteral stent is placed to open constricted areas. The term 'enteral' is used when it is placed in the gastrointestinal tract. Peter Mavrelis, M.D., and John Mirro, M.D., had been placing stents in the esophagus for several years but first performed it on a gastric outlet obstruction in December 2001.

Neighborly Care, SPRING 2002

"The secret of joy in work is contained in one word – excellence. To know how to do something well is to enjoy it."

~ Pearl Buck

Symptoms of Neuropathy

* numbness
* loss of feeling in the hands and feet
* slower reflexes
* tingling sensations in the fingers and toes
* sharp, shooting pains
* deep aches
* extra-sensitive skin

NEUROPATHY

In 2006, Podiatrists Michael Carroll, D.P.M.; Stephen Grandfield, D.P.M.; James Meade, D.P.M.; and Michael Nirenberg, D.P.M., were Northwest Indiana's only physicians credentialed in nerve decompression surgery that required special training by its founder, A. Lee Dellon, at John Hopkins School of Medicine. One patient, Ibeliza Goggins, who underwent the surgical procedure performed by Drs. Grandfield and Meade, said she felt immediate relief from longtime pain endured when she wore socks or shoes or put pressure on her foot with her automobile's gas pedal.

Vim & Vigor, SUMMER 2006

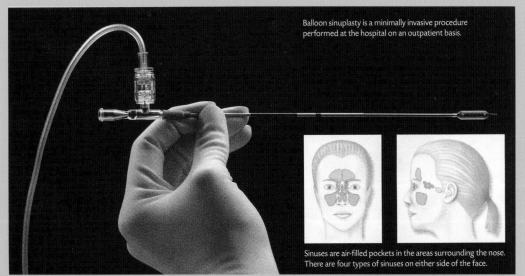

Balloon sinuplasty is a minimally invasive procedure performed at the hospital on an outpatient basis.

Sinuses are air-filled pockets in the areas surrounding the nose. There are four types of sinuses on either side of the face.

OTOLARYNGOLOGY

Balloon sinuplasty™ is a minimally invasive procedure performed at the hospital on an outpatient basis. It is a relatively new procedure in which a catheter with a guidewire positions a balloon into the sinus duct. When the balloon is inflated, it gently widens the walls of the nasal passageway without damaging the sinus lining.

Vim & Vigor, SPRING 2009

Dennis Han, M.D., and Thomas Tarin, M.D., both otolaryngologists at St. Mary Medical Center and Community Hospital, perform Balloon sinuplasty™ to relieve patients who suffer from sinusitis.

"Often, a combination of surgery and aggressive medical treatment are required to keep sinus disease under control," Tarin said. "Balloon sinuplasty™ is another excellent tool that we now have at our disposal to help us help our patients manage their disease – preserving the mucosal lining of the nose, and eliminating risk of scarring or making the condition worse."

Dennis Han, M.D.
Otolaryngologist

Thomas Tarin, M.D.
Otolaryngologist

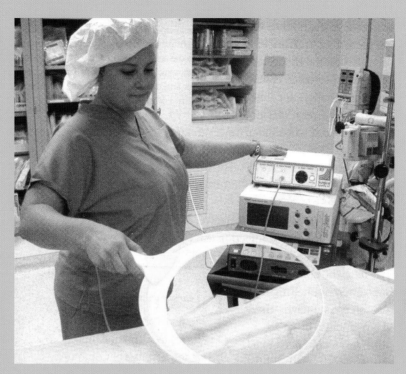

A NEW SURGICAL SYSTEM
Vanessa Byczko, RN, a surgical nurse at St. Mary Medical Center, demonstrates a new FDA-approved radiofrequency detection system for tracking and locating surgical sponges. The hospital is the first in Northwest Indiana to implement the system which enhances the already stringent safety measures used in the operating rooms.

Vim & Vigor, SPRING 2010

DID YOU KNOW?

The nurses at St. Mary Medical Center nominated Susan Hugus for the Nurse Hero Award, an award presented by the American Nurses Association and the American Red Cross. She was one of ten nurses nationwide to receive it and her daughter accepted the award on behalf of her mother at a ceremony in Washington, D. C.

IN MEMORIAM – SUSAN HUGUS
"Susan Hugus was a very dedicated, caring nurse in the Operating Room who specialized in open heart surgery. On her way to work one morning, she came across an accident on Route 130 in Wheeler and had gotten out of her car to help an injured man. She had called in to let us know she would be a little late. A short time later, we got a call that Susie herself had been injured. A car started to pull away from the scene of the accident, got caught in the wires that were down, and pulled a pole down on Susie. She was taken to Porter Memorial Hospital and was then transferred to Chicago. She passed away two weeks later.

"Susie was a perfect example of a good Samaritan and someone who was always thinking of others and giving of herself to those in need. She was the mother of two sons and a daughter. She took great pleasure in helping autistic children and was involved with individuals with special needs. We all miss Susie very much – a valued team member in the Operating Room and a very special individual."

Carol Burns, RN, BSN, Charge Nurse, Surgery
St. Mary Medical Center
(began in 1978 in Gary)

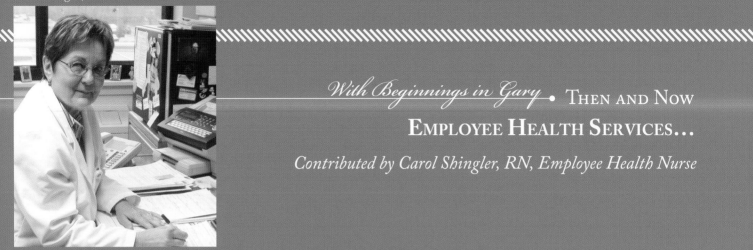

Carol Shingler, RN

With Beginnings in Gary • THEN AND NOW

EMPLOYEE HEALTH SERVICES...

Contributed by Carol Shingler, RN, Employee Health Nurse

There was no Employee Health Service at Mercy Hospital School of Nursing in Gary when I was a nursing student there in the late 1950s and early 1960s. I believe Miss Emily Mordi, RN, Emergency Room manager, was the first Employee Health nurse.

Since 1996, however, I have been at St. Mary Medical Center as the hospital's Employee Health nurse. My responsibilities include pre-employment screening and testing for new hires, annual tuberculosis (TB) tests for employees, physicians, volunteers and some contracted employees. I also take care of workers compensation injuries, reporting, referrals and follow-up care and I handle the filing of regular medical leaves, intermittent family medical leaves and follow-up paper work from physicians. My office also is responsible for fit-for-duty appointments and referrals.

The key to my position is having referral information ready, lending a listening ear and conveying compassion for those who need to find someone with whom they can talk. My biggest project has been the Employee Health fairs at St. Mary Medical Center. Since the first one in 1997, and for several years thereafter, 26–30 booths were represented from all over the area. While reconstruction and smaller space constraints downsized the size of the fair, it remains informative and fun for all.

The rewards of the Employee Health position are many – due in large part to wonderful co-workers and the people I meet each day at the hospital. Happily, I feel like the "mother hen" who needs to look after her children. That may be the result of 48 years of nursing experience.

IT'S BEEN *Said* IN 2009...

Mary Constandars: "When you first started working as an employee, you got a complete physical from Dr. A. S. Williams. (He was a family physician with a large practice.) You got an X-ray and all your blood work. Then every year on your anniversary, you got the whole nine yards again… and it was free."

Helen Urban: "The Sisters felt that by working in a healthcare facility, you should be healthy and you should get your tests done."

Mary Constandars: "Back then if you were sick, Miss (Emily) Mordi would give you anything you wanted. Now they give you nothing."

Helen Urban: "Also, once you were here for 60 days, you accumulated 60 days of sick time. Then, the following year if you did not miss any days, they gave you a bonus. They bought back half of your sick days."

Mary Constandars, HEALTH INFORMATION ANALYST
ST. MARY MEDICAL CENTER | (BEGAN IN 1975 IN GARY)
AND
Helen Urban, HEALTH INFORMATION ANALYST
ST. MARY MEDICAL CENTER | (BEGAN IN 1976 IN HOBART)

CLINICAL ENGINEERING/TELECOMMUNICATIONS DEPARTMENT...

Contributed by Russ Cain, Manager

IN THE EARLY DAYS
Shown here in the late 1970s in Gary is the
Biomedical (Bio-Med) Department
FRONT ROW (L-R): Marty Mendez, Ruben Santana,
Art Harmon, Lorenzo Baker, and Ray Gordon
TOP ROW (L-R): Scott Holly, Paul Piazza, and Clarence Voss

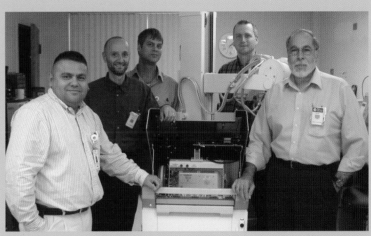

IN MORE RECENT DAYS
CLINICAL ENGINEERING DEPARTMENT STAFF PHOTO – 2009
SHOWN (L-R) with a portable X-ray machine are Roberto Mejia,
Martin Mendez, John Anco, William McCollum, and Ruben Santana

Manager Clinical Engineering Russ Cain

IT'S BEEN *Said* IN 2009...

"The (Biomedical) Department (later known as the Clinical
Engineering Department) was started in 1972 in Gary by Mike
Stallia and Ruben Santana."

Ruben Santana
BIO-MED TELECOMMUNICATIONS GROUP LEADER
MERCY HOSPITAL
(BEGAN IN 1971 IN GARY)

The primary goal of the Clinical Engineering Department is to ensure the safety of medical equipment used on our hospital patients. This is accomplished through properly maintaining medical equipment, keeping accurate records of maintenance performed, identifying repair trends, and instructing the owning departments on the proper use of equipment. The technicians within the Clinical Engineering Department typically have technical degrees in Electronics and receive continuing technical training on specific equipment as needed. The role of the technician has changed over the years but is mainly focused on having all medical equipment function properly whenever it is needed.

In order for the technicians to perform this work, they must be properly prepared and equipped. By providing the necessary tools such as meters, analyzers, simulators, and computers, they can expedite the repair process. All activity performed on medical equipment must be documented accurately. The technicians must follow guidelines set forth by various regulatory agencies such as The Joint Commission and the State Board of Health. All work performed is logged into an equipment management database program so that reporting can be easily accomplished. The technicians must be able to follow maintenance procedures that vary depending on the equipment serviced.

Accurate records and procedures are essential to a good maintenance program.

1970s Continued

Therapy Services

Outpatient Rehabilitation staff photo – 2008
Front row (l-r): Meghan Harper, Crisna Laxamana, Frank Kilian, Becky Mateja, and Lisette Talaga
Back row (l-r): Carlos DeJesus, Traci Goin, Jill Radas, Karie Knopf, Amber Artherhults, Tina Doctor, Ivelisse Beam, Amber Kimbrew, Jim Edwards, and Bonnie Wolfe

It's been *Said* in 2009...

"The person in the late 1970s or early 1980s who became in charge of physical therapy was Jack Gamet. He and Paul Bellendorf were very good friends. Jack Gamet was the man who supplied the funds and bought the first CAT scan in the area."

Bruce Lovell
X-ray Technologist
Mercy Hospital | (began in 1963 in Gary)

Physical Therapy staff photo – 2009
Shown (l-r): Mike Penna, Mary Kate Sosnowski, Stacy Gaza, Rebecca Lipe, Ivelisse Beam, Pennie Zimmerman, Jill Radas, and Meghan Harper

It's been *Said* in 2009...

"In 1996 or 1997 when I was a staff nurse, I was caring for an older terminally ill female cancer patient. Her last dying wish was to be baptized. Due to her religious beliefs, she needed to be immersed in water by her pastor. With the cooperation of administration and the Physical Therapy Department, I arranged for the woman to be taken down to the whirlpool where the baptism was performed. This was one of the moments that made me feel good about being a nurse. I not only cared for this patient's physical well being but also her spiritual well being."

Betty Lane, RN
Nurse Manager Oncology
St. Mary Medical Center
(began in 1990 in Hobart)

Pictured here is the Outpatient Rehabilitation building located adjacent to St. Mary Medical Center on Ash Street.

With Beginnings in Gary • THEN AND NOW

THERAPY SERVICES...

Contributed by Becky Mateja Lombardini, MPA
Community Relations Coordinator
St. Mary Outpatient Rehabilitation

It is said that Therapy Services date back to the early 1970s at Mercy Hospital and perhaps even before then. Today, like it was at the Gary hospital, Therapy Services are a very important aspect of "Helping People Regain Their Lives" within Community Healthcare System. Inpatient and outpatient services are provided at each of the three campuses – Community Hospital, St. Catherine Hospital, and St. Mary Medical Center. While some therapy is performed directly by the hospital, additional therapy is provided by the contractor, RehabCare. Frank Kilian of RehabCare has been at the helm of Therapy Services at St. Mary Medical Center since 2002, first reporting to Janice L. Ryba and then to Craig Bolda beginning in 2007.

Here at St. Mary Medical Center, we have inpatient and outpatient services of physical, occupational, and speech therapy. It is part of the larger continuum of Therapy Services that includes an Acute Rehabilitation Center and Home Health Services. The Inpatient Center is located on 2East while Outpatient Therapy is located in Hobart, Portage, and most recently in Winfield. Outpatient Therapy in Hobart was moved in 2003 from the Spectrum Building to the former Collective Image Center just west of the main hospital. The other two facilities are located in St. Mary's satellite buildings in Portage and Winfield until the Portage Outpatient Therapy Center moves to the St. Mary Medical Center Portage Health Center.

As we have expanded, our staff and programs have increased as well. We have more than 50 staff members and full-time programs at both Hobart and Portage to handle increased volume. Included with new equipment is a functional capacity evaluation machine and we recently added the Wii for rehabilitation. Another quality process that was implemented in 2005 was computerized documentation. Because of our commitment to excellence, we are also outsourcing our therapy services to private hospitals in the area.

Along with these additions, we provide monthly seminars and a public service radio program on www.midamericabroadcasting.com. Other aspects that set us apart are that we offer transportation and are exempt from government caps because we are a hospital-based therapy program.

Hearts of Hope

At the Hearts of Hope ceremony in 2008 are (l-r) Cardiologist Nazzal Obaid, M.D.; St. Mary Medical Center CEO and Administrator Janice L. Ryba; Mrs. Earl Friend; and her husband/heart patient Earl Friend.

Each year for the last six years, the Hearts of Hope trees at St. Mary Medical Center glow in honor or in memory of someone who has filled the hearts of others with love and joy. Located outside the west entrance, the crimson lights on the trees represent contributions made toward cardiovascular research. For a $5 donation, a light is reserved in the name of each designated person and helps support the Cardiovascular Research programs of Community Healthcare System (CHS). With vast experience in treating heart disease, the CHS hospitals are always working to improve the heart health of the community with local access to new treatment options available through research. These initiatives have allowed the CHS hospitals to participate in national research trials directed at better detection, treatments and the prevention of heart disease.

It's been *Said* in 2009...

"The one thing that's really changed over (the last) 10 years is the technology that we used to assist us in diagnosing heart disease and treatment. And the most exciting things are the ways that we can reverse disease or illness now. In the last 25 years, there have been tremendous gains in reversing (the effects of) heart attacks, and sparing people heart damage, and saving lives. There have been unbelievable strides in treating heart failure. People before that had a 50% chance of living five years. Now they live decades. So we have seen a huge change in treatment.

"Now we have to be expedient in the treatment. Before, when people had heart attacks, we were limited to use of a couple medications – sitting and watching what transpired because we couldn't reverse things. Now, we can be really aggressive in trying to reverse that process and reverse the heart attack. It puts a pressure on time because now there are a lot of situations where we have to come to the hospital immediately and apply those technologies. It's very gratifying because it makes an unbelievable difference not only in the course of the patients but also in their recovery, longevity and quality of life. It has been a huge change."

Jack Ziegler, M.D.
Cardiologist
St. Mary Medical Center
(began in 1982 in Hobart)

It's been *Said* in 2009...

Move that bus
"We had a young patient with a cardiac problem and he went into a very serious life-threatening rhythm disturbance that we had to monitor. The monitor was truly the size of a Volkswagen bus! I called it the Volkswagen bus. The doctor thankfully responded to the code that we called, and he was cardioverted. The 'bus' was on a set of wheels and we had to wheel it. Move that bus – I don't think people would believe it... and to think that today there are people walking around with pacemakers (that accomplish the same thing) who can go to the doctor's office for a reading of such and such a rhythm, at such and such a time, on such and such a day. The technology that came into medicine is mind boggling."

Shirley Makivich Urbanek, R.N., retired | St. Mary Mercy Hospital | (began in 1959 in Gary)

"Three years ago, a mother fell and hit her head and I was still working as a patient advocate and became very close to the family. The mother was in Intensive Care for a while so (I made) a point to go see them. I told them to call me any time and visited in the evening and sometimes had coffee with them. They were so grateful. After she was discharged, they wrote me letters. Several weeks ago, I was in Walmart and saw the daughter who came up and hugged me. That's one of my best memories. When you help people calm down and see that things will be better, that's a great feeling."

Dee Bedella, COORDINATOR, SLEEP LAB/COMMUNITY LIAISON
ST. MARY MEDICAL CENTER
(BEGAN IN 1988 IN HOBART)

"One of my colleagues is an internist. Two or three years into my practice – I was very young at that time – I was at Circuit City in Highland buying a stereo. I had a pair of cut-off shorts and a hat on. I was on call and they paged me that this doctor was having a heart attack. I got to the hospital in probably 18 minutes, flying down Main Street... His heart rate was 30. I got him to the cath lab and he fibrillated and started to have a seizure. We shocked him once and he woke up a little bit. We hadn't started the case and he fibrillated again. We shocked him again and he woke up. We put the tube in and he had 100% blockage in one of his arteries. I opened it, put a stent in and he went home in two days. He still works here.

"It is amazing. As anyone can imagine, as far as a reward, what else could you ask for? It is stressful but exciting. It is stressful but rewarding. I am very fortunate that I get to do something that I really love and enjoy."

Zlatan Stepanovic M.D., CARDIOLOGIST
DIRECTOR OF CONGESTIVE HEART FAILURE CLINIC
ST. MARY MEDICAL CENTER
(BEGAN IN 1997 IN HOBART)

HEART WATCH
"St. Mary Medical Center was very aggressive in developing the Electrophysiologic Program which involves not only pacemaker insertion but defibrillator insertions. (When Dr. Mark Dixon started here in 1996) the whole program really blossomed. It is an extraordinarily important adjunct to what we do in cardiology. On a local level, it was very aggressive in helping us deliver superior care in terms of life-threatening arrhythmias.

"Also of importance is the support of the hospital for continually improving our imaging technology... The administration and staff continually support the adaptation of new procedures and aren't afraid to do things at a community level like carotid stenting and peripheral vascular disease intervention – things that carry a risk.

"It becomes an issue of time and disposition. People don't want to go to Indianapolis or Chicago for that procedure if they don't have to. They're away from their family and away from their comfort zone. You know this stuff is frightening enough without removing them from their environment totally."

Jack Ziegler, M.D., CARDIOLOGIST
ST. MARY MEDICAL CENTER
(BEGAN IN 1982 IN HOBART)

DR. WRITE — THACH NGUYEN, M.D., CARDIOLOGIST/AUTHOR

In the early 1990s, Thach Nguyen, M.D., and St. Mary Medical Center Director of Cardiology, Paul Link, were members of a medical team that demonstrated angioplasty to cardiologists from around the world. They were attending the Third International Cardiology Conference in Guhan, China and presented a live demonstration of the procedure to more than 300 physicians. The practice of angioplasty in China was much less common because of the expense involved with equipment and medical care. The most important aspect of the trip, they said, was a chance to improve worldwide health.

IT'S BEEN *Said* IN 2009...

"I have written two books. The first one is called *Management of Complex Cardiovascular Problems*. It first came out in 2001. The second edition sold out and the publisher asked me to do a third edition in 2007. A review from Italy said that this is the guiding compass for cardiologists and the treatment of heart disease. So this is what is special about this book.

"The second book is called the *Practical Handbook of Advanced Interventional Cardiology*. In the second edition, we had to do two reprints because the book sold out. Now I am preparing the 4th edition, planned to be out in May 2011.

"I am finishing up a third book with the title *Evidence Based Cardiology Practice, a 21st Century Approach*. It was published in October 2009 by People's Medical Publishing House, the main medical publisher of China. The question in this book is: What difference are we doing now in the 21st century compared with what we did in the 20th century?

"Another publisher, Cardiotext Publishing in Hartford, CT, has asked me to write a book so I will do the fourth one to be published in December 2010. It will be called *Quality, Evidence Based, Cost and Time Effective Cardiology*."

Thach Nguyen, M.D., CARDIOLOGIST
ST. MARY MEDICAL CENTER | (BEGAN IN 1987 IN HOBART)

Evidence-Based Cardiology Practice, a 21st Century Approach

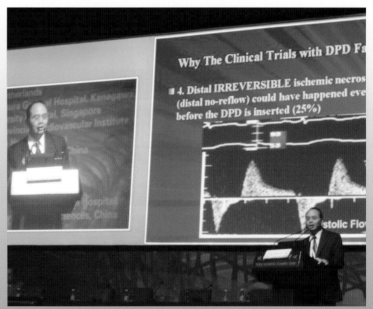

In 2008, Dr. Thach Nguyen gave a lecture in Beijing, China at the International Convention Center about management of a heart attack. Included in his talk was his case of an Indiana patient who suffered from both a heart attack and bleeding.

Cardiologist Thach Nguyen, M.D., examines American Indian Chief Basil Heath in his office. Dr. Nguyen, an American Indian enthusiast who collects artifacts, asked Basil Heath to share his history, talk to the nurses, and pose for photos. Basil Heath was an actor playing American Indians in many Hollywood movies.

1972 – First Open Heart Surgery in Gary

St. Catherine Hospital had pioneered unprecedented advances in cardiac care and heart surgery. Later, on the east side of the region, however, the first open heart surgery in a Gary hospital was performed on August, 23, 1972 – in the new open heart surgery suite.

And Later... Open Heart Surgery in Hobart

It's been *Said* in 2009...

"I began in cardiology in 1982 as the junior partner of Dr. Jerry Chip who was here approximately another 15 years after I started.

"In 1982, open heart surgery was still relatively new. The only hospitals in the immediate area that performed the surgery were St. Mary's in Gary and St. Anthony's in Crown Point. We had new and innovative treatments for heart attack and heart failure so it really was the dawn of a lot of advancements in treatment of cardiovascular illness. The decade of the '80s was when heart surgery was coming into its own. We had new ways to treat heart attacks, new ways to treat congestive heart failure, new ways to treat life threatening cardiac arrhythmias, so we were trying to figure out how we could pull those into a community setting.

"When I was here, it was Dr. Veera Porapaiboon, Dr. Kosin Thupvong and Dr. Sakda Suwan."

Jack Ziegler, M.D., Cardiologist
St. Mary Medical Center
(began in 1982 in Hobart)

It's been *Said* in 2009...

"I remember our first open heart patient in September of 1987. He was an extremely nice gentleman in his late 60s or early 70s. It was a culmination of so many months of preparation and wanting to make sure everything went well. We had a little party for him when he moved out of ICU and into the Step-Down unit. He would come back years later on a regular basis to let us know he was doing well. I believe he actually came from the Knox area. After our first open heart, we just soared from there."

Marsha King, R.N., M.S., M.B.A., C.N.A.A
former Vice President, Patient Care Services
St. Mary Medical Center
(began in 1987 in Hobart)

"Work lovingly done is the secret of
all order and all happiness."
~ *Pierre-Auguste Renoir*

It's been *Said* in 2009...

"We started doing open heart surgery here in Hobart also. I don't know the exact year but we started with the catheterization lab. We used to take the patients to Gary. Before I left the CCU downtown (in Gary) and went up to 6West, Dr. Veera Porapaiboon and Dr. Kosin Thupvong came to town. Dr. Jack Kamen was instrumental in getting them to come because Dr. Fred Weidman had left.

"In the meantime, when St. Anthony opened in Crown Point, they were enticed to go there to operate instead of downtown Gary. The Gary hospital was having more and more difficulty trying to get physicians because of socioeconomic changes that were rapidly destroying that city. Instead of taking cath patients downtown, I transported them to Crown Point until we got a cath lab of our own. Still, when the patients needed open heart surgery, we would take them to St. Anthony. Finally, they decided that didn't make sense so we began an open heart progam in Hobart in our little eight-bed unit with Dr. Porapaiboon and Dr. Thupvong. Dr. Porapaiboon was our Hobart physician. Dr. Thupvong was the surgeon at St. Anthony's and Dr. Sakda Suwan was at Methodist. This is when expansion plans began for a 12-bed unit to be moved downstairs.

"The Intermediate Care Unit (in Hobart) was right outside of the ICU. It was a medical unit that evolved into an Intermediate Care Unit with telemetry. When they put the telemetry on the IMCU, they projected the telemetry bank back into the ICCU unit. We had to have a staff nurse who was a telemetry monitor nurse. Her job was to analyze the monitors from both units until Hewlett Packard made a computer to detect arrhythmias. There were times when patients would go into a lethal arrhythmia and we would be out the door heading down there before they could even announce a code blue.

"When surgery was expanded on the west side of the hospital in the 1980s, a 12-bed, all-private-room Intensive Care Unit was also built adjacent to surgery. Beth Kaminski was the administrator at the time. We began doing many more open heart surgeries. Fortunately, I had Dr. Scully and Dr. Kamen to help guide me through a lot of this. Eventually Dr. Kamen retired and Dr. Scully stayed on as director of the ICCU downstairs until he retired..."

Maryanne Kerr, R.N., Nurse Manager, ICCU & Medical Oncology, retired
Mercy Hospital | (began in 1960 in Gary)

It's been *Said* in 2009...

"When we started here, we had a catheterization lab at Gary so we used to ride the ambulances that were owned by the funeral homes to Gary with our patients who needed cardiac catheterization and we would assist, stand and watch, etc. Patients had their cardiac caths done at Gary Mercy and then they would drive us back to St. Mary's and put the patients in their beds. That was probably around 1975. When they opened the cath labs here, of course they quit doing that (and) ambulances were no longer run by the funeral homes."

Catherine Wiseman, R.N.
Clinical Case Manager, Acute Rehabilitation Unit, retired
St. Mary Medical Center | (began in 1975 in Hobart)

It's been *Said* in 2009...

"I started as a junior cardiologist on the staff in general internal medicine. I developed a liking for Gary... (because) that is where I made my first dollar. I felt people in Gary had given me a lot of love, respect and recognition. As long as I am practicing, I will not leave the city of Gary."

Vijay Dave, M.D., Cardiologist
Mercy Hospital | (began in 1977 in Gary)

"(When) Dr. Vijay Dave came... on... he and his group were very instrumental with the cath lab development at Hobart Mercy."

John Birdzell, Former President of
Lakeshore Health System
(began in 1985 with Ancilla Systems Incorporated)

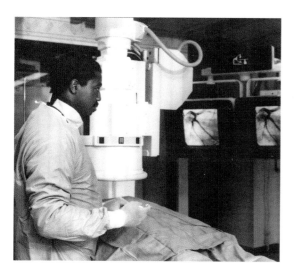

Cardiologist, Keith Artis, M.D., is shown here in 1991 performing a procedure at St. Mary Medical Center in Gary's all digital cardiac catheterization laboratory. More than 250 procedures were done in 1991. The lab, a computerized tomography (CT) scanner and a magnetic resonance imager (MRI), resulted from the partnership between the hospital and a group of 37 physicians.

Ancilla Systems Annual Report –1991

The Hobart Cardiac Unit was blessed in 1987 and was followed by an open house for the public. It was acknowledged as a premier facility.

IT'S BEEN *Said* IN 2009...

A STATE-OF-THE-ART LABORATORY

"This past year has been exceptional because we were able to install the two new (catheterization) labs with state-of-the-art, up-to-date technology. We have built a new diagnostic building and we upgraded to a 64-slice CT, and bought a new MRI to service both inpatients and outpatients."

Mary Sudicky

VICE PRESIDENT FINANCE AND CHIEF FINANCIAL OFFICER
ST. MARY MEDICAL CENTER | (BEGAN IN 2002 AT COMMUNITY HOSPITAL)

Interventional Cardiologist Cesar Jara, M.D.

In 2006, St. Mary Medical Center began offering carotid artery stent placement – a minimally-invasive procedure done in the cardiac catheterization laboratory to open clogged arteries in the neck. The procedure was pioneered by Community Hospital physicians Prakash Makam, M.D., and Arvind Ghandhi, M.D. "Just five years ago, someone who was not a good candidate for the standard carotid artery surgery had very few options for treatment and faced a situation much more grave than today," Jara said. "We have an opportunity to look at the evolution of medicine in the exciting field of vascular intervention as we move forward with the common goal of helping our patients obtain the best results."

A ribbon-cutting ceremony was held for the cardiac catheterization lab on January 28, 2009. Shown here (l-r) are Patti Robinson, cardiac catheterization lab RN: Cheryl Alderson, director of cardiology services; Rose Garcia, vice president, diagnostic and therapeutic services; and Janice L. Ryba, St. Mary Medical Center CEO and administrator. Notably, during the four-month renovation surrounded by construction and half the facility's capabilities, the staff maintained patient satisfaction scores in the 97th percentile.

Hospital Headlines, FEBRUARY 2009

CARDIAC CATHETERIZATION LABORATORY...

CARDIAC CATHETERIZATION LABORATORY
STAFF PHOTO — 2009

FRONT ROW (L-R): Director Cheryl Alderson; Patti Robinson, RN;
Charlene King, RN; Kristi Heinold, RT; and Suzanne Emig, RN
SECOND ROW (L-R): Jennifer Fraley, RT; Ashlee Kincaid, RT;
John Hunt, RN; and Karen Filko, RT

Contributed by Cheryl Alderson, B.S. RT
Director of Cardiology Services

In 1987, the cardiac catheterization lab (CCL) performed the first coronary angiogram at St. Mary Medical Center in Hobart, Indiana. The one-room procedure suite was staffed with two nurses, Debbie Krejci, RN, and Kristine Shocaroff, RN; two cardiovascular radiologic technologists, Jennifer Gould, B.S., RT (R) (CV) and Paul Link, RT (R). Jerold Chip, M.D., was the medical director.

In approximately 1994, the CCL added electrophysiology studies to our service line. These procedures, performed by an electrophysiologist, often would take hours to do and many times were scheduled to be performed in the evening. In 1996, SMMC opened a dedicated electrophysiology laboratory and these procedures were no longer performed in the CCL.

IT'S BEEN *Said* IN 2009...

CARDIAC CATHETERIZATION LABORATORY – IN GARY

"In the early to mid-1970s, I recall visiting Mercy Hospital in Gary to see a special procedure room in the Radiology Department where coronary angiograms were being performed. They were being done by one cardiologist, Dr. Jerry Chip from the Ross Clinic, and one radiologist, Dr. Heratch Doumanian. The chief technologist of the X-ray Department was Richard Marks. He was assisted by another technologist, Xavier Flores, whom I had trained at St. Catherine Hospital."

David Padilla
DIRECTOR, CARDIOLOGY SERVICES NON-INVASIVE
ST. CATHERINE HOSPITAL
(BEGAN IN THE EARLY 1970S IN GARY)

Not all peripheral vascular procedures were performed in the CCL in the early days. This was primarily due to the equipment limitations. Therefore, all (transcatheter) carotid angiograms and some other peripheral vascular angiograms were performed in the Radiology Department. In order to accommodate the growing patient volume in the CCL and to merge the service line into one location, a second procedure room with multiple imaging modalities was opened in July 1996. To this day, all transcatheter angiography of the heart and peripheral vascular systems are performed in the CCL.

At that time, many interventional radiology procedures were also shifted from the Radiology Department to the CCL. Again this afforded the physician better imaging and reduced the time of the procedure.

In 1987, a typical coronary angiogram took approximately 1½ hours to perform and percutaneous transluminal coronary angioplasty (PTCA) could take as long as four hours.

The standard of care at the time was to have a cardiovascular surgeon, anesthesiologist, open heart team, and perfusionist on standby for all PTCA procedures. During PTCA, a physician inflates a fluid-filled balloon according to the size of the artery to increase the blood flow to the heart muscle. Sometimes this procedure traumatizes the artery by causing sudden vessel collapse or acute closure. This was of great concern and the probability of that occurring was approximately one in five. In the mid-1990s, our CCL began using intracoronary stents. This technology, thankfully, reduced the risk of acute closure significantly and it was determined that it was not necessary to have surgical stand by on all PTCA procedures.

With the onset of new technology to enhance the safety and improve the outcome of coronary intervention procedures, the CCL began using drug-eluting stents and other technologies. With several options, our doctors are now able to use other tools – not only balloon, but also stents, atherectomy, thrombectomy, etc. The CCL now uses the acronym PCI (percutaneous coronary intervention) when describing the procedure.

Our CCL also provides percutaneous transluminal intervention (PTA) in treating disease of the peripheral arteries. PTA uses similar equipment as PCI and the purpose is exactly the same – to increase blood flow to the patient's extremities.

Our CCL also performs carotid artery stenting, endovascular aortic aneurysm graft insertions (much less invasive than the open procedure performed in surgery), and laser guided atherectomy in the treatment of chronic total occlusion in the peripheral arteries.

In the fall of 2008, St. Mary Medical Center did a complete renovation of the CCL. Philips Medical Systems FD-20 digital flat screen technology was installed and has greatly increased the image quality. The remodeling has made the department esthetically appealing and the millwork provides more space for greater efficiency.

Our staff has grown and our technological choices have broadened but our primary aim remains the same as it did in July 1987 – to provide the very best care to our patients.

IT'S BEEN *Said* IN 2009...

"When I was five years old, I was hospitalized with a serious illness. I was very frightened and I remember how wonderful the nurses were to me. From that time on, I wanted to be a nurse so I could touch someone's life the way they had touched me. Now, after all these years, I can still say that I made the right choice. I love what I do and I can't imagine doing anything else."

Kris Shocaroff, RN
CASE MANAGEMENT, ST. MARY MEDICAL CENTER | (BEGAN IN 1975 IN GARY)

IT'S BEEN *Said* IN 2009...

"We have two brand new cath labs and the images are phenomenal. They are up to par probably with any other catheterization lab in the country. One other thing we are doing is CT angiograms of the heart. Dr. Jayesh Thakrar and I are doing them in tandem. I am the cardiology department and he is the radiology department so the two of us are doing them. It is being done at Community Hospital, too. It is relatively new so we can now non-invasively image coronary arteries with CT scanning. This was one of the things that we wanted to have the ability to do. We did not want our patients to have to go outside of our (Hobart) community to have that test performed so we are very fortunate in that regard."

Zlatan Stepanovic MD., CARDIOLOGIST
DIRECTOR OF CONGESTIVE HEART FAILURE CLINIC | ST. MARY MEDICAL CENTER | (BEGAN IN 1997 IN HOBART)

NON-INVASIVE CARDIOLOGY DEPARTMENT...

Contributed by Cheryl Alderson, B.S. RT
David Padilla,
Director of Cardiology Services
St. Catherine Hospital

IT'S BEEN *Said* IN 2009...

NON-INVASIVE CARDIOLOGY STAFF PHOTO – 2009
PICTURED (L-R): Maria Bukorovic; Nadia Kargol; Irma Nelson; and Delane Sarkey

"My duties in Gary in the 1970s were to identify, expand and improve the delivery of echocardiograms by increasing the number of technicians. Advancements included standardizing the way in which stress tests were done, and providing holter scanning services. Initially, Echocardiogram Technician Jane Gonzales spent half days at the Gary and Hobart hospitals to administer the test. Within a year, we were able to utilize more technicians.

"Dr. John Scully was the medical director of the Cardiac Non-Invasive Laboratory – a true gentleman. With his vision and respect from the cardiologists and other physicians at St. Mary Medical Center, we were able to take leaps forward to improve cardiac services."

David Padilla, DIRECTOR
CARDIOLOGY SERVICES NON-INVASIVE
ST. CATHERINE HOSPITAL
(BEGAN IN THE EARLY 1970S IN GARY)

The Non-Invasive Cardiology (NIC) Department has existed since St. Mary Medical Center opened in Hobart in 1973. Known initially as the Electrocardiogram (EKG) Department, the staff performed EKGs, stress tests, and basic office work.

As the cardiovascular service line grew, so did the services provided by the Non-Invasive Cardiology Department. Almost from its inception, the NIC staff began assisting physicians with non-pharmaceutical and radio-pharmaceutical stress testing.

Echocardiography, or ultrasound of the heart chambers, was added to the service line to help our cardiologists in diagnosing various diseases of the heart. St. Mary Medical Center added echocardiography to its service line in approximately 1980.

Today, the NIC Department of St. Mary Medical Center provides a variety of non-invasive examinations with highly sophisticated equipment. Gone are the days when echocardiograms were recorded on a video tape. Today, they are transferred from the echocardiogram unit to a computer. The computer provides optimum images and assists the technician in obtaining more accurate measurements of the structures of the heart. The study is then sent to a server for long-term archiving. This has not only benefited the patient and physician with greatly improved image quality and more precise measurements, but also with simpler and faster data retrieval.

St. Mary Medical Center strives to remain on the cutting edge of medicine. We look forward (at this writing) to the installation of the state-of-the-art TraceMaster Vue electrocardiography system in June of 2010. This will enable the physician to have quick access to his/her patient's EKG and provide the staff with a more accurate tool when performing the examination.

Our daily focus – on the hearts of our patients – is performed by a Non-Invasive Cardiology Department staff that takes pride in delivering the best of the best in professional, compassionate care. To be sure – we are all heart!

Cardiac Rehabilitation... Letters/Data

A patient writes in 2009...

I have been going to St. Mary Cardiac Rehab since May 2008. I have gotten to know many of the patients there on a personal level (family, children, hobbies, etc.). Many of these patients have been going there for up to 20 years. Time and again, I will hear it is because of the personal attention that is directed toward them that makes the difference... The genuine care and concern that is demonstrated by this team of professionals is to be commended.

....

A patient writes in 2009...

The last time I visited my doctor I was telling him how glad I was that he sent me to Spectrum for instruction and therapy. Then I realized I should be telling this to you. I had been on oxygen for about four years. With the help of the staff – I am in stage three – and I will continue... the rest of my life. I feel so much better when I'm exercising regularly. I'm off oxygen, my heart and lungs are better, and I feel great. The staff at Spectrum is professional and still their caring shows through. I feel safe, too, for I have seen them in action. Thank you for providing this service.

....

A patient writes in 2009...

I have been attending cardiopulmonary phase three classes for almost six years. I have noticed a tremendous improvement in my overall health, benefited from a recent 13-pound weight loss, and have improved my outlook on life. (After two open heart surgeries – one of which was an aortic valve repair that later required a valve replacement – my physicians at the Cleveland Clinic said) my quick recovery was due to my participation in cardiac rehab at St. Mary. I feel like the staff – Dr. Gozo, Chris McGrew, Sandy, Lisa, Melanie, Gina, Cindy, Hosea and Cathy are like family to me. They have taken the time to get to know me and my family. They... let me know when I am doing a good job or if I need... more effort while exercising.

CARDIAC REHABILITATION DEPARTMENT...

Contributed by Cheryl Alderson, B.S. RT
Director of Cardiology Services

CARDIAC REHABILITATION DEPARTMENT
STAFF PHOTO – 2009
FRONT ROW (L-R): Cathy Cofer-Hines with red visor; Melonie Polley in front of her; Cecelia Hartgraves in pink, Chris McGrew, and Sandy Mills
SECOND ROW (L-R): Lisa Young (behind Cathy Cofer-Hines); Gina Harris, Jose Madrigal; Julie Konja; Debbie Brink; Felix Gozo, Jr., M.D., and Tom Coates

... AND THIS WAS THE CARDIAC REHABILITATION
STAFF IN 1990
SEATED: Amy Bachich, RN
STANDING (L-R): Mike Wegner, exercise physiologist; Paul Link, director of cardiology; Gail Pavese, RN; and Chris Tilka, RN

IT'S BEEN *Said* IN 2009...

CARDIAC REHABILITATION DEPARTMENT – IN GARY

"In the early 1970s, Cardiac Rehabilitation had only one nurse who floated between the Gary and Hobart hospitals to provide patient education. There was no exercise gym for phase II or III cardiac rehabilitation patients at the Gary site and limited service at the Hobart hospital.

"In August, 1987, I appointed a regional supervisor, Mr. Nick Rave, who managed and trained the staff in program development at all three hospitals – Gary, Hobart, and St. Catherine Hospital in East Chicago. Nick helped upgrade the programs and increase the services. Additional staff had to be hired because of demands made by the physicians. St. Mary in Gary finally got an exercise gym in the 1970s. St Mary's in Hobart expanded their program and exceeded their expectations. St. Mary in Hobart provided one of the premier Pulmonary Rehabilitation programs in the area and it quickly became well-known."

David Padilla, DIRECTOR, CARDIOLOGY SERVICES NON-INVASIVE
ST. CATHERINE HOSPITAL | (BEGAN IN THE EARLY 1970S IN GARY)

Did You Know?

Cardiac rehabilitation is clinically proven to improve a patient's quality of life and reduce recurrence of subsequent heart attacks and co-morbidities. Research shows that the average cardiac death rate was 26% lower in rehabilitation patients (exercise-trained) compared to those with "usual care." There were about 21% fewer non-fatal heart attacks, 13% fewer bypass surgeries, and 19% (less) angioplasties. Rehabilitation also includes psychosocial counseling, nutritional and smoke cessation counseling, control of diabetes, and adherence to medication schedules.

Journal of Circulation, 2005; 369-376.

IT'S BEEN *Said* IN 2009...

"In a study from our own research data, Community Healthcare System demonstrated a 57% decrease in re-admissions for ischemic events for coronary stent patients who participated in cardiac rehab versus stent patients who did not participate."

Felix Gozo, Jr., M.D.
CARDIAC REHABILITATION
(BEGAN IN 1984 IN GARY)

The Cardiac Rehabilitation program began in approximately 1983 in Hobart. The primary purpose was to rehabilitate patients who previously had an acute myocardial infarction.

Cardiac Rehabilitation, Phase I, was provided to the inpatient; Phases II and III were held in the Medical Arts Building on the second floor of the hospital. The Cardiac Rehabilitation, Phase II, patients attended classes for one hour, three times a week. The Phase III patients enjoyed coming to the hospital to work out under the supervision of a registered nurse or an exercise physiologist. At that time, the equipment consisted primarily of treadmills, a nautilus system and free weights.

In 2003, the Cardiac Phase II and III services were moved off-site to the Spectrum building located directly north of the hospital. The program began to grow and new equipment was purchased. More Phase II classes were added and the staff was scheduled to work later in the day to accommodate the Phase III patients.

In March 2008, the Cardiac Rehabilitation program began to offer peripheral artery disease (PAD) screening and in September 2008, we began our PAD rehabilitation services.

Throughout the year the Cardiac Rehabilitation Department provides various social events that reach out to our Phase II and Phase III patients. We celebrate National Heart Week each February with patients and provide educational opportunities.

In January 2006, we hosted a Mended Hearts meeting for our post-open heart patients who had completed Phase II Cardiac Rehabilitation and/or were participants of our Phase III program. Currently there are nine active members who attend meetings regularly and are committed to supporting the open heart surgery patients at St. Mary Medical Center.

Our staff is comprised of very dedicated, supportive professionals who care greatly about the well being of the patient. We are very fortunate to have Felix Gozo, M.D., who is very involved in the promotion of the Cardiac Rehabilitation program and conducts educational seminars for both the patients and the staff. We are very proud of our program!

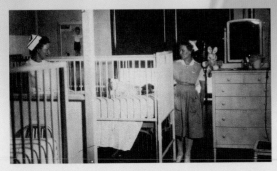

Mercy Hospital Pediatrics – Gary, 1945
*St. Mary's Mercy Hospital School of
Nursing yearbook – 1945*

FROM THE PHJC CHRONICLES – NOVEMBER 12, 1958

Our nursery boasts an all-time high of the 3,000th baby whose name is "Girl Lazarian."
CHJC, University of Notre Dame Archives

St. Mary's Mercy Hospital

Telephone 408-409   540 Tyler Street

To Board and Attendance		
Jan. 19 to Jan. 26	1.	50
Use of Operating Room	10.	00
Anesthetic		
Medicine		
X-Ray *Baby*	7.	00
Surgical Dressing	4.	00
Laboratory Fee	1.	00
Nurses Board	$ 39.	50

*Pd. in full.
S. M. Alphonsine, Supr.
per A.C.H.*

ORIGINAL

St. Mary's Mercy Hospital

540 Tyler St.

TELEPHONE 407-408-409   ::   Gary, Ind.

No. 28934   DATE *Jan 28 1928*

RECEIVED OF *Mr Jos Braunci*

ROOM *434*

Use of Operating Department		
Anesthetic		
Medicine *Baby*	2.	00
Surgical Dressing		
X-Ray Picture		
Laboratory Fee		
Nurses Board		
Board and Attendance	5.	00
Total	7.	00

S. M. Alphonsine, Supt.

Per *S. M. V.*

286565 BUSINESS UARCO SYSTEMS, CHICAGO

Marking Time...1971

- The 26th Amendment to the Constitution, lowering the voting age to 18, was ratified.

- Television commercials for cigarettes were banned, though print advertisements remained legal.

Shown (left) is a Labor and Delivery invoice issued in 1928 for a total of $39.50! The highest amount shown is a $10.00 charge for the use of the Operating Room. The mother's hospital stay was approximately a week; the fee for the baby (shown right) was $7.00 and additional medicine for the baby was $2.00.

Shown here with a young patient is auxiliary member, Mrs. E. H. Heilstedt, who served as volunteer chairman of the Pediatric Department. Her volunteer insignia is shown on the front of her red pinafore.

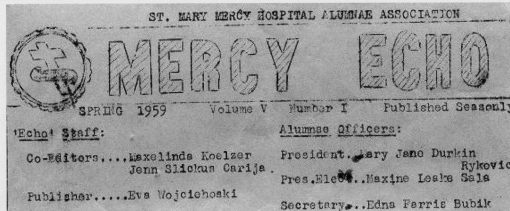

ST. MARY MERCY HOSPITAL ALUMNAE ASSOCIATION

MERCY ECHO

SPRING 1959   Volume V   Number I   Published Seasonly

'Echo' Staff:

Co-Editors....Maxelinda Koelzer
              Jenn Slickus Carije.

Publisher.....Eva Wojciehoski

Columnist....Mary Vygrala Donovan

Circulation.Pat McCormick Seicher
Managers..D.Jaznuski Harbottle

Alumnae Officers:

President..Mary Jane Durkin
                        Rykovic
Pres.Elect..Maxine Leake Sala

Secretary...Edna Farris Bubik

Treasurer...Pat Huber Sikich

TINY TOTS

Mrs. James (Betty Lou Locke) Bell
Class of '44
Boy 7 lbs 10 oz   April 1, 1958
"Gregory Charles"

Mrs. Philip (Catherine Christensen Comerford
Class of '46
Girl 6lbs 12 oz   April 4, 1958
"Phyllis Jean"

Mrs. John (Gaynell Farrell) Waldman
Class of '54
Boy 6 lbs 14 oz   April 4, 1958
"Joseph Carl"

Shown here is the "published seasonally" *Mercy Echo*, a newsletter of the St. Mary Mercy Hospital Alumnae Association. The spring 1959 edition reported recent arrivals in its *Tiny Tots* column, among them Mrs. Philip (Catherine Christensen) Comerford, from the nursing class of 1946, who gave birth to Phyllis Jean in 1958.

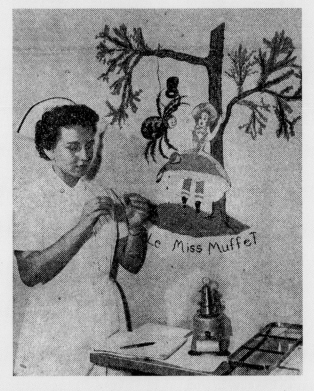

(Above) Mrs. Bruno Bernat, RN, reads a thermometer in the Pediatric Department admission room as Miss Muffet confronts a spider on the wall mural.
Reprinted by permission of the *Post-Tribune*, AUGUST 23, 1959

"(The murals of 'Get Well Island') distract the children," said Pediatrics Supervisor, Sister Ida Volk, PHJC. "They're usually emotionally upset – especially the youngest ones – but the nurses point to the storybook murals, tell them a story, and they calm down and practically forget that they are in the hospital for treatment."

IT'S BEEN *Said* IN 2009...

"I was an LPN student in Gary right out of high school in 1963. As a student, I got 50-cents an hour. We worked in the hospital and we worked fast. In the afternoon we would to go class.

"We worked with Sister Ida (Volk, PHJC) in pediatrics. She was a very small tornado... and very protective of her children. We did not have a neonatal unit at the time. It was just pediatrics.

"The oxygen tents would take up half of the bed. They came to the patient's waist or just below the waist and we tucked (them) in all around the sides as we made the bed. At the time, we were making crib beds, team beds and surgical beds."

Elizabeth A. Bethel, R.N, IMCU, RETIRED
ST. MARY MEDICAL CENTER
(BEGAN IN 1973 IN HOBART)

"Grandmother" Time

Mrs. John B. Radigan, affectionately called "Grandmother," is shown here reading to a group of children in the Pediatric Department at St. Mary's Mercy Hospital in Gary. Mrs. Radigan, the mother of seven grown sons, spent many hours each week reading, telling stories, feeding and playing with young people there.

Reprinted by permission of the *Post-Tribune*, 1953

To Serve with Love

In the 1980s, St. Mary Medical Center employees – at both hospital sites and in every department – were introduced to an initiative called "To Serve with Love," a slogan that was posted on billboards, in newspaper ads and hospital promotional material.

The hands-on training emphasized the practical application of serving each patient with love and C.A.R.E. – an acronym for Courtesy, Attitude, Respect and Enthusiasm.

"I CARE" pin

In 1982, Gary's St. Mary Medical Center Interim Administrator, Mary Gulyassy, said Reverend Kenneth E. Grabner was appointed administrative assistant for Mission and Philosophy. "He helps hospital staff understand providing loving care to the patients we serve," she said. "(We have) adopted a two-pronged slogan: To Serve with Love... and A Hospital Staffed by People Who Care. "The words in and of themselves are empty," she added. "Father Grabner is helping all employees to live those slogans."

Reprinted by permission of the *Post-Tribune*, FEBRUARY 14, 1982

To Serve With Love

At St. Mary Medical Center, those are not just empty words to be found on our motto.

They reflect St. Mary Medical Center's belief that each patient has an inestimable worth, and that worth is found in God.

We believe, therefore, that each patient must be treated as a person of intrinsic nobility - and must be treated as a whole person, body mind and spirit. We believe this wholistic care begins before a patient comes into our hospital, and continues after the patient leaves.

St. Mary Medical Center is part of a great Catholic health care system - care which traces its roots back to the very first Christian community and ultimately to Jesus Christ Himself.

Therefore, we believe that miracles of healing can and do occur, and that those miracles come from God.

We believe that

GOD IS ALIVE AND WELL

For the Children

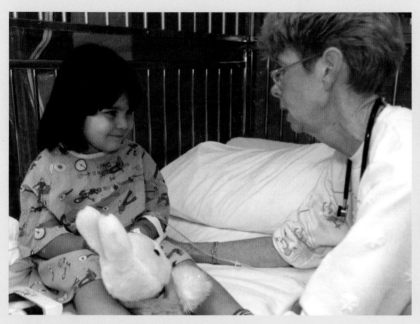

Helen Cavanaugh, LPN, tends to a young patient in the Pediatric Department at Mercy Hospital.

Jenitta Williams, RN, spends game time with two patients in the Pediatric Department at Mercy Hospital.

Shown here in the Gary hospital's Pediatric Unit in celebration of National Nutrition Month in the early 1980s are (l-r) Eneida Batista, Joyce Williams, Ellen Watson, Dottie Boatner, Nadine Hicks, Claudia Dixon and (seated) Norma Lobdell. All diet clerks dressed up as fruits and vegetables to help children enjoy learning about good eating habits.

In the 20th anniversary booklet of the St. Mary Medical Center Auxiliary, Pediatric Chairman Middi Sadowski wrote of supplies and equipment that had been purchased through auxiliary activities in 1973. Regarding some hands-on volunteering, she wrote: "The corridor sections were painted in soft pastels of blue, green, pink, and yellow as were the patient rooms. Through the generosity of the auxiliary president and board, your pediatric chairman was able to purchase and <u>hang</u> 93½ yards of 14" border wallpaper. The warm and beautiful result made the accompanying aching muscles worthwhile."

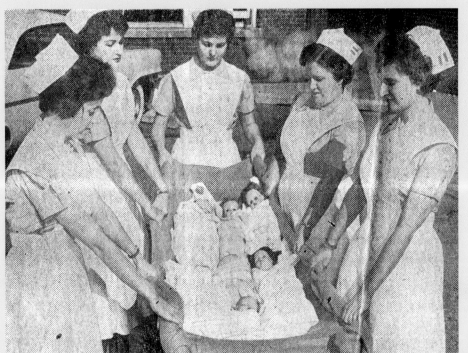

IT'S BEEN *Said* IN 2009...

IN DAYS GONE BY
"My son, Paul Jancarich, was born at St. Mary Mercy. In those days, things were a little different. The patient stayed in the hospital for 10 days. The new moms never moved; they were treated like queens; everybody loved them and the babies, too. The babies were not in the room with the patients and only grown-ups could visit – no little kids – and then just grown-ups two at a time. Sister was down at the door waiting. If a visitor came in and somebody was already up in the room, you had to wait until they came down before you were allowed to go up. Now you see them walking back and forth and then they wonder why all these germs are spread around."

Helen Petrovich, RN
ST. MARY MERCY HOSPITAL | (BEGAN IN 1934 IN GARY)
(NOTE: HELEN PETROVICH WAS 95 YEARS OLD AT THE TIME OF HER INTERVIEW.)

REMEMBERING OBSTETRICS AT MERCY HOSPITAL IN GARY

IT'S BEEN *Said* IN 2009...

"I worked in the Pediatric Department. Unwed mothers lived on the maternity floor – fourth floor of the hospital. They gave up their babies for adoption (no stork feathers and no birth announcements in the newspapers). After the mothers left the hospital, the babies were placed in pediatrics on the third floor until they were adopted."

Vivian Fugate Springer, RN, RETIRED
MERCY HOSPITAL
(BEGAN IN 1948 IN GARY)

IT'S BEEN *Said* IN 2009...

"All the patients were special but the children were extra special. The operating rooms were on the fifth floor at the south end. At the north end was a Pediatric Department.

"We brought the pediatric patients in wheelchairs to the Operating Room. A boy about six years of age slipped out of the chair at the Operating Room door and sped down the hall to his room in pediatrics. He did not have his tonsils out that day."

Marguerite Bendt, RN
OPERATING ROOM SUPERVISOR, RETIRED
MERCY HOSPITAL
(BEGAN IN 1946 IN GARY)

"I was born in Yugoslavia – came to this country in 1961… I came to Gary looking for part-time emergency work in July 1968… because I knew I was going into the Army in October. Emergency work was covered by local physicians… but there was a local OB/GYN, Dr. Chester Kmak, who was desperately looking for help at the Gary Clinic at 61st and Harrison. I was an OB/GYN just out of the Residency.

"I joined the Gary Clinic the next day. I met with the board of directors of the Gary Clinic. I gave them my credentials and all they checked was the Indiana license number and they called my professor where I graduated from the residency. He gave them an opinion about my work and that was it. I was put on temporary privileges at Saint Mary in Gary.

"I was still living in Chicago so whenever I was on-call, I would sleep at the hospital. I stayed like that until October… when I had to report down to Fort Walters, Texas for my service. That was the Vietnam time.

"I was gone two years but… while I was in service, since income was not like nowadays physicians, I drove every other weekend from Texas to Gary – a good 18 or 19 hours – and worked in the Emergency Room at the Gary Clinic. It was strenuous but it was fun, too. I was much younger. I was 32 years old at that time and nothing bothered me. (The Gary Clinic changed its name to the Ross Clinic when it moved from Gary to Merrillville.)"

Srbislav Brasovan, M.D., OBSTETRICIAN/GYNECOLOGIST
MERCY HOSPITAL
(BEGAN IN 1968 IN GARY)

"Our first daughter, Kelly, was born at Mercy Hospital in 1967, long before ultrasounds. Family Practitioner Joe Siekierski, M.D., gave us a due date of July 14th and believed that we had miscalculated when labor did not begin until August 15th. I will never forget going to a White Sox game the week before she was born and having a man sit down next to me and ask when my baby was due. When I told him three weeks prior, he said nothing – just left and never returned!

"Labor was intense and fast so when we arrived at the hospital it was an emergency situation. I will always remember how wonderful and caring everyone was at the hospital and how they marveled at Kelly lifting her head and looking around in the delivery room!"

Dian Reyome, LONGTIME NORTHWEST INDIANA RESIDENT

"The Sister who was up in OB – Sister Natalia (Bleise, PHJC) – always took very good care of her patients. She always encouraged them to come back! They offered to comply – if they had a good sense of humor."

Mary Ellen Donovan, SECRETARY TO THE DIRECTOR
ST. MARY'S MERCY SCHOOL OF NURSING
(BEGAN IN 1945 IN GARY)

OB student Barb Smolen is pictured working in Gary in 1959.

Joint Fund Drive Pledges

By the end of 1971, solicitation for the Mercy-Methodist Suburban Hospital Fund Drive was in full swing. City Chairman, Wilbur Nicholas, announced that pledges had surpassed $112,000. A portion of that amount, directed by Mayor L. J. Titus in his role as vice president of the fund drive, totaled nearly $6,000, was pledged by city employees including police and fire departments. Mrs. Paul Heuring, chairman of solicitation for Hobart residents, noted that 14 teams of more than 250 women were participating in the pledge effort.

Fund drive kickoff

A group gathered in Hobart for the kickoff of the $3.4 million Mercy-Methodist Suburban Hospital Fund Drive. Pictured (l-r) are Robert Vinzant, M.D., and Mrs. John Reed receiving campaign material from Orval Kincaid, president of the drive; Paul Heuring, Hobart vice chairman; and Willard C. Boehlke, general chairman.

Reprinted by permission of the *Post-Tribune* (date unknown)

Clerk's office pledge

Among community donors supporting the hospital effort were employees in the office of the Hobart City Clerk who each pledged one day's pay for three years to the Mercy-Methodist Suburban Hospital fund drive. Pictured (l-r) are Mrs. Frank Bohling, Mrs. Kenneth Hoeg, Miss Renee Shannon, Mrs. Evert Anderson, Mrs. Dwayne Evensen and City Clerk Treasurer Mrs. O'olah B. Evans. Not pictured: Mrs. Mike Carbine.

Hobart Herald, September 23, 1971

Pictured here in 1971 is a sign at the construction site of the Hobart hospital, St. Mary Mercy Southeast.

Photo published in the *Hobart Gazette*, January 1973

A Field with a Dream – April 12, 1972

> *"All glory comes from daring to begin."*
> —Eugene F. Ware

Breaking Ground for the Hobart Hospital

The Herald

Hobart Edition

Northern Indiana's Largest Weekly Newspaper

VOL. XXVII NO. 18   THURSDAY, SEPTEMBER 28, 1972   10¢ A COPY

Hospital to open in Feb.

DOMINIC BAY, director of public relations for St. Mary Mercy hospital, was the special speaker at the monthly general membership meeting of the Hobart Chamber of Commerce. He was introduced by Henry Dykstra.

~~AN~~

An audible response greeted Bay's announcement that the hospital in Hobart would be ready to open its doors in February of 1973. This is the good news that everyone has been waiting for in Hobart.

Bay said that the facility will have 159 beds, 25 of which will be unoccupied except by approval of hospital authorities. It will feature basic medical, surgical, and obstetrical facilities.

THE FIRST FLOOR will house administration, 16 obstetrical units, kitchen, dining room, pharmacy, surgical laboratory, radiology, emergency, physical therapy, and a lounge area. The upper floors will be devoted to patient care.

The total cost of the hospital is 4 1/2 million dollars. To date not enough money has been collected for this project. Hill-Burton funds were not used for construction of the hospital because, according to Bay, they are too restrictive and a more satisfactory arrangement for building the hospital was made with a St. Louis Hospital Building Corporation. This group hired local help.

However, Bay said that Hill-Burton funds will be used, in part, for some of the hospital equipment, about $75,000 worth.

WORK ON THE HOSPITAL is progressing from the top down. Ac-

Continued on page 2

In 1972, a copy of the *Hobart Herald* sold for 10 cents. In September, the low-cost weekly newspaper featured word of a new high-cost hospital destined to open in Hobart early in 1973. The new 159-bed facility would feature basic medical, surgical, and obstetrical facilities at an estimated cost of $4.5 million.

The Herald, Hobart Edition, September 28, 1972

On November 28, 1971, a groundbreaking ceremony was held for the new St. Mary Mercy Hospital Southeast in Hobart, located at Highway 51 and 61st Avenue. The five-story, 142-bed, full-service structure would cover approximately 100,000 square feet on 85.5 acres of land. Cost estimate reports ranged from $3.8 million to $4.5 million. Among those present were church and community leaders. Shown (l-r) are: Orval J. Kincaid, president of Mercy-Methodist Suburban Hospital Fund Drive; Sister Martine Tenholder, PHJC, vice president, board of directors; Willard C. Boehlke, chairman of the general campaign; Sister Clarice Van Hoedt, PHJC, provincial superior of the Ancilla Domini Sisters; L. J. Titus, mayor of Hobart; Andrew G. Grutka, D. D., bishop, diocese of Gary; Charles E. Daugherty, president, lay advisory board; John Brincko, M.D., president, St. Mary Mercy Hospital staff; and Paul C. Bellendorf, administrator, St. Mary Mercy Hospital in Gary.

Hospital Building and Equipment Company, 1972

Shown here is an artist's rendering of the 184-bed (Hobart) St. Mary Mercy Hospital Southeast designed for completion in early 1973.

Great Lakes Regional Bulletin, Hospital Building and Equipment (HBE) News, JANUARY, 1972

On Watch – the Hobart Hospital

A structure emerges – April 12, 1972

Hobart construction – June 28, 1972

By December 30, 1972 hospital construction was nearing completion.

Photo published in the *Hobart Gazette*, JANUARY 1973

In Gary – A New Hospital Wing – May 1972

THE NEWLY OPENED five-story wing of Mercy Hospital, viewed here from the parking lot at 6th and Polk, will be shown during an open house from 1 to 5 p.m. today. Tours will be conducted every 5 to 10 minutes in the main lobby located in the new wing. The main entrance now faces west in the 6th and Polk parking lot. Bishop Andrew G. Grutka, head of the Gary Catholic Diocese, today blesses the $6.5 million facility during a morning mass in the hospital chapel.

Open house at Mercy today

(Post-Tribune photo by Elmer Budlove)

OPEN HOUSE AND DEDICATION
OF

THE NEW ST. MARY MERCY HOSPITAL
SUNDAY, MAY 21, 1972

Sunday, May 21, 1972, marked the dedication and open house ceremonies for the new multimillion dollar wing of St. Mary Mercy Hospital. More than 2,000 people toured the facility to see the latest in diagnostic and therapeutic services. The additional 132 beds were intended to relieve the admissions problem by bringing the hospital's total bed count to more than 350.

Among those attending the St. Mary Medical Center dedication and open house in 1972, Sister Wilma Boeving, PHJC, included her own handwritten identification of some of the guests.

Acts of Mercy, Vol. 8, No. 6 – June, 1972

Acts of Mercy

Vol. 8, No. 6   ST. MARY MERCY HOSPITAL – GARY, INDIANA   JUNE, 1972

DEDICATION AND OPEN HOUSE ISSUE

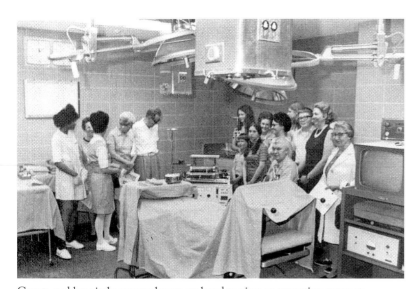

Guests and hospital personnel were on hand to view an operating room at the dedication and open house.

St. Mary Mercy Hospital, Gary

Acts of Mercy, Vol. 8, No. 6 – June, 1972

Meanwhile, Over in Hobart…

IT'S BEEN *Said* IN 2009…

"When St. Mary's was built in Hobart, it was considered a throw-away hospital. In other words… Ancilla Systems was going to… build a new hospital on the premises and tear down the existing hospital. That hospital was only supposed to last 10 years. The original hospital is still there even though it has been renovated. We also built the New Patient Tower, which truly was beneficial to St. Mary Medical Center and its status in the community."

Milt Triana, RETIRED HOSPITAL ADMINISTRATOR
ST. MARY MEDICAL CENTER
SPECIAL PROJECTS COORDINATOR
COMMUNITY HEALTHCARE SYSTEM
(BEGAN IN 1969 IN GARY)

IT'S BEEN *Said* IN 2009…

"When they built down here in 1972 in Hobart, everybody thought they were crazy… and they asked, 'Why are they building a hospital in the middle of a corn field'?

"The original plans were to tear the main hospital down. That's why they had all this land – to build a new facility – with doctors' quarters to teach – but it never went through. Instead… they just kept adding on to it."

Jim Wade, ENGINEERING MANAGER
MERCY HOSPITAL
(BEGAN IN 1960 IN GARY)
NOTE: At this writing in 2009, Jim Wade has worked at the Gary and Hobart hospital sites for 49 years and is the oldest active employee at St. Mary Medical Center.

IT'S BEEN *Said* IN 2009…

"There was a great need and people in the Hobart area had wanted this hospital for a long time. They wanted it to be the Hobart hospital. It of course was owned by Ancilla (Systems Incorporated) and I think there were some who were quite disappointed when it remained with Ancilla… and it did not belong to the city of Hobart."

Shirley Makivich Urbanek, R N, RETIRED | ST. MARY MERCY HOSPITAL | (BEGAN IN 1959 IN GARY)

1973 – Hobart to Have Long-Awaited Hospital

IT'S BEEN *Said* IN 2009…

"Laura Bracken was city clerk treasurer for around 43 years, longer than anybody. I believe she was in her 90s or maybe late 80s. Of course everybody in town was interested in getting this hospital and at one meeting, she said, 'I am absolutely not going to die until we get that hospital.' And, she didn't."

Virginia Curtis, LONGTIME HOBART COMMUNITY ADVOCATE/HISTORIAN

IT'S BEEN *Said* IN 2009…

"Before Hobart was built, I can remember having to drive neighbors into Gary and I would go through Glen Park to save time with people who were having a hemorrhage or something in my neighborhood. It's a scary thing to have to go that far to a hospital. So I went door to door to collect for this Hobart hospital."

Margaret Hart Swisher, AUXILIARY MEMBER, FORMER RN
GRADUATE OF ST. MARY'S MERCY SCHOOL OF NURSING, 1943

WAIT A MONTH

This sign, erected in January 1973, greeted southbound motorists on Interstate 65 near the 61st Avenue exits. Described as "probably premature" by a spokesman for the Indiana Highway Department District headquarters in LaPorte, it refers to St. Mary Medical Southeast in Hobart. At that time, the hospital was not scheduled to open until late February. Travelers who heeded the sign would have been further confused when they reached 61st Avenue because there was no indication which way to turn for the "mystery" hospital.

Reprinted by permission of the *Post-Tribune*, JANUARY, 1973

On January 28, 1973, the *Post-Tribune* reported that Hobart residents had a lot to be thankful for in 1973. The hospital they had dreamed about and worked on for years was about to become a reality with the official opening scheduled for February 1973.

The first floor was designed to house administration, an obstetrical unit, a kitchen, dining room, pharmacy, surgical laboratory, emergency room, outpatient service, physical therapy, information and admitting centers, chapel, gift shop, and employees' locker and lounge areas. The upper floors were to be for patient care. Vertical transportation was to be provided by four hydraulic elevators – two for passenger conveyance and two for food transportation and stretcher patients.

Nearly a decade later, a brochure touted the growth of the Hobart hospital: "The suburbs had grown. Availability of healthcare had not. In what had been a grass-filled field at the corner of Highway 51 and 61st Avenue, St. Mary Medical Center was built in Hobart. Easily accessible to all parts of Northwest Indiana… this growth is not at the expense of her sister hospital in Gary, but rather in concert with it – sharing services… to patients at both hospitals of talented hospital-based physicians and other key staff – sharing a commitment to provide quality healthcare – sharing a healthcare mission."

REACHING A FUND-RAISING GOAL
ST. MARY MERCY HOSPITAL SOUTHEAST

Hospital drive Hobart City Chairman, Wilbur Nicholas, points to the fund-raising goal that was reached early in 1973. Shown (l-r) are other local chairmen – Robert Vinzant, M.D., Bruce Sharp, M.D., and (kneeling) Charles Vigland. Standing next to Nicholas are District Chairman Paul Heuring and Business Collection Chairman, Nick Holzmer.

Hobart Gazette, JANUARY 11, 1973

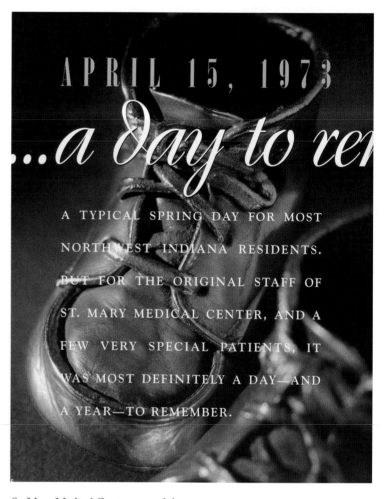

A welcome spring bloom

april 15/73 P.T.

METHODIST - SOUTH

HOBART MERCY

LASTER

Reprinted by permission of the *Post Tribune*, APRIL 15, 1973

APRIL 15, 1973 – AN OPEN HOUSE AT THE NEW HOBART HOSPITAL

APRIL 15, 1973

...a day to re

A TYPICAL SPRING DAY FOR MOST NORTHWEST INDIANA RESIDENTS. BUT FOR THE ORIGINAL STAFF OF ST. MARY MEDICAL CENTER, AND A FEW VERY SPECIAL PATIENTS, IT WAS MOST DEFINITELY A DAY—AND A YEAR—TO REMEMBER.

St. Mary Medical Center opened APRIL 15, 1973

Neighborly Care

The Board of Directors

and

The Sisters of St. Mary Mercy Hospital Southeast

of Hobart, Indiana

cordially invite you to

an Open House

in the new hospital

1500 So. Lake Park Avenue (Corner of 61st Avenue and Route 51)

on Sunday, April 15, 1973

from one to five in the afternoon

HOSPITAL LEADERS - 1973

SISTER MARTINE TENHOLDER, PHJC
Board of Directors President

PAUL C. BELLENDORF
Administrator

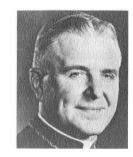

BISHOP ANDREW G. GRUTKA, D.D.
Gary Diocese

MARY GULYASSY
Assistant Administrator
Gary and Hobart

CHARLES E. DAUGHERTY
Advisory Board President

WALTER SALA, M.D.
Medical Staff President

SISTER CLARICE VAN HOEDT, PHJC,
Provincial

Inside the New Hobart Hospital

A spacious lobby greeted visitors.

Shown in the Physical Therapy Department is the large Hubbard Tank used for therapeutic treatments.

An auxiliary generator, located in the boiler room building, would handle all vital services in the event of a power failure.

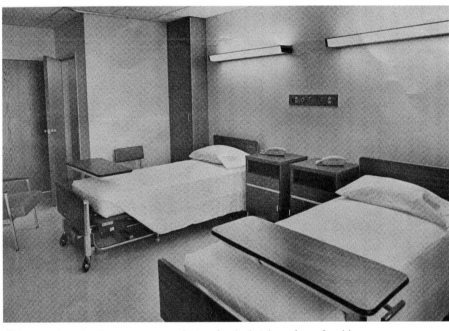

Private and semi-private rooms were designed to be bright and comfortable.

It's been *Said* in 2009...

"On October 13, 1987, we had a power outage in Gary. It was something because in those days we didn't have as much emergency power as today. Today, we could run the hospital on emergency power if we needed to. Back then we ran a lot of extension cords from our emergency power and we had to send a lot of our tests to Hobart."

Anthony "Tony" Costello, PhD
Site Director, Laboratory
St. Mary Medical Center
(began in 1976 in Gary)

A large well-equipped kitchen was designed for efficient food service to patients, visitors and personnel.

May 1973 – Bless This Hospital

Following the open house, the grand opening celebration for the new Mercy Hospital Southeast in Hobart was held in May 1973. Guided tours were arranged by hospital officials as the completion of the five-story, 184-bed general hospital marked the culmination of several years of planning and development. Crowds snaked along the perimeter of the hospital as visitors waited to catch a glimpse of their new facility.

Over 5,500 people toured the new Hobart hospital and were lined up to 61st Street outside the premises.

Acts of Mercy, Vol. 9, No. 5 – May, 1973

Bishop Andrew G. Grutka sprinkled holy water during the procession to bless the New Mercy Hospital Southeast in Hobart, located at 1500 S. Lake Park Avenue. Shown here (l-r) is Sister Wilma Boeving, PHJC, the hospital's associate administrator; Reverend Don Grass, pastor of Holy Angels Cathedral in Gary; and Bishop Andrew G. Grutka.

Acts of Mercy, Vol. 9, No. 5 – May, 1973

(l-r): Unknown, Myrtle King (second from left), unknown, Sister Esther Dolezal, PHJC, J. Delores Turner, Deloris "Cissy" Currin, Mary Turner, Sister Wilma Boeving, PHJC, Florence Jones, and unknown gentleman

Planting new life

Months later, in November, landscaping for the new Hobart Mercy Hospital was planned with funds provided by the St. Mary Mercy Hospital Auxiliary. Pictured (l-r) are: Mrs. Theodore Skager, co-chairman of the Hobart Gift Shop; Mrs. Mary Gulyassy, assistant administrator of Hobart Mercy Hospital; Mrs. R. P. Barnett, treasurer of the Gary Gift Gallery; Mrs. Earl Saxton of the Gary Gift Gallery; Mrs. Paul Heuring, auxiliary president; Mr. Paul Heuring; and Jerry Zelenka of the Hobart Nursery.

Hobart Gazette, November 1, 1973

April 24, 1973 — Open for Business and Babies

A collage of photos from one of the extensive St. Mary Medical Center Auxiliary scrapbooks shows people, events, and places in the brand new Hobart facility.

"For several years after the Hobart opening, we still had to go to Gary for Methodist and Mercy (hospitals), making rounds and observing Emergency Room coverage. We did that for several years but finally we were able to keep our practice only at St. Mary here in Hobart. That was a blessing.

"At the time they were talking about building the Hobart hospital, I can remember there was some discussion about Methodist and Mercy joining together to build one single hospital probably over in Glen Park… but it went by the wayside."

Dr. John O. Carter, M.D., Family Practice
Lake George Medical Center | (began at Mercy Hospital as an Intern in 1956)

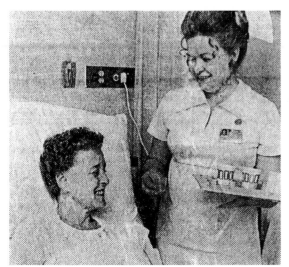

The First Patient

Photo reprinted by permission of the *Post-Tribune*, April 1973
Mrs. Larry Thomas of Merrillville (left), attended by Mrs. Sanford (June) Pangburn, RN, was the first scheduled patient admitted to Mercy Hospital Southeast after it opened.
For the record, the first female birth at the Hobart hospital occurred at 3:00 p.m. on April 24, 1973, when Mr. and Mrs. Joseph Johnston of Gary welcomed their infant daughter. The first newborn male was Patrick Higgins, born to Mr. and Mrs. Tom Higgins.
Acts of Mercy, Vol. 9, No. 6 – June, 1973

New Beginnings

Same Day Sisters

Mrs. Emanual Heridea and Mrs. William Cuevas of Gary, are sisters who each delivered daughters on the same day in the spring of 1974 at the Hobart hospital. Rosa Christine Cuevas, the older of the two newborns, was followed by her cousin, Corina Maria Heridea just seven hours and 40 minutes later.

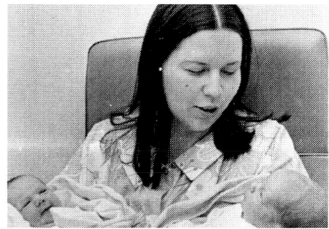

The First Twins

Mrs. Ronald (Sue) Monroe comforts Sharon and William, first twins born at the Hobart hospital. The Monroes, of east Gary, welcomed their newborns on May 8, shortly after the Hobart site opened on April 24, 1973. The Monroes also had three more children at home.

Acts of Mercy, Vol. 9, No. 6 – June 1973

Boy in Blue

IT'S BEEN *Said* IN 2009...

St. Mary Medical Center's First Boy

"Accustomed as I was to delivering babies, the eighth time for the Higgins family would prove to be somewhat different. On April 24, 1973, with our oldest daughter, Judy, at home to care for her siblings, I contacted Dr. Robert Penn of east Gary who recommended that we go to the new St. Mary Medical Center in Hobart.

"It was more convenient to our Merrillville home than the original St. Mary Mercy Hospital in Gary but, interestingly, the doctor was unfamiliar with the layout of the hospital and had to get directions from a staff member on how to get to the maternity area which may have been a first!

"A pink receiving blanket signifying the first baby girl born at the Hobart hospital was flying from a flag pole near the emergency entrance and I quipped to the Sister who met us that she might get a blue blanket ready for the arrival of our baby boy since we already had five girls and two boys. It was merely wishful thinking since I don't know if ultrasound even existed then.

"When I was taken into a room for the preliminaries, many of the required accessories were still in boxes – somewhere. Part of the wait was for the nurse leaving on a 'find' mission. Throughout the hospital, workers were still completing finishing touches, including in the labor rooms. When I was wheeled in to meet the doctor, there were two painters in white coveralls working on the walls. My immediate apprehension concerned their possible role. Were they going to watch, continue facing the walls, or just leave? It didn't take long. A birth was the last thing they wanted any part of so they left with their brushes and paint.

"As my husband, Tom Higgins, was waiting in the hallway, Dr. Donald Phillips – a friend of my husband's from the Army Reserves and the physician who delivered the first-born baby girl – passed the hall where Tom was standing and said to his nurses, 'See that guy? He has more kids than I delivered!'

"Patrick Edward Higgins was born at 5:05 p.m. and the Sister had a blue receiving blanket sent up the flag pole. Children were not allowed in the first floor maternity rooms, so during my recovery stay, Tom would bring our children to my outside window – across the mud since there was no lawn – so they could see the new family addition and talk through the screen.

"Just as it was at St. Mary Mercy Hospital in Gary, the hospital staff members, especially the Sisters, were magnificent – thoughtful, kind, and cheerful and willing to help in any way they could during that time."

Elizabeth (Betty) Higgins

Honoring the Babies — One Year Later

To mark the first anniversary of the opening of St. Mary Medical Center in Hobart, two guests of honor – the first girl and first boy born at the hospital – received honorary plaques. Shown (l-r) in 1974 are Mrs. Tom Higgins with son Patrick; Mrs. Virginia Rudovich, RN, head nurse of Labor and Delivery who was on duty during both births; Mrs. Joseph Johnston with daughter Lee Anne; and Assistant Administrator Mary Gulyassy.

Hobart Gazette, Thursday, May 1, 1974

Honoring the Babies — 25 Years Later

Taking care of you...for life.

St. Mary Medical Center

Patrick Higgins
Birthing Suites: 1973
Hospital's First Born

In 1998, 25 years after it opened, St. Mary Medical Center sponsored billboards around Northwest Indiana showing young adult, Patrick Higgins, holding his baby picture as the hospital's first-born male infant. "The slogan, 'Taking care of you… for life,' was certainly true," said Patrick's mother, Betty Higgins, "for hundreds of patients ever since."

Courtesy of Higgins family collection

Girl in Pink

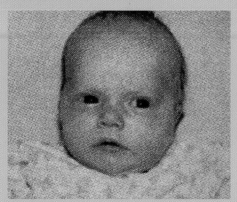

Lee Anne Johnston was the first female baby born at St. Mary Medical Center on April 24, 1973. She is shown here 25 years later in 1998 with her parents, Karen and Joe Johnston.

Reprinted by permission of the
Post-Tribune, May 25, 1998

Lee Anne Johnston - The first female baby.
Reprinted by permission of the *Post-Tribune*, May 25, 1998

In 1977, Hobart hospital's maternity ward was not only open to parental visits but also visits from both sets of grandparents. Proud parents Yolanda and Herman Matlock, Jr., show off newborn son, Lincoln Carl Matlock, (born March 9, 1977) to happy grandparents Sue and Herman Matlock, Sr.

Acts and Facts, APRIL, 1977

St. Mary Medical Center – Pediatrics in Hobart

From the PHJC Chronicles – May, 1986

MAY 21 – Open house was held for the Pediatric Department in Hobart. The Sisters attended. At this time, Father Langhals blessed the new department. The open house was for the medical staff and other interested people – employees, volunteers and those from the civic community.

CHJC, University of Notre Dame Archives

PEDIATRIC DEPARTMENT STAFF PHOTO – 2009

FRONT ROW (L-R): Sheila Davis, RN; Nurse Manager Alicia Hart; and Amanda Packham, RN

MIDDLE ROW (L-R): Heather Markwell, nurse fellow; Hollie Overman, RN; Melissa Thompson, RN; Janessa McKinley, unit assistant; and Amanda Scheuer, nurse fellow

BACK ROW (L-R): Heidi Koonce, RN; Mallory Zormier, unit assistant; and Donna Springman, unit assistant

THE PAINTINGS OF MADISON "MADI" CARTER

Madison "Madi" Carter

This is an excerpt of the tribute to Madi Carter that hangs beneath her photo in the St. Mary Medical Center Pediatric Unit:

"Madison 'Madi' Carter is the daughter of Dr. John E. and Kim Carter and the sister of Riley Carter. Madi passed away on January 16, 2006, after a long battle with liver disease. She was nine years old... Madi was very proud of her works of art and quite often gave them away as gifts. She left her family and friends with many beautiful treasures, some of which we hope you will enjoy while here in the Pediatric Unit. Madi would be so happy that her paintings are being shared with others."

"IN THE INNER PLACE WHERE TRUE ARTISTS CREATE, THERE EXISTS A PURE CHILD."

~ *Lawren Harris*

"*A new baby is like the beginning of all things – wonder, hope, a dream of all possibilities.*"

~UNKNOWN

A PATIENT'S MOTHER WRITES IN 2009...

My daughter is a young 19-year-old and she gave birth to my first grandson on January 24th. While our entire family was nervous, excited, and a bit frightened, all went well... From the moment we walked through the front doors and approached your greeters, my daughter was treated with warm welcomes, friendly soothing conversations, and nurturing treatments. I don't know the names of all the caring staff... but Cassie Johnson delivered the baby and was so comforting and reassuring, she made the delivery process seem easy. Jim, the anesthesiologist... was magnificent! Erin and Renee were two of the nurses who assisted.

I'm convinced it takes great leadership in any organization to build the kind of nurturing, welcoming culture we experienced during our visit. So, thanks also to you, Ms. Ryba, for your leadership at St. Mary Medical Center.

God bless you all,

Renee

Frances and Eddie Vega, of Portage, welcomed twin sons on December 14, 1990. Simos Joseph, was born at 1:38 p.m. and Angel Eddie was born at 1:39 p.m. The boys were the first twins to be delivered in the Labor, Delivery, Recovery and Postpartum (LDRP) Unit at St. Mary Medical Center in Hobart.

Hobart Gazette, DECEMBER 19, 1990

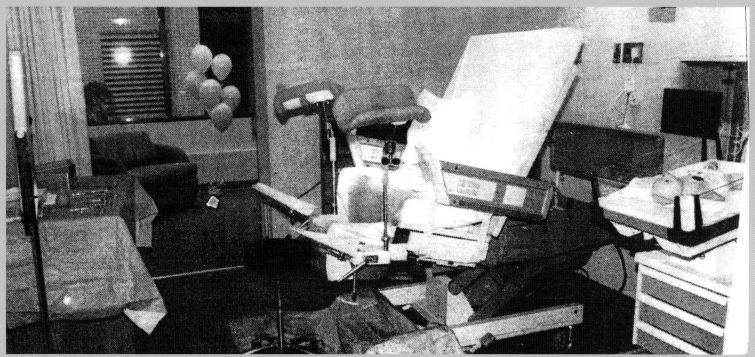

Shown here in 1990 when the Hobart hospital campus opened its new LDRP (Labor, Delivery, Recovery and Postpartum) Unit is a birthing suite with all its equipment. At various stages of a woman's pregnancy, some of the pieces would not be in the room simultaneously – only as needed.

Hobart Gazette, JANUARY 17, 1990

• THEN AND NOW

LABOR AND DELIVERY – LDRP...

Contributed by Nancy Sedoris, RN

LABOR, DELIVERY, RECOVERY AND POSTPARTUM DEPARTMENT STAFF PHOTO – 2009
FRONT ROW (L-R): Bea Williams, PCA II; Nurse Manager Alicia Hart; and Sheila Davis, charge nurse
MIDDLE ROW (L-R): Melissa Rivera, unit secretary; and Melissa Thompson, RN
BACK ROW (L-R): Tina Crum, RN; and Lynda Stringer, RN

POST-TRIBUNE

St. Mary center to reopen obstetrics facility in Hobart

By Steve Collins
Correspondent

HOBART — St. Mary Medical Center officials are planning to reopen the obstetrics unit at the hospital here.

Susan O'Leary, regional manager of public affairs for the hospital, said the project is under way and involves remodeling the building and adding on to the hospital. The cost of the project has not been announced.

She said the obstetrics unit will be put into an area of the hospital now occupied by the pediatrics ward. The pediatrics ward will be moved to another part of the medical center.

The obstetrics unit opened in 1973, but closed in February 1984, with hospital officials blaming a declining birth rate and a slow economy for the decision.

There were 9,666 live births in Lake County in 1980, but by 1986, that number declined to 6,829. Of that, there were 685 live births from Hobart and Lake Station in 1980, compared with 493 in 1986.

O'Leary said that in spite of the numbers, "The Hobart community has expressed a need for obstetrics services again."

She said that hospital officials hired a marketing research firm a year ago to survey the area to determine the need for obstetric services at St. Mary. The firm studied the number of births, the types of deliveries and other factors affecting mothers in Lake and Porter counties, she said.

O'Leary said the firm found that people preferred a more personalized, family approach to obstetrics.

The former obstetrics unit in Hobart had two labor rooms, two delivery rooms and 16 post-partum rooms, but the new unit will be smaller, O'Leary said. It will provide private birthing suites, each to be used for labor, delivery and post-partum.

Hospital officials are taking bids on the project, and no completion date has been announced.

Mike Fandl, regional director of facilities and plant for Lakeshore Health System Inc., which manages the hospital, appeared before a Hobart Plan Commission meeting last week to explain the project to city officials.

Fandl told city planners that the hospital addition will be 10 by 60 feet and that the area will be known as the Labor-Delivery-Recovery-Postpartum Birthing Center.

Plan Commission members decided the project does not represent major work and thus does not need Plan Commission approval.

The new Hobart obstetrics unit will compliment an obstetrics unit at another hospital managed by Lakeshore, St. Catherine Hospital in East Chicago.

In September 1989 it was announced that St. Mary Medical Center would reopen the Obstetrics Unit at the Hobart facility. The Pediatric Ward would be moved to another area to accommodate the obstetrical services. The Obstetrics Unit opened in 1973 but closed in 1984 with hospital officials citing a declining birth rate and a slow economy for the decision.

There were 9,666 live births in Lake County in 1980 but by 1986 the number had declined to 6,829. The Hobart community had nevertheless renewed its request for a personalized, family approach to obstetrical services. Mike Fandl, regional director of facilities and plant operations for Lakeshore Health System, Inc., said the new Obstetrics Unit would be known as the Labor, Delivery, Recovery, Postpartum Birthing Center.

Reprinted by permission of the *Post-Tribune*, SEPTEMBER 23, 1989

The word obstetrics is derived from the Latin word "obstare," which means "to stand by." Just as the field of obstetrics has undergone many changes over the years, the Labor, Delivery, Recovery and Postpartum (LDRP) unit at St. Mary Medical Center has maintained quality care for the Hobart area's women, infants and families.

The original unit opened in 1973 as a traditional labor and delivery area. Birth had gone from the natural, home-based process of earlier decades to a very sterile, orchestrated, and lonely affair. Labor rooms held more than one bed and patients were rushed down the hall to a cold, stainless steel table as they neared delivery. Dads were tolerated, barely, and visitor hours and numbers were strictly limited. Breastfeeding moms were a rare commodity and many staff members frequently discouraged moms from this type of feeding. Delivering physicians were both obstetricians and general practice doctors.

The Labor and Delivery Unit closed in the early 1980s but community demand brought the return of obstetrics to St. Mary Medical Center in January of 1990 when the hospital unveiled its new LDRP facility. Touted as a modern concept in birthing, the five suites combined labor, delivery, recovery and postpartum phases of birth in one room. The rooms themselves were very different from the former unit – this time providing a more homelike birthing process while providing a safe experience with medical and surgical intervention close at hand. Also added were Lamaze and breastfeeding classes for prospective parents. The delivery process had reverted to more of a natural occurrence than a pathology. The new facility surpassed expectations with more than 190 deliveries the first year. Dads were required to wear full surgical garb for delivery. The delivery area itself was open with little or no security. Visitors to other hospital departments often strolled through the unit to view the new babies. Obviously, there was a far greater fear of infection than of abduction! Many family physicians continued to deliver babies during this period. In the mid-1990s, the unit became locked with visitors required to register at a window before entering. The trend was to reduce the length of stay after a vaginal delivery to a mere 24 hours, as long as mom and baby seemed to be doing well. It wasn't long before insurers began to insist on a two-day stay for many postpartum problems that occurred after the first 24 hours. With the increase in patient stay and therefore patient census, and with deliveries increasing, an overflow unit with four beds and a small nursery was opened on the fourth floor of the hospital. The hospital averaged 30 deliveries per month by the year 2000 and continued to climb as did the national birth rate. Once more, change was coming to the labor and delivery area.

In February, 2005, a total of 10 LDRP suites and a four-bed triage and testing area were added. One suite contained a birthing tub to ease the pain of contractions and help the laboring mother relax. Part of the addition included a larger nursery capable of Level II newborn care. (Level II babies require more complex care than a "well" baby, such as oxygen or IV therapy.) The larger unit was welcomed by staff and patients alike but the rate of deliveries has continued to increase. Currently, the LDRP unit sees 80-90 deliveries per month and reached a record 96 births in June of 2009.

St. Mary LDRP offers many features to optimize the birth experience and give new families a successful start. In addition to the obstetricians and the few family practice physicians who deliver babies, several Certified Nurse Midwives are on staff to give low-risk mothers a more personal style of pregnancy care. Trained volunteer Doulas provide a specialized support for the laboring mother and her family, reducing the need for medication during the labor process. For mothers who seek more pain relief, several Certified Registered Nurse Anesthetists (CRNAs) are available around the clock to provide epidural anesthesia. Breastfeeding is no longer just tolerated, but strongly encouraged by the staff. Many of the LDRP staff nurses have become certified in specialties such as inpatient obstetrics and breastfeeding to better serve new mothers and their families. The staff of that original 1973 labor unit would be hard pressed to recognize LDRP today. Countless new grandmothers have commented, "My, how things have changed!" The LDRP unit at St. Mary remains open to future challenges and changes as the nurses and staff continue to stand by the mothers, babies and families in their care.

A Great Place To Start.

The Birthing Suites of St. Mary Medical Center, Hobart
The arrival of the Birthing Suites at St. Mary Medical Center was timely. Market growth indicated that a lot of young families were moving into the area, said Hospital Administrator Milt Triana, with families being attracted by a home-like environment with dimmed lights and soothing music. Further, labor, delivery, and recovery were available all in the same room, fathers could stay overnight barring health complications, and mothers could opt to have their newborns stay in the same room with them.
(Source: *Post-Tribune*, March 1, 2005)

"The angel statue sits in the Healing Hearts Garden. This is a garden that the nurses and doulas created to remember fetal loss.
We do remembrance services twice per year. In the fall we plant bulbs that bloom in the spring. We usually do the spring service around Mother's Day."
Alicia Hart, Nurse Manager
LDRP/Pediatrics

1973 – Joint Hospital Fund Drive Continues

At the time of the Hobart hospital opening, Broadway Methodist Hospital, a mile south of U.S. 30 on Broadway, had set a completion date of its new facility for late fall of 1974. While the majority of financing was being generated through Hill-Burton funds and special federal and private programs, both hospitals also continued to benefit from the joint Mercy-Methodist Suburban Hospital Fund Drive that was still under way in the communities the hospitals served.

(CHJC, University of Notre Dame Archives)

Shown here is Methodist Hospital - Northlake, 1972

The Joint Fund Drive – Disbursement and Opinion

Several years later, however, a *Post-Tribune* story of February 18, 1977, said St. Mary Hospital in Gary had been jeopardized from the expansion of suburban medical facilities, thereby creating a surplus of hospital beds that threatened the closing of the Gary hospital.

Jack Burton, director of planning at St. Mary Hospital, said at a Gary Public Library Information Center meeting that the state would advance the closing if it halted the use of beds in the oldest section. There were 160 beds in that section, built in 1917-1918.

Audience members questioned hospitals in the suburbs for planning and carrying on expansion to the detriment of healthcare in Gary.

As reported in the *Post-Tribune*, "Dr. Alfonso Holliday, III, director of the medical center of Gary, said there was no question that suburban expansion (had) resulted in a duplication of effort and an excess of facilities and services. He said (the) surplus of 500 hospital beds in the county came about because no one wanted to heed the studies. 'Racial factors were a motivating influence,' he said."

Holliday also said that the Joint Hospital Fund Drive did not fulfill the promise of fund drive organizers for the Gary hospitals and instead built in the suburbs out of all proportion to need. As a point of how much the Gary hospitals were shortchanged in disbursement of the 1967 fund drive proceeds, Holliday said St. Mary Hospital in Gary had facilities containing 168 beds that failed to conform to modern medical standards.

5WEST-MEDICAL ONCOLOGY/INFUSION CENTER STAFF PHOTO – 2009
BACK ROW (L-R): Camia Davis, LPN; Christian Isla, RN; Amanda Pundrich, PCA II (just left of B. Lane); Nurse Manager Betty Lane; Lakesha McLaurin, unit secretary (just right of B. Lane); and Scott Baker, RN
NEXT ROW (L-R): Tessie Biscocho, charge nurse (leaning on chair); Wanda Coates, RN; Kathy Barlog, LPN; Karen Bain, RN; and Pat Bridegroom, RN
SEATED (L-R): Laurel Meschede, RN; Alicia Ventura RN (a little back); Dana Reitz, PCA II; and Cindy Keller, RN

• THEN AND NOW

5WEST-MEDICAL ONCOLOGY/INFUSION CENTER...

Contributed by Betty Lane, RN, Nurse Manager

A PATIENT WRITES IN 2009...

Last Monday, my father once again needed to be admitted from Dr. Barai's office... My dad got the most wonderful care from every department and every person that touched him. From Joyce in dietary who made sure he got what I ordered at the last minute... to every CNA, tech, and nurse, Betty Lane can and should be so very proud of her staff. The warmth and kindness they display is special because you can tell it's (not just) 'their job'... They went that extra mile for us. A lot of people do great jobs every day, but you can always tell when it comes from the heart.

What is now known as 5West was previously located on the third floor of the East Tower. The unit was under the direction of manager Kay Wiseman, a longtime employee of St. Mary Medical Center. At that time, the Medical/Oncology Unit had 42 beds with 13 private rooms and 29 semi-private rooms. In the late 1980s and early 1990s, approximately 50% of the admitted patients were receiving chemotherapy. Sometime during the mid- to late-1990s, physicians began to open up infusion centers in their offices and chemotherapy treatments moved to the outpatient setting. The third floor evolved into more of a medical unit, caring for elderly patients with various disease processes as well as cancer. The unit size was decreased from 42 beds to 38 beds. In 1995, Maryann Kerr, the Intensive Care Unit (ICU) manager, became the manager of the third floor until 2004 when Betty Lane became the manager. When the New West Tower was being built, administration had a vision to revitalize the oncology program at St. Mary Medical Center out of a growing need within the community. In October 2004, the third floor found a new home on 5West with 27 spacious private rooms and a soothing décor along with an eight-chair Outpatient Infusion Center located on the south end of the unit. With the increasing oncology population in 2007, the oncology clinician role was developed. This has assisted in specialized training of staff along with increased confidence of our medical staff, knowing that their patients are receiving the very best care possible. Today, 5West cares for approximately 8,700 patient days a year while the Infusion Center continues to grow and sees approximately 3,600 patients a year.

IT'S BEEN *Said* IN 2009...

"(The field of orthopedics has changed dramatically since I began my practice.) I am now doing nothing that I was trained for in my residency. Total joints, arthroscopy, spine surgery and outpatient surgery are all new. Malpractice insurance was $2,000 a year and now it's $45,000 a year. Keeping up with medicine and surgery changes is a constant thing."

Robert S. Martino, M.D.
ORTHOPEDIC SURGEON | MERCY HOSPITAL
(BEGAN IN 1965 IN GARY)

A PATIENT WRITES IN 2009...

Dear Donna (Wieczorek, Joint Care Coordinator),

"Thank you!! Your humor, encouragement, and 'cheerleader' attitude made my stay in the Joint Academy much better! I was skeptical about the program since I thought I knew everything my second time around. Boy — was I wrong! I am so glad I participated — the pre-op education, 'Official Rules of Hips,' group therapy and lunch together were great. It is truly a great program you have started at St. Mary Medical Center..."
Best,
Nancy Moser

ORTHOPEDICS

A PATIENT WRITES IN 2009...

Dear Donna (Wieczorek, Joint Care Coordinator),

I want to thank you and all of the staff in the Joint Academy for the thoughtfulness and care that I received through both of my surgeries. I am not the most patient patient, but the nurses and aides went way beyond the call of duty... to make me as comfortable as possible at all times. To go downstairs to get me a diet Pepsi and not take money in return, or bringing me the morning paper are just small examples of the care that is given...
Sincerely,
David Z.

IT'S BEEN *Said* IN 2009...

"There was a 16-year-old boy who had a childhood problem with his hip and he just couldn't be around with his friends or do the things his friends were all doing. After his hip replacement, he was skateboarding and (joining) his friends. It was particularly gratifying to see that he would be able to enjoy his teen years and his young adult life without the burden of painful limps. It would have been a big stigma for him and now he is able to be pretty much normal."

Scott A. Andrews, M.D.
ORTHOPEDIC SURGEON
MEDICAL STAFF PRESIDENT, 2008-2010
(BEGAN IN 1994 IN HOBART)

IT'S BEEN *Said* IN 2009...

"I grew up in Crown Point and ultimately came back to join Dr. Robert Martino... One of the advances... that I brought from my training was to start patients moving the same day. Put them on a machine and let the machine bend the knee if it is total knee replacement. If it is a hip replacement, you get them up the next day and get them walking. Things like that — these little things we take for granted have made big, big advancements in the management of patients to get them through and get them out of the hospital."

Joe Koscielniak, M.D., ORTHOPEDIC SURGEON
MERCY HOSPITAL (EXTERN)
(BEGAN IN 1984 IN HOBART)

Joe Koscielniak, M.D., shown here in 1978 before beginning an internship.

Marking Time...1973

- *The Community Hospital in Munster opened for business.*

"In 1969, I did the first total hip replacement in Northwest Indiana at Mercy Hospital in Gary and was assisted by Dr. Luis DeMelo. The procedure took five hours compared to one hour today."

Robert S. Martino, M.D., ORTHOPEDIC SURGEON
MERCY HOSPITAL | (BEGAN IN 1965 IN GARY)

Young adults suffering from femoral bone-related conditions such as osteoarthritis, rheumatoid arthritis or avascular necrosis can find relief from a hip resurfacing procedure with the ReCap® Femoral Resurfacing System. Orthopedic Surgeon, Michael Leland, M.D., uses a model to demonstrate how the ReCap® Femoral Resurfacing Head obtains a more precise fit over the femur during a new minimally invasive procedure offered at St. Mary Medical Center.

Vim & Vigor, SPRING 2007

IT'S BEEN *Said* IN 2009...

GARY DAYS

"Ms. (Elvira) Bravo and I worked together at Mercy Hospital in Gary. She was a nurse's aide on the surgical/orthopedic unit where I worked on 3South. She was a hard worker and funny. She made everybody laugh and made everybody feel good. I think that was our atmosphere in those days. We were all a team and we all enjoyed some humor. There was not a lot of separation of, 'You do this and I will do this,' or 'This is my patient and that's your patient.' We all took care of everybody and all worked together."

Judy Elieff, DIABETES EDUCATOR, RETIRED
MERCY HOSPITAL | (BEGAN IN 1965 IN GARY)

"LET NO ONE EVER COME TO YOU
WITHOUT LEAVING BETTER
AND HAPPIER."

~ MOTHER TERESA

Shown here (l-r) in 2000 are a few staff members from the old orthopedic unit: Regina Wright, unit secretary; Romel Turner, PCA II; and Mary Munro, RN

Shown here in March 2009 on the new orthopedic unit are (l-r) Nicole Albrecht, RN; Arlene Evan, RN; Sue Chandler, RN; and Denise Niles, RN

Suzi Matheny, RN
Nurse Manager

• THEN AND NOW

3 WEST-ORTHOPEDICS...

Contributed by Suzanne Matheny, RN, BSN, NE–BC, BC
Nurse Manager 3West/Wound, Ostomy and Continence
Orthopedic Service Line Manager

Dating back to 1973, the 3West - Orthopedics Department was originally located on the old fourth floor in the old tower East Wing. There were 44 semi-private patient beds and the patients had to share rooms and bathrooms. The unit cared for general surgery and orthopedic patients with a length of stay that was much longer than it is today. It was not unusual for the first joint replacement patients to stay in bed for one week and remain in the hospital for at least two weeks after that. Many other surgical cases stayed for extended periods of time as well.

In 2004, this nursing unit moved to the New West Tower on the third floor and is now called 3West. The unit has 29 private rooms and provides care for surgical, orthopedic and general medical patients. There are still some long-term employees here from the old unit. Previous long-term nurse managers include Marianne Erdelac and Georgia Van Wormer from the 1970s and 1980s and Suzanne Matheny for 19 years since 1990.

In May 2008, we started a joint academy area on the new unit that allows for 10 beds for patients who have hip or knee replacements. The patients receive pre-op classes two weeks before surgery and bring their "coaches" with them to help during their recovery. They have group therapy in the "clubhouse" and group lunches for all patients, families and the coaches. The average patient length of stay ranges from one to three days.

Many of our general surgery cases stay less than a day now. We see shorter stays overall with an emphasis on outpatient surgery. Although this nursing unit has undergone changes over time, we still pride ourselves in premiere healthcare for all.

**CENTRAL STERILIZATION
STAFF PHOTO – 2009**
<u>Front row (l-r):</u> Mileva Miodragovic,
Beatrice Flores, and Kathy Fox, team leader
<u>Back row (l-r):</u> Cortnie Garrison, Willie
Macon, and Linda Simpson, team leader

Larry Winters
Central Sterilization Manager

● THEN AND NOW

1974 – CENTRAL STERILIZATION DEPARTMENT...

Contributed by Larry Winters, Manager

When the medical center opened in 1973, the Department of Central Sterilization did not exist as we know it today. The instrument cleaning, assembly and sterilizing were done by the nurses and Operating Room (OR) technicians. As the patient volume began to increase in the mid-1980s, an area adjacent to the Operating Room was designated for central sterilization.

Two pre-vacuum sterilizers, a sonic washer, and a new instrument washer were purchased for the "prep and pack" area and the new decontamination area of central sterilization.

The department also included the storeroom. The staff from the two areas was floated between the two departments. It wasn't until the early to mid-1990s that central sterilization became its own entity. Central sterilization was separated from the storeroom with its own staffing. The department reported to the director of surgical services with a team lead overseeing the day-to-day tasks of the department.

Later, in 2006, a manager was hired to take over the daily operations of the department. This was due to the increasing activities and volumes in the Operating Room and the changing requirements from the regulatory agencies that govern central sterilization.

There was also a need for more in-servicing of staff as the technology for the equipment and instrumentation became more advanced. Parallel to this is the development of different types of sterilization to sterilize the new equipment.

Training is also an important part of the daily operation of central sterilization. The team lead oversees the staff's performance and serves as a resource not only to our staff but also to the staff in surgery. Central sterilization and surgery work consistently as a cohesive unit to provide quality products to our valued customer, the surgeon.

Patient safety and physician satisfaction are the goals of central sterilization. Ongoing changes in healthcare require a well-trained staff. That is why we encourage the staff to become certified in central sterilization. The certification builds a solid foundation in the field and is becoming a requirement for employment at most hospitals. We recommend that any new uncertified staff members should become certified within 12-18 months of employment.

In 2009, two new instrument washers were purchased for the department with faster cycles and improved cleaning capabilities. Currently there are two decontamination rooms – one in surgery and one in central sterilization. Increasingly, the department cleans, assembles and sterilizes more than 1,350 trays a month.

Our departmental growth remains consistent with the volume of growth in surgery. This positions us as proud participants in the successful, future growth of St. Mary Medical Center.

HOSPITAL/COMMUNITY HAPPENINGS

1974 – MERCY HOSPITAL CHANGES ITS NAME

"Acts of Mercy," an in-house hospital publication for Gary and Hobart, featured a photo in October, 1974, of the Gary facility with its new name, St. Mary Medical Center. The name was legally changed and a sign was placed over the main entrance to reflect the new name. The name change, to apply to both hospitals in Gary and Hobart, followed the legal merger of the two institutions.

CHJC, University of Notre Dame Archives

LAW OFFICES
McCARTHY & TOOMEY

FRANK A. McCARTHY
JOHN E. TOOMEY

TIMOTHY C. TOOMEY
JOSEPH J. BURKE

JUN 10 1974

III WEST WASHINGTON STREET
CHICAGO, ILLINOIS 60602
TELEPHONE STATE 2-8577

June 6, 1974

Mr. Paul R. Kaiser
Administrator
St. Mary Mercy Hospital
540 Tyler Street
Gary, Indiana 46402

In re: Merger of Hobart into Gary

Dear Paul:

Enclosed please find the final Articles of Merger which have been filed and approved by the Secretary of State's Office in Indianapolis. You are now considered to be officially merged. We will now proceed in arranging for a change in name as was contemplated in the original agreement.

If you have any questions, just call. Kind regards.

Very truly yours,

McCARTHY & TOOMEY

By
Timothy C. Toomey

TCT:mmg
Enclosure

*Marking Time...*1974

- *On August 9, under pressure from the Watergate scandal, President Richard Nixon became the first president in the nation's history to resign. Vice president Gerald Ford succeeded and, on September 8, pardoned him.*
- *Vice President Gerald R. Ford of Michigan was sworn in as 38th president of the United States.*

In June 1974, Mercy Hospital Administrator Paul Kaiser received a letter from the law offices of McCarthy and Toomey in Chicago stating that St. Mary Mercy Hospital of Gary and St. Mary Mercy Hospital of Gary Southeast (as the Hobart hospital was then known) were officially merged. An official change in name was to follow.

The Bellendorf Hospital Plan

"Mary Gulyassy was top of the grade all the way around. She had a tremendous personality. She was accepted by everybody and was very outgoing. She was somebody who could think on her feet.

"Paul Bellendorf was an overall standout person who foresaw the whole hospital complex with plans for Gary and Hobart. He had a great vision and he had extensive administrative background. He, too, knew how to deal with people. He recognized Mary Gulyassy, for one thing. He wanted her to assume more responsibility, especially by starting the Department of Education."

Mary Ellen Donovan
SECRETARY TO THE DIRECTOR
ST. MARY'S MERCY SCHOOL OF NURSING
(BEGAN IN 1945 IN GARY)

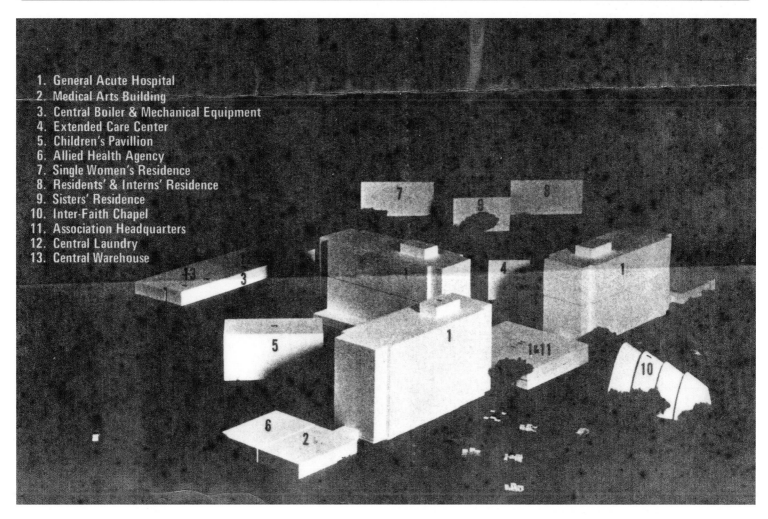

1. General Acute Hospital
2. Medical Arts Building
3. Central Boiler & Mechanical Equipment
4. Extended Care Center
5. Children's Pavillion
6. Allied Health Agency
7. Single Women's Residence
8. Residents' & Interns' Residence
9. Sisters' Residence
10. Inter-Faith Chapel
11. Association Headquarters
12. Central Laundry
13. Central Warehouse

According to Mary Ellen Donovan, Paul Bellendorf envisioned a long range hospital plan for St. Mary Mercy Hospital Southeast, as it was called, that would become a major 750-bed medical center with an extended care facility, a medical office building, a heliport, and a 1,500-car parking lot. The new plan – that originated in approximately 1974 or 1975 – was to follow a campus concept based on the latest demographic and hospital facilities studies. Studies showed an urgent need for such a center in east Lake County no later than 1985. Included in construction were the main portions of the hospital and additional areas like the Central Boiler and Medical Arts Building, etc. Among the concepts that never materialized were Extended Care, Allied Health Agency, a Single Women's residence, Children's Pavilion, and a Sisters' residence.

Courtesy of Mary Ellen Donovan
former Secretary to the Director
St. Mary's Mercy Hospital School of Nursing

Poor Handmaids of Jesus Christ – Silver Jubilee

(L-R) Bishop Andrew G. Grutka, D.D, bishop of Gary Diocese, poses with PHJC Sisters Wilma Boeving, Bertram Boeving, Agatha Niebrugge , Dorothy Marie Gaydos and Agnes Muehlenfeld. The occasion, June 25, 1974, marked the silver jubilee of the Sisters with the religious order of the Poor Handmaids of Jesus Christ. (Sister Wilma Boeving, PHJC, was assigned to St. Mary Mercy Hospital in Gary in 1967 as assistant administrator and two years later became associate administrator. In 1977, she advanced to fellowship status in the American College of Hospital Administrators, a professional society of more than 7,000 leading hospital and healthcare administrative personnel in the United States and Canada.)

Acts of Mercy, Vol. 10, No. 7 – July, 1974

Shown here in a photo from the mid-1970s are the Sisters of The Poor Handmaids of Jesus Christ associated with St. Mary Medical Center – Gary/Hobart.
Bottom row (L-R): PHJC Sisters Genevieve Biesiada, Beata Scherneck, Willibalda Heidt, Philomene Pawlik and Gabriel Giesken.
Top row (L-R): PHJC Sisters Ann Verbick, Wilma Boeving, Catherine Pavlovich, Andre Klein, Bertram Boeving and Catherine Thelen.

1975 – PAUL R. KAISER – INDIANA HOSPITAL ASSOCIATION BOARD

In 1975, St. Mary Medical Center Administrator Paul R. Kaiser was elected to a three-year term as a trustee on the board of directors of the Indiana Hospital Association.

Acts of Mercy, NOVEMBER, 1975

HOSPITAL/COMMUNITY HAPPENINGS

A UNION VOTE

1976 Convent Chronicle (Continued)

March 25   A red letter day in the history of the Hospital in form of Voting Day No 1 for Employees of St Mary Medical Center whether they want "Union" here in the Hospital. Sister Hillibalda was first to vote and her ballot was rejected as was that of all the sisters and certain employees

March 26   Voting also took place in Hobart today. The ballots were under strict security and brought to the Cafeteria Meeting Area and the votes were counted in presence of any one who wanted to observe. After much stress and tension the result was "No."

Father Longhels led the assembly in prayer of St. Francis "Make me an instrument of Peace." The Union was not welcome here.

Although the majority of PHJC chronicle entries were typed in later years, this 1976 *Convent Chronicles* entry is a handwritten account of a union vote taken at Mercy Hospital.

CHJC, University of Notre Dame Archives

ONE BIG PICNIC

September 12   A first in St. Mary Medical Center History in a Picnic for all Employees held at Sauzer's Park located on routes 30 at 41 in city of Schererville. All sisters were included in the near 1000 employees who took advantage of the food, contests, bingo, rides and fun.

September 7   Christian Life Commission, chaired by Sister Wilma met in C. Kasper Hall room 109, 4 PM to 6 PM followed by pick up supper in Cafeteria

As recorded in the 1976 *Convent Chronicles*, a first all-employee picnic was held at Sauzer's Kiddieland on September 12, 1976. Also noted on September 7 is the Christian Life Commission meeting. It is believed that this was the original Christian Awareness Committee.

CHJC, University of Notre Dame Archives

CHRISTIAN AWARENESS COMMITTEE – 2009

BACK ROW (L-R): Laura Labadie, Quality Assurance; Susan Nowak, Storeroom and Receiving; Carol Reeves, Storeroom and Receiving; Debra Jenkins, Mission Effectiveness; Karen Zanolla, Food and Nutrition Services; and Kelly Grata, Patient Registration
MIDDLE ROW (L-R): Carolyn Johnson, Food and Nutrition; Gale Hacker, Environmental Services; Kimberly Van Eerd, Human Resources; Len Ayers, Jr., Food and Nutrition Services; Roz Jevtic, Marketing and Community Relations; Carol Ochwat, CFNI Finance; and Sister Mary Ellen Goeller, PHJC, Mission Effectiveness
SEATED (L-R): Dee Bedella, Sleep Center; Sara Pierce, Managed Care; Laurie Edmond, Managed Care; and Irene Pacheco, Patient Accounting
NOT PICTURED: Irma Baca, Laboratory; Ann Dumbauld, Lake George Clinic; Heidi Smith, Nursing Administration; and Alberta Watts, Lake George Clinic

Judy Smith, compensation and benefits analyst at St. Catherine Hospital, previously worked at the Gary and Hobart hospital sites, and was a member of the Christian Awareness Committee for many years. She was instrumental in establishing St. Mary Medical Center's Memorial Tree located in the Memorial Walkway.

CHRISTIAN AWARENESS COMMITTEE...

Contributed by Sister Mary Ellen Goeller, PHJC Regional Director of Mission Integration

In January 1976, the "Christian Awareness Committee" was formed at St. Mary Medical Center Gary/Hobart. It was established to work hand-in-hand with the Pastoral Care Department in meeting the spiritual needs of the patients and employees. It was composed of the personnel of both hospitals. This resulted in having all involved with the spiritual aspects of the hospital complex.

Committee managers helped get the committee off the ground and, today, the group is also comprised of employees from diversified departments within St. Mary Medical Center. While members have served for varying lengths of time – some for many years – the committee conducts fund-raising drives for local citizens. Also sensitive to the needs of employees within the hospital, the committee has assisted "some of its own" hospital employees during the last several years.

One employee reach-out initiative is a special memorial for deceased staff members. A Memorial Walkway is located outside the East Tower below the flag pole and is comprised of bricks inscribed with the names of deceased employees. Generally held in the fall, the memorial service includes chaplains who partner in the committee's effort and is attended by family members and co-workers from the department where the employee worked.

IT'S BEEN *Said* IN 2009...

"Back in 1997, the Christian Awareness Committee began having memorial services for employees who passed away while they were employed at the hospital. I can remember during the first memorial service, Adele Dungy, a radiology technician, sang 'His Eye is on the Sparrow,' and there was actually a sparrow circling around above us as she was singing. Everyone was talking about it and how it was such a coincidence. They felt as if God was watching over the (service). This committee continues to have a memorial service acknowledging employees who have passed away."

Judy Smith
COMPENSATION AND BENEFITS ANALYST
ST. CATHERINE HOSPITAL | (BEGAN IN 1987 IN GARY)

Also under way is a restricted fund known as the Employee In Need Fund where employees can request assistance if they are in need of some emergency help. A sub-committee reviews the documentation and meets confidentially with the employee. We began giving out school supplies and smoke detectors in 2006 to assist with children's needs and to keep families safe.

The generosity of St. Mary Medical Center staff members, volunteers, and physicians allows the Christian Awareness Committee to answer the needs of many – inside the hospital and well into the Hobart community. In the end, in our focus to help others, we reap intangible benefits from those we serve.

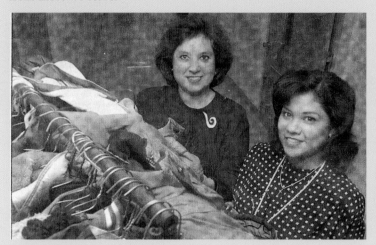

HOSPITAL COAT DRIVE – 1997
St. Mary Medical Center staff members Irene Pacheco and Teresa Pedroza were among volunteers who collected coats and other clothing for needy families. From the project's inception in 1993 until 1997, more than 1,600 coats had been collected.

Reprinted by permission of *The Times*, NOVEMBER 28, 1997

As a thank you to St. Bridget's School for the students' "penny wars" fund-raiser to purchase holiday gifts for the St. Mary Medical Center Giving Tree Program, members of St. Mary Medical Center's Christian Awareness Committee provided lunch at the school for students and faculty members.
COMMITTEE MEMBERS IN BACK ROW (L-R):
Gale Hacker and Jackie Juskevice
SECOND ROW (L-R): Karen Zanolla, Irma Baca, Debra Jenkins, and Carol Reeves
FRONT ROW (L-R): Susan Nowak and Len Ayers

Hospital Headlines, MARCH 2009

IT'S BEEN *Said* IN 2009...

"I became a member and continue to be a member of the Christian Awareness Committee because of my commitment to helping others less fortunate than myself, and providing a voice for others who are unable to speak or help themselves through no fault of their own. So many people have been instrumental in my life through my ups and downs, my trials and tribulations, and have given to me not only monetarily but spiritually as well. This is just my small way of giving back. I believe a man's best accomplishment is to love God first, love yourself, and love others as you would have them love you."

Len Ayers, Jr.
DIRECTOR, FOOD AND NUTRITION SERVICES
(BEGAN IN 1998 IN HOBART)

IT'S BEEN *Said* IN 2009...

"I joined the Christian Awareness Committee in 1995. I have been on it for 14 years and have never regretted joining. I had just lost my husband and I actually thought it was a prayer group and I wanted to be really close to God at that time in my life.

After attending several meetings, I found out it was a wonderful committee that helped a lot of people in the community... and helping other people brought joy to my heart. My favorite project is the Giving Tree... for children in the community who are less fortunate than we are. Employees, visitors and doctors purchase Christmas gifts... and we schedule a date and place before Christmas where the parents can pick up their gifts for their children.

"The Employee In Need Fund is a very touching project because the employees give to their fellow co-workers whether they know them or not. They just know that someone is in need."

Irma Baca, PHLEBOTOMIST II
ST. MARY MEDICAL CENTER
(BEGAN IN 1993 AT ST. CATHERINE HOSPITAL)

"A journey of a thousand miles must begin with a single step."
~Lao-Tsu

With Beginnings in Gary • THEN AND NOW

ALCOHOLISM TREATMENT PROGRAM...

Contributed by Gene Burkat, Former Director of Substance Abuse Services

The Alcoholism Treatment Program (ATP) was established in 1977 at St. Mary Mercy Hospital in Gary. It was later renamed the Center for Addiction Treatment. When the methadone program, called the New Life Center, opened in 1991, I was named the program supervisor. When the director of the Center for Addiction Treatment resigned in 1992, I was given that position to oversee the Center for Addiction Treatment inpatient and outpatient programs and the New Life Center methadone program.

Leo Cooper, M.D., was the medical director of the program when I began in 1981 and was followed a year later by William Washington, M.D. Dr. Washington is still the medical director for the New Life Center which is the methadone treatment program located in the old Ambulatory Care Unit right across the street from the former Gary hospital site.

With the methadone program there were a lot of regulations, a lot of different agencies involved. We had to get approval from the Food and Drug Administration, the State Methadone Authority which in our case was also the Division of Addiction Services, and the Drug Enforcement Administration. We had to put things into place so that all those agencies were comfortable with what we were doing.

One of the early patients left the program and opened Serenity Club, Inc., a social place where people could get involved after treatment. Father Ken Grabner obtained $1,000 seed money to help start the club in 1977 which is today known as Serenity House of Gary, Inc. Original facility planners purchased an old, closed tavern that still had a bar in it. Naturally, alcohol was no longer served once it became the Serenity Club. It was located at 3401 West 25th Avenue in Gary. In 1985, the club moved to 3825 Broadway. That location experienced some structural damage from a storm around 2006 and had to vacate its location.

IT'S BEEN *Said* IN 2009...

"The Drug Enforcement Administration (D.E.A.) officers had come to the unit to make their first inspection of our program after it opened. These were always surprise inspections with no warning. Part of the inspection involved taking an inventory of all methadone on the unit and a count of all dosage amounts we had dispensed since opening. After the inspection, they met with me to share their findings. They were amazed to discover that our dispensing records and inventory on hand were only off by one quarter of one tablet. They said that they had never encountered such a record."

Gene Burkat
FORMER DIRECTOR OF SUBSTANCE ABUSE SERVICES
ST. MARY MEDICAL CENTER
(BEGAN IN 1981 IN GARY)

Lisa Wein, drug abuse counselor for St. Mary Medical Center's Alcoholism Treatment Program, was featured in a 1988 *Times* story called *"Helping others live one day at a time,"* in which she described such things as her outpatient counseling sessions, intermittent calls from the in-patient wing of the hospital's treatment center, and the importance of teaching young children about drug prevention.

IT'S BEEN *Said* IN 2009...

"There was an obvious need. The Alcoholism Treatment Program at that time was considered state-of-the-art. It was the first inpatient hospital-based program that was opened in this area. Going from a non-medical detoxification setting to a hospital-based program was quite a change for me. It was very exciting.

"We need another addiction program like we had at St. Mary to operate in a hospital setting. I do see programs. In other hospital areas, they have detoxification but it is a far cry from inpatient care."

Lisa Wein, FORMER OUTPATIENT MANAGER
ALCOHOLISM TREATMENT PROGRAM, ST. MARY MEDICAL CENTER
(BEGAN IN 1978 IN GARY)

IT'S BEEN *Said* IN 2009...

"One woman in her early forties was supporting her addiction as a street prostitute by the time she came to us. She was so affected by her alcoholism and drug addiction. Her alcoholism was primary. I actually thought she had brain damage. I had really questioned her ability to benefit from the program. Down the road, she not only achieved recovery successfully but she eventually became a counselor in Illinois. So this was quite a change from being a street prostitute.

"What we did with everyone who came to our door was plant a seed. With addiction, like with other chronic illnesses, it really comes down to what the person is willing to do..."

Lisa Wein, FORMER OUTPATIENT MANAGER
ALCOHOLISM TREATMENT PROGRAM, ST. MARY MEDICAL CENTER
(BEGAN IN 1978 IN GARY)

May 4, 1993

Mr. John A. Giandelone, Deputy
Director/Contract Management
State of Indiana
Division of Mental Health
402 West Washington Street, Room W353
Indianapolis, Indiana 46204-2739

RE: New Life Center
       DAS I.D.# 93-4538

Dear Mr. Giandelone:

It is with deepest regret that I inform you that Lakeshore Health System, d/b/a St. Mary Medical Center, is unable to extend our contractual relationship beyond June 30, 1993.

New Life Center has provided a vital service in our community and Lakeshore Health System is proud to have been its sponsor. Due to financial considerations that must be urgently addressed, Lakeshore cannot renew the contract for another year. I trust you will seek another agency in our community willing to carry forth with this much needed service.

Sincerely,

Beth Kaminski
Senior Vice President, Operations
Lakeshore Health System

cc: Robert F. Tyburski
       Office of Resource Development
       Division of Mental Health

BK/wt

When the sale of St. Mary Medical Center - Gary was imminent, Lakeshore Health System canceled its contract with New Life Center. A letter followed shortly thereafter in which patients were reassured that the New Life Center would not close.

June 3, 1993

TO ALL NEW LIFE CENTER PATIENTS

Many of you have been following the recent articles in the newspapers regarding the sale of the hospital and negotiations with Summit Medical Management, Inc. All indications are that Summit will be purchasing St. Mary Medical Center, Gary.

We felt that it was important to inform you as to what the sale means to you. We have been busy trying to secure the position of the New Life Center since the announcement was first made on March 6, 1993 of the sale of the hospital. In talking with outside organizations, we decided to support an agreement with the Gary Board of Health to take over the operation of our program. We believe that this arrangement will prove to be the most beneficial to you, our patients. The State of Indiana, Department of Mental Health, who certifies substance abuse programs in our State and who further provides part of our funding, is supportive of this change. We are currently in the process of obtaining needed approval from Federal agencies. We have been assured by St. Mary Medical Center that we can continue to occupy our current space. As the opportunity presents itself, we will be talking with the new buyer (Summit) in the hope of establishing a mutual relationship whereas New Life Center can remain at its current location. Should that not be possible, we will negotiate a temporary agreement for the current location until such time as another location can be established and approved by State and Federal agencies.

Please be assured that New Life Center will not close after June 30th. We are working for you but we need your help in accomplishing this. Our only revenue besides the partial assistance we receive from the State is our patient fees. We need both to survive. We are doing our part - please do yours by paying regularly and keeping your account current.

We will provide more information as it is available to us.

KEEP THE FAITH.

_____
GENE BURKAT
Director

_____
DEBRA D. DOTSON
Program Supervisor

*Marking Time...*1977

1978

- *Nobel Prize in Science – Allan McLeod Cormack (US) and Godfrey Newbold Hounsfield (UK), for developing computed axial tomography (CAT scan) X-ray technique.*

Heroin center to open in Gary

Methadone is treatment

By Robin Biesen

Staff writer

The first hospital-based program for methadone treatment of drug addiction in Northwest Indiana is set to open today at St. Mary Medical Center in Gary.

According to Eugene Burkat, who will oversee operation of the outpatient facility, there is a great need for methadone treatment in the area.

"Even before anything about the facility was published, we were getting calls from people who felt they needed the treatment," Burkat said. "We have more than 50 people on a list waiting for the program to begin.

"Once we're open, we think every person we see will bring another 10 to the center," he added.

A similar program based at Wishard Hospital in Indianapolis typically treats 200 patients per day, he said.

There is one private methadone program in Northwest Indiana.

Reprinted by permission of the *Post-Tribune*, APRIL 1, 1991

ABSTINENCE PLEDGE

Gary Mayor Richard G. Hatcher (left) signs a placard pledging to abstain from alcohol in observance of the "I'm Not Drinking Today" campaign of St. Mary Medical Center and its Alcoholism Treatment Program. Pictured with him are St. Mary's Administrator John Dandridge, Jr., and Associate Administrator Denise Williams. The program focused on greater public awareness on alcohol abuse and the problems caused from it both locally and nationally.

Reprinted by permission of the *Post-Tribune*, APRIL 5, 1984

DID YOU KNOW?

Serenity House of Gary, Inc. opened in 1980 as a continuum of care after primary treatment for alcoholism and drug addiction is provided. Staff members are comprised of recovering alcoholics and/or those who are trained to assist people with addiction. Services were originally provided for eight male residents but were expanded to include eight female residents in November 1990.

Care continues today at Serenity House where people live and are helped with their needs, including job placement. The patients who have no other place to go and have no family support are given structure to their lives. Serenity House opened in August of 1980 at 439 Marshall Street in Gary. On September 1, 1998, it moved to its present location on a nine-acre site at 5157 Harrison Street in Gary.

The Alcoholism Treatment Program closed in approximately 1994 and probably stayed open another year after Summit Medical Management bought St. Mary Medical Center - Gary.

1977
HOBART HOSPITAL EXPANSION ANNOUNCED

The $6.4 million Hobart hospital expansion plan was to include a Medical Arts Building and ancillary services.

In May 1977, plans were announced by Administrator Paul R. Kaiser to expand St. Mary Medical Center in Hobart. Several areas of the hospital were to be housed in the new quarters, including the Department of Education, Pastoral Care and physicians' offices. In providing rental space for 25 to 30 physicians, the close proximity to the hospital would be beneficial to both patients and physicians, hospital officials said.

Additionally, it would include X-ray, laboratory, physical and occupational therapy, an emergency room, pulmonary services, electrodiagnostic services, nursing services, obstetrical, pharmacy, surgery, dietary, a 25-bed pediatric unit, and administrative offices.

Kaiser said the need for the expansion came quickly. The hospital had opened several years earlier as a 159-bed facility and by 1977 was operating at a capacity of 184 beds. Hospital occupancy surpassed 90-percent.

"Healthcare needs in both Gary and Hobart are expected to increase in the years to come," Kaiser said in a *Hobart Gazette* article of May 1977. "It is our intent to prepare today for tomorrow's expected increase in demand for services."

Construction was scheduled for completion at the end of 1979.

1978
HOSPITAL/COMMUNITY HAPPENINGS

Calvin Green, mayor of Hobart (seated) issued a proclamation in honor of National Hospital Week to Administrator Paul R. Kaiser (left) and Mrs. Mary Gulyassy, associate administrator – Hobart operations. A similar proclamation was issued by Gary Mayor Richard Hatcher.   *Acts and Facts,* MAY, 1978

Hobart Adds Five-story Ancillary Facility

Under construction in 1978 was the five-story Hobart ancillary facility. Work on the addition was approximately 25% complete in this photo.

Acts and Facts, Vol. 14, No. 5 – May, 1978

This photo, taken in early September, 1978, shows construction progress. The "old" section is obscured by the new construction when viewed from Indiana 51 at the previous entrance to the visitors' parking lot.

Acts and Facts, St. Mary Medical Center publication Gary and Hobart, September, 1978

Mother Mary Katherine Kasper Beatification in Rome

Mother Mary Katherine Kasper was beatified in Rome, Italy, on April 16, 1978. The order received official word that Pope Paul VI would announce that Mother Mary was among the Blessed of the Church. Poor Handmaids from America, Europe and India made the pilgrimage to the Vatican for the three-day beatification ceremonies. Overflow crowds estimated at 10,000 were present inside and outside the church.

His Holiness Pope Paul VI pronounced the proclamation of beatification. *Acts and Facts*, Vol. 14, No. 5 – May, 1978

(Above) This portrait of The Blessed Mother Mary Katherine Kasper was displayed in the Vatican as she was beatified.

(Right) Thousands gathered in St. Peter's Square to witness Mother Mary's beatification.

Acts and Facts, Vol. 14, No. 5 – May, 1978

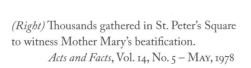

Gary Intensive Care Unit Dedicated

A spacious new Intensive Care Unit (ICU) on the fourth floor of the Gary hospital was dedicated in 1978. With room for seven patients, one separate room was designated as an isolation area. Provision was also made for specialized equipment for Pediatric Intensive Care. The new unit included such features as centralized monitoring of heart rate and rhythm. Heart patterns from each of the seven bedside monitors would appear on a centralized scope and the nursing staff could maintain 24-hour surveillance of each patient.

A Career in Gary and Hobart –
One Nurse's Story Spanning the Decades

It's been *Said* in 2009...

Maryann Kerr during nursing school days

"I started right out of high school in 1957 and trained at St. Mary Mercy Hospital. I graduated from the School of Nursing in Gary in 1960 and was hired as a pediatric staffer. I fell in love with pediatrics. Sister Ida (Volk, PHJC) was the nun there and she was just a little fireball who loved kids.

"Eventually, I went to 3North which was a surgical unit and did that part-time for several years until the West Wing of St. Mary's opened sometime in the late 1960s. Then I moved to 3West and worked part-time around my husband's schedule. I ended up having three daughters. In those days, there was no such thing as pregnancy being an illness. You had to quit your job and then come back again.

"We started doing open heart surgery in downtown Gary in the early 1970s and Dr. Fred Weidman was our first open heart surgeon. The postoperative patients after ICU would come up to 3West so I really became interested in that field.

"Sister Judian (Breitenbach, PHJC), who was the director of nursing at the time, wanted me to develop a Cardiovascular Postoperative Unit in downtown Gary. They transferred me to the Coronary Care Unit to learn critical care, EKG, and that kind of thing. I went from coronary care to 4West. That was my first nursing manager job.

"I was approached one day to see if I would be interested in opening the Intensive Care Unit in Hobart. I set up an eight-bed Intensive Care Unit on the second floor of St. Mary in Hobart when it opened in 1973.

"The first day was pretty wild although we had everything, at least all the equipment we needed. At the time Dr. Jack Kamen was the head of the Intensive Care Unit in downtown Gary. He was a wonderful man. Dr. John T. Scully was actually the first internist in the city of Gary. They became co-directors of the Intensive Care Unit here. It was called Intensive Coronary Care Unit or ICCU. They really helped teach me and guide me in the patient care that I needed to learn more about. At first, I had to work weekends because there was not enough staff. Eventually, being a new hospital, we attracted new nurses. They told me they would only open enough beds that we had staff to take care of, but of course that didn't happen. Soon we had all eight beds filled. It was very interesting and very challenging but fun."

Maryann Kerr, R.N., RN, Nurse Manager
ICCU & Medical Oncology, retired
Mercy Hospital | (began in 1960 in Gary)

Intensive Care in Hobart

Don't give up

"Ten years ago, a gentleman who was a dentist and a real workaholic wasn't very good at taking care of himself. Apparently, he had hypertension for a long time and never treated it. He came in and he had a large intracerebral hemorrhage and it took every medical specialty a month, basically, just to get him to survive. About three days into it, there was some thought that maybe what we were doing really wasn't in his best interest. I explained to all of the other attendings and to his family that the size of the hemorrhage was very large but it was also not necessarily indicative of the final injury. We had to get him through the point where the injury would resolve and the blood would resolve before we could really see how much damage was really done. I sort of stuck to my guns and said, 'We have to keep going.'

"This gentleman was 'type A' before he had this problem and after. He wasn't going to give up and he went from the ICU to the medical floors and he was still pretty debilitated. He ended up going to a nursing home for about six months but continued his therapy. He is not able to work in his profession now but he lives at home. He walks, he talks, he drives, he does the cooking for his wife who is still working. He has a little bit of a limp and some trouble with a hand but he is otherwise pretty much able to do whatever he wants to do.

"Neurologists sometimes tend to be the last ones to jump off the ship because we have seen these incredible recoveries. The brain sometimes can do some amazing things."

Mark Simaga, M.D., Neurologist
St. Mary Medical Center | (began in 1997 in Hobart)

A patient writes in the mid-1970s…

I spent five weeks in the Hobart hospital with a heart attack. My Intensive Care and floor care were excellent. I had open heart surgery three months later in your Gary hospital. My care in C. V. U. was something to write a sonnet about. Your Sister Esther (Dolezal, PHJC) and her exceptional crew were like angels, not only with me but with all of the patients.   - C.A.G.

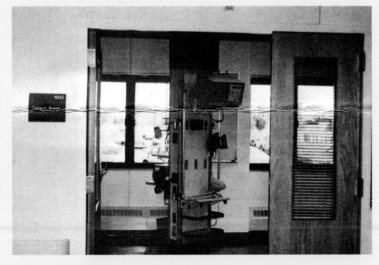

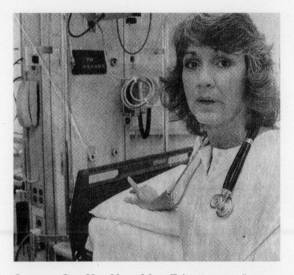

The new Intensive Care Unit that opened in 1988 at St. Mary Medical Center in Hobart featured the latest technology in a comfortable setting for patients and families. All patient rooms were built along outside walls for outside visibility. "The area outside the Hobart hospital is really beautiful all year around, said Director of Facilities Services, Mike Fandl, who worked with Hobart Chief Operating Officer Beth Kaminski in construction of the new addition.

Intensive Care Unit Nurse Mary Zak points to a "power column" unit at St. Mary Medical Center's new Intensive Care unit/surgical suite addition in Hobart. The wing was part of a $6 million expansion and renovation project.
Reprinted by permission of the
Post-Tribune, Thursday, June 2, 1988

"We've purposely aimed the facility at letting the patient see out. It's much more relaxing, much more calming, much less clinical."
Summary, June 1988

INTENSIVE CARE UNIT STAFF PHOTO – 2009
FRONT ROW (L-R): Brenda Toby, unit secretary; Kristen Vandenburgh, RN
MIDDLE ROW (L-R): Sheena Tinner, RN (standing); Dianna Ketchem, RN (seated); Dawn Credille, RN; Jennifer Somers, RN, clinical nurse leader; and Nurse Manager Beth Navarro, RN
BACK ROW (L-R): Ann Simpson, RN; Mike Gozo, RN; Sherry Gouveia, RN; Lori Jucknowski, PCA II; Tom Kulick, RN, critical care clinician; Joe Hulse, RN; Mercy Moto, RN; Judy Ward, RN; Rich Zimmerman, RN; and Christine Sobocinski, RN

With Beginnings in Gary • THEN AND NOW

INTENSIVE CARE UNIT...

Contributed by Jen Somers, RN,
Clinical Nurse Leader, ICU/CCU

The original Intensive Care Unit (ICU) in Hobart opened in 1973 and was located on the second floor where the Endoscopy Department is now. It was an eight-bed unit that expanded to ten beds and later was reduced to eight beds again.

In 1991, when I started working at St. Mary, the second floor ICU was a five-bed overflow unit for the first floor ICU. The newly built ICU opened in 1988. The second floor ICU closed in 1992. The staff stayed the same, only our location changed.

We take pride in tremendous longevity. Many of our staff members have worked in this ICU for 15 years or longer: Ann Simpson, Sherry Gouveia, Donna Lipman, Carol Prince, Patty Lucas, and Jennifer Somers. Tina Doolin, who recently retired, worked for St. Mary Medical Center for more than 30 years and started her ICU career on the second floor unit.

St. Mary Medical Center purchased new monitoring equipment in early 1992 before the upstairs unit closed. Monitors were also upgraded in approximately 2004 and again in the spring of 2009. We have always had current state-of-the art monitoring equipment. A case in point is when I received my first open heart patient from surgery. I was (accustomed) to emptying drainage bags into graduated cylinders to measure outputs. Now I had a machine that did it for me! We still use those machines today.

Additionally, our monitoring equipment has the capability of calculating medication doses and converting weight in pounds to kilograms. We have gone from counting drops of IV fluid to being able to calculate specific weight-based dosages via infusion pumps that are wirelessly connected to a mainframe. We can connect an IV catheter to a machine and it will tell you how much blood your heart is efficiently pumping minute by minute. These tasks used to be done with pencil, paper, and the memorizing of formulas. We still use our formulas and calculate the old-school way, but the ICU is full of technology that helps us do our job quickly and more efficiently!

Evidenced-based nursing has changed how nurses practice, not what they practice. It gives us the reasoning and the science behind the way we do things. Giving antibiotics earlier, turning a patient every two hours, administering oral care every four hours when on a ventilator, getting patients out of bed after surgery – these interventions are all grounded on research and patient outcomes. Our education never stops.

Through the years, St. Mary has given (us) the tools, knowledge, and technology we need to continue to give quality nursing care.

DEDICATING THE ICU IN HONOR OF JOHN T. SCULLY, M.D.

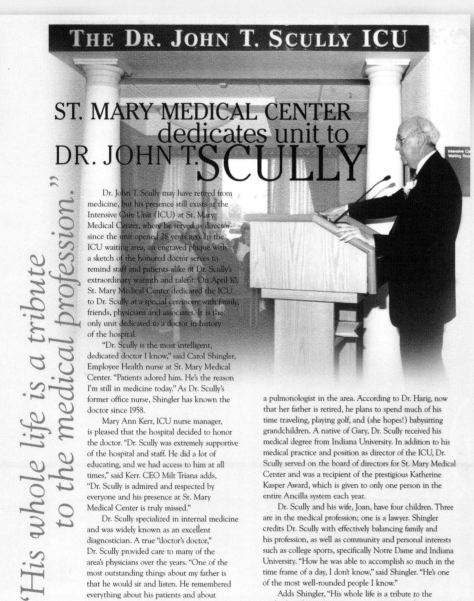

THE DR. JOHN T. SCULLY ICU

ST. MARY MEDICAL CENTER dedicates unit to DR. JOHN T. SCULLY

"His whole life is a tribute to the medical profession."

Dr. John T. Scully may have retired from medicine, but his presence still exists at the Intensive Care Unit (ICU) at St. Mary Medical Center, where he served as director since the unit opened 28 years ago. In the ICU waiting area, an engraved plaque with a sketch of the honored doctor serves to remind staff and patients alike of Dr. Scully's extraordinary warmth and talent. On April 10, St. Mary Medical Center dedicated the ICU to Dr. Scully at a special ceremony with family, friends, physicians and associates. It is the only unit dedicated to a doctor in history of the hospital.

"Dr. Scully is the most intelligent, dedicated doctor I know," said Carol Shingler, Employee Health nurse at St. Mary Medical Center. "Patients adored him. He's the reason I'm still in medicine today." As Dr. Scully's former office nurse, Shingler has known the doctor since 1958.

Mary Ann Kerr, ICU nurse manager, is pleased that the hospital decided to honor the doctor. "Dr. Scully was extremely supportive of the hospital and staff. He did a lot of educating, and we had access to him at all times," said Kerr. CEO Milt Triana adds, "Dr. Scully is admired and respected by everyone and his presence at St. Mary Medical Center is truly missed."

Dr. Scully specialized in internal medicine and was widely known as an excellent diagnostician. A true "doctor's doctor," Dr. Scully provided care to many of the area's physicians over the years. "One of the most outstanding things about my father is that he would sit and listen. He remembered everything about his patients and about medicine," said his daughter, Dr. Sharon Harig,

a pulmonologist in the area. According to Dr. Harig, now that her father is retired, he plans to spend much of his time traveling, playing golf, and (she hopes!) babysitting grandchildren. A native of Gary, Dr. Scully received his medical degree from Indiana University. In addition to his medical practice and position as director of the ICU, Dr. Scully served on the board of directors for St. Mary Medical Center and was a recipient of the prestigious Katherine Kasper Award, which is given to only one person in the entire Ancilla system each year.

Dr. Scully and his wife, Joan, have four children. Three are in the medical profession; one is a lawyer. Shingler credits Dr. Scully with effectively balancing family and his profession, as well as community and personal interests such as college sports, specifically Notre Dame and Indiana University. "How he was able to accomplish so much in the time frame of a day, I don't know," said Shingler. "He's one of the most well-rounded people I know."

Adds Shingler, "His whole life is a tribute to the medical profession."

IT'S BEEN *Said* IN 2009...

"I learned of the Intensive Care Unit being named after me for the first time at my retirement party which was given by my associates in 2000. It was presented by (former St. Mary Medical Center CEO) Milt Triana, and it was very gratifying. I think it was gratifying for the nursing staff to feel that it was an important entity within the hospital."

John T. Scully, M.D.
INTERNIST, RETIRED
MERCY HOSPITAL
(BEGAN IN 1955 IN GARY)

IT'S BEEN *Said* IN 2009...

"One of my greatest honors was to be asked to sing for Dr. Scully at his retirement party. My choice of song was, appropriately, 'Wind beneath My Wings.'

Dr. Scully is just that to me. I have soared and have accomplished much because of his patience, care, guidance and teaching. I would be nothing without him."

Mary Ann Wolfe Reeves
LONGTIME PATIENT OF
DR. JOHN SCULLY

Shown here on April 10, 2001, is John T. Scully, M.D., when the St. Mary Medical Center Intensive Care Unit was dedicated in his honor.

Neighborly Care, SPRING 2001

"When I was a staff nurse working on 2North at Gary Mercy in 1956, I was honored that Dr. Scully asked me to come and work for him and I did so until 1961. I have deep admiration for him. He is one of a kind. He was a born teacher who was eager to share his knowledge. He was able to instill confidence in his patients as well as his staff. He never failed to say please when asking me to do something and always replied with a 'Thank you,' even at the end of long days in the office.

"I worked intermittently with Dr. John Mirro and Dr. Scully and remain active filling in for nurses on vacation or sick leave. Those of us from our day have witnessed dramatic changes in healthcare. There was a time when patients were never addressed by their first names and nurses, likewise, were always 'Miss' or 'Mrs.' We did not have disposable supplies. Syringes had to be washed, soaked, and autoclaved at the end of each shift. Needles had to be cleaned, sharpened and autoclaved. Oxygen was supplied in large, very heavy tanks that had to be taken by the nurses to each patient's room where the patients were in oxygen tents (no cannulas or anything plugged into the walls). We did not have a central supply unit. Foley catheters were made of rubber tubing that also had to be cleaned and autoclaved after each patient's use. Instead of the disposable bags, we had tin cans that sat on the floor with the tubing draining into them. I kicked a lot of cans over and mopped up a lot of urine!"

Margaret Wolfe, R.N., RETIRED
MERCY HOSPITAL
(BEGAN IN 1955 IN GARY)

"I will never forget Dr. Scully. He actually scared me the first time I met him... because he was so business-like. But he was so smart... He felt that nurses needed to be able to read EKGs, for example. Now that is completely a doctor realm but he taught us how to read EKGs. You could read them, you could not interpret, but at least you knew what you were dealing with... (and you) knew how to act. He respected us. It was nothing for him to ask, 'Well, what do you think?' He made us a team and I loved him for it."

Pat De Neal, R.N., FORMER DIRECTOR OF NURSING
MERCY HOSPITAL
(BEGAN IN 1964 IN GARY)

DIABETES CARE

"I owe my life and that of my daughter, Katie, to Dr. John Scully. So how do I put into words what he means to me?

"I was diagnosed with Type I Diabetes at the age of six. To say that Dr. Scully cared for me is a gross understatement. He taught me how to live a healthy and productive life – a life that just happened to include diabetes. Imagine a physician whose guidance and teaching helped me to pursue every dream I ever had – from traveling around the world, to cheering at every high school game, to attending camp, and most importantly, to giving birth to a healthy baby after having lived with diabetes for over 20 years – something people said was impossible."

Mary Ann Wolfe Reeves, LONGTIME PATIENT OF DR. JOHN SCULLY

DID YOU KNOW?

Diabetes was the seventh leading cause of death listed on U.S. death certificates in 2006. There are an estimated 23.6 million children and adults in the United States, or 7.8% of the population, who have diabetes. While an estimated 17.9 million have been diagnosed, unfortunately 5.7 million people are not aware that they have the disease.

If present trends continue, one in three Americans, and one in two minorities born in 2000 will develop diabetes in their lifetime. Approximately 4,384 people are diagnosed with diabetes each day. In 2007, 1.6 million new cases of diabetes were diagnosed in people age 20 years or older.

Department of Health and Human Services
Centers for Disease Control and Prevention

Scully and Kamen – A Doctor Duo

IT'S BEEN *Said* IN 2009...

"Dr. Scully was… absolutely the most precise diagnostician who could diagnose the most difficult case and be absolutely right on – so well respected for his demeanor, his stature, his abilities as a physician and then his close collaboration with nursing. He was very much a hero at St. Mary hospital. He rounded every day in ICU and would sit down and talk with the nurses any time there was a difficult patient whether it was his patient or not. He was absolutely a hands-on medical director and never afraid to tackle a difficult situation."

Marsha King, R.N., MS, MBA, CNAA
FORMER VICE PRESIDENT, PATIENT CARE SERVICES
ST. MARY MEDICAL CENTER
(BEGAN IN 1987 IN HOBART)

"THE MOST ENJOYABLE PART OF MEDICINE TO ME WAS MAKING A DIAGNOSIS. IT'S KIND OF LIKE BEING A DETECTIVE."

John T. Scully, M.D.
INTERNIST, RETIRED
MERCY HOSPITAL
(BEGAN IN 1955 IN GARY)

IT'S BEEN *Said* IN 2009...

"Dr. John Scully, a doctor's 'doctor,' was of great help if I needed urgent ICU consultation. He would always respond even in the wee hours of the morning. The cardiovascular surgery groups and many other general and specialist surgeons would also come in immediately if personally contacted. The response rate was, overall, excellent."

Marsha King, R.N., MS, MBA, CNAA
FORMER VICE PRESIDENT, PATIENT CARE SERVICES
ST. MARY MEDICAL CENTER
(BEGAN IN 1987 IN HOBART)

IT'S BEEN *Said* IN 2009...

"One doctor who probably deserves as much credit as anyone for doing great things at St. Mary's in Gary, and subsequently in Hobart, is Dr. Jack Kamen. He was an incredibly talented anesthesiologist but he was also a true hospitalist. Hospitalists now are common in hospitals but I can't think of anyone I respected more and did more for patients than Dr. Kamen. We used to have an old adage that when the nurses would say, 'So and so is having trouble,' the reply would be, 'Call Kamen.' I never knew when he slept. I would say he saved more lives in the hospital than the rest of the medical staff combined."

John T. Scully, M.D.
INTERNIST, RETIRED
MERCY HOSPITAL | (BEGAN IN 1955 IN GARY)

A HOSPITALIST

"A hospitalist is a physician who basically will focus his practice in the hospital. The theory is that if you have a group of physicians who are busy with an office practice and they need to admit a patient to the hospital, the hospitalist will look after that patient in the hospital. It saves a lot of time for the office practitioners because they are not running back and forth between their office and the hospital."

John Birdzell
FORMER PRESIDENT OF LAKESHORE HEALTH SYSTEM
(BEGAN IN 1985 WITH ANCILLA SYSTEMS INCORPORATED)

"Dr. Kamen was really a legend in Gary. He was an anesthesiologist who became a Critical Care specialist. He did so much for the people and the city of Gary. He would take money out of his pocket if they didn't have money for food or medicine. He was so kind. He never expected anything in return. He lectured all over the country. He stuttered and yet still had a wonderful sense of humor and was wonderful at teaching."

Maryann Kerr, RN
NURSE MANAGER, ICCU & MEDICAL ONCOLOGY, RETIRED
MERCY HOSPITAL
(BEGAN IN 1960 IN GARY)

"... HE (JACK KAMEN) WAS MY GOOD FRIEND. WE WORKED TOGETHER FOR MANY, MANY YEARS AND NO ONE HAD MORE TRUE DEDICATION THAN JACK. HE IS STILL ALIVE AND HE HAS BEEN RETIRED FOR SOME TIME."

John T. Scully, M.D.
INTERNIST, RETIRED
MERCY HOSPITAL | (BEGAN IN 1955 IN GARY)

"The thing was, I stuttered. In high school, I should have been the salutatorian, but I stuttered so bad I couldn't have given a speech, so they gave me third place. I think that is why when I met Dr. Kamen I really respected him because he stuttered and still stutters. I really admired him to go all... through medical school... and he stutters."

Flora Dean Meeks, RN
RADIOLOGY, RETIRED
MERCY HOSPITAL
(BEGAN IN 1960 IN GARY)

DID YOU KNOW?

In 2000, John T. Scully, M.D., was the recipient of the prestigious Sagamore of the Wabash award from the governor of Indiana.

CRITICAL CARE CONFERENCES

"Many of the critical care seminars, sponsored by St. Mary Medical Center, and held at the Radisson convention center, had more than 300 attendees – many from Ohio and Illinois. Mary Ann Kerr, RN, and Pat DeNeal, RN, were the engines responsible for their success. Our respiratory care seminars, which also saw attendance in the hundreds, were also sponsored by St. Mary Medical Center and led by Tony Lucsevic, RRT. Both seminars featured outstanding local and outside speakers – experts in their fields."

Jack M. Kamen, M.D.
DIRECTOR OF I.C.U., DIRECTOR OF ST. MARY MEDICAL CENTER PAIN CENTER, CHIEF OF DEPARTMENT OF
ANESTHESIOLOGY, DIRECTOR OF RESPIRATORY CARE, DIRECTOR OF MEDICAL EDUCATION, RETIRED
MERCY HOSPITAL | (BEGAN IN 1952 AT ST. CATHERINE HOSPITAL)

"Dr. Kamen wanted the nurses to learn so he started having classes. We would go to a hotel conference room in the evening, and he and Dr. Scully would pay for the dinners and many ICU, CCU nurses would always go and they taught us. We were the first ones to start reading EKGs... We were the first ones to do (Peripherally Inserted Central Catheter) PICC lines. At that time it wasn't called a PICC line, but you would still insert a long catheter into a cubital vein. They also taught us about CVP lines, arterial lines. We were the first to do those things – and at the time we had to piece every part together. Now they come all assembled. They were ahead of their time in teaching us. Now maybe the educators in nursing are teaching them. We would have a class for each specialty."

Flora Dean Meeks, RN
RADIOLOGY, RETIRED
MERCY HOSPITAL | (BEGAN IN 1960 IN GARY)

A LOGO IN PARTNERSHIP

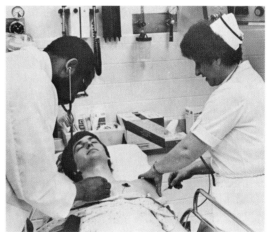

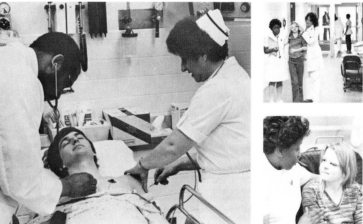

This is St. Mary Medical Center's logo and slogan with the two partnering hospitals as shown in the January 18, 1987, edition of the *Northwest Indiana Catholic Newspaper.*

St. Mary Medical Center   *To Serve with Love* brochure, 1984

Hobart hospital rendering   *To Serve with Love* brochure, 1984   Gary hospital rendering   *To Serve with Love* brochure, 1984

HOSPITAL/COMMUNITY HAPPENINGS

FROM THE PHJC CHRONICLES – OCTOBER, 1985

Monday, October 21, the auxiliary of St. Mary Medical Center Gary – Hobart, honored Sister Cornelia (Leible, PHJC) for her birthday and 70 years in the convent. Sister will be 90 years old on the 22nd. She received candlesticks as a gift from the auxilians and plaques to be placed in each facility. The plaques honor Sister Cornelia for her many years of service for the hospital and the community. PHJC Sisters Kathleen, Candace, and Carol Ann were present along with the Sisters at St. Mary Medical Center. Mr. Dandridge, Mary Gulyassy and many auxilians were present for the occasion.

CHJC, University of Notre Dame Archives

In 1980, Sister Wilma Boeving, PHJC, was appointed vice president of Ancilla Domini Health Systems, Inc., (ADHS) the corporate parent of St. Mary Medical Center. ADHS included seven hospitals in the health care apostolate of the Poor Handmaids of Jesus Christ. Sister Wilma began with St. Mary Medical Center in 1967 as assistant administrator. In 1969 she became associate administrator, Professional Services, and served in that role until her new ADHS role in 1980.

Photo from *Word-Gathering*, SPRING 1980

In 1980 St. Mary Medical Center Personnel Director Howard Jack was elected president of the American Society for Hospital Personnel Administration (ASHPA), with a roster of more than 1,500 members. The organization, as an affiliate of the American Hospital Association, promoted the advancement of effective personnel administration in hospitals.

Acts and Facts, JULY 1980

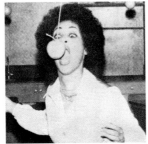

(Middle) Halloween time during "coffee break" at the Gary hospital was the scene of apples suspended from the cafeteria ceiling or swimming in tubs of water as employees tried to better the score of previous contestants. Jowanna Ivy from the business office tried to take a mighty bite from her apple.

Acts and Facts, NOVEMBER, 1980

Shown here at a 1981 gathering at the home of Bruce Lovell is an animated Bea Sparber, secretary to Jack Kamen, M.D.

(Far Right) Joan Orton, surgery supervisor at Mercy Hospital in Gary, dressed in a flapper dress for a 1981 Halloween party at the home of Bruce Lovell.

*Marking Time...*1981

- The world's first combined heart-lung transplant was carried out.
- First laparoscopic appendectomy was performed.

Then and Now

Intermediate Care Unit...

Contributed by Beth Navarro, BSN
Nurse Manager ICU, IMCU
2Medical–Telemetry

The Intermediate Care Unit (IMCU) at St. Mary Medical Center in Hobart (established in the early 1980s) has changed in many ways over the years. Originally, the rooms were small with shared bathroom space. Private rooms were uncommon.

With changes in healthcare and availability of services, the New Patient Tower was built in 2004 with 32 large private rooms designated for IMCU (2West). This met the need to accommodate patients and their families.

In July 2008, 2West was restructured, separating the 32 beds into two more manageable units (IMCU and 2Medical-Telemetry). The IMCU consists of 19 beds, three of which could be ICU-step-down, meaning if a patient's condition warrants closer care but not ICU, we can utilize a patient ratio of 3:1 instead of 4:1. The 2Medical-Telemetry, known as 2MT, has 13 telemetry beds.

Although IMCU serves a variety of patients with various medical conditions, our primary focus is care of the cardiac patient. The 19-bed unit allows the nursing care to be focused on those patients who need advanced specialized care.

We now have the pneumatic "tube" system that provides an efficient means of transportation between departments. This can include small supplies and certain medications from pharmacy. The larger nurses' station accommodates the nursing staff and our multidisciplinary team (social service, case management, etc.) as well as the physicians. Our physicians also have the luxury of a private dictation area as dictated by the Health Insurance Portability and Accountability Act (HIPAA), whereas in the recent past, there were no rules to protect patient privacy.

With advanced research and the use of EBN practices, we are able to achieve better patient outcomes. Continuous nursing research helps us render the quality of care we provide today. Patient safety and satisfaction have become a major focus as well as collaboration with patient and family regarding the patient's plan of care. It used to be that what the doctor said was what happened – no questions asked. We now have a multidisciplinary team that interacts with the patient (and family) for the best outcomes.

Increased technology has brought sophisticated, advanced electronic monitors and various other equipment to specifically meet the needs of our patients. New mobile computers have been added to allow the nurses to (spend more time) at the patient's bedside.

Today (in 2010), there are more career opportunities for nursing that include specialized fields within the Intermediate Care and Intensive Care departments as well as other areas within the hospital environment.

IT'S BEEN *Said* IN 2009...

"I once cared for the father of a friend who had a heart attack. His daughter was a longtime friend. One day after he was transferred from ICCU to IMCU, he went into a lethal arrhythmia, and a Code Blue was called. After working on him, we were unable to save his life. I reluctantly came out of that room because I was having trouble with my own emotions. The family was there. I walked up to the man's son-in-law and daughter and started sobbing. They were comforting me more than I could comfort them. The family said later how important it was for them to know that somebody who cared was with him when he died."

Maryann Kerr, RN
Nurse Manager, ICCU &
Medical Oncology, retired
Mercy Hospital
(began in 1960 in Gary)

CASE MANAGEMENT/SOCIAL SERVICE...

*Contributed by Lori Koziczynski, Director
and Barbara McDonald, RN, Case Manager*

A DECADE EARLIER –
1999 CASE MANAGEMENT DEPARTMENT
STANDING (L-R): Rosemarie Ehrhardt,
Director Sherry Brewer, Pete Otero, and Barbara McDonald
SEATED (L-R):
Sandra Wytovicz, Marsha Coots, and Darlene Woodley

CASE MANAGEMENT STAFF PHOTO – 2009
FIRST ROW (L-R): Birute Pumputis, M.D., Jennifer Schoonveld, Rosa Mazzocco, Kathleen Djuric, Kris Shocaroff, Teri Delreal, and Director Lori Koziczynski
BACK ROW (L-R): Susan Schmidt, Carolyne Wiesinger, Dee Bedella, Barbara McDonald, and Nikki West

SOCIAL SERVICE DEPARTMENT STAFF PHOTO – 2009
PICTURED (L-R): Birute Pumputis, M.D.; Debbie Thompson; Rita Luczac; Lora Darmofalski; and Director Lori Koziczynski

In the early 1980s, concern increased about the viability of the hospital insurance, supplementary medical insurance, protection of beneficiaries, and quality of care reimbursed through Medicare. These concerns led to changes in Quality Management and the reimbursement structure of Medicare. In 1984, the Deficit Reduction Act mandated development and implementation of the Medicare Prospective Pay System (PPS), designed to contain spiraling health care costs by reimbursing providers at a fixed rate based on Diagnosis Related Groups (DRGs). DRGS reflected the group and quantities of resources typically used per instance of a specific diagnosis. DRGs replaced the prior reimbursement system that was based on reasonable or prevailing charges. With the advent of PPS, hospitals across the country increased the importance of quality assurance and utilization oversight of health care services provided to Medicare beneficiaries.

The ever-changing reimbursement issues for hospitals with Medicare under the PPS initiative caused providers to reduce the resources expended per hospital stay either by reducing the kinds or amounts of services provided, or by reducing patient length of stay. Hospitals around the country were working on ways to do just that. Under the nursing leadership of Marsha King, a pilot program for Case Management was started with Barbara McDonald. The program started with Congestive Heart Failure (CHF) and Cardiac Artery Bypass Graft (CABG) diagnosis. The purpose was to initiate discharge planning early to identify any barriers that could increase length of stay and to follow the patient's case to make sure that resources were used appropriately. The pilot program for Case Management was successful. Case Management responsibilities now encompass utilization review, discharge planning, and quality indicators.

The director of Case Management and Quality was Connie Blaine. The case managers were Sherry Brewer, Claudia Olszewski, Greta Coady, Barbara McDonald, Darlene Woodley, and Amy Bachich. The team covered both SMMC in Hobart and Gary.

Case Management and Quality Management became so big that as time progressed they were separated into two separate departments. Sherry Brewer was awarded the title of director of Case Management and Social Service and Connie Blaine was awarded the title of director of Quality Management. From the late 1990s until 2004, three licensed practical nurses (LPNs) Freida Graves, Marcia Coots, and Pete Otero did the Utilization Review and the registered nurses (RNs) were responsible for Case Management.

In the process of UR and CM developing, the UR committee was chaired by John O. Carter, M.D. Other members included Scott Andrews, M.D.; Milton Gasparis, M.D.; Raja Devanathan, M.D.; and Phillip Kellar, M.D.

In 2003, the Case Management and Social Service departments included four full-time case managers – Barb McDonald, Debbie Watson, Sandy Wytovicz, and Darlene Woodley. Two part-time case managers were Rosa Mazzocco and Donna Wasko. The Social Service Department consisted of two full-time social workers – Nancy Becker and John Boguslawski. Robert Fields was the evening social worker and on-call social worker.

In 2004, Sherry Brewer became the director of Quality and Risk Management and Peggy Baxter became the director of Case Management and Social Service. Through Peggy's leadership, a total of seven full-time case managers were hired as well as three full-time social workers, one part-time social worker, and one PRN social worker to cover weekends and 24/7 on-call. Carolyne Wiesinger, RN, was hired as a Denials Resolution specialist and Teri Delreal, Registered Health Information technologist (RHIT), was hired as a Utilization technician.

From 2007 until currently (2009), the leadership of the Case Management and Social Service Department falls under Lori Koziczynski. The afore-mentioned full-time employees (FTEs) remain with the addition of Emergency Department Case Manager Kathleen Djuric and part-time Utilization Review Technician Dee Bedella. In 2009, and still in its infancy, a Clinical Documentation Improvement program was developed by Lori Koziczynski; Inpatient Coding Manager Sandy Plummer; and Case Manager Kris Shocaroff.

Our department prides itself in quality professionalism and we remain focused on ongoing changes and the day-to-day management of important healthcare issues.

IT'S BEEN *Said* IN 2009...

"I recall when the Social Service Department at St. Mary Medical Center consisted of Director Mark Kowalski, full-time Social Worker Amanda Jones and part-time Social Worker Nancy Becker. Mr. Robert Fields was the evening social worker and… was loved by all. He was a very kind man who was always in a pleasant mood and would do anything for anyone."

Barbara McDonald, R.N, CASE MANAGER
ST. MARY MEDICAL CENTER
(BEGAN IN 1981 IN HOBART)

Finance

"St. Mary was the smaller of the two hospitals that served the city of Gary so everyone knew each other. I had a good time but the budget was challenging every year because we had to roll up our sleeves and see what we had to do to get through the next year on such a tight profit margin.

"St. Mary - Gary was a Disproportionate Share Hospital (DSH) which means it served a high Medicaid and indigent population. The challenge was to make sure we managed our costs so we could continue providing health services for the community. We also had physicians who... understood our struggles. We were one of the first hospitals to start a Cardiac Catheterization Lab and MRI joint venture in Lake County. The doctors got behind it and it was doing pretty well until... they sold the hospital."

Lou Molina, VICE PRESIDENT FINANCE AND CHIEF FINANCIAL OFFICER
COMMUNITY HOSPITAL
(BEGAN IN 1986 IN GARY)

"I always remember the one meeting where our administrator, George Burrell, got up and he said, 'Well, I want to talk to everyone here about DRGs,' and he wrote the letters and he asked, 'Do you know what this stands for?' No one answered and he said, 'Well, I am going to tell you. It stands for Da Revenue's Gone.' It was the beginning of hospitals having to run operations like a business and since that time we have succeeded in doing that through strengthening our systems."

Lou Molina, VICE PRESIDENT FINANCE AND CHIEF FINANCIAL OFFICER
COMMUNITY HOSPITAL
(BEGAN IN 1986 IN GARY)

"I was payroll supervisor for the whole system – St. Catherine in East Chicago, Mercy Hospital in Gary, and St. Mary in Hobart. I had four clerks reporting to me.

"People got paid every two weeks and we would actually get a stack of time cards for the clerks to check each time. For the most part, if you were salaried they were handwritten. If you were hourly you punched a clock. At payroll time some supervisors would add the hours and some wouldn't and even if they did, the clerks always had to go back and make sure the correct hours were there. If there was any overtime, they had to calculate that. So everything the clerks did was up in their heads. They had to know the rules. They had to pretty much do everything manually and there were approximately 700 employees there at the time."

Joe Winterhaler, VICE PRESIDENT FINANCE AND CHIEF FINANCIAL OFFICER
ST. CATHERINE HOSPITAL
(BEGAN IN 1986 IN GARY)

"Hobart was built in 1973. To me, that was the most exciting time. I never moved (my office) to Hobart but I helped open Hobart. One of the things they wanted to do in accounting was make sure all the accounting records were done appropriately. I got the IT piece of it which was key-punching data to get Hobart up and running. I can remember 12–14 hour days and it was just incredible. If I could pick one time to go back and do over, that would be it because I just loved the excitement of setting up the whole new hospital."

Judy Candiano, REVENUE CYCLE CONTROL SUPERVISOR, PATIENT ACCOUNTING
MERCY HOSPITAL
(BEGAN IN 1969 IN GARY)

"The one thing the government has instituted is what is called 'never' events. Those are things they will not pay for – if there is injury from a fall, if there is a pressure ulcer that developed while the patient is in the hospital. Ninety percent of them nursing has total control over. Nursing has always been seen in a hospital as a cost. It has never been seen as a revenue-generating department. This is primarily because our costs or our nursing care is factored in with the room and board charge so we always look like an expense. With these 'never' events, I told nursing this is where we can prove our value to the organization and the impact nursing has on the outcomes. This is not just clinically but also financially as well. I don't see it as a negative thing because I know with good nursing care and evidenced-based nursing practice, we can prevent 'never' events."

Tammie R. Finn-Jones, VICE PRESIDENT AND CHIEF NURSING OFFICER
ST. MARY MEDICAL CENTER
(BEGAN IN 2007 IN HOBART)

With Beginnings in Gary • THEN AND NOW

FINANCE DEPARTMENT...

Contributed by Joseph P. Winterhaler, CPA
Vice President Finance and Chief Financial Officer
and Arthur Vasquez, CPA, Controller

FINANCE DEPARTMENT STAFF PHOTO – 2009
SEATED (L-R): Janice DeMercede, senior accountant: and
Vice President Finance and Chief Financial Officer Mary Sudicky
STANDING (L-R): Arthur Vasquez, controller; Tonya Witt, staff accountant
staff accountant; Jennifer Grafton, senior cost and budget analyst;
and Raelene Cooper, administrative assistant

The Finance Department of St. Mary Medical Center has undergone many changes during the last several decades.

In the late 1980s, the departments of both St. Mary Medical Center and St. Catherine Hospital were housed in the basement of St. Mary Medical Center – Gary. From this location all the aspects of finance (from budgets to payroll to patient billing) were performed for Lakeshore Health System, which was comprised of St. Catherine Hospital as well as St. Mary Medical Center's Gary and Hobart campuses.

In 1993, Ancilla Systems Incorporated (which at that time owned several hospitals in Indiana and Illinois) sold the Gary campus to a healthcare corporation headquartered in Georgia. As a result of this sale, the finance operations were moved to the Ancilla corporate office in Hobart, Indiana. Throughout the years, the departments were absorbed back into the hospitals. The patient billing office remained at the Hobart location.

On October 17, 2001, the Community Foundation, Inc. (CFI), parent company of Community Hospital, announced the acquisition of two Northwest Indiana hospitals operated by Ancilla Systems Incorporated. The foundation name was later changed to Community Foundation of Northwest Indiana, Inc. (CFNI). Under the banner of Community Healthcare System, the three hospitals – Community Hospital, St. Catherine Hospital, and St. Mary Medical Center – were integrated. Since this transaction, the accounts payable and payroll duties have once again been centralized.

The St. Mary Medical Center Finance Department has changed considerably over the years. All of the finance positions are currently occupied by employees who are new to the St. Mary Medical Center organization within the last three years. The finance staff consists of a controller, senior accountant, junior accountant and senior cost and budget analyst. The responsibilities of this team encompass everything from financial statement preparation to business expansion pro forma development.

Hospital/Community Happenings

1981 – Ambulatory Care Center Accepts Patients

When the U.S. government listed the city of Gary as a "Medically Underserved Area," a new medical concept was initiated for local citizens. Gary Administrator Paul R. Kaiser announced that the newly-opened Ambulatory Care Center – right off Fifth Avenue across from the hospital – would be staffed by five physicians with specialties in internal medicine, obstetrics and gynecology, pediatrics, and general practice.

"The St. Mary Medical Center Ambulatory Care Center is ideally suited to people who need to see a doctor but do not presently have a physician caring for their medical needs or the healthcare needs of their families," said the Ambulatory Care Center's Medical Director, Alexander S. Williams, M.D., in an *Acts and Facts* hospital publication of September 1981. "It has been estimated that as many as 250,000 patient visits a year are not being attended to by doctors because of the shortage," he added. "Many of Gary's doctors are so over burdened that they cannot possibly see new patients."

This center later became known as the Turner-Grutka Clinic.

IT'S BEEN *Said* IN 2009...

"Bishop Grutka was a good friend of mine and I used to take care of him and the next bishop who came, too. They were outstanding religious leaders. Bishop Grutka was kind and very well known in the city of Gary and also internationally."

Jose H. Roig, M.D.
OPHTHALMOLOGIST, RETIRED
MERCY HOSPITAL
(BEGAN IN 1967 IN GARY)

THE TURNER-GRUTKA CLINIC

IT'S BEEN *Said* IN 2009...

"In the late 1980s or so, Dr. Alexander Williams was bringing in African-American doctors and they opened the Turner-Grutka Clinic. It was for anyone but it was just in a black area so most of the patients were black. It was located on Fifth and Filmore. It worked as a clinic. The doctors had their own patients that came in and we would take new admissions. There was OB/gynecology, pediatrics, internal medicine, etc."

Flora Dean Meeks, RN
RADIOLOGY, RETIRED
MERCY HOSPITAL | (BEGAN IN 1960 IN GARY)

FROM THE PHJC CHRONICLES
JANUARY 5, 1984

On Thursday, January 5, the hospital opened a new Ambulatory Care Center in a renovated building at 1110 West Fifth Avenue. The former unit, in the lobby of the (Gary) hospital, was closed. The center was dedicated by public officials and community leaders. The new center was named for two outstanding Gary community leaders. One was Dudley Turner, M.D., who died in 1981, and practiced medicine in Gary from 1920 until a heart condition forced his retirement at age 98. The other was Bishop Andrew Grutka who became the first bishop of the Gary Diocese in 1957. He has been a leader in the human rights struggle in the area. The new Ambulatory Care Center has private doctors offering services in internal medicine, obstetrics/gynecology, pediatrics and family practice. In addition to the physicians, four nurses and seven clerical personnel are included in the staff. We are very proud of the Dr. Dudley Turner/ Bishop Andrew G. Grutka Ambulatory Care Center.

CHJC, University of Notre Dame Archives

1982 – Diamond Anniversary
75 Years of Gary's First Hospital

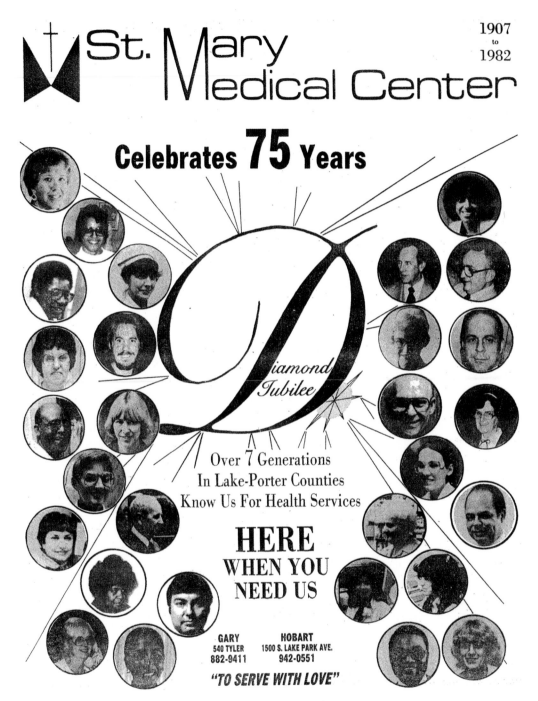

✝ St. Mary
Medical Center

1907
to
1982

Celebrates 75 Years

Diamond Jubilee

Over 7 Generations
In Lake-Porter Counties
Know Us For Health Services

HERE
WHEN YOU
NEED US

GARY
540 TYLER
882-9411

HOBART
1500 S. LAKE PARK AVE.
942-0551

"TO SERVE WITH LOVE"

Celebrating the 75th anniversary of St. Mary Medical Center, Gary and Hobart, from 1907-1982,
the Diamond Jubilee was publicized in the *Post-Tribune* with its "To Serve with Love" slogan.
Reprinted by permission of the *Post-Tribune*, April 30, 1982

In 1982, plans were in place for the Diamond Anniversary of the opening of Gary's first hospital. The 75-year recognition, on November 9, was to include Holy Mass at Holy Angels Cathedral in Gary and again November 11 in the Chapel of St. Mary Medical Center in Hobart. Bishop Andrew G. Grutka celebrated Mass at the cathedral followed by a flag-raising ceremony in the Gary hospital parking lot. The American flag, provided by Senator Richard G. Lugar, had been flown over the Capitol building in Washington, D.C. and was raised by the United States Marines attached to Reserve Company A – 6th Engineering Battalion. Also raised for the first time was a custom-designed flag commemorating the hospital's 75th anniversary.

1982 – John Dandridge, Jr., Administrator

John Dandridge, Jr., executive director of St. Mary Medical Center, was named a Young Leader in the healthcare industry by *Hospitals*, a magazine published by American Hospital Publishing, Inc. Honorees were identified as "up-and-comers representing new, innovative leaders in the healthcare field."

Acts and Facts, MAY, 1986

In March 1982, John Dandridge, Jr., of Virginia, assumed his new position as St. Mary Medical Center administrator of the center's hospitals in Gary and Hobart. Mary Gulyassy had served as interim administrator since the departure of former administrator Paul Kaiser. Dandridge, 33, was described in a 1982 *Post-Tribune* article as "a deeply religious man committed to his family and the Sisters' statement of philosophy to emphasize the spiritual as well as the physical, psychological and social needs of human person." Dandridge was to oversee a total of 469 beds at the two facilities.

1985 – Gary and Hobart Construction Projects OK'd

The March 13, 1985, edition of the *Post-Tribune* publicized modernization and expansion plans for St. Mary Medical Center hospitals in Gary and Hobart – with approval from the Indiana State Board of Health for the $34.5 million project. St. Mary Executive Director, John Dandridge, Jr., said in his announcement that the Gary hospital would cost approximately $21.3 million and the Hobart hospital was estimated at approximately $13.2 million.

Plans included a three-floor addition to a section of the Gary hospital's West Wing, and new but not as extensive construction at the Hobart hospital. Both hospitals were in line for some remodeling of existing space, the *Post-Tribune* reported. The Gary hospital's bed total was to be reduced by 26 to 259 and the Hobart facility's bed total was to be increased by 25 for a total of 209 beds.

In Gary, a new laboratory was to be created, a new area for radiology would be established, and eleven new critical care beds would bring the total to 32. Fewer medical/surgical beds would remain.

New for the first time in Hobart would be a pediatric facility of eight beds. Six more critical care beds would be added for a total of 26, and eleven more medical/surgical beds would bring the total to 175.

CHJC, University of Notre Dame Archives

From the PHJC Chronicles – August, 1985

The Blessing and Dedication of the Gary hospital's new lobby was held on August 14 in the afternoon. Many board members, Sisters, volunteers, employees and visitors attended. Mr. Dandridge welcomed everyone. Father Grabner performed the blessing ceremony. Tours and refreshments were given.

CHJC, University of Notre Dame Archives

Marking Time...

1983
- *Medicare began paying for hospice care.*
- *Burn patients received grafts of artificial skin grown from cultured cells.*

1984
- *Ibuprofen hit the market as an across-the-counter analgesic.*
  (May 27 – Post Tribune article)

With Beginnings in Gary • THEN AND NOW

MISSION EFFECTIVENESS DEPARTMENT...

Contributed by Sister Mary Ellen Goeller

MISSION EFFECTIVENESS DEPARTMENT
(L-R) Debra Jenkins, regional assistant, and
Sister Mary Ellen Goeller, PHJC, regional director

Mary Gulyassy was appointed assistant executive director for Mission Effectiveness for the St. Mary Medical Center Gary-Hobart and St. Catherine Hospital sites on July 7, 1986. In her role, she was responsible for patient relations, guest relations, pastoral care and Sister visitors.

"In this approach, the mission and values will be a living part of the lives of all the persons we touch in the healing ministry," said Sister Mary Ellen Goeller, PHJC, today's regional director of Mission Integration. "The Mission Effectiveness Department is still active today. The mission and values of the Poor Handmaids who sponsored the hospital as well as the Community Healthcare System mission and values continue to be lived out through all of the employees."

IT'S BEEN *Said* IN 2009...

"I have been working for Sister Mary Ellen Goeller, (PHJC), for over 15 years. She is a very dedicated, caring, and giving person. She is always concerned about others and I believe people realize that."

Debra Jenkins, REGIONAL ASSISTANT OF MISSION EFFECTIVENESS
ST. MARY MEDICAL CENTER | (BEGAN IN 1985 IN GARY)

IT'S BEEN *Said* IN 2009...

* "When some major event happens in the world, one remembers exactly where he/she was at the time. We were in a board meeting when the Challenger disaster took place. It was almost impossible to finish the meeting because of the great shock and sorrow in the group."

Sister Nora Hahn, PHJC, PROVINCIAL
DONALDSON, INDIANA

Marking Time...1986

- The world's first combined heart, lung, and liver transplant was successfully carried out in England.
- Super Bowl – Chicago defeated New England (46-10).
- Space shuttle Challenger exploded after launch at Cape Canaveral, Florida, killing all seven aboard including teacher Christa McAuliffe (Jan. 28).*

"As the patient advocate, I am available to address questions or concerns our visitors, patients and their family members may have. My role is to interpret hospital policy and procedures by giving referrals, direction, information or resolving issues in coordination with all involved parties.

"As volunteer manager, I provide overall direction with the hospital volunteer groups and ensure that services are provided in a courteous, considerate manner advantageous to the reputation of the hospital.

"Working in this capacity allows me to live out our mission on a daily basis by ensuring we're respecting the dignity of our patients and serving the needs of our customers."

Teresa Pedroza
Manager, Volunteers/Patient Advocate

IT'S BEEN *Said* IN 2009...

"Back in the 1980s, we had some pretty tough recessions and volatile times. Back in the 1960s we went through all the civil rights unrest. We've had some tumultuous periods during my time in healthcare but we always were able to 'weather the storm.' A lot of people say that healthcare is pretty much recession proof.

"The flip side of that is you don't have your elective surgery done when times are tough. You put off everything but the true emergencies. Where the hospitals like St. Catherine run into a real pinch is they are reliant for almost 80-90% of their revenue on government-based programs that don't pay what it costs to deliver the care so you really kind of end up behind the eight ball in an economic downturn. A lot of what people are trying to figure out with this current move toward reform is what it is really going to mean if there is more government control over healthcare as we know it today."

John Birdzell, FORMER PRESIDENT OF LAKESHORE HEALTH SYSTEM
(BEGAN IN 1985 WITH ANCILLA SYSTEMS INCORPORATED)

LAKESHORE HEALTH SYSTEM
MISSION, PRINCIPLES AND VALUES

Lakeshore Health System, organized in 1986, was a not-for-profit healthcare corporation sponsored by the Poor Handmaids of Jesus Christ. In organizing eight hospitals of the Ancilla System into regions, one easily-identified region was in Northwest Indiana where the three Ancilla-owned facilities – St. Catherine Hospital in East Chicago and the two St. Mary Medical Center locations in Gary and Hobart – were operating independently of each other but were all in a 20-mile radius. It is said that the Lakeshore system, which existed for approximately seven years, worked well in creating a corporate culture and coordinating management and staff members. Founded on Christian principles, focused on customer needs, and driven by a commitment to total quality service, Lakeshore Health System was dedicated to continually learning and adapting its services to achieve improvements that resulted in higher levels of satisfaction for its customers.

Adapted from *Lakeshore Health System handbook*, 1994

HOSPITALS IN COLLABORATION

During the summer of 1986, John Birdzell was chief executive officer of the "program on affiliation" among the three Ancilla Systems hospitals in Northwest Indiana – St. Mary Medical Center in Gary and Hobart, and St. Catherine Hospital in East Chicago. He had been hired in April and was shuttling among the three locations as he selected members of the senior management team. He named Larry Mangold as chief financial officer; Karen Burniston as chief operating officer at St. Catherine; Beth Kaminski as director of Hobart operations; Robert Bergin as director of marketing, planning, and community affairs; and Susan Bodenhorn as director of human resources.

The focus of the collaboration, Birdzell said, was to focus on greater efficiency through consolidation of some of the service departments. Prior to his appointment, Birdzell had served as St. Catherine Hospital administrator for 15 months beginning in 1985.

In September, 18 staff cuts were announced among managerial and salaried professionals at St. Catherine Hospital and St. Mary Medical Center locations in Gary and Hobart.

"This is a necessary move in our development strategy," Birdzell said in a *Post-Tribune* story of September 27, 1986. "In building the regional system it is important to develop a departmental structure that is flexible, efficient and responsive to a changing healthcare environment. The decision to make a staff reduction such as this is always difficult but we must strike a balance between the needs of the individual and those of the system and the people it serves."

By October, the *Post-Tribune* reported that the $32.8 million construction/renovation plans for the Gary and Hobart facilities would be scaled down significantly under the new management. Ensuing publicity covered reports of threatened picketing related to union employees' reduced health benefits and the elimination of 220 jobs at the Gary and Hobart hospitals.

Development continued, however, and the following spring, in 1987, Birdzell spoke of plans at the Gary facility for a newly-constructed and more efficient Emergency Room, the new design of Intensive and Critical Care units, the relocation and re-design of the Pediatric Department, expansion of surgery facilities and more.

Hobart, also poised for growth, would proceed with remodeling of its physical and occupational therapy units, expansion of cardiovascular services and an addition to the pharmacy. Half of a designated $12 million improvement plan was for the Hobart hospital site.

A number of hospital departments were established during this period of time and are included in this section of the book's chronology.

IT'S BEEN *Said* IN 2009...

"I am the provincial superior of the American Province of the Poor Handmaids of Jesus Christ. Many of our Sisters have devoted a great part of their lives to the services of the sick in Gary and Hobart. We have partnered with many wonderful doctors and hospital personnel during those years and continue today with Sister Mary Ellen Goeller's presence there."

Sister Nora Hahn, PHJC, PROVINCIAL
DONALDSON, INDIANA

FROM THE HANDBOOK
We expect all individuals associated with our system – associates, physicians, auxiliary members and volunteers – to perform in a manner consistent with the values. The five principles that guide our organization are Dignity of the Person, Compassionate Care, Community, Quality, and Stewardship.
Lakeshore Health System Handbook, 1994

St. Catherine, St. Mary unite under common hospital board

In 1986 John Birdzell became Chief Executive Officer of St. Catherine Hospital and St. Mary Medical Center in a collective move to make Ancilla Systems Incorporated the largest provider of acute hospital care in Northwest Indiana. John Dandridge, Jr., continued to serve as executive director of St. Mary Medical Center during the transition. St. Catherine Hospital and the St. Mary Medical Center facilities in Gary and Hobart were to be governed by a common board of directors headed by former Gary City Councilman Thomas Crump, Jr. It was the first merger of its kind among area hospitals.
Reprinted by permission of the *Post-Tribune*, APRIL 15, 1986

IT'S BEEN *Said* IN 2009...

"In 1986, I joined Ancilla Systems Incorporated as chief operating officer of St. Mary Medical Center – Hobart. At that time, the Poor Handmaids of Jesus Christ were forming Lakeshore Health System. This was the first initiative to align their three hospitals in Lake County. John Birdzell, CEO of St. Catherine's Hospital, became the CEO of Lakeshore Health System which was comprised of St. Catherine in East Chicago, St. Mary Medical Center in Hobart and St. Mary Medical Center in Gary. Merging of the three into one organization presented opportunities for sharing resources and achieving efficiency. In the early 1990s, I became the COO for Lakeshore Health System and later CEO of Lakeshore Health System. During this time, St. Mary's in Gary was sold to a for-profit company which operated the facility for two years."

Beth Kaminski, FORMER CEO
ST. MARY MEDICAL CENTER AND ANCILLA SYSTEMS INCORPORATED | (BEGAN IN 1986 IN HOBART)

IT'S BEEN *Said* IN 2009...

"During my time as head of Lakeshore Health System, my biggest priority was creating a regional system where everybody took ownership of the three hospitals. Even though we were all part of the same 'parenthood' – i.e., Ancilla Systems – I was astounded when I took over that there were people at St. Catherine who said they didn't even know that Mercy Hospital was part of the same order.

"There were people in Gary and Hobart who said the same thing – that they didn't know they were related to St. Catherine and wondered why we should be getting along. There was pretty clear divide between Gary and Hobart. Some of it was racially-based and some of it was just suburban versus inner city. Trying to get everybody on the same page and buying into the fact that we are one system all going down the road together took time, but by the time I left in the early 1990s, I was pretty pleased with the spirit and teamwork that had evolved toward Lakeshore Health System. I think it was pretty healthy and people were generally on board with the idea of the three-hospital system.

"The biggest challenge, on the other side of the coin, was trying to find a way to help Gary Mercy survive. You hate to be 'on watch' and responsible when a hospital has to close. You always second guess yourself in terms of, 'Did we do everything that we could have done?'"

John Birdzell, FORMER PRESIDENT OF LAKESHORE HEALTH SYSTEM | (BEGAN IN 1985 WITH ANCILLA SYSTEMS INCORPORATED)

IT'S BEEN *Said* IN 2009...

"I was hired in October of 1990 as vice president of Mission Effectiveness. At that time, John Birdzell was CEO of Lakeshore Health System – comprised of St. Mary Medical Center in Gary and Hobart and St. Catherine Hospital in East Chicago.

"Prior to becoming an employee for Lakeshore Health System, I was on the St. Mary Medical Center Board of Directors. I remember meeting in Whiting at that wonderful fish place – Phil Smidt's. That's when the board talked about becoming Lakeshore Health System. Not only did we have lunch there, but we had dinner there. That's how long we met – for two meals, you know. John Birdzell and Beth Kaminski would have been there as well as others."

Sister Mary Ellen Goeller, PHJC
REGIONAL DIRECTOR OF MISSION INTEGRATION | ST. MARY MEDICAL CENTER | (BEGAN IN 1990 AT ST. CATHERINE HOSPITAL AND ST. MARY MEDICAL CENTERS GARY/HOBART)

Beth Kaminski – Hospital Administrator

Beth Kaminski became CEO of St. Mary Medical Center in 1993.

"When I came to St. Mary's in 1986 (as senior vice president and COO), one of the patient floors was closed. There seemed to be a demand as patients were turned away. There were not enough beds on the other units. Working with the management team, it was determined we could open this floor and hire additional staff and discontinue the policy of turning away patients.

"It was clear there was a need for cardiology services. We were able to revive a plan for a catheterization lab and locate it next to the Surgery Department for easier access. The teams were put in place and developed an excellent cardiology program. This became a very important service financially. The orthopedics program was enhanced with additional space in a building adjacent to the hospital. Physician office space, occupational health and cardiac rehabilitation occupied this building and enhanced the beginning of a very successful outpatient service."

Beth Kaminski, FORMER CEO
ST. MARY MEDICAL CENTER AND ANCILLA SYSTEMS INCORPORATED
(BEGAN IN 1986 IN HOBART)

"Beth Kaminski treated everybody with respect. I never saw her out of line with anybody. She was someone I admired and looked up to and I learned many things from her. She was absolutely a wonderful leader. She amazed me how she treated everybody the same way. She would walk the halls and talk to people and take them where they needed to go. She would go visit with people after hours and she literally worked right along side them. She spent a few evenings in housekeeping, helping them, seeing how they did their jobs. She cleaned toilets. You don't know how they do it unless you do it."

Sharon Forszt, FORMER ADMINISTRATIVE ASSISTANT TO CEO
ST. MARY MEDICAL CENTER
(BEGAN IN 1975 AT ST. CATHERINE HOSPITAL)

"Beth Kaminski was instrumental in the technological and clinical development of St. Mary's. She was a visionary at that time and truly was a leader for St. Mary Medical Center."

Marsha King, R.N., M.S., M.B.A., C.N.A.A.
FORMER VICE PRESIDENT, PATIENT CARE SERVICES
ST. MARY MEDICAL CENTER | (BEGAN IN 1987 IN HOBART)

"In 1994, Bill Harkins, CEO of Ancilla Systems, asked me to serve as the CEO of the start-up physician company, Ancilla Health Services. It was interesting and exciting to be on the ground floor of a new company. Milt Triana, then vice president at St. Mary Medical Center (Hobart), succeeded me as CEO.

"The nationwide trend in the 1990s was to employ primary care physicians to build physician networks for managed care systems that would be supportive of your hospital system. The physician company grew to 86 physicians in Northern Indiana – from Lake County to the Ohio border."

Beth Kaminski, FORMER CEO
ST. MARY MEDICAL CENTER AND ANCILLA SYSTEMS INCORPORATED | (BEGAN IN 1986 IN HOBART)

**6WEST-MEDICAL TELEMETRY
DEPARTMENT STAFF PHOTO – 2010**

FIRST ROW (L-R): Corby Clark, RN;
Thelma Mariano, RN, admissions/discharge
nurse; Nichole Wojcehowski, PCA II;
Haley Stoica, RN; Jennifer Walczak, RN;
Ashley Hershman, RN Fellow; and
Doris Barnes, LPN

SECOND ROW (L-R): Annette Doyen, RN;
Leigh Cotton, PCA II; Monica Castro, PCA II;
Jenny Murray, RN; JoAnn Haas,
unit secretary; Joanne Zickuhr, RN,
charge nurse; Tina Centifanto, PCA II;
Aleta Williscroft, unit secretary; and
Nurse Manager Shannon Blaney

BACK ROW (L-R): Nadia Exl, RN; and
Krystal Baum, RN

● THEN AND NOW

6WEST-MEDICAL TELEMETRY...

*Contributed by Shannon Blaney, RN, Nurse Manager
Joanne Zickuhr, RN, Charge Nurse and Annette Doyen, RN*

What is now known as 6West-Medical Telemetry was previously located on the fifth floor of the East Tower. The unit originally opened in the fall of 1986 as a 10-bed Primary Care Medical Unit. The nurse manager at that time was Carol Lajcin with a staff of all registered nurses. As the hospital census increased so did the number of beds on the unit – first to 16 beds and then to approximately 28 beds by early 1987. The staff then was also comprised of licensed practical nurses and nursing assistants.

In the early 1990s, the staff attended electrocardiogram (EKG) classes and 16 telemetry monitors were installed in the department. The patient population grew to include cardiac patients and stable patients on tridil and lidocaine drips. Patients scheduled for cardiac catheterization procedures were admitted as 23-hour observation patients and were admitted to the fifth floor which was labeled a Medical Telemetry Unit. In 1992, Kim McBrayer became the nurse manager of the department. The unit was the "catch-all" floor of the hospital with patient diagnoses ranging from medical issues such as pneumonia or urinary tract infections to cardiac issues such as chest pain, rule-out myocardial infarction, and congestive heart failure. We began to assist cardiologists and anesthesiologists in the performance of cardiac cardioversions on the unit. The unit began to take more critically ill patients but still with many restrictions. A patient undergoing his/her first dialysis treatment, for example, had to be transferred to the Intermediate Care Unit for closer observation. The nurse-to-patient ratio was six-to-one at that time and it was team-style nursing. The staff consisted of registered nurses, licensed practical nurses, nursing assistants, nurse apprentice technicians and unit secretaries.

In 2004, under the management of Shannon Blaney, the unit moved to our current location on 6West of the New Patient Tower, a 22-bed all-telemetry unit. The unit truly became an all-inclusive Medical Telemetry Unit. The staff underwent extensive education and began to take more critically ill patients, including the heart failure patients on natrecor and dobutamine drips. We also began to titrate tridil on patients with chest pain. First-time dialysis patients stayed in the department. The patient population still varied from medical patient to more critically ill patients. The nurse patient ratio decreased from six to eight patients per nurse to four to five patients per nurse.

Today's highly-educated staff is continuously trained on new procedures and medications. Just as the medical staff is confident in the care administered to their patients of the 6West-Medical Telemetry Unit, so too are the patients who feel confident and safe in the caring hands of the 6West Medical-Telemetry Unit.

RADIATION ONCOLOGY

IT'S BEEN *Said* IN 2009...

"Most of my time was spent on the oncology floor. I was the nurse manager for 18 years. I was hired by Colleen Chirinos who was the director of nursing. I met with her and told her that I lived in Hobart, was very dependable, and had a very good background. She hired me. She told me to go home and put on my white shoes and my uniform and my hat. I began working midnights in 1975. When I started, you gave back rubs. You tucked people in at night. You had more time to do that. I worked that year part-time and then I became the nurse manager of the oncology unit until I went into case management. When we saw a patient go home, that was the highlight of our lives."

Catherine Wiseman, R.N., CLINICAL CASE MANAGER
ACUTE REHABILITATION UNIT, RETIRED
ST. MARY MEDICAL CENTER
(BEGAN IN 1975 IN HOBART)

IT'S BEEN *Said* IN 2009...

"With specimens that we have in the morning, we'll have results that afternoon. If you're a woman who has a breast biopsy and you're concerned that you might have cancer and it needs treatment, you don't want to agonize over a 24 to 72-hour period to wait for that answer. The results certainly bring peace of mind if it's negative or if it's positive, and you can say, 'Okay, let's get something done.'"

Anthony "Tony" Costello, Ph.D., SITE DIRECTOR, LABORATORY
ST. MARY MEDICAL CENTER
(BEGAN IN 1976 IN GARY)

"Cancer is a word, not a sentence."
- JOHN DIAMOND

• THEN AND NOW

RADIATION ONCOLOGY/MEDICAL PHYSICS DEPARTMENT...

Contributed by Matt Matushek, Director
Michael Mysz, Medical Physicist
and Koppolu Sarma, M.D., Radiation Oncologist

RADIATION ONCOLOGY STAFF PHOTO – 2009
BACK ROW (L-R): Director of Radiation Oncology Matt Matushek;
Mike Mysz, medical physicist; Biljana Terzioski, radiation therapist;
and Koppolu Sarma, M.D., radiation oncologist
FRONT ROW (L-R): Kathy Blakeley, radiation therapist;
Connie Swartz, department assistant; and Judy Garza, RN

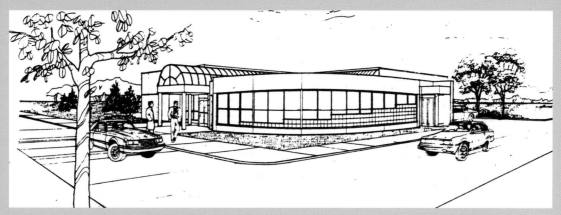

Shown here is an artist's conception of the $7 million cancer diagnostic center that was built in 1985 at St. Mary Medical Center in Hobart.

Reprinted by permission of the *Post-Tribune*, FEBRUARY 23, 1985

The newly refurbished Center for Imaging and Radiation Oncology (CIRO) re-opened in the fall of 2005 with the following diagnostic specialties: mammography, bone density, ultrasound and CT scanning. This complimented the MRI and radiation oncology services already available in the building. These services provide patients with the easily accessible convenience of premier detection and treatment.

Located in the Center for Imaging and Radiation Oncology just off 61st Avenue, the beautiful Women's Center prides itself in giving same-day results.

On March 17, 1986, the Diagnostic Outpatient Center opened on five acres of land owned by St. Mary Medical Center but leased to a private investor. The Diagnostic Outpatient Center, also known as "DOC," was specifically designed for the detection and treatment of cancer. The facility was equipped with Magnetic Resonance Imaging (MRI), a linear accelerator, a low dose mammography, and breast ultrasound.

The inpatients from St. Mary Medical Center were transported to the DOC by ambulance for their daily treatments. The center prospered and worked closely with area medical oncologists to provide comprehensive treatments. The DOC continued to provide state-of-the-art equipment and services. The MRI was upgraded and replaced in the early 1990s. The linear accelerator was replaced in February, 2000, with fully digital capabilities and multi-leaf collimation that uses mechanical shields in the machine to shape and control radiation instead of external lead blocking. Computerized Tomography (CT) simulation was added at that time to replace the two-dimensional simulator. This equipment allowed for more complex treatment planning and treatments utilizing Intensity Modulated Radiation Therapy (IMRT). The DOC was one of the earliest adopters of IMRT, ahead of many area hospitals.

On January 1, 2004, the DOC was acquired from the private investors by St. Mary Medical Center and renamed The Center for Imaging and Radiation Oncology (CIRO). The facility continued to provide Magnetic Resonance Imaging (MRI) as well as radiation treatments using the linear accelerator. The other diagnostic studies, ultrasound and mammography, were provided at the main hospital while the center was completely remodeled and updated.

The newly refurbished center re-opened in the fall of 2005 with the following diagnostic specialties: digital mammography, bone density, ultrasound and CT scanning. This complimented the MRI and radiation oncology services already available in the building.

As part of the Radiation Oncology Department, professional staff members in the Department of Medical Physics help provide for the safe and effective use of radiation in diagnostic and therapeutic procedures. Medical physicists perform calibration and quality assurance testing on radiation-producing equipment such as linear accelerators, CT scanners, and X-ray machines. Medical physicists are consulted when radioactive isotopes are used in treatment and diagnostic procedures. Medical physicists and dosimetrists from the Department of Medical Physics are especially involved in patient care at the Center for Imaging and Radiation Oncology where they assist physicians with planning and setup to achieve the prescribed doses during external beam irradiation or internal radioactive source placement.

These services at The Center for Imaging and Radiation Oncology now provide patients with the easily accessible convenience of premier detection and treatment, with premier services available within Community Healthcare System.

IT'S BEEN *Said* IN 2009... ~~~~~~~~~~

"St. Mary Medical Center, in partnership with its sister hospitals in Community Healthcare System, offers the benefit of efficient referral for oncology patients who need specialized radiation services. St. Catherine Hospital in East Chicago, Indiana, has the only CyberKnife™ in Northwest Indiana with the ability to irradiate areas of the body that would be extremely risky to treat with other forms of radiation. Community Hospital in Munster, Indiana, has High-Dose Rate Brachytherapy that allows the patient to have temporary radioactive sources placed within or near the tumor to treat the cancer while reducing dosage to healthy tissues."

Koppolu Sarma, M.D.
RADIATION ONCOLOGIST
ST. MARY MEDICAL CENTER
(BEGAN IN 1986 IN HOBART)

Marking Time... 1987

- *A gene that causes cancer of the colon was pinpointed on a human chromosome.*
- *On Black Monday, October 19, the Dow Jones industrial average dropped a record 508.32 (22.6 percent). The Crash of '87 was costly to many investors but did not trigger a recession or depression.*

HOME HEALTH DEPARTMENT STAFF PHOTO – 2009

<u>TOP ROW (L-R):</u> Rebecca Siminiski, department assistant; Rosanne Hutchins, patient care coordinator/supervisor; Janet Craig, occupational therapist; Roland Novales, physical therapist; Diane Krzanowsky, scheduler; Teena Culig, operations assistant; Tracey Vanvuren, patient care coordinator/supervisor; Al Flores, physical therapist; Ibikunle Salami, physical therapist; and Kristy Snyder, RN

<u>MIDDLE ROW (L-R):</u> Joan Rodriguez, RN; Lori Alicea, clerk/receptionist; Leann Richmond, coder; Debra Maxin, patient care coordinator/supervisor; Polly Rushmore, RN; Carol Andjelich, RN; and Renee Fuller, RN

<u>FRONT ROW (L-R):</u> Chelsea Hagan, RN; Laurice Yangson, physical therapist; Marsha Frank, RN; Jennifer Johnson, RN; and Romeo Roldan, physical therapist

---

• THEN AND NOW

HOME HEALTH...

Contributed by Lori Passine, Administrator

Lori Passine, Administrator
Home Health

Home Health of St. Mary Medical Center had its beginning on March 1, 1987, as Ancilla Home Health. The agency, a division of Ancilla Systems Corporation, was a free-standing agency although physically located at St. Catherine Hospital. The agency serviced clients in Lake and Porter counties.

In 1994, the Home Health Agency was relocated to Highland, Indiana. Then in January, 1996, Ancilla Home Health divided and became Ancilla Home Health of St. Catherine Hospital and Ancilla Home Health of St. Mary Medical Center under the ownership of each hospital.

In 1997, each agency relocated to its host hospital. Ancilla Home Health of St. Mary Medical Center was relocated near the Garden Café. In 1999, the agency moved to St. Mary's Portage Outpatient Health Center on Willowcreek Road. It would be home for approximately three years with big changes to come. In 2001, with the development of Community Healthcare System, our department name was changed to Home Health of St. Mary Medical Center – no longer Ancilla. We acquired a new vice president of Home Care and underwent numerous changes such as staff turnover, new methods of operation, a change in our director and, yes, one more change in location.

Lori Passine began as Home Health administrator in 2002 and a year later Home Health moved back to Hobart across the street from the hospital where it still remains in 2010. In 2008, we serviced over 900 patients and provided over 22,000 visits involving skilled nursing, physical therapy, occupational therapy, speech therapy, home health aid, and social services.

It takes a special nurse and a special person to remain in Home Health Care, not only through orientation but also for 10-20 years of service, as our office nursing staff has done. The stories remain unique to healthcare as patients are cared for in their homes – in diversified environments with interesting family dynamics. We do not discriminate among the patients we serve, having been in beautiful homes and homes without running water, homes that are "rent by the hour," and homes where staff members are the only "family" patients have.

In Home Care, we get to make a difference on a very personal level.

IT'S BEEN *Said* IN 2009...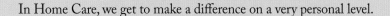

"When Ancilla Home Health was located near the Garden Café at the Hobart facility, our small office space was somehow home to a cat! At the same time, the Acute Rehabilitation Unit (ARU) was being added to the hospital and the cat took up residency in the ceiling. Staff heard the meowing one night and left a bowl of food on the table. The next morning the extremely frightened cat couldn't be contained by the staff. After assistance from security, Hobart police and animal control, the cat was rescued and the office assistant was sent to the Emergency Room to be treated for cat scratches from the rescue attempt."

Rosanne Hutchins
PATIENT CARE COORDINATOR/SUPERVISOR
(BEGAN IN 1990 IN HOBART)

IT'S BEEN *Said* IN 2009...

"One time during an orientation, we learned that a 90-year-old patient had let a stray cat into her home that in turn delivered kittens. The preceptor was buying food for all the felines since the patient was unable to do so. When the patient's health declined and she was sent by ambulance to the hospital, her last words were, 'Please take care of the cat and kittens.' She did not want them to be euthanized, so when the little lady died, the nurses kept their word. The cats have been a part of their homes for 14 years."

Rosanne Hutchins
PATIENT CARE COORDINATOR/SUPERVISOR
(BEGAN IN 1990 IN HOBART)

IT'S BEEN *Said* IN 2009...

"Smiles arise remembering the day when the new vice president of Home Care arrived unannounced looking for the director. It was Halloween and the director, Paula Shaw, was decked out in a witch's costume with a green face, wart and all. A short time later, the vice president and director were seen leaving in the vice president's car with the witch's black wig and cape blowing in the wind… destination unknown."

Debra Maxin
PATIENT CARE COORDINATOR/SUPERVISOR
(BEGAN IN 1995 IN HOBART)

QUALITY/RISK

IT'S BEEN *Said* IN 2009...

"The system has been wonderful for quality. We were given a lot more financial support, a lot more people and more tools. Ancilla just didn't have the money to do it. They would have if they could have but they couldn't. So I was able to increase my staff and things I needed. Milt (Triana) always looked at the quality and Janice (Ryba), coming from the quality background, is even more supportive of quality. You can do a more thorough job when you have the tools and the resources to keep the quality good here."

Sherry Brewer, R.N., Ph.D
DIRECTOR, QUALITY RISK MANAGEMENT
ST. MARY MEDICAL CENTER
(BEGAN IN 1974 IN HOBART)

With Beginnings in Gary • THEN AND NOW
QUALITY/RISK MANAGEMENT...

Contributed by Sherry Brewer, RN, Ph.D.
Director of Quality/Risk Management

QUALITY AND RISK MANAGEMENT STAFF PHOTO - 2009
SHOWN (L-R): Performance Improvement Coordinator Laura Labadie; Operations Assistant Regina Sabo; Director Sherry Brewer; Clinical Data Specialist Gloria Kvachkoff; and Performance Improvement Coordinator Nancy Cline

Since its beginning in 1987, the Quality Management Department has undergone tremendous growth. Originally, there was one person who reviewed physician charts. The department covered two hospitals – St. Mary Medical Center in Hobart and St. Mary Mercy Hospital in Gary. Initially, there wasn't a department that looked at staff or departmental quality indicators, but a 1987 Joint Commission visit presented standardized quality indicators and found that both hospitals were not in compliance. They were given six months to improve performance or risk losing accreditation.

Don Barnes and Jack Seebee, M.D., headed up a task force to meet The Joint Commission requirements. Peggy Kamysz served as Quality Review director from 1987-1989. There was a Physician Quality Review committee already in place and Peggy formed a subcommittee to address hospital quality and report to the Physician Quality Review committee chaired by Steve Simpson, M.D. In mid-1987, Sister Nora Hahn, PHJC, initiated a Corporate Quality Review committee comprised of all five Ancilla System hospitals. The standardization of Quality indicators became a corporate responsibility with subsequent quarterly reports to Ancilla System board members.

Anthony "Tony" Costello and Karen Gerke were among team members who conducted in-depth self-departmental reviews plus those of other departments, and sent reports to the Physician Quality Review committee. The basic hospital review process remains in use today. Managers who conducted Quality Assurance Program (QAP – not to be confused with QIP mentioned above) reviews at both hospitals wore orange badges and were known as Quality Assurance evaluators.

Laura Gilliam was later moved to the Quality and Utilization Department and joined Connie Blaine, Lynn Olszewski, Sharon York, Tina Smith and Darlene Woodley who were hired to perform Quality reviews for both hospitals. Pre-admission and Infection Control nurses, Charlotte Vellines, Barbara Crawford and Mary (Cathy) Adams, worked with the Quality director and assisted with chart reviews. In 1991, Connie Blaine became Quality director for both Gary and Hobart with nurses who helped with physician peer review and hospital quality review. During this time, Medicare and insurance case reviews began as part of Utilization Review. From 1991 – 1996, Barb McDonald, Amy Bachich and Greta Coady were assigned to Quality Management and all staff moved between the two hospitals. The two St. Mary hospitals held joint physician departmental/quality meetings with Methodist Hospital until 1997.

QUALITY ASSURANCE EVALUATOR

The Badge
Managers who conducted Quality Assurance Program (QAP) reviews at both hospitals wore orange badges and were known as Quality Assurance evaluators."

Risk Management was a separate entity under Ron Morris and later Trina Lynch. The chart reviews for risk cases were always done by Nursing or Hospital Quality, and later this area of responsibility was transferred to Hospital Quality. In addition to Director Sherry Brewer, current staff members in 2009 include Nancy Cline and Laura Labadie who are full-time case reviewers, Gloria Kvachkoff who reviews core measure cases part-time, and Regina Sabo who is operations assistant.

Managers still assist in some quality review efforts, but not to the extent they did in 1987 when the department was in its infancy. In 2001, when we joined with Community Healthcare System, Janice L. Ryba was appointed regional director for Quality at Community Hospital, St. Mary Medical Center, and St. Catherine Hospital. Because of the sound quality footing designed back in 1987, she found it very easy to merge the three hospital Quality departments into a cohesive group with the same quality processes.

Janice now serves as CEO and administrator of St. Mary Medical Center and Nancy Moser is vice president Compliance, Quality and Risk Management. Over time, the purpose of the department has been carefully scrutinized and defined. Progress continues. As Laura Labadie noted, several years ago review charts were not available for several days. Today, we have the luxury of instantaneous computer information. Now that is history!

Shown here is Connie Blaine, RN, in 1978.

It's been *Said* in 2009...

"When I had the opportunity to become a head nurse in 1978, I was in the Hobart facility on a medical-surgical unit… (with) a wonderful team. I called our floor the potpourri unit. Changes were occurring in healthcare in terms of reimbursement; patients were coming out of ICU sooner, and we had a mix of patients – from pediatric patients to critical patients on ventilators. It was a challenge to keep up the skills necessary to care for the wide variety of ages and conditions…

"I look back on my career from 1960-1999, beginning with St. Mary Mercy Hospital and ending with St. Mary Medical Center, with a sense of pride and accomplishment, proud to have been part of the wonderful profession of nursing in the St. Mary 'family'."

Connie McCarthy Blaine, R.N, BSHA
Director of Quality Management, retired
St. Mary Mercy Hospital
(began in 1963 in Gary)

It's been *Said* in 2009...

"We started the QIP system. We had little orange badges for Quality Insurance inspection and each department listed points of excellence that they should fulfill for quality work. For example, I as a laboratory person would go to the warehouse to review everything on their list and someone from the warehouse would come to the laboratory and check our list. I'll never forget going down to the warehouse on Fifth Avenue and Lorenzo Crowell, who is now the leader of our union, worked in the warehouse and took me around. That was an attempt to bring quality to your departments and get everybody looking at everybody else so you appreciate what's going on in another department."

Anthony "Tony" Costello, PhD
Site Director, Laboratory
St. Mary Medical Center | (began in 1976 in Gary)

HOSPITAL/COMMUNITY HAPPENINGS

Shown here (left - right) at a Hobart surgery gathering in 1988 are
William Glover, M.D.; Lin Lovell, CRNA; and William Nowlin, M.D.

LARRY MANGOLD

In 1986, Larry Mangold was named chief financial officer of the newly-formed Northwest Indiana System (officially named Lakeshore Health System shortly thereafter), comprised of St. Mary Medical Center – Gary and Hobart, and St. Catherine Hospital in East Chicago.

GEORGE BURRELL

George Burrell, who had been vice president of operations for Lakeshore Health Systems, was appointed chief operating officer at St. Mary Medical Center in Gary in 1988. He replaced Larry Mangold who was appointed chief operating officer at St. Catherine Hospital. Burrell said a top priority was "for the Gary campus to have a closer working relationship with the community surrounding the campus and the communities we serve."

Reprinted by permission of the *Post-Tribune*, SEPTEMBER 9, 1988

THOMAS J. CRUMP

Thomas J. Crump, former chairman of the board of directors for Lakeshore Health System

THOMAS L. GLEASON

Thomas L. Gleason, controller of Inland Steel Industries, Inc., was appointed chairman of the board of directors for Lakeshore Health System in September 1988. He succeeded Thomas J. Crump, who had served on the combined board as chairman since its formation in 1986, and had also served on St. Mary Medical Center's board of directors since 1980.

1988 – The Lithotripter

In 1988, the Dornier Kidney Lithotripter became available for faster relief of kidney stones. The process was introduced to eliminate the stones through a specially-targeted shock wave treatment in which the stones are non-invasively shattered. A mobile semi-trailer was shared with hospitals in Elkhart, South Bend, and Kokomo but traveled locally among St. Mary's Gary and Hobart sites as well as to St. Catherine Hospital.

Lithotripsy came to Ancilla Systems hospitals in Northwest Indiana in 1988. Urologist Bassem Atassi, M.D., and Lithotripter Technologist Karen Bingham demonstrate the computerized mechanism for electronically crushing gall stones or kidney stones.

Hobart Gazette, June 15, 1988

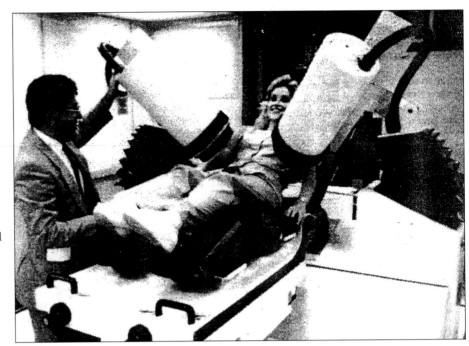

The Strike

From the PHJC Chronicles – July, 1988

Our bargaining Union #1199 began to strike at 6:00 a.m. on July 18th. Employees (non-bargaining) are working 12 hour shifts. This includes the Sisters.

CHJC, University of Notre Dame Archives

A workers' strike began July 18 after a vote by members of the National Union of Hospital and Health Care Employees/SEIU Indiana Local 1199. The union represented 418 service and maintenance workers at St. Mary Medical Center's Gary and Hobart hospitals.

Under discussion were such issues as wage increases, short-term disability, and pro-rated benefits. Picketers stood outside both hospital locations as the strike moved into its second week. In an effort to reach a strike settlement, Gary Mayor Thomas V. Barnes stepped in; he and his attorney met separately with three representatives from both sides at the mayor's home.

The *Hobart Gazette* reported that the 12-day strike between the two St. Mary Medical Center campuses and Local 1199, National Union of Hospital and Health Care Employees ended on July 29, 1988, after union members overwhelmingly voted to ratify a new contract.

It's been *Said* in 2009...

"I was a vice-president during the workers' strike in the 1980s. The Service Employees International Union (SEIU) includes such groups as environmental services, food service, maintenance, and unit secretaries. This group decided to strike and it lasted almost two weeks. John Birdzell was CEO of Lakeshore Health System and we decided, with John's direction, that all the managers from all three hospitals would work in different positions... of the hospital. I was assigned to clean rooms with Dave Padilla and we flipped a coin to see who would clean the room or the bathroom. I lost and I wound up cleaning all the bathrooms. We must have done 30 or more rooms every day for 14 days straight until the strike was settled.

"It was a tough strike. The employees were picketing and our hospital volume was down. Patients in unions decided they would not use St. Mary because of their union ties. It was difficult financially for the hospital during those two weeks. All of us in management realized the importance of the jobs that they did."

Milt Triana, retired Hospital Administrator, St. Mary Medical Center
Special Projects Coordinator, Community Healthcare System | (began in 1969 in Gary)

1989

HOSPITAL/COMMUNITY HAPPENINGS

Sister Florence Kuhn, PHJC, gave one of the readings at the 1989 Nativity scene blessing ceremony at St. Mary Medical Center. Standing behind her is hospital chaplain, Reverend David Nowak.

Herald News Group, DECEMBER 20, 1989

*Marking Time...*1989

- *First successful liver transplant using portion of living donor's organ.*
- *Spiral CAT scanning was introduced.*

DID YOU KNOW?

MERCY'S HELIPORT CAME FIRST

In the 1970s, Mercy Hospital's heliport was a large "H" painted within a large red medical cross symbol on the playground/parking lot of Holy Angels School in Gary. It was used for emergency pick-up or delivery to the hospital which was located directly across Sixth Avenue from Mercy's Emergency Room entrance.

The 1974 heliport was located on the playground/parking lot of Holy Angels School directly across the street from the hospital's emergency entrance.

Reprinted by permission of the *Post-Tribune*, June 6, 1974

1989 – HOBART ADDS A HELIPAD

The first helipad at St. Mary Medical Center in Hobart was added on the hospital grounds in August, 1989. It would mean quick transportation for patients who needed to be flown to or from the Hobart campus. The helipad was made possible through donations from the Fraternal Order of Police Lodge 121, Veterans of Foreign Wars Post 5365, and Boyd Construction Co. It was located at the southwest corner of the hospital.

Shown here is the helipad outside St. Mary Medical Center in Hobart. Sgt. Chuck Bernhardt, retired (left), of the Lake County Sheriff's Police, and Officer Greg Shaginaw of the Hobart Police Department stand on the new helipad. Shaginaw was president of the Hobart Fraternal Order of Police, the group that started the fund drive for the 324-square foot helicopter pad.

Source unknown

1999 – HOBART HELIPAD UPGRADED

At an unveiling of the new Hobart helipad in 1999, Hospital Administrator Milt Triana touted it as the best in the country. The $44,000 50 x 50-foot heated structure was made of corrugated aluminum, was surrounded by landing lights, and could be approached from any direction. Hartley Thomas, M.D., the hospital's Emergency Room director, was an in-flight physician. His father, Gerald Thomas, M.D., a general surgeon at St. Mary Medical Center for 50 years, was a strong advocate for the needed upgrade. The new helipad replaced the former, smaller concrete landing site near the Emergency Room entrance and remains there today (in 2010).

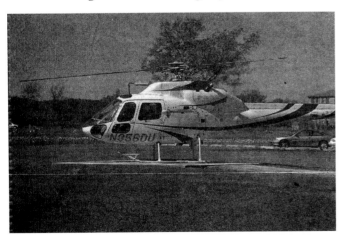

A helicopter from the University of Chicago Burn Unit landed at St. Mary Medical Center as part of the unveiling of the hospital's new helipad in 1999.

Reprinted by permission of the *Post-Tribune*, OCTOBER 6, 1999

The Podiatric Residency Program

The Podiatric Residency Program was established at St. Mary Medical Center in 1990, jointly sponsored by the hospital and Broadwest Surgical Center. It was one of 200 nationally approved Podiatric Residency programs, certified through the Council on Medical Education.

Stephen Grandfield, D.P.M.

The program was approved for four residents – two PSR-12 (one year) and two PSR-24 (two year) residents who rotated through medical and surgical services as well as hospital-based rotations. Stephen Grandfield, D.P.M., responsible for overseeing the program's certification standards, also processed applications submitted by those at the end of their podiatry medical school training.

This was a quality program with sufficient trauma and other surgical situations to make it one of the more sought after programs," Dr. Grandfield said. "It featured prolific numbers of podiatric and orthopedic procedures."

A total of 25 podiatrists matriculated through the Podiatric Residency Program until it ended in June 2007. Many graduates practice locally, contributing to St. Mary Medical Center and other area institutions.

MediMex

MediMex was formed in 1990 to go beyond our borders to care for those in need. It was initiated by Jerry Cassity and two of Community Healthcare System's own – Ken Vanderhye, then director of Imaging Services at St. Mary Medical Center and Rory Melendes, Community Hospital nurse educator. Northwest Indiana involvement in the initiative lasted for approximately 15 years, exemplifying a strong avenue of volunteer outreach.

Food, medicine, beds and X-ray machines (hospital equipment replaced with new technology) were shipped to the underdeveloped region or Mexico's Baja peninsula where people travel miles to be seen by a physician. From delivering babies to assisting with appendectomies, additional Community Healthcare System volunteers helped the local people build modest shelters that they call home.

St. Mary Medical Center Clinical Engineer, Ruben Santana, who speaks fluent Spanish, repaired equipment when something went wrong.

"I was born in Puerto Rico and lived there until I was seven years old," he said in a *Vim & Vigor* magazine issue in the fall of 2005. "We were very poor. Seeing these children and families made me remember. There was a connection there and now I'm hooked."

1990s – A Mission of Mercy to China

IT'S BEEN *Said* IN 2009…

"Healthcare in this country is the finest in the world – not perfect but the finest. I went to China as a representative of the hospital back in the mid-1990s. I went with one of the Operating Room (OR) nurses and Dr. O'Yek, who was a Chinese Philippine open heart surgeon. We performed two open heart surgeries there. The staff there was eager to learn and was very cordial to us. We took a lot of supplies with us – things that we would have thrown away. If a suture is taken from a packet and put on a sterile field, we can't use it. They could use it as it remained sterile inside the package. At that time, China was truly a third world country in medicine."

Maryann Kerr, R.N, Nurse Manager
ICCU & Medical Oncology, retired
Mercy Hospital | (began in 1960 in Gary)

Victorio O'Yek, M.D.
Cardiothoracic Surgeon

ALSO IN THE 1990S

LAKESHORE HEALTH SYSTEM – TOTAL QUALITY MANAGEMENT

In 1991, 35 team leaders and 125 team members were trained for TQM, or Total Quality Management, a unified problem-solving initiative of Lakeshore Health System. With additional teams planned, the basic premise was to resolve problems by team examination of the facts and have all associates participate in the decision-making process.

GARY MEDICAL PARTNERSHIP

One of several partnerships initiated by Ancilla Systems Incorporated was the Gary Medical Partnership which elected Alexander Williams, M.D., as Chairman of the Board. He and 36 other physicians joined with St. Mary Medical Center in ownership of the facility's CT scanner and other diagnostic equipment.

1990 Ancilla Systems Annual Report

• THEN AND NOW

MANAGED CARE DEPARTMENT...

Contributed by Jim Hilburger, Director

MANAGED CARE DEPARTMENT STAFF PHOTO – 2009
PICTURED (L-R): Managed Care Analyst Laurie Edmond, Director Jim Hilburger and Credentialing Manager Sara Pierce

Marking Time...

1990
• Congress passed Nutrition Labeling and Education Act, requiring all food products to carry detailed labels describing nutritional content.

1991
• The Chicago Bulls, led by Michael Jordan, won their first of three consecutive National Basketball Association championships, this time over the Los Angeles Lakers.

"Where will healthcare be in the next decade? Healthcare will advance in technology and in controlling various diseases. I think the number one concern, however, now and in the future, is the declining reimbursement from insurance providers. St. Mary's was very profitable in the '90s even though our inpatient volume and our average daily census were approximately 80-90 – maybe 100 at their peak. When I first became the administrator, the reimbursement was very good from private insurance and Medicare but it soon changed. Medicare started reimbursing less, managed care came into existence and there were more HMOs and PPOs so we had a big emphasis on cost savings and cost reductions. We had to cut back."

Milt Triana, RETIRED
HOSPITAL ADMINISTRATOR, ST. MARY MEDICAL CENTER
SPECIAL PROJECTS COORDINATOR, COMMUNITY HEALTHCARE SYSTEM | (BEGAN IN 1969 IN GARY)

When the Poor Handmaids of Jesus Christ founded St. Mary Mercy Hospital in Gary in 1913, health insurance was not available as it is today. Patients paid out of pocket with help from family and friends as well as the charity of the Poor Handmaids. Advances in the science of medicine led to standardized medical education, licensure, accreditation, new technologies, and improved facilities. These advances helped to increase demand and raise the costs of providing quality health care to the surrounding community.

Around our country in the 1920s, physicians offered to care for rural communities or company employees for a set fee per person per month. This was the beginning of Health Maintenance Organizations (HMO). Similar pre-paid hospital care led to the development of Blue Cross plans. Soon Blue Shield plans developed for physicians. Special enabling legislation allowed these plans to form as non-profit mutual benefit insurance organizations. Over time, commercial insurers saw the success of Blue Cross Blue Shield plans and entered the health insurance market. During and post World War II, our nation witnessed a boom in the employer health insurance market.

Coincidentally, in 1973 we saw the birth of St. Mary Medical Center in Hobart as well as the passage of The HMO Act of 1973. This act authorized the development of pre-paid health plans to enroll patients and arrange for all of their health care needs within a designated provider network. This was the birth of managed care as we know it today. Over the last half century, we have continued to seek solutions to issues of health care cost containment, coverage for the uninsured, access to services for the poor, consumer rights, efficient health care delivery systems and the provision of quality health care.

The term "managed care" encompasses the acronym soup of HMOs (health maintenance organizations), PPOs (preferred provider organizations), and POS plans (point of service). It also includes hospital and physician delivery systems that contract with such health plans, as well as the techniques and models utilized by organizations in coordinating the delivery of quality healthcare. As the HMOs and insurance companies sought to create their provider networks and delivery systems for their enrollees, they proposed contracts to St. Mary Medical Center requesting discounts from billed charges. As these proposals became more frequent and more complicated, there was a need to manage and coordinate all of these arrangements and the Department of Managed Care was created. Today, the Managed Care Department is integrated across all three hospitals of Community Healthcare System, contracting with all of the major health plans and insurance companies doing business in our service area.

In the mid 1990s, the hospital collaborated with our physicians to form the St. Mary Medical Center Physician Hospital Organization (PHO). Our PHO currently has over 200 physician members and provides health plans with a single point of access to propose business relationships. In addition to managed care contracting, our PHO also assists its physicians and their offices by providing information through newsletters, in-services with health plans, liaison and problem solving resources, and streamlined health plan credentialing.

Another key component of our Managed Care Department is our MDwise delivery system. In 2002, Community Healthcare System partnered with MDwise to offer Medicaid beneficiaries a managed care program as part of the Indiana Hoosier Healthwise initiative. Our MDwise Network, which includes over 400 physicians, is a managed care program providing quality healthcare to over 18,000 children, pregnant women and low income families in the Community Healthcare System service area.

In 2008, the Managed Care Department undertook two new initiatives for residents of the State of Indiana. The Healthy Indiana Plan offers a basic health insurance benefit to eligible low income Hoosiers without access to employer sponsored health insurance. The Indiana Care Select program for the aged, blind and disabled is designed to improve the patient's health status, enhance quality of life, and improve the patient's safety, autonomy and adherence to treatment plans. Indiana Care Select also strives to control healthcare costs by providing care in a less fragmented and more holistic managed care program.

Through its relationships with the commercial insurance industry, the Managed Care Department provides a critical link in the revenue chain that supports our mission at St. Mary Medical Center.

Hospital/Community Happenings

Did you know?

In August 1992, St. Mary Medical Center in Hobart opened its new Chest Pain Emergency Center. The center was created to bring awareness to the importance of early cardiac care and to encourage people to become familiar with the early warning signs of a heart attack and to call or come into the hospital if they have chest pain.

Smoke-Free

On November 19, 1992, on the day of the American Cancer Society's Great American Smokeout, St. Mary Medical Center, at both locations in Gary and Hobart, became smoke-free inside their hospitals to uphold its mission of promoting health and wellness.

Furthermore, on April 15, 2010, Community Healthcare System hospitals became smoke-free on all hospital properties and off-site locations. This included parking lots and surrounding areas.

"Kick the habit"
In 1992, Milt Triana, then St. Mary Medical Center vice president of operations and chairman of Lakeshore Health System Smoke-free committee, extinguished what could well have been his last cigarette.

Summary, February 1992

1992 – Health and Rehabilitation Spectrum

In the spring of 1992, St. Mary Medical Center in Hobart opened its new Health and Rehabilitation Spectrum just north of the hospital at 1354 South Lake Park Avenue. Designed as a multi-purpose outpatient rehabilitation facility dedicated to the prevention, evaluation, treatment, and rehabilitation of injured workers and athletes; the new facility was also being used by St. Mary cardiac patients. The spacious facility, with more than 12,000 square feet, included five major programs: industrial rehabilitation, sports medicine, Phase III cardiac rehabilitation, occupational health, and wellness and fitness. Staff physician, Robert Wylie, M.D., was Spectrum's first medical director.

"The Health and Rehabilitation Spectrum is by far the most comprehensive… facility in the hospital's service area," said Ed Grogg, responsible for administration, sales, and marketing.

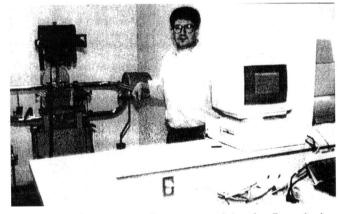

Mark Leto, athletic trainer at Spectrum, stands beside a B-200 back analysis machine. The device was designed to test for any type of back disfiguration.

Hobart Gazette, March 11, 1992

At the opening of the Health & Rehabilitation Spectrum on March 21, 1992, then Chicago Bears quarterback, Jim Harbaugh, was on hand to help with the St. Mary Medical Center celebration. He is shown autographing a football for a young fan.

Summary, April, 1992

Marking Time...1992

- *First report on sentinel node biopsy for breast cancer was issued.*
- *Johnny Carson hosted "The Tonight Show" for the last time.*

Hospital/Community Happenings

Collaborating with another Provider

Demonstrating collaboration with another provider, St. Mary Medical Center, Hobart, and St. Anthony Medical Center, Crown Point, opened the Valparaiso Physician and Surgery Center early in 1993. The lobby adjoined physician offices and four surgical suites, full-service laboratory, EKG and pulmonary function testing, and other diagnostic services.

Special Dental Care Center

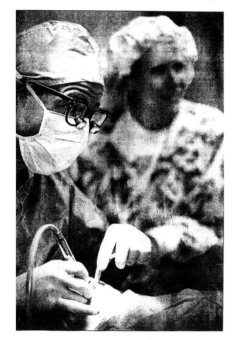

The Special Dental Care Center opened in the Medical Arts Building of St. Mary Medical Center in December, 1993, under the directorship of James Lipton, D.D.S., and Dental Program Coordinator Cynthia Van Zant. The program moved from St. Margaret Mercy Healthcare Center in Dyer where Dr. Lipton developed it in 1987.

The Special Dental Care Center, cited by the *Journal of American Dental Association*, took a multidisciplinary approach to the dental care of medically compromised patients whose conditions could range from congenital heart disease to mental retardation.

"We will work very closely with the patient's referring dentist or physician," Lipton said in a *Hobart Gazette* story (January 26, 1994). "In turn, we return the patient to the dentist's private office to perform any non-invasive procedures that the patient can tolerate in that setting."

The program was in existence until 1999.

Dr. James Lipton performs oral surgery on a patient while Anesthesiology Nurse Mary Ellen Pierce assists at the St. Mary Medical Center Dental Clinic.
Reprinted by permission of *The Times*, May 17, 1994

1993 – St. Mary Mercy Hospital for Sale

It's been *Said* in 2009...

"I had to go back to the Gary hospital for a meeting and there was rumor that the hospital was going to close. I went downtown and while I was there I had the desire to roam through that hospital. I had trained there and I had lived there, and I had established so much in that building with all of the people. I was by myself. It is a wonder security didn't get me and haul me out of there but I went up to the fifth floor where the pediatric area was and where the old surgery was. I made my way down to the different floors. It was just a real gratifying feeling. It was a very nostalgic feeling thinking of all those years I worked there and everything that had happened and the people that I knew. That was the last time I was in that hospital. It closed a few months later and I thought, 'I'm so glad I did that.'"

Shirley Makivich Urbanek, R.N
RETIRED
St. Mary Mercy Hospital| (began in 1959 in Gary)

It's been *Said* in 2009...

"Our mission is to serve the poor but our mission also is to give quality healthcare to all persons who come. We stayed in Gary as long as our services were needed. I said that even if we moved to Hobart we were still going to fulfill our mission. Hobart was not an elitist community. It was a community that also needed the services for those who could not afford it."

Sister Kathleen Quinn, PHJC
Board Member, Community Foundation of Northwest Indiana, Inc.
Former Chairman of the Board, Ancilla Systems Incorporated

"(The city of) Gary could not support two hospitals. Somebody had to make a move and it was (Gary's) St. Mary Medical Center that did."

Sister Jolise May, PHJC, GENERAL SUPERIOR OF THE INTERNATIONAL CONGREGATION OF THE POOR HANDMAIDS OF JESUS CHRIST DERNBACH, GERMANY

Sister Jolise May, PHJC, General Superior of the International Congregation of the Poor Handmaids of Jesus Christ, offered her recollections during a visit to the Hobart office of Ancilla Systems Incorporated in June 2009. She came from Dernbach, Germany.

Gary's health care

11-12-93
POST-TRIB.

New hospital owners have a niche to fill

The long-anticipated sale of St. Mary Medical Center in Gary is essentially complete. The new owner, Summit Medical Management of Atlanta, takes over a hospital that has not been a financial success.

Summit has an admirable track record of operating hospitals in urban areas similar to Gary. That expertise should serve the company well, particularly in the current environment of health care reform.

Gary is an underserved market concerning hospitals. Lakeshore Health System, which sold the hospital to concentrate on its other hospitals and clinics, conducted a study which found Gary needs more outpatient surgery centers and primary care units. It also found that Gary needs far more long-term care beds than it presently has.

In assuming the mantle of hospital leadership from the Poor Handmaids of Jesus Christ, the religious order which has operated the hospital since 1913, Summit must provide services to a health care-starved community where almost half the residents seek hospital care outside the city.

Summit should consider honing its expertise to fit the specific needs of Gary. At present, the hospital is operating at less than half of its licensed capacity. It must do better if it is to be successful, and much of that hinges on referrals by doctors.

The purchase of St. Mary closes one chapter and opens another in the medical history of Gary. With proper management and better planning, there's no reason why this chapter can't be a healthy one.

Our opinion

St. Mary's new owners ought to focus on Gary's health care needs.

Frequent publicity surrounded the sale of St. Mary Medical Center in Gary, as it was called in this 1993 *Post-Tribune* editorial.

Reprinted by permission of the *Post-Tribune*, NOVEMBER 12, 1993 CHJC, University of Notre Dame Archives

Hope remains alive at hospital

▶ St. Mary's public relations committee has recommended alternatives to selling the Gary facility.

Post-Tribune staff report

GARY — Lakeshore Health System Inc. officials have agreed to consider keeping St. Mary Medical Center afloat through a merger or some other cooperative arrangement with Methodist Hospital Northlake Campus.

"I will be happy to sit down and talk with anyone with a proposal."
Charlie Brown, D-Gary

St. Mary's beds full, but pockets empty

▶ A high occupancy rate doesn't translate into operating funds.

Politicians offer petitions to keep Gary hospital open

Reprinted by permission of the *Post-Tribune* CHJC, University of Notre Dame Archives

Amendment would keep St. Mary hospital open

By Joseph Conn 4-1-93
Staff writer POST-TRIB.

An amendment filed Wednesday by State Rep. Charlie Brown, D-Gary, could create an Indiana law permitting a court-appointed receiver to take over a hospital that is threatening to close.

Though the Indiana Constitution bars targeted legislation, there was little doubt that the situation at St. Mary Medical Center in Gary was being addressed by the amendment to a health-related bill, which passed the House Health Committee that Brown chairs by an 11-1 vote.

"Every step needs to be taken to assure that hospital stays open," said Brown Wednesday. "This is just another step."

Brown said it sends a clear message to Ancilla Systems Inc., the Gary hospital's corporate parent, that "all bases will be covered" to stop its move "to desert" Gary.

Ancilla announced March 6 its intention of selling St. Mary Medical Center in Gary. Few area health care experts believe a buyer will emerge. St. Mary has been losing money for years and has been buoyed financially by its satellite hospital in Hobart and by its sister, St. Catherine Hospital in East Chicago.

Debate in committee Wednesday centered on the state-wide implications of the amendment, which was grafted onto Senate Bill 451 that deals with blood transfusions and donations. So Brown used population limits to make the bill applicable only to Lake County.

The bill gives the state health commissioner the authority to ask the Indiana Attorney General to petition a circuit or superior court to appoint a receiver to take control of a hospital under certain conditions.

Those conditions are:
■ If the hospital is operating without a license.
■ If the hospital plans to close and "adequate arrangements have not been made for the orderly transfer of patients at least 90 days before closing."
■ If "extraordinary conditions" present a major threat to patients' safety, security or welfare.

"There is really nothing we can say about it," said Sue O'Leary, spokeswoman for Lakeshore Health Systems, the Ancilla subsidiary that operates Ancilla's three Northwest Indiana hospitals.

"Every step needs to be taken to assure that hospital stays open."
Charlie Brown D-Gary

A HOSPITAL PERSPECTIVE

"There was a disaster in 1993 when they had the South Shore derailment in Gary (between Gary and Hessville). A code yellow was called and St. Mary was ready to accept patients. It was a very big disappointment because the majority of injured were taken to Community, St. Catherine Hospital, Methodist and St. Mary Hobart. Only three patients came to St. Mary Gary. The accident happened in Gary but we didn't get to treat the patients. I think this was a sign of the times – that St. Mary's Gary was closing."

Juanita Grimes, SWITCHBOARD OPERATOR | ST. MARY MEDICAL CENTER | (BEGAN IN 1982 IN GARY)

In March 1993, Lakeshore Health Systems President, John Birdzell, said, "It's time to pass the baton," when referring to putting St. Mary Medical Center - Gary up for sale. The hospital was not closing, he said in a *Post-Tribune* story of March 7, 1993, and hoped something positive would come from the transaction.

Birdzell said the decision to sell the hospital was made by the Ancilla board and affirmed by the hospital's council.

"They have put their hospitals where their mission statement says 'taking care of the poor'," he added. "It's not a system that is rich in capital and profitability." Nearly 70% of the Gary hospital's patients were on some form of public healthcare program and "we get paid about 45-cents on every dollar we charge," he added.

Mayor Thomas V. Barnes and Representative Charlie Brown (D-Gary) were scheduled to hold a press conference to discuss steps to ensure good healthcare.

1993 – ST. MARY MERCY HOSPITAL SOLD TO SUMMIT MEDICAL MANAGEMENT

James Dittoe, left, vice president of Public Affairs for Ancilla Systems Incorporated, addresses protestors at Ancilla's Hobart headquarters. Calumet Township Trustee Dozier T. Allen, Jr., and Johnnie B. Ward, third and fourth from left, listen intently.

Reprinted by permission of the *Post Tribune,* MAY 25, 1993

"We were told later on that they were building another hospital that would be like a stand-by in case Gary got too full but that was not the case. I think they got tired of Gary because we had so many indigent patients. Business started dropping off and they sold it.

"Hobart was newer than Gary. It had newer equipment. Gary equipment was failing and was not replaced. When it was replaced, it was with what Hobart had used. There was a vast difference from the old Mercy."

Jamesetta Meadows
STENOGRAPHER, RADIOLOGY DEPARTMENT, RETIRED
MERCY HOSPITAL | (BEGAN IN 1967 IN GARY)

After numerous lawsuits and petitions to keep the 300-bed Gary hospital open, Ancilla Systems Incorporated acted upon the shaky future of the hospital and finalized the sale of St. Mary Medical Center in Gary to Summit Medical Management, based in Atlanta, Georgia. Summit, headed by President/CEO Rembert T. Cribb, was described as a company that specialized in turning around ailing inner-city hospitals and was to begin running the facility by the end of November 1993. The hospital was expected to stay open during the transition and would be known as Northwest Family Hospital.

The Poor Handmaids of Jesus Christ had owned the hospital since 1913, marking 80 years of medical service at the Gary facility. They announced the need to sell or close the facility because of substantial financial losses in net operating income between 1988 and 1992.

Larry Jagnow, left, vice president of communications for Ancilla Systems Incorporated, parent company of Gary's St. Mary Medical Center, explains the hospital's situation to Dozier T. Allen, Calumet Township trustee.

Reprinted by permission of the *Post Tribune,* 1993

THE ISSUES

In the late 1980s, years before the hospital was sold, those keeping pulse on Mercy Hospital and trends in the hospital industry felt the pinch of financial pressures.

The Times ran a feature story, "Financial problems mount as competition increases."

"Hospitals, local and nationwide," the article said, "face continued financial pressures with no relief in sight. Changes in the way Medicare is distributed have hurt many hospitals and the problem of uninsured patients who can't pay their bills is growing," local hospital representatives said.

Statistics, the representatives further said, showed there were additional issues adding to problems facing St. Mary Mercy Hospital: Patient stays averaged 116 per day, considerably less than the hospital's licensed capacity of 300 beds. (Source: *Post-Tribune*, May 1993)

The drop was due in part to many surgical procedures that were being performed on an outpatient basis and an upward trend in outpatient visits was expected to continue.

The racial climate in Northwest Indiana saw scores of white patients and their physicians who ceased to utilize both downtown Gary hospitals. From 1970 to 1993, Gary's population dropped by more than 58,000.

As the city's economy dwindled with the U.S. Steel industry, larger numbers of Gary hospital patients were using government-financed healthcare – Medicaid, Medicare and Hospital Care for the indigent. The programs did not pay the full share of treatment costs and the hospitals felt the financial pinch even further.

The insurance companies, under pressure by corporate clients over rising healthcare costs, started cutting payments to hospitals. St. Mary Mercy was not included as a preferred provider by Blue Cross/Blue Shield, one of the state's largest networks. Still, few employees were expected to be laid off and Summit pledged its commitment to maintaining all services including the Emergency Department. It even hoped to add such services as obstetrics and mental health.

George Burrell, then vice president of operations for St. Mary Gary who stayed on as acting CEO and was being considered for the permanent position said, "The community is really the big winner as a result of this sale. (Summit) values community input. I would tell my neighbors to give us a chance, to use us. We're here for the community."

Summit planned to improve the hospital's financial performance by fostering "a much more cooperative relationship with the community and the physicians."

IT'S BEEN *Said* IN 2009...

"The time between 1990 and 2000 was probably when the economics of Mercy in Gary became precarious and... the hospital was functioning at a real deficit. With losses of up to $5 million or more per year, the Hobart hospital could not supply the differential.

"During this same period, Ancilla Systems (Incorporated) was losing other hospitals. They had one in East St. Louis, one in Fort Wayne, and St. Catherine's in East Chicago was not going real well at that time.

"Beyond the economic standpoint, there were some other reasons for the demise of Mercy. For one, the Medicaid funding for Methodist was much higher. Methodist had a legislative arrangement from Indianapolis whereby Wishard Hospital, a large hospital in Indianapolis, got special funding for Medicaid. Methodist also was of sufficient size that it fell within the same purview for Medicaid funding. So they got more Medicaid funding and it made it somewhat more solvent.

"At the same time the Emergency Medical technicians (EMTs) and ambulances in Gary were run by the fire department. EMTs were well trained and did a good job but they also formally or informally brought the paying patients to Methodist and the indigent to Mercy."

John T. Scully, MD.
INTERNIST, RETIRED
MERCY HOSPITAL | (BEGAN IN 1955 IN GARY)

SUMMIT

"It was my impression from day number one that Summit had their own agenda. They milked whatever money was left. With the changing dynamics in Gary, steel mill industry, government, reimbursements and what not... the Sisters faced a dilemma. They did their very best to keep the hospital going but when your services are not needed then you know your time has come."

Heratch Doumanian, M.D.
RADIOLOGIST, RETIRED
MERCY HOSPITAL | (BEGAN IN 1967 IN GARY)

"(The Gary hospital's closing in the early 1990s) was a slow death but inevitable for the hospital to concentrate its work into Hobart. It became successful and utilized and over utilized; it became apparent that there really didn't have to be two non-profit hospitals downtown.

"Most of the movement from the city to the suburbs by whites had been made by that time and blacks were moving out to the center of the city where there was more violence, corruption, city government corruption, prostitution and all kinds of things.

"As a pathologist, we got to see some victims of that and it really was a vicious place for some people to try to exist, but racially it was just a matter of surviving.

"All of us – the whites and the blacks – we all felt the need to not be in the middle of the corruption path and that made for changes in the hospital population and plans that took place in establishing more hospital investments in the southern part of the county. It was more like a family atmosphere in the hospital. I don't remember any black and white hospital tension at all."

Earl J. Mason, Ph.D., M.D.
FORMER DIRECTOR OF THE LABORATORY, RETIRED
MERCY HOSPITAL | (BEGAN IN 1965 IN GARY)

THE FOUNDATIONS

GARY COMMUNITY HEALTH FOUNDATION

"...When the hospital was sold, the (Poor Handmaids of Jesus Christ) made a sizeable contribution to establish the Gary Community Health Foundation. The Foundation worked with and funded other agencies to promote healthcare within the community. I was asked to sit on the foundation board for several years. It was a good program that tried to get out into the community through the ministers, the churches, or different non-profit agencies."

Lou Molina, VICE PRESIDENT FINANCE
AND CHIEF FINANCIAL OFFICER
COMMUNITY HOSPITAL | (BEGAN IN 1986 IN GARY)

"We established the foundation and I was on the board for quite a while. It was to serve the public healthcare needs of Gary. We were reaching out to the community."

Sister Kathleen Quinn, PHJC
BOARD MEMBER, COMMUNITY FOUNDATION OF
NORTHWEST INDIANA, INC.
FORMER CHAIRPERSON OF THE BOARD, ANCILLA
SYSTEMS INCORPORATED

"The foundation helps fulfill a pledge to the community that Ancilla Systems and the Poor Handmaids made when we announced our decision on March 6 to sell the hospital," said Sister Kathleen Quinn, PHJC, Ancilla Systems chairperson, in a *Word Gathering* publication of November/December 1993. "Since the first Poor Handmaids came to St. Mary Mercy Hospital... in 1913... we have built up a close relationship with the people of Gary. We are happy that the healthcare needs of the people will continue to be met..."

A HARD SELL

Carol Ochwat
Contract Specialist
CFNI

"It was a sad day when Gary was sold to Summit on November 22, 1993. Having worked at all three facilities (St. Mary Medical Center-Gary, St. Catherine Hospital, and St. Mary Medical Center-Hobart) in Human Resources, Administration and Quality Management, what I remember most about the people at the Gary hospital is that they seemed to be more like my family. It really is true that when one door closes, God opens another and the opportunity became available for me at St. Mary Medical Center Hobart where the best of the old and the new continue to work together to provide the very best of healthcare to those who are in need. A lot of the people I have known for 20+ years from Gary are now here in Hobart and the family atmosphere continues."

Carol Ochwat, CONTRACT SPECIALIST
COMMUNITY FOUNDATION OF NORTHWEST INDIANA, INC. | (BEGAN IN 1981 IN GARY)

ECONOMIC ILLS FORCE HOSPITAL CLOSING

"Initially, I understood that Hobart was constructed with a 20-year life in mind. I think there were fears, especially by many of the employees in Gary that Hobart would become the dominant hospital and the Gary hospital would be closed. I understand why the Gary hospital was closed but that had to do with market forces and not any kind of plot to deprive the city of a hospital."

Mike Adler, FORMER DIRECTOR OF PUBLIC RELATIONS
MERCY HOSPITAL
(BEGAN IN 1977, GARY AND HOBART)

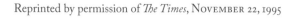

Employees at Northwest Family Hospital in Gary went their separate ways by the end of November as the owners closed the financially troubled hospital. Judy Jacobs, a staff nurse for 10 years, and Sue Burns, with the hospital for 11 years, embraced after learning of the failed talks to keep the hospital open.

Reprinted by permission of the
Post-Tribune, NOVEMBER 22, 1995

Reprinted by permission of *The Times,* NOVEMBER 22, 1995

"… One of our issues was that we shared much of the same physician staff with Methodist Hospital less than a half mile away. Methodist Hospital was a 350 – 400-bed hospital and it was difficult for us to provide all the same medical services."

Lou Molina, VICE PRESIDENT FINANCE AND CHIEF FINANCIAL OFFICER
COMMUNITY HOSPITAL | (BEGAN IN 1986 IN GARY)

WHEN A HOSPITAL CLOSES… ONE WOMAN'S STORY

IT'S BEEN *Said* IN 2009…

"When the actual St. Mary closed (was sold to Summit, and called Northwest Family Hospital) it was devastating. I remember our manager, Karen Gerke… came into the recovery room. She had tears in her eyes, and she said, 'I have some bad news. St. Mary's Hospital is going to be sold. They are actively looking for a buyer.' We all just said, 'What?' We were just… devastated. Nobody knew it. Nobody saw it. Summit did try to save St. Mary's and they tried to get Methodist to help us but they gave us no help at all. So now I'm thinking, 'Healthcare has really gone down in Gary.'

"Summit took over in 1993; I think it was two days before Thanksgiving. They left in 1995, two days before Thanksgiving. I was there. I went through that. The first day after they purchased the hospital I really didn't notice anything different. Things seemed to be status quo. Summit told us that we would keep our seniority. They gave us half of our vacation, sick time, and stuff like that. They said it would be a smooth transition. That's what we were told. It would be a smooth transition. They made you think it would work.

"Initially, I think I was happy. Things seemed to be going well but then things began changing. It wasn't quite what it was. I worked as the assistant director of Surgical Services so I started to notice things were different when we couldn't get equipment in and we couldn't get X-ray film. We were out of X-ray film. We asked what was happening and things weren't going right. I asked to get a sales representative in for surgery because their company had received no funds from this hospital group and they wouldn't come unless they got some funds. Something was up. You knew it wasn't quite right.

"When I found out about Summit closing the hospital (as assistant director of Surgical Services), it was at meetings they periodically scheduled. They called us up that day about one o'clock, Summit did, and said, 'We were trying to save the hospital and it didn't work.' They said, 'Go back and tell all your people that today is their last day.' They could get whatever they needed out – all of their belongings – because they would not be allowed back into the hospital after 3:30 p.m. Yes!

"We knew it was going to happen. We just didn't know when. They had already started moving patients out of the hospital a couple days before and not really admitting new patients. The surgery schedule was almost nothing.

"I went down and got my staff together and I told them. My staff was probably 40 or 50 people at the time – surgical nurses, surgical technologists, and recovery room nurses as well as a few nursing assistants.

"People just couldn't believe it. Then we got directions to get our paychecks. We had to come back because that next week was pay week. We were told to bring our badge. We could pick up our check and drop our badge off in a bucket or something they had there.

"People were up and moving around. We had to call some of the vendors. We had eye implants there that were on consignment. We had to call them and say, 'Hey, we're closing. You need to come and get your equipment out of here because you will not be able to get anything after tomorrow.'

"It was quite a feat. I came in the next day to work because I had things to finish. There were instructions to take the files of all the employees over to personnel – clean up this and that. The day before, I had to get all the narcotics out of the department. Pharmacy came and we gave all the narcotics to them. We were closing the place down. After I got everything done, I dropped my keys off and that was it."

Etta Weatherspoon, R.N, MS, MEDICAL-SURGICAL CLINICIAN
ST. MARY MEDICAL CENTER | (BEGAN IN 1974 IN GARY)

When Northwest Family Hospital Closed

IT'S BEEN *Said* IN 2009...

"After the hospital closed… it sat there for eight years or so until the city of Gary wanted it for their police station. They call it a Public Safety Facility.

"They had an open house when they bought it and I wanted to go into the place. It looked nothing like the hospital. The Emergency Department was replaced by something else. Right when you walked in, there was the window with the police officers right behind it. It was kind of bizarre because when you walked into the hospital when it was the hospital, it was just wide open, like most hospitals – more like St. Mary Medical Center is today as you walk into their New Patient Tower – expansive. We took a tour up to the second floor where they had (jail) cells so it was kind of sad."

Joe Winterhaler, VICE PRESIDENT FINANCE AND CHIEF FINANCIAL OFFICER
ST. CATHERINE HOSPITAL | (BEGAN IN 1989 IN GARY)

1994

Hospital/Community Happenings

St. Mary Medical Center Appoints Community Case Manager

As part of its effort to promote wellness throughout the community, St. Mary Medical Center established a new program designed to follow-up on high at-risk patients after they have been released from the hospital. Kay Wiseman was appointed by Vice President of Nursing Marsha King to fill the new post as Community Case Manager.

IT'S BEEN *Said* IN 2009...

Kay Wiseman, RN
Community Case
Manager, 1994

"Case management is very good. It is a collaborative role that the nurse, case manager and the doctors do together. When they came in with what they call DRGs (Diagnosis Related Groups), they should have started with the doctors first. A lot of doctors in the past – if they had to have tests done – didn't figure out how they logistically should be done. They would schedule tests… and if one couldn't be done after the first test, the patient had to stay in the hospital a little longer. They don't allow that now and the case managers are the ones who have to work with the doctors and are responsible for seeing that the patients are discharged in an appropriate time. I was one of the first case managers and that was about 1994."

Catherine Wiseman, R.N, CLINICAL CASE MANAGER, ACUTE REHABILITATION UNIT, RETIRED
ST. MARY MEDICAL CENTER | (BEGAN IN 1975 IN HOBART)

The goal of the Community Case Manager initiative, Wiseman noted, is to enable patients to remain in the community as long as possible and to reduce admissions to nursing homes and re-admissions to the hospital. Those who benefit from such a service are patients who don't qualify for home healthcare or need to be seen more frequently than some agencies can handle.

ELECTROPHYSIOLOGY DEPARTMENT...

Contributed by Cheryl Alderson, B.S. RT
Director of Cardiology Services

ELECTROPHYSIOLOGY LABORATORY DEPARTMENT STAFF PHOTO – 2009
SEATED (L-R): Dan Demo, RN; Christine Abraham, RN; and Dale Perry, RN
STANDING (L-R): Melissa Schultz, RN; Michelle Nieckula, RT; Patti Bottos-Campano, RN; Amy Booth CVT; Rayna Ehrhardt, EP coordinator; and Martin Marquez, RT

In 1994, in order to provide a full array of electrophysiology procedures, St. Mary Medical Center opened its dedicated Electrophysiology Laboratory (EP Lab).

The unit began with one procedure room located in a renovated patient room on the second floor. As the patient volume grew, so did the need for a larger area to house the patient records, the physician dictation area, procedure room, and equipment. In 1996, the department was relocated to its existing area on the first floor.

The new area included one procedure room and was staffed with three nurses and two dedicated electrophysiologists, Mark Dixon, D.O., and Scott Kaufman, D.O. The procedures performed were primarily Permanent Pacemaker insertion and Internal Cardiac Defibrillator (ICD) insertion.

Shortly after the relocation, Drs. Dixon and Kaufman opened the Electrophysiology Clinic within the EP Lab. Visits to the patient clinic grew rapidly and more staff was hired to accommodate the increased patient volume.

During this time, Dr. Dixon was principle investigator for a number of research studies. Dr. Kaufman actively participated in research, too. Together they brought the program up to a new level and began to do Cardiac Resynchronization Therapy (CRT).

In 2002, a second procedure suite was added to accommodate the patient procedure volume. Shortly thereafter Ragu Dasari, M.D., joined the group.

In 2007, the EP Lab added CartoMerge and CartoSound technology. These technologies help the physician locate areas within the heart that initiate aberrant arrhythmias. These areas are then ablated to eliminate the aberrancy.

In March 2009, the EP Lab added Lead Management to the list of services using Excimer Laser. The laser ablates the scar tissue formed around a lead to enable lead extraction. This is a less invasive procedure that, if not available, could require surgery to extract the lead.

The Electrophysiology Department, an integral part of St. Mary Medical Center, is a proud participant in state-of-the-art medical care. The best is yet to come!

In 2003, *Vim & Vigor* Magazine featured clinical trials that focused on cardiac care. The St. Mary Medical Center laboratory was among the first to practice biventricular pacing, a procedure to pace the beating of the heart by monitoring the right and left ventricles with the use of a CONTAK CD® bi-ventricular defibrillator/pacemaker. Shown here in the Electrophysiology Lab are (l-r) Mark Dixon, D.O.; Scott Kaufman, D.O.; Chris Atherton, RN, MHA; Patti Campano, RN; Michele Panek, RN; and Ed Truman, RN. Not pictured: Destiny Whitaker, RN; and Amanda Coates, medical assistant.
Vim & Vigor, SPRING 2003

1995

HOSPITAL/COMMUNITY HAPPENINGS

AREA HOSPITALS TEAMING UP

Early in 1995, Larry Jagnow, vice president of Communications for Ancilla Systems Incorporated, announced that an affiliation between Ancilla Systems and the University of Chicago Hospital would help patients in terms of both cost and care. Ancilla, at that time, operated St. Mary Medical Center in Hobart and St. Catherine Hospital in East Chicago.

Jagnow said that although an agreement had not been reached, patients could be referred to the University of Chicago for specializations not available and vice versa.

"The focus today in healthcare is not only quality but cost," Jagnow added. "We are seeking ways to offer programs and services more cost effectively."

THE COLLECTIVE IMAGE

The Collective Image sign

IT'S BEEN *Said* IN 2009...

"I was also the manager at The Collective Image. It was a fitness center based on research regarding women and heart disease. We felt, as a hospital, we needed to do something for women and heart disease. It was located in a separate building on the grounds of the hospital in the late 1990s. It started with Beth Kaminski and it was her project while she was administrator. The PHJC Sisters, our sponsors at the time, were involved because they wanted it to be more holistic, an outside of the hospital-kind-of feeling. So we had massage therapy, a kids' corner, a hair salon, women's fitness, cooking demonstrations, a library, and educational sessions. We all know that women are the caregivers and we take care of everything else before we take care of ourselves. This was a place where they could take care of themselves.

"We had a member who had very low self esteem, had some health issues (i.e., high blood pressure) and had never exercised before – was too embarrassed and was overweight. We worked with her. She lost weight, improved her blood pressure, was taken off blood pressure medication and felt good about herself. We featured people like her in a couple of our ads, and all of a sudden people were seeing successful examples of what we could do... It would be really wonderful if we could get back to it sometime."

Bobbi Homola, MPA, RD, CD, REGIONAL CLINICAL MANAGER
FOOD AND NUTRITION SERVICES | ST. MARY MEDICAL CENTER | (BEGAN IN 1976 IN HOBART)

"Take care of your body. It's the only place you have to live."

~ JIM ROHN

Milt Triana – Hospital Administrator/CEO

Milt Triana, retired
Hospital Administrator
St. Mary Medical Center
Special Projects Coordinator,
Community Healthcare System
(began in 1969 in Gary)

It's been *Said* in 2009...

"Milt (Triana)… was just like a dad or a father who really cared about all of his employees. He just made you feel like you were something special. He was just one great man. The last time I saw him a few months ago when he visited our new office; he was still the same."

Gayle Brumley, Telephone Analyst
Patient Accounting, St. Mary Medical Center
(began in 1982 at St. Catherine Hospital)

Did you know?

In 1997, Milt Triana received the Crystal Globe Award from the Asian American Medical Society for being a leader in healthcare administration to all physicians.

In 1998, he also received the American College of Healthcare Executives' (ACHE) Indiana Regent's Award as Senior Level Executive of the Year for the northern Indiana region.

It's been *Said* in 2009...

"When I first took over as administrator, one of the major challenges around 1995 was that we had a lot of employed physicians for the Ancilla hospital system. What Ancilla decided to do, however, was take the physician-employed ownership that was under their umbrella and transfer it to each hospital to manage. When it came to St. Mary we would look at each physician practice and with input from my CFO and some other staff members, we decided which physician practices were profitable and beneficial to the hospital. We decided to divest almost all of those physician practices and that was not an easy task. There were approximately 7-10 practices under consideration and fortunately we were able to divest them and not lose their business."

Milt Triana, retired Hospital Administrator, St. Mary Medical Center
Special Projects Coordinator, Community Healthcare System | (began in 1969 in Gary)

It's been *Said* in 2009...

"When Milt Triana was brought in as St. Mary Medical Center's full-time administrator, he spent the first year or two smoothing the feathers of the medical staff and was very successful. I think Milt's claim to fame as an administrator was his relationship with the medical staff which is extremely important. Those are the people who admit your patients – where you get your revenue – and Milt did a great job of that."

Bill Schenck, President, Board of Directors, St. Mary Medical Center
Board Member, Community Foundation of Northwest Indiana, Inc.

It's been *Said* in 2009...

"I can remember the first pre-holiday Christmas party back in 1997 at the Greek Hall on Harrison Street in Merrillville, Indiana. It was sponsored by Milt Triana, administrator, (complete with) hors d'oeuvres, dinner, and a cash bar. I didn't know Milt could dance but the night of this party was when he really showed his dancing moves… and oh my – everyone was so impressed. The nurses loved him. They would gather around and take turns dancing with him… These were memorable evenings and it was always such a nice time of food and fellowship with co-workers."

Judy Smith
Compensation and Benefits Analyst
St. Catherine Hospital
(began in 1987 in Gary)

In the Community

It's been *Said* in 2009...

"(Former Hospital Administrator) Milt Triana was on the Hobart Chamber of Commerce board. He was very friendly, very helpful, very dependable and very knowledgeable. And did I say efficient?"

Virgina Curtis
Longtime Hobart Community Advocate | Historian

CARDIOVASCULAR OUTPATIENT UNIT AND HEART FAILURE CENTER...

Contributed by Shannon Blaney, RN, Nurse Manager
April Schutter, RN, Charge Nurse, HF Nurse
and Kathy Nelson RN, CVOP

CARDIO-VASCULAR OUTPATIENT UNIT AND HEART AMBULATORY CLINIC STAFF PHOTO — 2009
FRONT ROW (L-R): Kathy Nelson, RN; Veronica Hall, LPN; and Sandy Cano, RN
BACK ROW (L-R): Donna Wasko, RN; April Schutter, RN; and Jaime Francis, RN

In 1995, the Cardiovascular Outpatient Unit (CVU/CVOP) and Heart Failure Center (HFC) opened in what was once the Intensive Care Unit (ICU) on 2East. The unit was under the direction of Kim McBrayer, who also managed the Medical Telemetry Unit on 5East. The unit was a dedicated unit for outpatient cardiovascular procedures and infusions. It consisted of five beds and four infusion chairs, and was open 24 hours a day, Monday through Friday. Coronary and peripheral angiograms, angioplasties, electrophysiology (EP) studies, ablations, and pacemaker/defibrillators were the main patient focus. At that time, the Cardiovascular Outpatient Unit (CVOP) functioned as the Heart Failure Center (HFC) also, caring for those outpatients who needed frequent assessments, IV diuretics, and infusions of dobutrex, primacor and/or natrecor to manage their disease process. Many of these patients came two or three times per week for infusions and became a second family to the CVOP staff. As American Heart Association (AHA) and Medicare guidelines changed, outpatient infusions decreased and eventually stopped altogether, slightly altering the focus of the HFC and the way in which it would best serve those suffering with chronic congestive heart failure. In 2003, Bobbie Herron, clinical nurse specialist, was hired to initiate the HFC as its own entity apart from CVOP.

In 2004, Shannon Blaney, a longtime employee on 5East, became the manager of CVOP and the HFC. That same year, the hospital added a dedicated Inpatient Heart Failure Nurse, HFC. Donna Wasko, a longtime employee of SMMC, became inpatient educator. This initiative helped provide patients and their families with the knowledge and resources required to manage heart failure effectively. It also allowed for follow-up so that the patients of St. Mary Medical Center were being given the very best care and educational opportunities.

In 2005, CVOP moved into an expanded patient care area on 2East. The new unit consisted of eight beds, four private and two semi-private rooms. Outpatient cardiac procedures remained the primary focus but overflows were also admitted along with Emergency Room/direct admits with a dedicated staff of six employees. In 2008, the CVOP and HFC were partially combined with both departments under the management of Shannon Blaney. April Schutter assumed the role as Heart Failure nurse for the outpatients and assisted Donna Wasko with inpatient education. Along with some talented new physicians, the staff of CVOP and the HFC has had the privilege of being on the front lines of advancing cardiac medicine, whether it has been a new procedure as in carotid stenting and CT angiography or a new product or device as in Syvex and Angioseal. CVOP and the HFC will continually strive to provide their patients with the very best care available.

THEN AND NOW

WOUND, OSTOMY AND CONTINENCE CENTER...

Contributed by Suzanne Matheny RN, BSN, NE–BC, BC
Nurse Manager 3 West/Wound, Ostomy and Continence
Orthopedic Service Line Manager

IT'S BEEN *Said* IN 2009...

"Suzi Matheny was head of the Burn and Wound Center of Excellence and I think she still is. At the time we had to answer the phone, 'St. Mary Medical Center Health and Rehabilitation Spectrum and Burn and Wound Center of Excellence.' We would register their patients. They had an area down in physical therapy... and we coordinated our departments together over there.

"I do remember them bringing in a little girl from a daycare center. I felt really bad for her because hot food spilled on her. She did (really) well. She was really good. Everyone was concerned and took great care of her and we felt better for her when she left."

Donna Seeley
REGISTRATION REPRESENTATIVE
ST. MARY MEDICAL CENTER PORTAGE
OUTPATIENT CENTER
(BEGAN IN 1993 IN HOBART)

St. Mary Medical Center opened its Wound and Burn Clinic on July 14, 1997. The Center was located at the Spectrum Building next to the hospital in a time-share area. It was under the direction of Suzanne Matheny, RN, nurse manager, and Nicholas Retson, M.D. As we grew in volume a new area was designed just for the Center. In 2002, the center was relocated to St. Mary Medical Center Outpatient Facility in Portage. The move allowed access to the laboratory, X-ray, CAT scan and physical therapy services.

Most recently in March of 2009, we opened our second site which is located inside the Hobart hospital facility in Suite 1103. The service has been expanded to include continence services and is reflected in our new name, St. Mary Medical Center Wound, Ostomy and Continence Center. Our volume at the centers has averaged 154 visits per month. We serve patients with any type of diabetic wound, chronic wound, traumatic wound, vascular wound, ostomy care and fecal and urinary problems.

Their focus, as noted in a May/June 2009 publication of *Hospital Headlines*, is "to offer expert, compassionate care to patients requiring these services."

BACK ROW (L–R): Craig Bolda, vice president, Therapy and Rehabilitative Services; Denise Weaver, M.D., co-chairman, Environmental Infection Control committee; Barbara Chavez, RN; and Suzan Hoeksema, RN, NP
FRONT ROW (L–R): Marianne Brush, medical assistant; Suzanne Matheny, RN, BSN, NE-BC, BC, nurse manager; and Cheryl Mestrovich, RN

Shown here is Claudia Olszewski, RN, MSN, NP, as she puts an Unna Boot on a patient suffering from complications from a spider bite. The boot of special salve and moist gauze exemplifies the modern application of moist wound therapy.
Vim & Vigor, WINTER 2002

*Marking Time...*1997

- *Air bags became mandatory for all cars made in the United States.*
- *Tiger Woods won the Master golf tournament. At age 21 he was the youngest player ever to win the Masters.*

HOSPITAL/COMMUNITY HAPPENINGS

THE ST. MARY MEDICAL CENTER FOUNDATION

By the end of the 1990s, activities of the St. Mary Medical Center Foundation were flourishing. The foundation, created several years earlier in 1995, was designed as a fundraising vehicle for the hospital.

Robert J. Welsh, chairman of the St. Mary Medical Center finance committee, said support for the hospital was critical because of the important changes in healthcare. Cutbacks in federal and state subsidies continued, and insurance companies were adjusting the length of hospital stays and the portion of a hospital bill they agreed to cover.

Welsh further said donations could be earmarked for specific services or facilities – perhaps new hospital equipment, educational programs, or community outreach activities.

Progress on the hospital included the addition of the Coronary Care Unit; the opening of Spectrum for athletic, job-related and cardiac problems; the re-opening of the Obstetrics Ward with Birthing Suites; the opening of the Portage Health Center; and construction work on Collective Image.

Specifically, funds came to the foundation from a number of sources:
1. Planned giving from the community with stocks, property, or charitable trusts;
2. Fund-raising events such as the annual gala and employee payroll deductions;
3. Contributions from other foundations;
4. The St. Mary Medical Center Auxiliary.

FORMER CHAIRMAN OF THE BOARD – BOB WELSH

> "Over the years, Bob Welsh has been a loyal supporter!"

Sister Kathleen Quinn, PHJC
BOARD MEMBER, COMMUNITY FOUNDATION OF NORTHWEST INDIANA, INC.
FORMER CHAIRMAN OF THE BOARD, ANCILLA SYSTEMS INCORPORATED

Bob Welsh

IT'S BEEN *Said* IN 2009...

ADMIRING THE LEADERSHIP

"Don Powers is one of the most remarkable persons I have ever known. He is a very intelligent visionary who built Munster Community Hospital when everyone told him it was foolish to build and would fail. He bought (the Hobart hospital) and St. Catherine's when many of his advisors told him it was foolish.

"Today, Community, Hobart Mercy, and St. Catherine's are all the shining stars of all the hospitals in Lake and Porter counties. They are all first-class facilities – up-to-date, profitable, and well structured to serve our area for many years – thanks to Don Powers."

Robert J. Welsh, FORMER ST. MARY MEDICAL CENTER
ST. CATHERINE HOSPITAL BOARD MEMBER
ST. MARY MEDICAL CENTER CHAIRMAN OF THE BOARD (1997 – 2001) | CFNI BOARD MEMBER

RIDING THE WAVE OF CARE AND FRIENDSHIP

"When I went to Gary, one of the first women I met was a nurse whose mother was a patient there (with) a fractured hip. I had taken care of her before she died and not too long after that her husband came in as a patient. I had him as a heart attack (patient) and the reason I am telling this is because this gentleman was Bob Welsh's father, and that is how I got to know the Welsh family. I got to know Bob and his wife and we became good friends.

"Bob Welsh is a great guy. He was on the board for many years. He was kind of shy and quite laid back. His wife was real outgoing and always so thoughtful. Once he said, 'We have to do something for you. I don't care how many Sisters you bring but we are going to take you out on the boat we have. It has sleeping room for 10. My brother-in-law is an obstetrician and he lives in Michigan City, and I am going to have him come and the whole group of us is going out,' and he made arrangements. He did the cooking and planned the meals so I took a whole bunch of Sisters with me. We spent the whole day on Lake Michigan and then he parked in the middle of the lake and we had a chicken dinner. I can remember I said to him, 'You know, Sister Jeanette (PHJC) would love to drive the boat.' So I took Sister Jeanette to the top and he put her behind the wheel and had her drive that very big boat. She was in her glory!"

Sister Philomene Pawlik, PHJC, RN, RETIRED
DONALDSON, INDIANA | (BEGAN IN 1955 IN GARY)

"Sister Philomene, (PHJC), was a very, very compassionate, caring nun who cared for my father, Robert Welsh, Sr. He was in Gary Mercy Hospital for three weeks prior to his death on October 9, 1968.

"My mother, Catherine Volk Welsh, was a registered nurse for several years at Gary Mercy Hospital. She had a stroke and was in a coma at Hobart Mercy Hospital for several months. She died at Hobart Mercy Hospital on May 18, 1984. Her care by the wonderful nuns and nurses and Dr. John Scully was 'world class'. Our family will never forget this."

Robert J. Welsh, FORMER ST. MARY MEDICAL CENTER
ST. CATHERINE HOSPITAL BOARD MEMBER
ST. MARY MEDICAL CENTER CHAIRMAN OF THE BOARD (1997 – 2001) | CFNI BOARD MEMBER

FOUNDATION FUNDRAISING EVENTS

▶ FIRST ANNUAL GALA HELD BY ST. MARY MEDICAL CENTER FOUNDATION

St. Mary Medical Center Foundation Inaugural Gala '97 was held on March 1, 1997, 280 plus were in attendance, The Allen Sterns Orchestra provided music to compliment the new orleans theme of the evening. The Gala was held at the beautiful, new, Sand Creek Country Club in Chesterton. Cocktails were served at 6:00 p.m. accompanied by a silent auction. Dinner began at 7:00 p.m. and was followed by dancing.

A good time was had by all who attended and it was an excellent way to support our foundation.

Tickets were $100 per person with all proceeds benefiting the St. Mary Medical Center Foundation.

THE GALAS IN THEIR DAY....

In the late 1990s through 2003, St. Mary Medical Center Foundation hosted an annual gala to raise funds to help the hospital better serve its surrounding communities. The event always followed a big city theme such as New York or San Francisco. Co-chairmen and committee members worked hard to present big bands, silent auctions, program booklets, and a lively evening for a good cause. The gala in 1999 raised more than $75,000.

An Auto/Cash Raffle, a joint venture between the St. Mary Medical Center Foundation and the St. Mary Medical Center Auxiliary, included a generous first prize – a 1999 Jeep Laredo or $20,000 in cash. A Ford Explorer was also part of an Auto/Cash Raffle in 2000.

"The tireless support of the employees and this community overwhelmed me," said Jeane Ziegler, who co-chaired the event with Kathy Koscielniak, Marietta Cebedo, and then Mayor Linda Buzinec. "Hospital directors and department heads came out in full force. Employees bought tickets to the event and then worked all evening; and many businesses in the community really responded."

Anthony "Tony" Costello and Elizabeth Yee were co-chairpersons representing hospital employees.

"To do the amount of work we had to do in a short amount of time, the results were really amazing," Costello said. "It was the best time I've had in the 23 years I've been with the hospital."

(Source: "*Neighborly Care,*" SPRING 1999)

In 1999, a New York-themed gala was held at the Center for Visual and Performing Arts with proceeds designated for St. Mary Medical Center. More than 425 guests responded to this invitation.

Following a San Francisco theme, the St. Mary Medical Center Foundation Gala 2000 was held at the Center for Visual and Performing Arts. Among nearly 400 guests were (top photo, l-r) Jeane Ziegler and Kathy Koscielniak; (bottom photo, l-r) Dick Sierra, Lois Miller, Jim Miller and Debra Jenkins.

The St. Mary Medical Center Foundation earned the Grand Prize for its entry in Hobart's 1996 Fourth of July parade. Participation in the event was to promote the foundation as a philanthropic arm of the hospital.

Herald News Group, JULY 17, 1996

IT'S BEEN *Said* IN 2009...~~~~~~

"I worked with the St. Mary Foundation as executive secretary. Its purpose was to assist with funding of hospital programs and sponsor several events within the community. We held several galas and auto/cash raffles. One gala in particular was in 1999 which I helped plan. There were many doctors and business people from the community in attendance. The theme was "New York." It was a big event and we had many items for silent auction. All the money raised from our gala and auto/cash raffles went toward helping the hospital purchase equipment, etc."

Debra Jenkins, REGIONAL ASSISTANT OF MISSION EFFECTIVENESS
ST. MARY MEDICAL CENTER | (BEGAN IN 1985 IN GARY)

1997 – HEALTHCARE ADVOCACY GROUP

IT'S BEEN *Said* IN 2009...

HEALTHCARE ADVOCATE CATHERINE WISEMAN

"I finished my career in acute rehab. I was the discharge planner, utilization review, case manager, and social service designee. I wore four hats. It was a wonderful way for a registered nurse to end her career because then when I retired and was approached about being part of the Healthcare Advocacy Group, I could use my background with helping people find nursing homes, home health services, and different avenues for taking care of their spouse or their elderly parent. It was wonderful how it worked out."

Catherine Wiseman, R.N, CLINICAL CASE MANAGER
ACUTE REHABILITATION UNIT, RETIRED | ST. MARY MEDICAL CENTER | (BEGAN IN 1975 IN HOBART)

IT'S BEEN *Said* IN 2009...

ABOUT THE DESIGNEE

"Kay Wiseman would be the first person to help you in any situation, the first person to volunteer for any committee, the first person to offer comfort to anyone. Any questions that I had when I first started: Kay Wiseman."

Dee Bedella, COORDINATOR, SLEEP LAB/COMMUNITY LIAISON
ST. MARY MEDICAL CENTER | (BEGAN IN 1988 IN HOBART)

IT'S BEEN *Said* IN 2009...

ABOUT THE DESIGNEE

"At least once a quarter, I would work the unit as a supervisor or staff nurse. They wanted to test me in terms of what I would do. I hadn't worked the floor for a long time and thought the best place to start was Kay Wiseman's floor because if I passed Kay's test I knew I would be acceptable to the rest. I worked her unit and she gave me five patients. One was a tracheotomy, one was comatose, one was a cerebrovascular accident (CVA) or stroke victim and I thought, 'Oh brother.' While Kay gave me the hardest patients, she also worked with me to take care of them and the patients were patient themselves. I told them who I was and what I was doing and they accepted it, well except for the one who was comatose, but just Kay's interjection was very helpful."

Peggy Kamysz, R.N, MPA, INFORMATION TECHNOLOGY
ST. MARY MEDICAL CENTER | (BEGAN IN 1982 IN GARY/HOBART)

Donald Phillips, M.D.

PHYSICIAN OF THE YEAR

Donald Phillips, M.D., was named Physician of the Year by the Indiana Academy of Family Physicians in 2004. He founded the not-for-profit Healthcare Advocacy Group, Inc., an organization to support those who experience major impediments with health insurance. Phillips, on staff at St. Mary Medical Center since 1966, founded the group to champion patient rights. He was nominated by former colleague Marcia Speer.

Vim & Vigor, WINTER 2004

1997 – Hobart's Sesquicentennial Citizen of the Year Awards Begin

Citizen of the Year award

St. Mary Medical Center celebrated Hobart's sesquicentennial (1847 – 1997) by recognizing a Citizen of the Year who demonstrated citizenship through civic pride, neighborly kindness, and concern for the general community. The committee consisted of the hospital administrator; regional director of mission integration, marketing; and approximately eight employees who resided in Hobart. Committee employees were to be rotated to obtain varied ideas on individuals from the community.

The award continued from 1997 through 2003. Those recognized were: Dorothy Ballentyne in 1997; Mary McIntyre in 1998; Kay Wiseman in 1999; Helen Galler in 2000; Carol Shingler in 2001; Virginia Curtis in 2002; and Mary Adams in 2003.

Citizens of the Year – leading by example
Employee Health Nurse Carol Shingler was honored as St. Mary Medical Center's outstanding Citizen of the Year award. "She cannot do enough for people," said Dr. John T. Scully in a *Post-Tribune* article. "I think your choice… could not have been better."

Reprinted by permission of the *Post-Tribune*, April, 2002

1998

Poor Handmaids of Jesus Christ/Ancilla Systems Incorporated

Did you know?

The corporate legal name of the American Province of the Poor Handmaids of Jesus Christ is Ancilla Domini Sisters. In the spirit of Blessed Catherine Kasper, the mission of Ancilla Systems Incorporated is to enhance the Poor Handmaids of Jesus Christ ministries to the poor and underserved. Ancilla Systems provides services and support to Ancilla Domini Sisters, Inc., and to the PHJC ministries through collaboration and compassionate sharing of its talents and resources. Ancilla Systems Incorporated is located in Hobart, Indiana.

It's been *Said* in 2009…

"The most important aspect of the sale of these two hospitals is that the Sisters feel great about what is happening with St. Catherine's and St. Mary Medical Center today, many years later. Don Powers has been instrumental in the success of Community Hospital and now in all three of the hospitals. The Sisters feel very good that their 'letting go' has been very good for healthcare in the communities. They have found other ways to continue to serve in the hospital communities with such initiatives as Sojourner Truth in Gary, Nazareth Home in East Chicago and HealthVisions that serve all of Northwest Indiana. The Sisters also continue to individually serve in areas such as pastoral care at Community Healthcare System hospitals. Today, I believe the Sisters would say their decision to exit acute care, in the best interest of the continuation of high quality community healthcare, was absolutely the right thing to do at the time. The success of the hospitals is evident."

Beth Kaminski, former CEO
St. Mary Medical Center and Ancilla Systems Incorporated | (began in 1986 in Hobart)

It's been *Said* in 2009…

"The corporate office was down the road at 1000 Lake Park Avenue in the old Prudential building. It had 60 or 80 people there and we practically had the entire building. Later, Ancilla Systems moved to a five-person office in the shopping center across the street from the hospital."

Peggy Kamysz, R.N., MPA, Information Technology
St. Mary Medical Center | (began in 1982 in Gary/Hobart)

HealthVisions Midwest

IT'S BEEN *Said* IN 2009...

"St. Mary Medical Center has always been very committed to the community and willing to put resources into community health programs. They were instrumental in the creation of HealthVisions Midwest in 1998 with our focus on community health and wellness to the underserved. We have always found them to be a willing partner in our efforts to improve community health."

Don Barnes, PRESIDENT/CEO OF HEALTHVISIONS MIDWEST

HealthVisions Midwest works within local communities served by the Poor Handmaids of Jesus Christ or where called to work with other partners. HealthVisions strives to build healthy communities by reducing health disparities among the poor and underserved. They are empowered to improve their own health... and are impacted through advocacy efforts and systemic changes.

THE LINDEN HOUSE

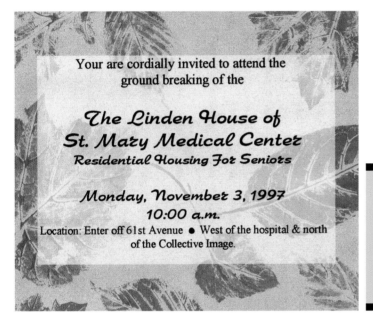

Your are cordially invited to attend the
ground breaking of the

**The Linden House of
St. Mary Medical Center**
Residential Housing For Seniors

**Monday, November 3, 1997
10:00 a.m.**
Location: Enter off 61st Avenue ● West of the hospital & north
of the Collective Image.

On November 3, 1997, ground was broken for The Linden House of St. Mary Medical Center. The hospital and Ancilla Systems Incorporated received a $3.4 million Housing and Urban Development grant to aid in the planning and construction of the assisted living facility for senior citizens. The linden is a tree whose leaf is part of the Ancilla trademark. It reflects a symbol of life for the Poor Handmaids of Jesus Christ, the Roman Catholic order that operates Ancilla Systems Incorporated.

DID YOU KNOW?

The Linden House of Chicago, Gary, Hobart, and Mishawaka – sponsored by Ancilla Systems Incorporated – is affordable housing for seniors and individuals with special needs. The Linden House is dedicated to enriching the quality of life for its residents by respecting the dignity of each person and by providing a sense of community through proper management.

1998 – ST. MARY MEDICAL CENTER — CELEBRATING 25 YEARS

St. Mary Medical Center – 1973-1998
Neighborly Care, SPRING 1998

When St. Mary Medical Center celebrated its 25th anniversary in 1998, the hospital's director of Marketing and Community Relations, Marlena Lagina, said the hospital's commitment to the future was as strong as its growth from the day it opened as a 186-bed facility on April 15, 1973. In celebration of a quarter-century of progress, a festive spring day was marked by an early-morning outdoor Mass and an all-day potluck supper.

The Hobart hospital opened in the early 1970s as the 12th medical facility sponsored by the Poor Handmaids of Jesus Christ. Although the new Hobart location was originally described as a satellite of St. Mary Medical Center in Gary, the Gary site closed in 1993. In 1974, its first year – operating as an acute-care facility with a focus on accidents and injuries – St. Mary Medical Center in Hobart admitted nearly 7,500 patients, handled more than 1,300 births, and had an average daily census of 150-159. In 1974, it employed 450 people. By 1998, the hospital had nearly doubled its staff to 800 employees and boasted 350 hospital volunteers. A 25-year commemorative advertisement said, "(At) St. Mary Medical Center... with a bright future ahead, the community can look forward to another 25 years of technology, innovation and, of course, some of the most caring smiles you've ever seen."

• THEN AND NOW

PHYSICIAN PRACTICE – MANAGEMENT...

Contributed by Lisa Logan, Director

Lisa Logan, Director

With the ever-changing healthcare environment and multiple demands placed upon physicians, the need of physicians to balance the practice of medicine with the business of medicine has become a continuous challenge. It was out of the needs expressed by physicians to find this balance that Physician Practice – Management evolved and began in 1999.

There are many facets that are needed to run a medical practice smoothly and effectively: employing medical and office personnel; purchasing and updating computer systems; ordering and maintaining supplies, equipment, and medications; billing and coding for patient visits, payroll and benefits for employees; and marketing the practice to the community, just to name a few. Focusing on these areas of running a medical office can take time away from what physicians were trained for and want to do – to be with their patients and practice the art of medicine! That's where Physician Practice – Management steps in and provides business assistance to physicians.

Those physicians who become part of Community Healthcare System's Care Network form a partnership with St. Mary Medical Center. The business side of the medical practices is then handled by Physician Practice – Management. What a great combination that provides the best patient care possible – so no wonder our patients are so satisfied and rate us highly!

With the financial and time demands placed upon physicians, this cohesive team approach brings the best of both worlds together. More and more physicians are realizing the benefits of this and Physician Practice – Management has grown by more than 100%!

We value the dedication and expertise of our physicians and staff. With their committed focus and partnership, we know that our patients are receiving the best quality of care and that's truly why we are all here!

*Marking Time...*1999

- *The world awaited the consequences of the Y2K bug, with more drastic millennial theorists warning of Armageddon.*
- *The number of Internet users worldwide reached 150 million by the beginning of 1999. Over 50% were from the U.S.*
- *U.S. cancer survivor Lance Armstrong won cycling's Tour De France.*

HOSPITAL/COMMUNITY HAPPENINGS

THE WELL CITY USA PROJECT IN HOBART

HOBART – A WELL CITY
Through the Well City USA project, Hobart, Indiana, was awarded Well City status in 2000.
Photo provided by Wellness Council of America (WELCOA)

WELL CITY – SMALL TOWN, BIG RESULTS

Well City was an ambitious project that was designed to improve the health and well-being of its citizens. A report issued prior to the Well City USA campaign showed that Hobart, like other Northwest Indiana cities, had significant health risks. Lake County was leading the state in the late 1990s in incidents of heart disease and cancer, and the statistics on obesity and lack of exercise were also of concern.

"If 'Well City USA' sounds like an important title, it is," said St. Mary Medical Center Administrator Milt Triana. "We are part of a truly elite group – one that is doing something tangible, something real – to foster not only a healthy workplace, but also a healthy community and beyond."

To help introduce the idea of worksite wellness and its positive ramifications for businesses and the business community, the Wellness Council of Indiana hosted a number of gatherings which added to those who became involved in the initiative.

Patrick Midkiff, then vice president of Planning and Business Development at St. Mary Medical Center, said, "We've actually improved on several health status factors. Employers have indeed seen an impact and are now striving for even better results."

When the city was awarded "Hobart Well City" status in October 2000, the population was 21,000. The top five industries within the community were manufacturing, healthcare, retail, services and education. The number of Well Workplace participants was 20 and the number of employees within the Well City Project was 5,000.

Source: Wellness Council of America (WELCOA)

IT'S BEEN *Said* IN 2009...

"We partnered with the city of Hobart for achieving a Well City designation and the goal was to get approximately 20 businesses in the city to develop wellness programs for their companies. So St. Mary developed a program along with (then) Mayor Linda Buzinec's office and the city government, the YMCA, Hobart Federal Savings Bank, Greener's Store for Men/Women, Hobart School System, and other local businesses. We submitted our goals and results to the Wellness Council of Northwest Indiana for final selection. The city of Hobart was selected in 2000 as the first city in the state of Indiana to be designated as Well City. St. Mary Medical Center was the main sponsor for this project."

Milt Triana, RETIRED HOSPITAL ADMINISTRATOR
ST. MARY MEDICAL CENTER
BUSINESS DEVELOPMENT, COMMUNITY HEALTHCARE SYSTEM | (BEGAN IN 1969 IN GARY)

Marking Time...2000

• *Human genome (genetic content) deciphered; expected to revolutionize the practice of medicine (Jun. 26).*

ACUTE REHABILITATION CENTER...

Contributed by Valori Kolarczyk
Program Director

ACUTE REHABILITATION CENTER
STAFF PHOTO – 2009
BACK ROW (L-R): Gretchen Mercer; Floyd Bristol; TJ Docena; Mardee Newton; and Sandy Morrison
MIDDLE ROW (L-R): Stephen Karol, M.D.; Stephanie Mullin; Bethany Buckner; Cindy Fenik; Deb Kelnhofer; Nurse Manager Joyce Plukas; and Karen Malone
FRONT ROW (L-R): Program Director Valori Kolarczyk; Maren Johnson; Hope Wells; Quintella Benson; Rudo Swain; Andrea Moon, charge nurse; and Deb Griggs

Recovering from a serious illness or injury can be one of the greatest challenges a person can face. Physical rehabilitation helps patients resume healthy, happy and productive lives. Therefore, St. Mary Medical Center made a commitment to our community by opening the Acute Rehabilitation Center on December 7, 2000. The Rehabilitation Center is equipped with 20 private patient rooms, a patient dining room, a dedicated gym and an area for Activities of Daily Living. The ability to assist individuals in reaching their highest level of independence is accomplished through an interdisciplinary team including a rehabilitation medicine physician, registered nurses, physical therapists, occupational therapists, speech-language pathologists, and a social worker. This interdisciplinary team offers intensive inpatient rehabilitation services to those who have limitations in mobility, self-care, and communication. Most of the time, these limitations are the result of one of the following medical conditions: stroke, major multiple trauma, spinal cord injury, brain injury, amputation, fractures of the hip, polyarthritis, and other neurological disorders – all of which require individualized treatment programs.

In 2001, St. Mary Medical Center came together with Community Hospital and St. Catherine Hospital as Community Healthcare System. As a three-rehabilitation system, we began our journey of establishing common systems, programs and processes. We offer education to our patients and the community through our "Moving Forward after Stroke" program. We also established and maintain a Guest Speaker Bureau and Peer Support for patients and their families.

The Rehabilitation Centers of Community Healthcare System received three-year accreditations from CARF (Commission on Accreditation of Rehabilitation Facilities) in 2004 and 2007, thereby demonstrating compliance with nationally recognized standards in rehabilitation.

In 2008, the Rehabilitation Center at St. Mary Medical Center was able to acquire therapy equipment that minimizes gravity and facilitates better mobility and walking patterns for patients with neurological impairment. Most recently, in 2009, we implemented a Wiihabilitation Program which uses the Wii system to address balance, coordination, strength, socialization and fun!

A professional, caring staff and state-of-the-art equipment are key components to offering the very best at the Acute Rehabilitation Center. Every day is dedicated to our patients' success and satisfaction.

DID YOU KNOW?

The Transitional Care Unit (TCU) was established in March 1998 as a 30-bed, $2.5 million facility to accommodate patients who required a longer length of stay. It became a unique option for those who no longer require acute inpatient care but are not medically ready to return home. They meet the requirements for long term care and can be moved to the Transitional Care Unit. These "sub-acute" care patients include those recovering from stroke or major joint replacement surgery as well as individuals in need of nutritional assessment or wound care. Due to the drastic decrease in reimbursement for patients going to a Transitional Care Unit, the unit was converted from a sub-acute to an acute unit. Before the conversion to an Acute Rehabilitation Center, the unit was temporarily closed for remodeling. It is currently managed by RehabCare Group.

HOSPITAL/COMMUNITY HAPPENINGS

ARRHYTHMIA MAPPING

To help patients with certain types of cardiac arrhythmias, a new tool was implemented at St. Mary Medical Center in 2001 to help physicians navigate their way through the heart. Arrhythmia mapping, as it is known, is used during a cardiac ablation procedure to help correct atrial flutter, atrial tachycardia and other types of rhythm problems that were previously difficult to remedy. St. Mary Medical Center began using arrhythmia mapping in March 2001 as the only hospital using such technology.

Neighborly Care, SUMMER 2001

THE ACQUISITION – COMMUNITY HEALTHCARE SYSTEM

In October 2001, the Community Foundation, Inc. (CFI), parent company of The Community Hospital, announced the acquisition of two Northwest Indiana hospitals operated by Ancilla Systems Incorporated. The foundation name was changed to Community Foundation of Northwest Indiana, Inc. (CFNI). Under the banner of Community Healthcare System, The Community Hospital, St. Catherine Hospital, and St. Mary Medical Center were integrated to offer a network of collective, quality medical services.

Mylinda Cane, regional director of Marketing and Corporate Communications for Community Healthcare System, said Donald Powers, president and CEO of Community Foundation of Northwest Indiana, Inc., wanted to strengthen the quality of healthcare in Northwest Indiana and believed that this new partnership would raise standards among all three facilities.

"He certainly saw a lot of promise in the growth potential of St. Mary Medical Center and the need to invest in expanding its capacity and technology," she said. "But the most important commitment made to this newly formed healthcare system was the focus on identifying best practices and efficiencies that could be achieved by working together. We owed it to the communities we served to make healthcare better, more accessible and more affordable. By working as partners and tapping into the strengths of each hospital, we were able to bring about these improvements much quicker."

IT'S BEEN *Said* IN 2009...

"The Catholic Health Association envisioned Catholic hospital systems coming together to form large entities to support managed care initiatives. Ancilla Systems (Incorporated) explored several opportunities, however, and did not find an option that fit their mission and values.

"The Sisters began to explore opportunities within each of the hospital markets and were successful in finding partners that would further the continuation of each of the Catholic hospitals. The Sisters had acute care ministries for more than a hundred years in some markets. This was a major decision and was very progressive for Catholic Orders at the time.

"In Lake County, Ken Herlin, a partner with Ernst & Young, facilitated a meeting to explore potential partnership. Don Powers and Sister Kathleen Quinn, (PHJC), initially met to discuss this opportunity. At the beginning of these discussions, I became the CEO of Ancilla Systems. Ancilla respected the vision Don Powers had with Community Hospital in Munster. The discussions continued. Issues such as St. Mary's and St. Catherine's remaining Catholic were important to the Sisters.

"Don respected and valued the position of the Sisters. We appreciated his position and respected his astute business skills and willingness to make this a successful partnership. We each learned from each other and this facilitated the discussions."

Beth Kaminski, FORMER CEO
ST. MARY MEDICAL CENTER AND ANCILLA SYSTEMS INCORPORATED
(BEGAN IN 1986 IN HOBART)

Marking Time...2001

- Terrorists attack United States. Hijackers flew jetliners into twin towers of New York City's World Trade Center and the Pentagon. A fourth hijacked plane crashed 80 miles outside of Pittsburgh (Sep. 11).

- New class of cancer drugs announced. Researchers at San Francisco conference report new drug, Gleevec, showed promise in treating patients who do not respond to chemotherapy (May 13).

"I think the acquisition was one of the best things that happened because Community at the time was sort of the premiere hospital in Northwest Indiana and we were able to partner with them. They had the money – and the first thing they did was to come in and… really upgrade the hospital which we couldn't have done on our own. So making this facility better for the patients… and also having the three hospitals as partners strengthened each of them."

Sister Nora Hahn, PHJC, PROVINCIAL
DONALDSON, INDIANA

"When Community Healthcare System was formed, there were four people named to the board through Ancilla Systems – Ed Williams, Monsignor (Joseph) Semancik, Bob Welsh (and me). We tried to be selective. Monsignor and Ed Williams came from St. Catherine and Bob Welsh came from St. Mary Medical Center. Both Ancilla and our religious community determined that they were very faithful and supportive."

Sister Kathleen Quinn, PHJC, BOARD MEMBER, COMMUNITY FOUNDATION OF NORTHWEST INDIANA, INC.
FORMER CHAIRMAN OF THE BOARD, ANCILLA SYSTEMS INCORPORATED

"(The acquisition) has been very good for us. We have been very blessed. We say the morning prayer and the evening prayer on the PA system and we have been able to maintain the mission and the values. We have various priests from the area who come in to say Mass. Father David Gosnell comes from St. Elizabeth Seton in Valparaiso, Father Thomas Mischler is from St. Mary of the Lake in Miller, and Father Joseph Kelchak is retired but comes in from Lake of the Four Seasons. If they can't come, I have Father Lourdu Pasala from Assumption in New Chicago and Father Plavcan comes from the diocese. So I have a good roster of them."

Sister Mary O'Hara, OP, CHAPLAIN, PASTORAL CARE DEPARTMENT
ST. MARY MEDICAL CENTER | (BEGAN IN 1989 IN GARY)

"Look at the beautiful hospital we have… I mean it's insane. I can't thank Community Healthcare System, Mr. Powers, and John Gorski enough for the physical plan that we have in which to deliver our care. This community has never had anything that nice and it's certainly something that's superior to our immediate surrounding hospitals. You can't measure how uplifting it is to this staff to come to a clean, new, and more efficient facility. Every part about it makes some part of their job easier. With all the increasing strains on nursing and the increase in their responsibilities, all of us are feeling the load of a change in economic times, changes in reimbursement, pressures to be perfect. Just to walk into that physical plan… and the patients are happier. It really is an immeasurable difference."

Jack Ziegler, M.D., CARDIOLOGIST
ST. MARY MEDICAL CENTER | (BEGAN IN 1982 IN HOBART)

"The culture is the great benevolence of a not-for-profit hospital. We are here to serve all the patients in need in the communities where we are located. Mr. Powers' philosophy also means the hospitals(s) will be dedicated to technological advances to make sure we have the very best to offer to the community. The Community Healthcare System reinvests in the community to make sure we meet their needs. For those of us who have had the opportunity to interact with him, it is interesting that he accomplishes so much with a non-ostentatious manner. With very few words you clearly understand what kind of man he is. We wouldn't all be here in these positions without him leading us in that direction. He is a unique individual. I don't know anybody else like him."

Janice Ryba, CEO AND ADMINISTRATOR
ST. MARY MEDICAL CENTER
(BEGAN IN 1984 AT COMMUNITY HOSPITAL)

Technology

"When I first started working we were the bedside nurses. But then as the technology came about, the patients still needed everything, but the computers and paperwork were a new era. It was terribly important; it helped people get well and be diagnosed a lot quicker."

Shirley Makivich Urbanek, R.N., RETIRED
ST. MARY MERCY HOSPITAL | (BEGAN IN 1959 IN GARY)

"Back in the earlier days, we were still using the manual typewriters with the carriages. We used to have little index cards where we had to type the patient's name, the date and their X-ray number, and then we would attach it with their paperwork because there was still paperwork involved. We had to type on the actual requisition too. We had to get three sheets, a white sheet, a yellow sheet and a blue sheet. One went into the folder, one went to the doctor's box, and one went into medical records for their files."

Beverly Armenta, COORDINATOR RADIOLOGY SUPPORT, RADIOLOGY
ST. MARY MEDICAL CENTER | (BEGAN IN 1972 IN GARY)

"Computerized nursing documentation was important to ongoing changes in medicine. We implemented the Meditech System in the late 1990s at St. Mary Medical Center and St. Catherine Hospital... Handheld computers, a Meditech function, were adapted by nurses so they could take vital signs and download their information into the device at the patient's bedside...

"Brenda Metros, who was an Operating Room (OR) nurse, and I developed our own computerized nursing documentation notes. Brenda, some staff nurses, and I then taught other staff. We started with the Intensive Care Unit first since those nurses were willing to learn something new."

Maryann Kerr, R.N., NURSE MANAGER, ICCU & MEDICAL ONCOLOGY, RETIRED
MERCY HOSPITAL | (BEGAN IN 1960 IN GARY)

"I started between the Gary and Hobart facilities as an assistant director of Quality Review for nursing. I am an RN but I know computer systems. The software that was in use at St. Mary's for many years was Meditech...

"Several years ago, we changed from Meditech to Affinity at St. Mary's with the plan of going through all three facilities. There are some major issues with Affinity so our facilities decided to look to either Epic or Meditech."

Peggy Kamysz, R.N., M.P.A., INFORMATION TECHNOLOGY
ST. MARY MEDICAL CENTER | (BEGAN IN 1982 IN GARY/HOBART)

"I was responsible for taking payments and registering patients for tests. My most important experience was going from doing everything by hand to computers. We had to load all insurance lists into the computer by hand. This was an enormous task in the beginning, but as time went on it really helped us out. I transferred to Hobart in 1974 and retired in 1992."

Jennie Purcell
FORMER HEAD CASHIER, BUSINESS OFFICE
MERCY HOSPITAL | (BEGAN IN 1968 IN GARY)

INFORMATION TECHNOLOGY STAFF PHOTO – 2009
BACK ROW (L-R): Gary Ludwig, Kathy Tomczak, Cecilia Helson, Jim Nida, and Ryan Szarkowicz
FRONT ROW (L-R): Brenda Metros, Bryan Neece, and Peggy Kamysz
NOT PICTURED: Jay Mummey and Sue Demitroulas

• THEN AND NOW

INFORMATION TECHNOLOGY...

Gary Weiner
Vice President and Chief Information Officer

Gary Weiner

The Information Technology Department was formed in 2001 when St. Mary Medical Center, St. Catherine Hospital and Community Hospital came together as Community Healthcare System. The Community Hospital Information Technology (IT) Department and elements from Ancilla Support Services were joined and located at St. Catherine Hospital. Initially, Ancilla continued to host the major hospital applications for both St. Mary Medical Center and St. Catherine Hospital until computers were transferred and the new IT Department staff assumed the work and responsibilities of the applications and support. The IT Department continues to serve all three hospitals with some IT staff located at each facility to provide local and prompt support of an ever-growing list of applications.

A strategic plan was developed in 2001 and 2002 that called for common information systems to support the hospitals from the Business and Hospital Information System (HIS) perspective. The laboratory system was the first to be standardized followed by PeopleSoft applications for Finance, Human Resources, and Materials Management departments. The next major effort was the Hospital Information System in which a single patient accounting application was implemented followed by the clinical applications of the HIS. St. Mary Medical Center volunteered to be the first hospital in each of the HIS efforts and played an instrumental role in proving out the applications and highlighting the strengths and weaknesses for the other hospitals. The hospital staff and leadership should be commended for their efforts and perseverance.

Modern high speed wireless communications "pipes" link the three hospitals and major clinics providing communications, patient information and radiological images from the central computer rooms where the hardware and applications run.

Community Healthcare System has made significant progress in creating integrated information systems that provide secure patient data at any of our patient treatment locations. Planned HIS improvements will provide future-looking technology to support growth and improved capabilities.

2002

HOSPITAL/COMMUNITY HAPPENINGS

DID YOU KNOW?

Neighborly Care, a healthcare information magazine, published until the spring of 2002, was replaced with a new publication, *Vim & Vigor Magazine* – a free quarterly magazine with continuing healthcare information and a link to Community Healthcare System hospitals – Community Hospital, St. Catherine Hospital, and St. Mary Medical Center.

2002 – TriVex Surgery Performed at St. Mary Medical Center

In 2002, St. Mary Medical Center became the first hospital in Lake County to utilize the TriVex surgery performed by Cardiovascular Surgeon, Benjamin Tang, M.D. The procedure, a new method of removing varicose veins, was touted for its level of accuracy, Dr. Tang noted. Ultrasound imaging helps the physician know exactly which vein or veins to remove. The surgeon makes as few as two incisions per vein cluster. An illumination device is inserted in one of the incisions and a power resector is inserted into the other incision to remove varicose vein clusters.

DID YOU KNOW?

Varicose veins are large, bulging veins more than two millimeters in diameter. In a healthy vein, valves allow the blood to flow back to the heart but in varicose veins the valves don't work properly and allow blood to pool in the leg. This causes the vein to swell and bulge.

Reticular veins are medium-sized visible veins on the leg, often accompanied by varicose veins. Patients are usually told not to be concerned about having them removed.

Spider veins are the tiniest visible veins on the leg. They are generally purple and less than a millimeter in diameter. They pose no health threat.

Source: *Vim & Vigor,* summer 2002

2004

HOSPITAL/COMMUNITY HAPPENINGS

HOSPITAL FRIENDS
When Marie Czarnecki and Annie Soto returned to visit in 2004, a group of longtime hospital friends met at Giovanni's Restaurant in Munster to reminisce. **FRONT ROW (L-R):** Judy Candiano, Irene Pacheco, Mary Ann Danko, and Marie Czarnecki. **BACK ROW (L-R):** Monita Puckett, Margie Salinas, and Annie Soto

*Marking Time...*2002

- *U.S. health officials issued new guidelines on mammograms, strongly recommending that breast cancer screening begin at age 40 instead of 50. Recommendation followed months of controversy over the effectiveness of breast cancer screening (Feb. 21).*

Know Your Hospital... and Look How We've Grown!

The building under construction (red arrow at right) is the Admitting/Outpatient Center, built in 1992. Although several additions to the campus are also shown, St. Mary Medical Center was aligning itself to begin a growing surge. Patients entered the facility on the east side (Route 51 as noted). The large parking lot at the bottom of the photo was designated for employee parking. Courtesy of Ismael "Izzy" Alicea

This aerial photo, dated in the summer of 1999 or 2000 because of the existing maintenance office building, was taken from the northeast – around the time of initial preparations for the New Patient Tower. Running north and south on the bottom left corner is Route 51. Running east and west at the top of the photo is 61st Avenue. Shown above the lake is the Diagnostic Outpatient Center (DOC) which later became The Center for Imaging and Radiation Oncology (CIRO) and Women's Diagnostic Center. The Collective Image is shown at top right and later became the Outpatient Rehabilitation Center.
Courtesy of Ismael "Izzy" Alicea

St. Mary Medical Center – The Hobart Construction Chart

Since St. Mary Medical Center opened in Hobart in 1973, its growth has been significant, as shown in the chart below.

Building/Area	Year Built	Project Inclusion
Patient Tower – East	1972	Initial Patient Tower
Medical Arts Building, 1st Floor, Lab and Emergency Room	1978	This included the front and South side of the facility
"D.O. N." Fundraising Project	1987	Intensive Care Unit, Cardiac Cath. Emergency Power building
Physical Therapy/Occupational Therapy	1987	Physical Therapy, Communications Switch Board
Storage Building	1990	Individual Department Storage
Labor, Delivery, Recovery and Post-Partum	1990	Re-Modeling of existing unit
Sports Medicine Facility/Spectrum	1991	Currently houses Cardiac Rehabilitation
Admitting/Outpatient Center	1992	Admitting Stations/Administrative Offices
Engineering Office Building	1996	Engineering Services
Women's Health Center	1997	Women's care center-satellite facility
Physician Office Building/Transitional Care Unit	1998	Professional Office Building, Transitional Care Unit – Currently Services as Acute Rehab Unit
New Patient Tower – West	2004	Patient tower, Conference Center, Gift Shop, Auxiliary work rooms, Cafeteria serving and dining area.
Family Birthing Center	2005	Renovation of Labor, Delivery, Recovery and Post-Partum area
Diagnostic Imaging Center – Magnetic Resonance Imaging	2009	MRI, CT Scan, Ultrasound/Radiology administrative offices
Cardiac Catheterization Laboratory	2009	Renovation of existing area
Emergency Room	Fall-2010 (Anticipated Completion)	Expansion and Renovation of existing area

This map, published in March 2009, is used by volunteers to direct visitors through the hospital. Indicated here are the west entrance and many changes over time.

The New Patient Tower

When Community Healthcare System partnered with the Bachman Partnership, P.C., of Highland, to design a multi-million dollar, state-of-the-art, six-story New Patient Tower at St. Mary Medical Center, it was important to obtain the input of the professionals who would utilize the area day after day. Staff nurses, physicians and technicians assisted with details – all in an effort to make their jobs easier, safer, more efficient, and more pleasant for themselves and their patients.

"… Thanks to the diligence and belief of all these groups, we're seeing it through today," said former Administrator Milt Triana at the groundbreaking ceremony on November 20, 2002. "And what we'll have on the ground in two years is the best of all the ideas."

It was a proud day in the history of St. Mary Medical Center when, after months of anticipation, the New Patient Tower was completed in September 2004 by Berglund Construction, of Chesterton. On hand for the open house were Governor Joe Kernan and U.S. Representative Pete Visclosky, D-Merrillville. Milt Triana noted that it was extremely gratifying to share the new 124,000 square-foot facility with the public. Those seeing it for the first time raved about its functionality and remarkable presence in the community.

Shown here is St. Mary Medical Center's New Patient Tower under early construction.

MAKING PROGRESS
The St. Mary Medical Center's New Patient Tower nears completion. The six-story, $40 million structure was finished in 2004.

The six-story tower features modern inpatient care in private rooms designed to accommodate patients and families in a comfortable setting. Reclining chairs and Internet access are included as well as telemetry monitoring and Computers on Wheels for bedside charting. A pneumatic tube system, physical therapy room, a large infusion room and a bright, cheerful Pediatric Unit help complete the amenities.

From October 2004 to January 2010, the New Patient Tower has welcomed and discharged nearly 4,500 newborns, handled more than 135,000 emergency visits, served more than 22,000 outpatient surgery patients, and accommodated approximately 332,000 patient days.

"We intend to keep pace with the advances in healthcare that will help area residents enjoy a higher quality of life and health," said Donald S. Powers, president and CEO of Community Foundation of Northwest Indiana, Inc. "By investing in our hospitals, we are helping to keep our community strong and vital and, as not-for-profit hospitals, we serve to protect and heal our most vulnerable citizens."

THE NEW PATIENT TOWER
In September 2004, lines formed outside the New Patient Tower when the public was invited to see it for the first time. Former Chicago Bears player, Dick Butkus (left), and former wrestler, Mick Foley (right), were on hand to sign autographs.
Reprinted by permission of the *Post-Tribune*, SEPTEMBER 20, 2004

New Patient Tower lobby

IT'S BEEN *Said* IN 2009...

"The biggest change was the addition of the New Tower. Certainly the patients are a lot happier with the beautiful building and the design; and the ergonomics of it all really made a big difference for the doctors and the nurses."

Mark Simaga, M.D., NEUROLOGIST
ST. MARY MEDICAL CENTER
(BEGAN IN 1997 IN HOBART)

St. Mary Medical Center – Satellite Locations

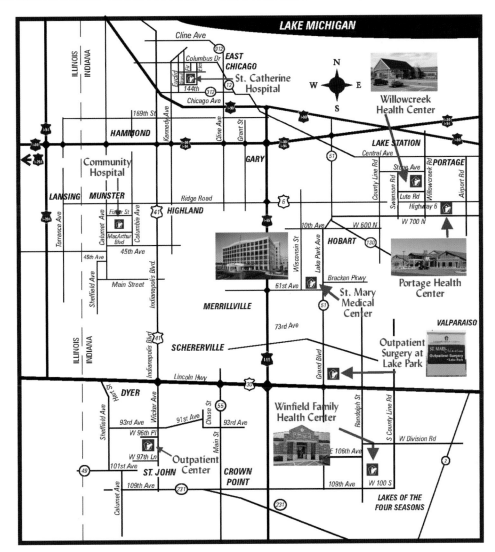

Shown here is a current map of St. Mary Medical Center and its off-site locations – Willowcreek Health Center, Portage Health Center, Outpatient Surgery at Lake Park, and Winfield Family Health Center.

IT'S BEEN *Said* IN 2009...

"The trend from inpatient to outpatient was probably driven by two things: one was technology, and the other was financial. Early on, it was close to an 80/20 kind of situation where 80% of your business was generated on the inpatient side. You knew if you came in to have your gallbladder out you were going to be there for at least a week. If you had a torn meniscus fixed in your knee, they were going to open your knee and you were going to be off your feet and rehabilitating for months. It would probably be two weeks until you got out of the hospital.

"Technology and drugs and new procedures came along. Suddenly you found you could scope the knee, do the same kind of thing in an hour's time and have the patient in and out of the hospital on the same day. That was tremendous advance. Laparoscopic gallbladders, arthroscopic surgeries, and all those kind of things were really significant in shifting the care from the inpatient side to the outpatient side. Financially, if you could do those things on an outpatient basis, while the initial cost might be significant, you were saving maybe a week's room and board and therapy and other expenses in the hospital.

"It all happened over a period of years but we saw a significant shift in the way patients were treated. One of the old jokes about the doctor making house calls and carrying his little black bag was the fact that most of the medicines that were available to him to take care of a patient he could put in a little black bag. Well, today that's a whole different situation."

John Birdzell
FORMER PRESIDENT OF LAKESHORE HEALTH SYSTEM
(BEGAN IN 1985 WITH ANCILLA SYSTEMS
INCORPORATED)

1 Spectrum
of St. Mary Medical Center
1354 S. Lake Park Ave.

2 Outpatient Rehabilitation Center
320 W. 61st Ave.

3 Center for Imaging and
Radiation Oncology Services (CIRO)
300 W. 61st. Ave.

4 Women's Diagnostic Center
300 W. 61st Ave.

Shown here are St. Mary Medical Center and its Hobart campus facilities – Spectrum, Outpatient Rehabilitation Center, Center for Imaging and Radiation Oncology Services (CIRO), and the Women's Diagnostic Center.

WINFIELD FAMILY HEALTH CENTER

Winfield Family Health Center

The Winfield Family Health Center was unveiled on February 8, 2001 and officially opened in April 2001 as a 12,000-foot satellite facility on Randolph Street just north of the Winfield Government Center. Features of the new structure included a laboratory, radiology and physical therapy services, and physician offices. Patients in the area were provided with access to X-rays, blood draws and other tests performed closer to home.

Among the crowd visiting the new facility were: Father Joseph Murphy of Holy Spirit Catholic Church who offered the invocation; St. Mary Medical Center CEO, Milt Triana; Vice President of Planning and Development, Patrick Midkiff; Winfield Township Trustee John Curly, who was instrumental in bringing the center to Winfield; center Medical Director, Brent Jacobus, M.D.; and Ancilla Board Chairperson, Sister Kathleen Quinn, PHJC.

In September 2009, the husband and wife team of Karin Patterson, D.O., family medicine, and Jonathan Patterson, D.O., general surgery/cosmetic surgery, began seeing patients. In October 2009, at Innovative Women's Health, Douglas Dedelow, D.O.; Colleen Sahy, CNM; and Kelly Oney, FNP-BC; also began seeing patients. Urologist David Wilks, M.D., began seeing patients in the spring of 2010.

IT'S BEEN *Said* IN 2009...

"I used to work at a site called Broadwest Lab in Merrillville for St. Mary... They actually did on-site laboratory work for the surgical center that was in that building. We did any pre-surgical testing and EKGs. Specimens they had were brought down to us and we would do them.

"While at Broadwest, I also registered patients from our Winfield Center in Winfield that is still in existence. Upstairs in that building, St. Mary's has an office that does X-ray and laboratory work. Their materials are brought to St. Mary's by courier. They opened physical therapy on the lower level in May 2008.

"While at Broadwest, I also registered patients from our Merrillville Health Center located by the Merrillville post office. This facility catered to doctors in that area. Dr. Clark Kramer was a big supporter of referrals."

Donna Seeley, REGISTRATION REPRESENTATIVE
PORTAGE OUTPATIENT CENTER | (BEGAN IN 1993 IN HOBART)

WILLOWCREEK HEALTH CENTER

Willowcreek Health Center

Willowcreek Health Center (formerly Portage Outpatient Health Center) opened in 1996 at 3170 Willowcreek Road in Portage. Today, it provides CT, MRI, and ultrasound services as well as lab services and physician offices. St. Mary Medical Center's Wound/Ostomy/Continence Center also offers services at the Willowcreek Health Center.

OUTPATIENT SURGERY AT LAKE PARK

Outpatient Surgery at Lake Park

In January 2010, St. Mary Medical Center opened its new facility, Outpatient Surgery at Lake Park (formerly Lake Park Surgicare, LLC) located on Grand Boulevard/SR 51 just north of U.S. Route 30. The facility performs a wide variety of outpatient surgical procedures.

PORTAGE HEALTH CENTER

Portage Health Center

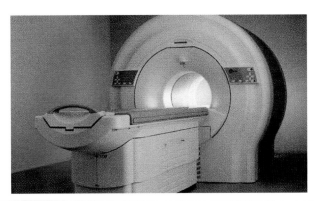

The newest addition to the Portage Outpatient Health Center in 2002 was an MRI (Magnetic Resonance Imaging) that uses digital technology for the sharpest image quality possible in one of the most open environments for patient comfort. The MRI is used to diagnose conditions such as brain and nervous system disorders, cardiovascular disease, and cancer and organ disease.

Neighborly Care, SPRING 2002

Portage Health Center opened in August of 2009 when Outpatient Rehabilitation Services moved there from the Willowcreek location. Staff physicians (in 2010) are Urologist David Wilks, M.D.; Douglas Dedelow, D.O.; and Wallace Sherritt, D.O., both of obstetrics/gynecology.

St. Mary Medical Center's Occupational Health services opened offices there as well, and Innovative Women's Health, St. Mary's OB/GYN physicians and nurse specialists see patients at this location, as well as Winfield, and at new offices opening in 2010 in Hobart and Valparaiso.

2005

Hospital/Community Happenings

2005 – Patient Safety – A Reminder

In Hospital Administrator Milt Triana's premier quarterly in-house publication, he issued a reminder.

"While it goes without saying that patient safety is an utmost priority here, I urge you all – regardless of whether you are in a clinical department – to keep patient safety in the forefront of all you do."

2005 - 2008

St. Mary Medical Center Lauded with National Recognition

Teamwork at its finest
In 2008, for the fourth consecutive year, St. Mary Medical Center received national quality recognition from HealthGrades®, the nation's leading independent rating agencies for hospital quality.

*Marking Time...*2005

- Cancer replaced heart disease as No. 1 cause of death for people 85 years and under.
- Hurricane Katrina wreaked catastrophic damage on the Gulf coast; more than 1,000 died and millions were left homeless on (Aug. 29).
- U.S. President George W. Bush endorsed a nationwide tiered plan for the electronic medical record.
- Number of deaths of U.S. soldiers in Iraq reached 2,000 (Oct. 25).

MEDICAL-SURGICAL

"I began working at St. Mary in 1959 two days after I graduated from nursing school. I worked as a registered nurse for the hospital until 1998 when I retired. I worked on Gary's medical unit, 2South, when I graduated. The Hobart hospital was just a corn field at that time.

"I remained in Gary and more than a decade later, when they were beginning to expand the Gary hospital, I was asked if I would open one of the west wings so I did. A couple of years later, in 1973, the Hobart hospital had taken off and they were ready to open the building. Again I was asked if I would come and open a (third floor Medical-Surgical) unit which I did, and was there for about eight years. I was so fortunate to take the people who had the experience of opening 4West in Gary with me. Janet Wade was the clerk who had kept all of the paperwork from the Gary opening so when she came to Hobart she just did everything for me. We had nothing. We didn't have pencils, paper, bed pans, water pitchers or anything; and we had to go about getting all of it because it was so busy. I tried to keep it organized."

Shirley Makivich Urbanek, RN, RETIRED
ST. MARY MERCY HOSPITAL | (BEGAN IN GARY IN 1959)

ALL DRESSED IN WHITE – ON HER WEDDING DAY
Shown here are Evelyn Charbonneau Ryan and Kenneth Ryan on their wedding day, September 29, 1962. Standing between the newlyweds is Father William Martin who presided at the wedding that was held at St. Luke's Church in Gary before the couple – still dressed in their wedding garb – stopped at the hospital to visit Evelyn's department, the 3North surgical floor.

"When I graduated in 1957, I got the floor of my choice and I picked the Medical-Surgical (Med.-Surg.) floor, 3North, and I absolutely loved it.

"One very special thing – I got married in September of 1962 and I got to come up on 3North in my wedding gown with my new husband and go room to room to see the patients. A lot of these long-timers happened to be there and it made the day just wonderful. On the floor at the south corner were rooms where we had three of the elderly nuns who were ill. We had to get special permission for my husband to come back there so the bedridden nuns could meet him. That was just a special thing to get to do and then we heard, 'When are we going to see kids?'"

Evelyn Charbonneau Ryan, RN
INFECTION CONTROL, RETIRED
MERCY HOSPITAL
(BEGAN IN 1957 IN GARY)

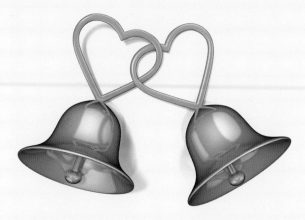

3East-Medical-Surgery staff photo – 2009
Front row, seated (l-r): Nurse Manager Kelly Loudermilk; Ashley Smith; and Tricia Pierce
Middle row (l-r): Loleta Pope; Tracy Lewis; Kortni Centracchio; Susan Schmidt; Mary Munro; and Michele Ferrell
Back row (l-r): Jeton Valentin; Marilou Propeck; Sophia Tolliver; Christina Dowling; Andrea Sielski; and Alysha Nolan

• Then and Now

3East – Medical-Surgery Unit…

Contributed by Kelly Loudermilk, RN, Nurse Manager

Sometime in the late fall of 2005, probably in November after the New West Tower opened, it quickly became apparent that additional medical beds were needed to meet the needs of the high census. A portion of 2East was quickly set up to admit up to eight additional patients. When this unit opened, Shannon Blaney was the interim nurse manager. Using two registered nurses from the hospitals float pool, patients were admitted, orders received, and patients cared for until they could be placed in a bed in the New Patient Tower. This worked well until patients were not being placed for up to 24-48 hours. It was then decided that there needed to be an area that could accommodate patients on an inpatient basis. Two East was used on an "as needed" basis, opened in high census times, and closed as the census dropped. With the census continuing to increase, 2East quickly ran out of rooms. Three East had some renovation work done and the 2East unit was moved.

When the unit transferred to 3East, a small staff was hired, and it began with six to eight beds. It was closed on weekends and holidays. During this period, 3East was under the management of Sheerin Moss. Suzanne Matheny assisted Sheerin with its development. Again, during low census times, the staff was designated to other units in the hospital. Gradually the census increased, however, from its original six to eight beds to a 28-bed unit. Through the next three years many changes were initiated.

The unit, now known as 3East-Med-Surg., has 16 beds and is under the leadership of Kelly Loudermilk, RN. The staff consists of 29 employees, some of whom have been here since the very beginning, including Kelly. The unit cares for diversified patients ranging in age from 18-103. There is now a full-time case manager and a dedicated social worker shared between 3East and 3West.

In November 2009, 3East increased to a total of 19 beds. There was also a successful pilot program initiated in January 2009 for a four-bed medical admission unit known as the Express Admission Unit (EAU). The unit is also managed by Kelly Loudermilk.

At this writing (in 2010), the EAU has eight beds, accepts telemetry patients and is open 24 hours. The entire EAU staff successfully completed basic electrocardiogram (EKG) training certification. Kelly Loudermilk and Shannon Blaney have worked closely to develop the telemetry admission criteria for this expansion. The basic EAU plan is to decrease Emergency Room overflow and staff overtime, increase core measure compliance, and admit patients in a fast-paced, efficient manner. The unit will admit patients for 3East, 3West, 2Medical Telemetry, 5West and 6West.

The 3East-Medical-Surgery Unit has a unique staff that has become a tight-knit family. It has been through numerous challenges including patient care with a unit under construction, a fluctuating census ranging from 6 to 28, and the opening and closing of the unit. Yes, a lot of dedicated, professional St. Mary Medical Center employees have delivered positive energy, a healthy attitude and excellent patient care – now and for years to come.

HOSPITAL/COMMUNITY HAPPENINGS

DID YOU KNOW?

With matching support from the Community Foundation of Northwest Indiana, Inc. (CFNI), the employees and physicians of Community Healthcare System donated $194,140 to help the victims of Hurricane Katrina. The donation was the largest made to the local Red Cross agency by a single corporation in Northwest Indiana.

Vim & Vigor, SPRING 2006

Community Healthcare System representatives (l-r) Mylinda Cane, regional director of Marketing and Corporate Communications, and Donald S. Powers, president and CEO, present a check for Hurricane Katrina relief to American Red Cross Public Support Officer, Tula Gogolak, and Financial Development Chairman, Dr. Gary Jones.

Vim & Vigor, SPRING 2006

2006 – "HOT AUGUST NIGHTS"

On August 9, 2006, "Hot August Nights" – a spinoff of "American Idol" – was organized to boost employee morale and showcase the talent of St. Mary Medical Center's "own." Ismael "Izzy" Alicea, maintenance worker III, kicked off the event by singing and playing guitar with his original composition, "Hot August Nights."

Ten contestants performed in Hobart's outdoor band shell to an audience of nearly 400 people. Committee members were Yvonne Hoff, Ismael "Izzy" Alicea, Russ Cain, Randy Norris and Julia Smith. Judges were then Mayor Linda Buzinec, Hobart High School Musical Director Dean Wolff, and *Times* Columnist Adele Mackanos.

The Christian Awareness Committee sold concessions to raise funds for the Employee in Need Fund and other community outreach programs. Contest winners were Respiratory Therapist, Kim Berrier, first place for singing "Wind beneath My Wings"; Emergency Department Unit Secretary, Lisa Wilson, second place; and 6West Nurse Fellow, Nicole Green, third place.

⏱ *Marking Time...2006*

- *In the first Space Shuttle flight after Columbia's 2003 explosion, Discovery delivered supplies to the International Space Station and conducted three spacewalks (Jul. 4-17).*

- *Gerald R. Ford (38th president of the United States, 1974-1977) died at 93 (Dec. 26).*

"HOT AUGUST NIGHTS" PARTICIPANTS
FRONT ROW (L-R): Nicole Green, 6West; Lisa Wilson, Emergency Department; Tina Anderson, IMCU; Amanda Packham, 6West; Gary Coppinger, maintenance; Annie Mumford, Acute Rehabilitation; and Marc Williams, Laboratory
BACK ROW (L-R): Peggy Baxter, Case Management; Michelle Owens, Emergency Department; Milt Triana – host; and Kim Berrier, respiratory therapy

HOSPITAL/COMMUNITY HAPPENINGS

"ST. MARY'S HEALING TOUCH" – THE CHELICH OIL PAINTING

Northwest Indiana artist Michael Chelich stands with his original oil painting, "St. Mary's Healing Touch," which is hung on the wall near the Labor and Delivery family waiting room, just off the hospital's east lobby. St. Mary Medical Center commissioned Chelich to create an image that accurately reflects (Community Healthcare System's) mission to "provide the highest quality care in the most cost-efficient manner, respect the dignity of the individual, provide for the well-being of the community, and serve the needs for ALL people, including the poor and disadvantaged." The figures in the painting, Chelich said, are the images of Mary, the mother of Jesus, and a young boy who looks to the Blessed Mother for healing and comfort. A dove, representing the Holy Spirit, hovers nearby and is symbolic of protection.

Marking Time...2007

- *California Democrat Nancy Pelosi took the gavel after being elected Speaker of the House of the 110th Congress. Democrats took control of both houses of Congress for the first time. (Jan. 4)*
- *Richard J. Daley was elected to a sixth consecutive mayoral term, the only Chicago mayor to do so. (Feb. 27)*

The Studer Program

It's been *Said* in 2009...

"The major attributes of St. Mary Medical Center are its emphasis on patient and employee satisfaction, its emphasis on quality service, and its excellent relationship with the medical staff. St. Mary Medical Center is perceived by the community of Hobart and even surrounding communities as a first-class hospital."

Milt Triana, RETIRED HOSPITAL ADMINISTRATOR, ST. MARY MEDICAL CENTER
SPECIAL PROJECTS COORDINATOR, COMMUNITY HEALTHCARE SYSTEM
(BEGAN IN 1969 IN GARY)

It's been *Said* in 2009...

"In January 2007, Community Healthcare System had its first Leadership Development Institute (LDI) after signing a contract with the Studer Group®. This was the start of our journey of Operational Excellence to become a great place for patients to receive care, physicians to practice medicine, and employees to work. Our focus was to improve our patients' perception of care. We knew we gave very good care and wanted to make sure we were all speaking the same language. System goals were set under our five pillars: Service, Quality, Finance, Growth and People. When patients and families walked through our hallways, we wanted them to feel our commitment to Operational Excellence. It is all about the patient experience.

"As a result of our hard work, Studer Group® presented Community Healthcare System with the Fire Starter award in November 2009. Receiving this award is a great honor and reflected how our patients are receiving care."

Kris Garcia, INTERNAL OPERATIONAL EXCELLENCE COACH
COMMUNITY HEALTHCARE SYSTEM

Janice L. Ryba
CEO and Administrator
St. Mary Medical Center

Janice L. Ryba – CEO and Administrator

In 2007, Janice L. Ryba was appointed CEO and administrator of St. Mary Medical Center, overseeing the 190-bed, not-for-profit hospital in Hobart, Indiana.

It's been *Said* in 2009...

"I was first employed by the system in February of 1984 at Community Hospital as a Senior Technologist in the Laboratory Hematology Department.

"I have been in my role of St. Mary Medical Center CEO and administrator for nearly three years now. I love the facility, but it is really more than bricks and mortar. It is more about the people and the physicians here. Personally, I could not have had a warmer welcome. Walking down the halls every day you immediately recognize the culture of caring, and the compassion exhibited by the staff is so evident. We hear it from the patients and even from the physicians consistently. As a healthcare provider, it is really about the patient – providing "patient-centered care.""

Janice Ryba, CEO AND ADMINISTRATOR
ST. MARY MEDICAL CENTER
(BEGAN IN 1984 AT COMMUNITY HOSPITAL IN MUNSTER)

"St. Mary Medical Center is doing very well both clinically and financially under Janice Ryba's direction and the supervision of her management team. I believe it will continue to do well as long as there are ongoing advances in technology and infrastructure. St. Mary Medical Center must and will continue, I believe, to be the hospital of choice in East Lake and Porter counties."

Milt Triana, RETIRED HOSPITAL ADMINISTRATOR, ST. MARY MEDICAL CENTER
SPECIAL PROJECTS COORDINATOR, COMMUNITY HEALTHCARE SYSTEM
(BEGAN IN 1969 IN GARY)

"Janice can be described as highly competent and involved while remaining personable. She prioritizes excellence in healthcare for all our patients and the communities we serve."

John R. Danielson, MD., MEDICAL DIRECTOR, QUALITY MANAGEMENT

"Janice Ryba is very analytical data driven. She wants to do what's right. When I greeted her in the board room when we all met her, I told her my name and that I worked in the Medical Records Department as director and I said, 'I will do my very best under your leadership.' She also promised to do her very best for me and for the hospital. I don't think most leaders would feel the need to reciprocate like that. She was very humble with her reply. I like that."

Jo Toigo, RHIT, CCS
DIRECTOR, HEALTH INFORMATION MANAGEMENT
ST. MARY MEDICAL CENTER
(BEGAN IN 1980 IN GARY)

"...There are so many patients in need and I just feel privileged to be part of such a great facility where we care so much about (them). You know how much suffering goes on. It's a privilege to play a part in helping those families and patients deal with their healthcare challenges. In the best of all worlds, we see great outcomes and the patients are able to return home with their families."

Janice Ryba, CEO AND ADMINISTRATOR
ST. MARY MEDICAL CENTER
(BEGAN IN 1984 AT COMMUNITY HOSPITAL)

THE FIELD OF NURSING – GIVING AND RECEIVING... THEN AND NOW

SAFE IN MY HANDS

"When I teach new nurses, I always say that a patient can tell a lot about you when you touch them. I think that is very important. When I go in to see a patient and say, 'Good morning' with just a handshake, they can tell a lot about me. Or when I tell them, 'I'm going to turn you,' and I put my hands on them to turn them, that patient can tell a lot about me. I like for my patients to know that they can feel secure... and know I am competent in what I am doing. They can then feel safe in my hands. That's what I like patients to know."

Etta Weatherspoon, R.N., M.S, MEDICAL-SURGICAL CLINICIAN
MERCY HOSPITAL | (BEGAN IN 1974 IN GARY)

"I think our nursing care was more than what I ever realized. I recall a patient who was probably in his forties in Gary in the mid-1960s. He had a routine appendectomy and developed gas gangrene and we thought he was going to die. His recovery was awesome. Gas gangrene was unheard of and he was on a routine medical floor. He was so terribly, terribly ill and he was there for a long time. I was working midnights and his dressings had to be changed every two to three hours. When the man got well, Dr. Walt Robinson wrote a note to the nursing staff saying that there was one thing that had saved that man's life and that was the nurses. He was a surgeon. He was a man of few words but I had a lot of respect for him. Everyone did."

Shirley Makivich Urbanek, R.N, RETIRED
ST. MARY MERCY HOSPITAL | (BEGAN IN 1959 IN GARY)

"As director of nursing at Mercy Hospital, one of the biggest issues I encountered in medicine was doctor/nurse relationships. Establishing a respectful, appreciative relationship between physicians and nurses was achieved through dialogue and effective boundaries, yet recognizing and supporting nurse initiatives related to patient care."

Sister Judian Breitenbach, PHJC
FORMER DIRECTOR OF NURSING
MERCY HOSPITAL | (BEGAN IN 1970 IN GARY)

"There was a really loyal, dedicated group that went through a lot over at Gary Mercy. They spent a lot of years really struggling, trying to compete against Methodist Southlake. (If you talked) to a lot of doctors – and they (would) tell you – you could always count on the excellent nurses at St. Mary Medical in Hobart."

John Birdzell
FORMER PRESIDENT OF LAKESHORE HEALTH SYSTEM
(BEGAN IN 1985 WITH ANCILLA SYSTEMS INCORPORATED)

"Nurses are angels in comfortable shoes."
-UNKNOWN

"When I was a kid, I was on my bike and got hit by a car… After I had been bed-ridden… for about four months, I remember asking a nurse if I was ever going to walk again. I guess I was too scared to ask the doctor. And I will never forget it, and I'm 57 now. She said, 'You are going to be able to walk if you get out of bed and start walking.' That day I braced myself and tried to walk and I did a little every day. I ended up playing sports again and everything. I wish I could remember her name. That was the best advice I ever got."

Jesse Bravo, FORMER TELECOMMUNICATIONS TECHNICIAN
ST. MARY MEDICAL CENTER
(BEGAN IN 1992 IN GARY)

"The nurses are the ones dealing with the hardest part of patient care – their pains and their complaints and their infirmities – more than the physicians. They are the ones who have to be there with the patient a lot of the day… and without them the hospital couldn't be here. The care couldn't be here. The physicians are providing some direction and some orders but the nurses are actually doing the care thing."

Scott A. Andrews, M.D., ORTHOPEDIC SURGEON
MEDICAL STAFF PRESIDENT, 2008-2010
(BEGAN IN 1994 IN HOBART)

"My life is in the Education Department and I just wish that people would realize how important education is and how complicated healthcare is nowadays – and keeping up with skills. I don't know if nursing is appreciated. There are so many things for nurses to learn and be on top of so it's a difficult job. It is 365 days a year, 24 hours a day. (Nursing) doesn't take a holiday or vacation. Women and men really dedicate their lives to helping others. It is not a job. It is truly a profession. It is a way of life. It is within you. It's what you want to do and how you feel about people – that interaction with people."

Judy Elieff, DIABETES EDUCATOR, RETIRED
MERCY HOSPITAL
(BEGAN IN 1965 IN GARY)

"Shirley Makivich (Urbanek) was a marvelous head nurse on the third floor when I started working in Hobart. She kept a tight rein on her unit. She could sit in her office down at the end of the hall… and she could hear what was going on at that nurses' station. That is a good distance. She was an excellent example for her girls."

Elizabeth A. Bethel, R.N, IMCU, RETIRED
ST. MARY MEDICAL CENTER | (BEGAN IN 1973 IN HOBART)

In Remembrance – June Pangburn

It's been *Said* in 2009...

"Betty Hill was a registered nurse who recommended (hiring me) for the oncology floor and then June Pangburn later became director of nurses. She stood behind her nurses. Those two persons I remember as being influential in my attitude and care.

"June developed ovarian cancer. She has a memorial stone monument out in the parkway in front of the hospital on the east side here. She was a very caring, personable leader."

Catherine Wiseman, RN, Clinical Case Manager
Acute Rehabilitation Unit, retired | St. Mary Medical Center
(began in 1975 in Hobart)

IN MEMORY OF
JUNE PANGBURN, R.N., B.S.N.
VICE PRESIDENT OF NURSING
YEARS OF SERVICE 1972-1990
ST. MARY MEDICAL CENTER
GARY / HOBART

It's been *Said* in 2009...

"June Pangburn was 45 when she developed ovarian cancer. She had surgery and came to work even though she was in pain. June was determined to put in a full day's work and I was amazed at her strength and courage. I remember one Christmas I helped her bring in Christmas presents for her managers. I could see she was not having a good day and suggested she return home, but she insisted on staying and told me this was going to be a very good Christmas. She passed away the following month and I believe she knew her death was imminent. June was a remarkable person. Her daughters formed a nursing scholarship in her name which is still in existence."

Dee Bedella, Coordinator, Sleep Lab/Community Liaison
St. Mary Medical Center
(began in 1988 in Hobart)

Nursing Today

According to the U.S. Department of Labor in 2009, the demand for nurses has been increasing for several years, spurred on by various economic and demographic factors. The demand for nurses is expected to increase by 23% between 2006 and 2016. Nursing jobs that are in the highest demand include registered nurses, licensed practical nurses, certified nurse assistants, and certified medical assistants.

It's been *Said* in 2009...

"The nurses, I think, are some of the best I've ever worked with. I've worked in probably 25 different hospitals and I've never found nurses that were better.

"I trained at Rush. I was at M.D. Anderson Cancer Center. These are 1,000-bed institutions and the quality of care provided on a day-to-day basis for patients in this community hospital easily compares – you couldn't find a better place."

Mark Simaga, M.D., Neurologist
St. Mary Medical Center
(began in 1997 in Hobart)

NURSING ADMINISTRATION STAFF PHOTO – 2009
SHOWN (L-R): Heidi Smith, administrative assistant; Kathleen Carrico, lead nursing supervisor: Vice President and Chief Nursing Officer Tammie R. Finn-Jones; and Deborah Krejci, manager, Systems & Regulatory Quality

NATIONAL NURSES WEEK – PILLAR AWARDS

St. Mary Medical Center 2009 Nursing Pillar Awards were presented during National Nurses Week. The awards recognized each nurse's contribution in five categories – Service, Quality, Finance, Growth, and People – that represent the foundation of the hospital's operational goals and mission of care
FRONT ROW (L-R): Therese Dristas, RN; Thelma Mariano, RN; CEO and Administrator Janice L. Ryba; Vice President and Chief Nursing Officer Tammie R. Finn-Jones; Kindra Rodgers, RN and Danielle Geib, RN.
BACK ROW (L-R): Nurse managers Kelly Loudermilk, RN; Shannon Blaney, RN; Beth Navarro, RN and Betty Lane, RN
NOT PICTURED: Quality award winner Lynelle Sibich, RN

Employer Choice Award – Top Five

Advance for Nurses, a publication of Greater Chicago, Wisconsin, and Indiana, compiled an *ADVANCE Readers Choice* survey in which it said, "There are plenty of lists that rank hospitals based on outcomes, awards and having top doctors, but those good things don't always trickle down enough to make working as a nurse in the facility a postitive experience."

In the survey, nurses were asked to rank hospitals in categories that would make a difference to them – quality of care, organizational culture, communication, professional development, and retention efforts. St. Mary Medical Center and Illinois Masonic Medical Center were the only two hospitals to be ranked in all five categories.

Removing boundaries and fostering communication are most important. St. Mary Medical Center was described as a facility that builds on the notion of giving nurses a voice, promoting monthly staff meetings and town hall meetings as an opportunity to give nurses a voice. At the town hall meetings where hospital updates and future plans are explained, nurses can question meeting moderators about issues and daily needs with responses posted for everyone on the hospital intranet.

It's been *Said* in 2009...

"I think the biggest challenge for me in my role with nursing is the rapid change in science and technology. We are starting to see patients who have more serious sickness here at St. Mary. Our case mix index is going up to demonstrate that. The challenge is bringing nursing to that next level.

"There is a large geriatric population but we're getting more patients because they are happier when they come here. Physicians like to bring their patients here. We used to be passed up because St. Mary was perceived to be a small community hospital. I think there is a greater confidence level in our abilities so they're challenging us with sicker patients. It is a multitude of factors – the aging population and the level of obesity, diabetes, and all the other co-morbidities that come along with that. I also think it is due to the confidence that the medical staff has in nursing care and the technologies we have that are starting to bring in more patients."

Tammie R. Finn-Jones
Vice President and Chief Nursing Officer
St. Mary Medical Center | (began in 2007 in Hobart)

"Nurses are I.V. Leaguers!"
~ Unknown

2008 and 2009
HOSPITAL/COMMUNITY HAPPENINGS

IT'S BEEN *Said* IN 2009...

VOICES OF MEDICINE

"We are at a critical junction of medicine in general in the United States... and I think the key is what the government has in store for us. We are in a very trying time for healthcare and I think as physicians we have to stand up and really have our voices heard because we are going to be in deep trouble if we don't do that. We are very poor at organizing ourselves to get our word out to express what is important. The bottom line is what happens to the patient."

Zlatan Stepanovic, M.D., CARDIOLOGIST
DIRECTOR OF CONGESTIVE HEART FAILURE CLINIC
ST. MARY MEDICAL CENTER
(BEGAN IN 1997 IN HOBART)

COMPASS AWARDS

In 2008, St. Mary Medical Center was awarded two Press Ganey Compass Awards for patient satisfaction improvements in the areas of Ambulatory Surgery and Outpatient Services.

A WORD FROM THE HOBART CHAMBER OF COMMERCE

Mike Adams
Executive Director
Hobart Chamber
of Commerce

IT'S BEEN *Said* IN 2010...

"St Mary Medical Center is the largest employer in Hobart and the major provider of healthcare but that just touches the surface. St Mary's is a 'Great Neighbor'! Virtually every event in Hobart enjoys the sponsorship of the medical center as well as the participation of its employees. From a more personal perspective, St. Mary's is a gathering place for the welcoming of new life, and providing a lifetime of healthcare to the gentle passing of our loved ones. One also notes that St. Mary's is a place where Hobart residents can participate. The volunteer programs are very important to a myriad of senior citizens.

"From a personal perspective, my sister, Christine (Adams) Caplinger graduated from St. Mary's School of Nursing in 1958 and that event changed her life for the better in more ways that can be listed here. Finally, did I mention that in 1949 I entered this life into the loving hands of St. Mary's staff?"

Mike Adams, EXECUTIVE DIRECTOR, HOBART CHAMBER OF COMMERCE

Marking Time...

2008
- *The Federal Reserve bank cut interest rates by .75% in response to the global market plunge – the largest single-day reduction in the bank's history.*
- *U.S. suffered 4,000th soldier death in Iraq war (Mar.23).*
- *In Beijing, U.S. Swimmer Michael Phelps became first athlete in Olympic history to win 11 career gold medals.*
- *Barack Obama was elected the 44th U.S president – the first African American to do so.*

2009
- *U.S. Airways Flight 1549 crashed into the Hudson River after allegedly striking a flock of geese. All 155 aboard survived (Jan. 15).*

2008 – LARGE BUSINESS OF THE YEAR AWARD

BUSINESS OF THE YEAR
PICTURED (L-R): Hobart Chamber of Commerce Executive Director
Mike Adams; St. Mary Medical Center CEO and Administrator
Janice L. Ryba; and U.S. Representative Pete Visclosky, D-Merrillville.

St. Mary Medical Center was named the 2008 Large Business of the Year by the Hobart Chamber of Commerce. Chamber Executive Director, Mike Adams, recognized the hospital's exceptional support for the community through sponsorships, volunteers, employment opportunities, and a commitment to the quality of life for Hobart residents through extraordinary medical care. U.S. Representative Pete Visclosky, D-Merrillville, presented the hospital with a citation entered into the U.S. Congressional Record.

"St. Mary has a strong tradition of community support and we're honored to receive this award and citation," said Janice L. Ryba, CEO and administrator of St. Mary Medical Center. "True excellence in healthcare means going beyond our hospital walls to build strong business and neighborhood partnerships that are fundamental to the goals we share in building healthier communities."

2009 – A WORD FROM THE MAYOR – BRIAN SNEDECOR

Brian Keith Snedecor
Mayor, City of Hobart

"I was 13 years old and living in Gary when the hospital was first built in Hobart. Since then, and more recently with Community Healthcare System being on board, the leadership of St. Mary has been commendable. We are proud of continued progress with several additions and specialized quality services.

"There is a close partnership between the city of Hobart and St. Mary Medical Center which I refer to as the 'medical community'– in place for a viable future infrastructure. We work closely within the framework of public safety and quality-of-life issues, particularly with our emergency ambulance service provider.

"With the continued demand for quality healthcare, I look forward to continued growth at our Hobart hospital. The emergence of more specialized care means that local patients no longer have to travel to Chicago and other areas for treatment.

"Our medical needs are now met right here in Hobart's own 'back yard'. Staff members treat patients with love and care. They are true professionals!"

Brian Keith Snedecor, MAYOR, CITY OF HOBART

IT'S BEEN *Said* IN 2009...

"For St. Mary Medical Center, healthcare isn't just about a patient's acute illness that brings them to the doors of our facility... Because we are a non-profit, community-based organization, we are here to help them... across the continuum of care. This includes outpatient services, home health care, education and a wide variety of community health services. Healthcare is about improving and, in some cases, sustaining a patient's quality of life.

"Families need to feel comforted by a high-quality facility that is easily accessible to them and their families. We emphasize access... because there is tremendous emotional strain on a family when a patient needs care (and) we need to provide services on a local level whenever possible. A dominant aspect of our mission is to continue to grow and mutually meet the needs of our community."

Janice Ryba, CEO AND ADMINISTRATOR | ST. MARY MEDICAL CENTER
(BEGAN IN 1985 AT COMMUNITY HOSPITAL)

National Recognition – Thomson Reuters

In 2009, through Thomson Reuter's *100 Top Hospitals: Health Systems Quality/Efficiency Study*, Community Healthcare System received national recognition for hospital quality and efficiency as one of the nation's top performing health systems. It was the only healthcare system in Northwest Indiana ranked in the top 50 by this new study that highlights the potential of health systems and their impact on the quality of healthcare.

The hospitals of Community Healthcare System – Community Hospital in Munster, St. Catherine in East Chicago, and St. Mary Medical Center in Hobart – were each involved in this quality analysis by Thomson Reuters, with follow-up information published in August 2009 in *Modern Healthcare Magazine*. It found significant contrasts between high and low-performing systems in terms of patient survival, complication, patient safety, and how quickly patients may return to daily activities.

The Chanute Prize

Community Healthcare System's team members were recognized in 2009 with the Chanute Prize for their innovative same-day results initiative.

Standing (l-r): Mike Marocchi, supervisor, CT/MR/US, St. Mary Medical Center; Kelli Dijak, operations director, Systems Laboratory, Community Hospital; Glyn Porter, M.D., medical director, Laboratory, St. Mary Medical Center; Sheila Miller, general specialist, Pathology, Community Hospital; Pete Dyba, director of Imaging Services, St. Mary Medical Center; Suzanne Ruiz, RN, M.S. NP-C, breast health navigator, Women's Diagnostic Center; Anthony "Tony" Costello, Ph.D, site director, Laboratory, St. Mary Medical Center; Jayesh Thakrar, M.D., director of radiology, St. Mary Medical Center.

Seated (l-r): Brenda Eriksen, M.D., medical director, Laboratory, Community Hospital; Janice L. Ryba, CEO and administrator, St. Mary Medical Center; and Mary Nicholson, M.D., medical director, Women's Diagnostic Center. *Vim & Vigor*, FALL 2009

"THE SECRET OF JOY IN WORK IS CONTAINED IN ONE WORD — EXCELLENCE. TO KNOW HOW TO DO SOMETHING WELL IS TO ENJOY IT."

~ Pearl Buck

A Visit from Sister Jolise May, PHJC
General Superior of the International Congregation of the
Poor Handmaids of Jesus Christ

IT'S BEEN *Said* IN 2009...

Shown here during Sister Jolise May's visit to Northwest Indiana in June 2009, (l-r) are: Toni Mola, administrator, Ancilla Systems Incorporated; Sister Jolise May, PHJC, general superior of the International Congregation of the Poor Handmaids of Jesus Christ; and Sister Mary Ellen Goeller, PHJC, regional director, Mission Integration, St. Catherine Hospital and St. Mary Medical Center.

"God bless Mr. Powers. In the mission statement it is caring for the poor and vulnerable and that is part of who we are. It has only become stronger... Mr. Powers had the vision... to do these kinds of things.

"With one visionary by himself, however, nothing is going to happen. If you have a whole line of visionaries who can talk to each other and work together, then I think we can fulfill the whole picture and not just a piece of it. It takes everyone to have a good health system in their area. I really believe that."

Sister Jolise May, PHJC
General Superior of the International
Congregation of the Poor Handmaids
of Jesus Christ
Dernbach, Germany

Jubilarians of the Poor Handmaids of Jesus Christ
PHJC Sisters Boeving, Quinn, Schleper, and Weiner

In honor of the 2009 Jubilarians of the Poor Handmaids of Jesus Christ, a gathering of friends, family members, and longtime associates took place on May 16, 2009, at the Motherhouse in Donaldson, Indiana. Among those recognized were PHJC Sisters Bertram and Wilma Boeving for 60 years and Sister Kathleen Quinn, PHJC, for 60 years. The celebration included a Eucharistic Liturgy at the Ancilla Domini Chapel. Sister Georgine Schleper, PHJC, was also honored for 60 years in 2010 and Sister Nola Weiner, PHJC, was honored for 75 years.

Sister Bertram Boeving, PHJC
60-year Jubilee celebration
Word Gathering, SUMMER, 2009

Sister Kathleen Quinn, PHJC
60-year Jubilee celebration
Word Gathering, SUMMER, 2009

Sister Wilma Boeving, PHJC
60-year Jubilee celebration
Word Gathering, SUMMER, 2009

2009 – Doing unto Others – Unger and Lessard

Helen Unger (left) and Rae Lessard agreed to this photo with the hope that others would be inspired to donate handcrafted items to the hospital. Helen has sewn more than 350 surgical caps, many of which have been given to St. Mary Medical Center pediatric patients. Helen has made more than 85 afghans and Rae has joined her friend with afghans, baby items, and hand knit hats.

August 18, 2009

Speaking the Same Language

It's been *Said* in 2009...

"I used to have to speak to my dad in Serbian so I have some knowledge of the language. I would be asked to interpret a little when patients came in. I had an incident once where they were having a problem with a patient and they didn't understand him. He was of Slovak descent. Because of the depth of his medical condition, I called my mother, Amelia Orlich, and my aunt, Mildred Chulibrk, to discuss his medical situation with him. He was grateful to be able to express his concerns. The patient had both his legs amputated. The hospital assisted this patient in obtaining medical assistance, getting him fitted with prostheses for both legs, and placing him in a senior high rise. This was probably the most traumatic of all my patient-related incidents."

Joni Bucko
Financial Counselor, retired
St. Mary Medical Center
(began in 1975 in Gary)

It's been *Said* in 2009...

"A few years ago, the (number of Spanish speaking) Latin patients was very limited, but now more have made this their hospital. I'm one of the few Latins in my department and you can just see the relief on their faces because there is somebody here who could understand. A lot of them don't speak English. They need us and I am going to be there for them. They call me to the Emergency Room, they call me to the catheterization lab, and they call me wherever needed."

Beverly Armenta
Coordinator Radiology Support, Radiology
Mercy Hospital
(began in 1972 in Gary)

Education and Opportunity

Did you know?

In 1971, under Administrator Paul Bellendorf, employees were introduced to a tuition reimbursement program that would encourage continuing education in programs related to their present jobs or other hospital-related careers.

It's been *Said* in 2009...

"There were four of us from Indiana University who were looking for a place to start our internships and one of the guys was from Gary, so we visited Mercy Hospital along with two or three other hospitals in the area and we liked what we saw. We kind of liked the Mercy staff. They seemed to be very welcoming. John Gallinatti was the one from Gary and we were with Andrew Russo and Richard Philbert."

Dr. John O. Carter, M.D., Family Practice | Lake George Medical Center
(began in 1956 at Mercy Hospital as an Intern)

"We had the best of both worlds at St Mary, extensive clinical experience and a full load of college courses from St. Joseph's College. While I'm sure I am biased, I feel the diploma program afforded students the best preparation and experiences for the realities of the nursing profession."

Connie McCarthy Blaine, RN, BSHA
DIRECTOR OF QUALITY MANAGEMENT, RETIRED
ST. MARY MERCY HOSPITAL
(BEGAN IN 1963 IN GARY)

"I wanted to go to college but there were 10 of us. I wanted to be a CPA, but my father didn't have money to send me to college; and nursing at that time was probably about $300 a year so I went into nursing. Nursing is really my niche.

"As my mother, Cornelia Styles, would tell me when I would come home complaining about how busy we were and what a hard day I had, she would tell me, 'Be patient with the patients because one day you might be a patient.' That is something I never forgot."

Flora Dean Meeks, RN
RADIOLOGY, RETIRED
MERCY HOSPITAL | (BEGAN IN 1960 IN GARY)

"My dear mother, Rosemary Knapp Beckham… delivered me at Mercy Hospital with Dr. Carl Bendler's expertise at 11:50p.m., 10 minutes prior to St. Patrick's Day. Being of Irish heritage, my late father, Malachy Beckham, was wishing for a son who would be born on St. Patrick's Day. For the daughter who was born on March 16th, however, Dr. Bendler's professional fee was a bottle of White Horse scotch!

"My mother is a 1934 graduate of St. Mary's Mercy School of Nursing and, as a new graduate nurse, worked in direct patient care throughout the hospital on 12-hour shifts. She also did private duty for affluent patients when the hospital patient census was down.

"In 1955, Rosemary enrolled in the University of Chicago hospital's Refresher Course for RNs. After completion of this program, she was able to pass naso-gastric tubes, monitor blood pressures, and do intravenous procedures. At that time, only physicians in the Calumet area took blood pressures and started IVs."

Rosemary Beckham Ofsaiof
ST. MARY'S MERCY SCHOOL OF NURSING
(CLASS OF 1961)

"Education is simply the soul of a society as it passes from one generation to another."
~ Gilbert Keith Chesterton

"This job here at St. Mary has helped me raise and support my children, helped me buy a home, helped me put my daughter through school, and still be able to provide. It's all due to St. Mary's. I bought my home by myself with three kids. I am grateful. I have never taken my job for granted and I even tell my boss now that if it ever comes up where they want to eliminate my position, I will be glad to take any position that is open within the hospital. I want to stay with St. Mary's. I can't imagine working anywhere else."

Beverly Armenta
COORDINATOR RADIOLOGY SUPPORT, RADIOLOGY
MERCY HOSPITAL
(BEGAN IN 1972 IN GARY)

"I have been with St. Mary since March 1973. I started at the Gary campus in the storeroom and transferred to the storeroom in Hobart. I could not speak English when I was hired but my girlfriend helped me get my job through the storeroom manager. I took classes while working at St. Mary and learned how to speak English. Today, St. Mary's offers Spanish classes to our employees. When the storeroom split into two departments, I worked in Central Sterilization until 10 years ago when I transferred to the Registration Department."

Minerva Yanez
REGISTRATION REPRESENTATIVE
ST. MARY MEDICAL CENTER
(BEGAN IN 1973 IN GARY)

Shown here is Bettie Robinson at her desk abstracting charts.

"I worked in Medical Records at the Gary facility for more than 20 years and retired in 1995 as Release of Information Clerk and ICD-9 Coder. My most important experience with St. Mary Medical Center was the opportunity to attend college and excel in my career as a Health Information manager.

"What is so different today in the department is that most facilities utilize electronic medical records with the records stored on disk for future reference."

Bettie Robinson
RELEASE OF INFORMATION CLERK AND ICD-9 CODER
RETIRED
MERCY HOSPITAL | (BEGAN IN 1973 IN GARY)

A STORY OF DETERMINATION

"I came to the United States to pursue a dream of being a medical technologist. I was accepted as a student at the Gary facility of St. Mary Medical Center in 1977. All alone in a new place was very difficult but humbling. During the first few months, I lived at various Filipino homes. It was through the help of Sue Demitroulas, then the program coordinator, and Sister Wilma (Boeving, PHJC) that I was able to have a permanent residence – the third floor of the hospital building across from the hospital. I stayed there for five years. The nuns of the Poor Handmaids of Jesus Christ – Sisters Philomene, Bertram, and Wilma – have nurtured and assisted me throughout those years.

"The now defunct School of Medical Technology, directed by Dr. Earl Mason, was known in the area to be of high standards and high expectations. It provided a $150.00 stipend with free lunch. It allowed some students, including me, to work as phlebotomists after six months of training. I worked mainly in the evening shift.

"I was fortunate to find employment at St. Mary after my graduation. I was so excited. I said to myself, 'I will make my parents proud. Their sacrifices to put me through school will not go in vain.' And I did!"

Elizabeth Yee
VICE PRESIDENT, CLINICAL ANCILLARY SERVICES
COMMUNITY HOSPITAL
(BEGAN IN 1977 IN GARY)

"I am where I am today as executive director of Haven House Domestic Violence Shelter because of the opportunities that St. Mary gave me. I have my master's degree because I was able to apply for reimbursement from the hospital to acquire (it). I was working full-time and going to IU Northwest. I have the skill level with patient/client care with families because of my experience and training at St. Mary's. I was able to get licensed, too. I am forever grateful for St. Mary's.

"For a lot of us, St. Mary's was really a springboard. I hated to see the hospital close but many of us got opportunities in life. I run into people who are old co-workers I have known over the years. None of us really ever said good-bye to St. Mary's."

Lisa Wein
FORMER OUTPATIENT MANAGER
ALCOHOLISM TREATMENT PROGRAM, ST. MARY MEDICAL CENTER
(BEGAN IN 1978 IN GARY)

"I really enjoy working in healthcare. When I worked in Quality Management, I was exposed to the legal end of healthcare with malpractice suits and things of that nature. That exposure encouraged me to go back to school and become a Paralegal. For a period of time I worked at the Ancilla Systems corporate office and then I returned to St. Mary Medical Center-Hobart as a Contract Specialist/Paralegal. Currently I work with the physician contracts for all the Community Healthcare System hospitals and serve on various committees, all of which have enhanced my passion for healthcare and helping others."

Carol Ochwat
CONTRACT SPECIALIST
COMMUNITY FOUNDATION OF NORTHWEST INDIANA, INC.
(BEGAN IN 1981 IN GARY)

"When I was a medical student, (Mercy Hospital) actually was a fun place to learn... It was sort of like what Forrest Gump said – like a box of chocolates where you never knew what you were going to see. There were days when you had two hospitals in Gary and U.S. Steel had something like 30,000 employees. It was not unusual to see some really major trauma from the mills and then see a woman giving birth. It was the whole (gamut) of things – gunshot wounds, knifings – and a learning repository if you knew who to follow around. We as medical students all gravitated to a fellow by the name of Jack Kamen because he would sit and teach you and treat you like you actually knew something when you didn't know anything. John Scully was another one and Bob Martino and Phillip Kellar were all into mentoring of medical students.

"There are things that Dr. Scully and Dr. Kamen taught me that I still use. I have nurses and therapists look at me like, 'Where... did you learn that? You are an orthopedic surgeon; you are not supposed to know stuff like this.' The adage says that you are a doctor first and an orthopedic surgeon second."

Joe Koscielniak, MD., ORTHOPEDIC SURGEON
MERCY HOSPITAL (EXTERN)
(BEGAN IN 1984 IN HOBART)

A MOM'S COLLEGE EXPERIENCE

"I was 39 years old when my husband died in 1999 and I needed a future to care for my two young children. With a high school education, but no college experience, something drew me to Purdue University Calumet. Terrified of setting foot on campus, I managed to complete a sociology class with a good grade and went on to do well in three more classes the following semester. I paid for all of my classes on my own and did not know of any help available with tuition expenses. Eventually, however, I completed a Federal Assistance Student Financial Aid (FASFA) form, and received my first award letter that would cover tuition, books and some miscellaneous expenses.

"With enough pre-requisites out of the way, I introduced myself to the dean of the Nursing Department and was soon accepted into their program. In 2002, I entered the Best and Brightest Program offered by Community Healthcare System. It was a program for future graduates to determine which area of the hospital they liked. I chose St Mary to follow nurses on their units and visit different departments. I saw a fascinating procedure of the heart in the catheterization lab and the electrophysiology lab. I had always wanted to be a nurse and was pleased to be hired by the IMCU nurse manager as a Nurse Fellow in January, 2003, while I finished school. After I graduated in 2004 and began working at St. Mary's, I met Lynelle Sibich, RN, who helped me get oriented to the unit and became my mentor.

"I have worked for the past 5 ½ years and I still go to Lynelle if I have a question. This past year our floor transitioned from one to two separate units – known as IMCU and the new Medical Telemetry Unit. I now assist the manager and serve as clinical nurse leader for the 2West Medical/Telemetry Unit.

"You're never too old to learn something new. Just go out there and do it."

Donna Lynch, RN, CLINICAL NURSE LEADER
2WEST MEDICAL/TELEMETRY UNIT
ST. MARY MEDICAL CENTER | (BEGAN IN 2004 IN HOBART)

EDUCATION AND CUPID

"My son, David Coil, went to IU Northwest as an undergraduate. (His initial application)... to medical school... was not accepted so he got a job at the Hobart hospital as an orderly. This was around 1994 and he worked in the Emergency Room and in ICU for one year. The next year he was accepted at Downers Grove Osteopathic School. His future wife, Tammy, was working as a new nurse on the fifth floor and a relative of hers who worked in ICU with David said that Tammy would be a good gal for David. They all knew David and they all knew Tammy so they kind of... the two started dating. David went off to medical school and Tammy hung in there during those four years. Now she is Tammy Coil."

Phyllis Mattingly Coil, RN
FORMER STAFF NURSE, EMERGENCY ROOM
MERCY HOSPITAL
(BEGAN IN 1952 IN GARY)

• THEN AND NOW

STROKE CENTER OF EXCELLENCE...

Contributed by Kimberly Sgouroudis, RN, BSN
Stroke Coordinator

Kimberly Sgouroudis
Stroke Coordinator

St. Mary Medical Center has spent many years researching the need for a stroke program. Stroke is the third leading cause of death in America, affecting over 700,000 people each year. On September 8, 2009, the Stroke Program at St. Mary Medical Center began.

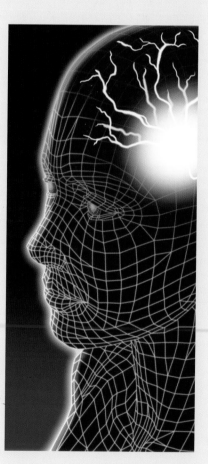

The program focus is to provide urgent, comprehensive and consistent care to stroke patients through detection, prevention, diagnosis and treatment. All patients with a diagnosis of stroke or TIA (Transient Ischemic Attack) will follow a specific protocol related to stroke. The protocol encompasses many facets of the stroke team which consist of neurologists, stroke coordinator, intensive care, acute care, rehabilitation, radiology, laboratory, pharmacy, physical therapy, occupational therapy, speech/language pathology and case management. A multi-disciplinary team of professionals has developed diagnostic tools to provide consistent care of stroke patients. Patients will benefit from state-of-the-art diagnostic testing including CT (Computed Tomography), CTA (Computed Tomography Angiogram), MRI (Magnetic Resonance Imaging), and MRA (Magnetic Resonance Angiogram). The medical director of the Stroke Program has expertise in stroke and oversees the program. The process of data entry into a national database will allow us to stay informed of best practices and receive direct feedback.

Through the dedication and support provided by the multi-disciplinary team, physicians, and administration here at St. Mary Medical Center, our Stroke Program will be the first disease-specific program requesting recognition by The Joint Commission as a Primary Stroke Center.

SOMETHING NEW IN SURGERY – SMARTRACK SYSTEM

FAMILY NOTICE		
✓	BIRTHDATE	ID #
☐	9/11/1934	530520
☐	3/21/1935	534295
☐	1/28/1936	533548
☐	4/27/1937	531811
☐	8/10/1937	530721
☐	5/2/1939	526442
☐	4/3/1942	532549
☐	12/14/1945	527634
☐	2/23/1947	534031
☐	10/15/1947	521010
☐	12/7/1949	531772
☐	9/29/1953	532193
☐	8/29/1955	531353
☐	11/11/1955	532175
☐	12/16/1955	527628
☐	11/20/1961	533563
☐	1/22/1962	518307
☐	4/10/1962	527113
☐	4/30/1965	527629
☐	5/23/1965	533905

In place at St. Mary Medical Center is a new SmarTrack system that allows family members to track their patient during surgery and know exactly where he/she is at all times. The interactive patient tracking technology, available in waiting rooms, updates the status of patients as they move from a pre-operative area to holding rooms, then through surgery and back to recovery rooms. Patient identity is listed by anonymous number.

"While it won't replace our personal approach or surgical staff updates every hour, families can look at a screen and know the status of their loved one at any time during their wait," said Karen Gerke, director of surgery. "It's very reassuring to them."

The new SmarTrack System offers interactive tracking technology so loved ones may follow a patient during surgery.

THE ST. MARY MEDICAL CENTER BOARD OF DIRECTORS

THE ST. MARY MEDICAL CENTER BOARD OF DIRECTORS – 2010
STANDING (L-R): Peggy Buffington, Ph.D.; Attorney Nick Thiros; Peter Mavrelis, M.D.; Kenneth Krupinski; John Burton; Scott Andrews, M.D.; Bill Joiner; and Sister Michele Dvorak, PHJC
SEATED (L-R): Lisa Field; Linda Buzinec; William Schenck; and CEO and Administrator Janice L. Ryba
NOT PICTURED: Milton Gasparis, M.D.; and Judge James Moody

Marking Time...2010

- A 7.0 magnitude earthquake ripped through Port-au-Prince, the capital of Haiti; over 200,000 killed (Feb. 9).

- March 23, 2010 – Following months of legislative debate, the Affordable Care Act became law. Shortly thereafter, www.HealthReform.gov was archived.

IT'S BEEN *Said* IN 2009...

"I think St. Mary Medical Center is going to become the cornerstone of healthcare on the east side of the county. I think it is just starting to hit its stride in terms of the building projects. Their progress is excellent. They have a great board of directors. They have a lot of long term employees who are dedicated to providing excellent services to our patients."

Lou Molina
VICE PRESIDENT FINANCE AND
CHIEF FINANCIAL OFFICER, COMMUNITY HOSPITAL
(BEGAN IN 1986 IN GARY)

LONGEVITY WITH HONOR – EMPLOYEES WHO SHINE

Undoubtedly there are thousands of employees, past and present, who have dedicated a lot of time to St. Mary Medical Center in both Gary and Hobart. While all of you are too numerous to mention, this section of the book honors ALL of you by naming a few – individually and in general.

IT'S BEEN *Said* IN 2009...

"From the standpoint of a physician, we do not spend all day long and all night long in the hospital. The people who are really important here are the nurses and the techs and the ancillary professionals who are at the hospital all day long. Having the group that we have makes it a heck of a lot easier to take care of somebody through a major illness or injury."

Joe Koscielniak, MD., ORTHOPEDIC SURGEON
MERCY HOSPITAL (EXTERN) | (BEGAN IN 1984 IN HOBART)

THIRTY YEARS AND COUNTING

Shown here are employees who began February 15, 1960 through October 29, 1979 and reached 30 years by December 31, 2009.
FRONT ROW (L-R): Linda Adler, Beverly Armenta, Susan Boney, Deborah Brink, Cindy Brito, and Joanne Budzevska
SECOND ROW (L-R): Helen Urban, Sandra Childs, Mary Constandars, Thera Dean, Claudia Dixon, Karen Gerke, and Anita Gerodimos
THIRD ROW (L-R): Paula Valentine, Patty Gutowski, JoAnn Haas, Bobbi Homola, Julie Konja, Derek Long, Cindy Macko, and Davaga Magee
FOURTH ROW (L-R): Joanne Zickuhr, Chris McGrew, Jacqueline Pratl, Antonia Reed, Melissa Saroff, Kristine Shocaroff, Lorraine Thomas, and Pamala Woodward

THIRTY YEARS AND COUNTING

Shown here is another group of employees who began February 15, 1960, through October 29, 1979, and reached 30 years by December 31, 2009.
FRONT ROW (L-R): Karen Bain, Charlotte Barber, Janet Barefield, Kathleen Barlog, Tessie Biscocho, and Carol Burns
SECOND ROW (L-R): Jil Cannon, Anthony "Tony" Costello, Ana Dabu, Sue Demitroulas, Annette Doyen, Karen Filko, and Tom Post
THIRD ROW (L-R): Ruben Santana, Beatrice Flores, Joy James, Jackie Juskevice, Irene Ortiz, Irene Pacheco, and Sampaguita Youngren
FOURTH ROW (L-R): Minerva Yanez, Sandy Wytovicz, Rosa Semovski, Pam Taylor, Dennis Williams, and Joyce Williams
NOT PICTURED: Sherry Brewer, Susan Chandler, Marilou Delacruz, Judith Garza, Martha Gibson, Bruce Grant, Cecelia Hartgraves, Barbara Haviza, Glenn Hepp, Diana Huminsky, Deborah Husek, Jowanna Ivy, Charlene King, Deborah Krejci, John Laskowski, Carolyn Lewis, Brenda Maupin, Patricia Nescak, James Nettles, Alberta Nettles, Charlene Neyhart, Darla Robinson, Lucy Rodriguez, Rosemarie Schmelter, Cheryl Smolinski, Diane Surma, Karleen Sutkowski, Carla Szarkowicz, James Wade, Sandra Wiechnik, Beatrice Williams, and Linda Wronko

Longtime Service

Ten years later in 2005, Jim Wade (far right) was recognized as the sole 45-year St. Mary Medical Center employee. Several 35-year honorees were (l-r) Susan Chandler, Brenda Maupin, and Marcia Keilman. Judy Elieff was a 40-year honoree.

Reprinted by permission of the *Post-Tribune*, MARCH, 2005

Among those from St. Mary Medical Center honored for 35 years of service were (l-r): Jim Blaine and Jim Wade of Plant Operations, and Ernestine Bell, Laboratory/Chemistry.

At the end of 1995, more than 193 associates from St. Mary Medical Center and St. Catherine Hospital were recognized for their years of service.

"Thanks to their dedication, expertise, and compassion, the hospitals of Lakeshore Health System are leaders in providing quality, state-of-the-art medical care to the residents of Northwest Indiana," said Joseph M. Mark, CEO of Lakeshore Health System.

Summary, NOVEMBER/DECEMBER 1995

IT'S BEEN *Said* IN 2009...

"Anybody who stays with an organization over 40 years is committed to it. It has been a wonderful organization to work for. I have been lucky to have been provided with many opportunities and challenges. I have had the opportunity to work with many talented and motivated people."

Sue Demitroulas
BUSINESS ANALYST, IT DEPARTMENT
MERCY HOSPITAL
(BEGAN IN 1967 IN GARY)

Family Physicians

In 1986, Raymond Carmody, M.D. and Joseph Sala, M.D. were honored by St. Mary Medical Center for serving 50 years on the medical staff. The 100 combined years of these physicians was increased by additional family members – Timothy Carmody, M.D., son of Raymond Carmody, M.D., who joined the St. Mary Medical Center staff in 1983, and Walter Sala, M.D., brother of Joseph Sala, M.D., who joined the St. Mary Medical Center staff in 1945.

All in the Family

John O. Carter, M.D. (father) – Family Practice – joined the staff July 1, 1957.
Mark Carter, M.D. (son) – Family Practice – joined the staff July 15, 1988.
John E. Carter, M.D. (son) – Family Practice – joined the staff June 30, 1993.

John T. Scully, M.D. (father, retired) – Internist – joined the staff from October 11, 1955 to August 31, 2000.
Sharon Harig, M.D. (daughter) – Internal Medicine/Pulmonary Medicine – joined the staff September 18, 1986.

Prinn Stang, M.D. (father) – Obstetrics-Gynecology – joined the staff September 20, 1979.
Perkin K. Stang, M.D. (son) – Family Practice/Obstetrics-Gynecology – joined the staff September 1, 2007.

Stephen K. Grandfield, D.P.M. (father) – Podiatry – joined the staff September 15, 1977.
Christopher Grandfield, D.P.M. (son) – Podiatry – joined the staff September 30, 1999.

Gerald Thomas, M.D. (father, retired) – General Surgery – joined the staff from August 19, 1950 to September 18, 1992.
Hartley Thomas, M.D. (son) – Emergency Medicine – joined the staff from November 17, 1995 to September 24, 2002.

A 55-Year Certificate

A Service Award Presentation

Mercy Hospital Administrator Paul R. Kaiser presents a 55-Year Certificate to Sister Willibalda Heidt, PHJC, (right) as 35-year veteran Florence Patchell and 20-year veteran Dorothy Kisylia look on. The Annual Service Award Presentation took place at Teibel's Restaurant in Schererville on November 5, 1973.

"I began working as a file clerk at St. Mary's in Gary in September 1973 right out of high school. I had to take a typing test on a manual typewriter. I was nervous but I got the position. Mr. Bob Nichols was my boss and Paul Kaiser was the administrator. I swore up and down that I was only going to work there for five years. Here I am almost 36 years later."

Irene Pacheco
PATIENT FINANCIAL COUNSELOR
PATIENT FINANCIAL SERVICES
ST. MARY MEDICAL CENTER
(BEGAN IN 1973 IN GARY)

"I lived out this way and Methodist Hospital at Southlake wasn't open at that time so I came here and it was going to be a temporary job until Methodist opened. Thirty-five years later I'm still here. I love St. Mary."

Sherry Brewer, R.N., PhD, DIRECTOR, QUALITY RISK MANAGEMENT
ST. MARY MEDICAL CENTER | (BEGAN IN 1974 IN HOBART)

"I remember St. Mary's in Gary so well in the 1980s because I had to graduate mid-term due to a policy President Ronald Reagan put into place. Seniors in high school who were receiving Social Security benefits were required to graduate in the middle of the school year and enroll in a college. I enrolled in Ivy Tech until I received my associate's degree as an administrative secretary and began working as a student intern at St. Mary in the personnel department. I enjoyed my internship and met so many beautiful people that I wanted to remain. After completing my internship, they hired me as a clerk typist in 1985 and I have been here ever since in various positions.

"My goal was to work at St. Mary's for five years – long enough to be vested with a pension. Somehow five years turned into 24 years! St. Mary has always been a very close-knit family and you can feel the camaraderie among the employees. From then until now, I have made many lifelong friends. I always try my best to work with everyone I come in contact with."

Debra Jenkins, REGIONAL ASSISTANT OF MISSION EFFECTIVENESS
ST. MARY MEDICAL CENTER | (BEGAN IN 1985 IN GARY)

"My memories of the Gary hospital go back to before I worked there. My aunt, Julia Ihnat, worked there for 43 years. She was a Labor and Delivery nurse. My mother, Marguerite McMahon, worked there. She graduated from St. Mary's Diploma Program in Gary and she met my father, Ted Ihnat, there. He was a policeman...

"They got married and had kids. My family is very religious. We frequently went to the hospital and we would go to the chapel. The grotto is a really big memory from when I was probably three years old. I remember that distinctly. I would go there with my mom and my aunt to say a prayer. It was just a very reverent and beautiful place to be – and a very peaceful place. I always wanted to be a nun until I found boys."

Kathy Carrico, R.N, LEAD NURSING SUPERVISOR
ST. MARY MEDICAL CENTER | (BEGAN IN 1982 IN GARY)

COMBINED FAMILY SERVICE

Four members of the Bayus family together contributed over 80 years of service to the Gary hospital site. Shown here (l-r) are: Donna Bayus-Wilson, former director, Medical Records, 41 years from 1963-2004; Danica Bayus, Dietary Service cook, 30 years from 1940-1970; Steve Bayus, Laundry attendant, 10 years from 1954-1964; and Violet Bayus-Lanis, Business Office clerk, three years from 1964-1967.

HONORING JIM WADE –
50 YEARS OF DEVOTED SERVICE

In February 1960, a young man by the name of Jim Wade landed a job at Mercy Hospital in Gary as a maintenance helper. The rate of pay for the 18-year-old in those days was $2.38 an hour. Ranked among the hospital's early staff members, his employee number is 263.

Fifty years later, on February 15, 2010, the soft-spoken, kindly man who is well respected and well known by his fellow employees has become a welcome fixture of the St. Mary family. Jim's longevity with the hospital – five decades of service – makes him the longest, currently active employee at St. Mary Medical Center.

Jim, who has rarely missed work, has a file replete with commendations for perfect attendance. In 1982, he was promoted to senior maintenance man and later named maintenance worker III. In 1993, with 33 years of employment to his credit, Jim was promoted to plant supervisor over Plant Operations in Hobart. In 1996, he was named manager of Plant Operations. The year 2005 marked 45 years of service.

And today, in 2010 – marking 50 years of devoted service – the South Bend native who settled in Northwest Indiana and refers to St. Mary Medical Center as his "extended family," has served the Gary and Hobart medical facilities well.

Hospital CEO and Administrator Janice L. Ryba presents Jim Wade with his plaque for 50 years of service at St. Mary Medical Center. Jim is the longest-serving active employee at St. Mary Medical Center.

IT'S BEEN *Said* IN 2009...

"I've found that we're all working toward the same thing – helping sick people feel better and live healthier. It makes me feel like I have a large, extended family."

Jim Wade, MANAGER OF PLANT OPERATIONS
MERCY HOSPITAL| (BEGAN IN 1960 IN GARY)

Speaking of the Doctors

Represented here are some of the many physicians at the Gary and Hobart hospital sites. While photos and quotes were not available for each individual, we have included information from and about many of them – as a collective honorarium to <u>all</u> of the physicians who have cared for the sick and injured at Mercy Hospital and St. Mary Medical Center.

Wall of Honor

The Wall of Honor is located in the Physician Office Building (POB). The middle glass encasement was the first artistic display – with a plaque donated by the parents of Jeffrey A. Tritsch, M.D., in memory of their son. Dr. Tritsch was a young ophthalmologist at St. Mary Medical Center who passed away in 1997.

Jeffrey A. Tritsch, M.D.
Ophthalmology

A Special Tribute to a Man Gifted with Healing Hands and a Compassionate Heart.

There is no one shining moment, no singlular event-- rather, it has been an accumulation of dedicated work, quality patient care and love for his family, friends and co-workers that made him stand alone.

It's been *Said* in 2009...

"Some of the outstanding physicians I worked with were Dr. Oscar Almquist, general surgery; Dr. Frank Michael, urologist; Dr. Raymond Carmody, ophthalmologist; and Dr. William Glover who worked with Dr. Almquist."

Marguerite Bendt, R.N., Operating Room Supervisor, retired
Mercy Hospital | (began in 1946 in Gary)

William Glover, M.D.

It's been *Said* in 2010...

By the way...
"We had a wonderful head nurse in surgery in Gary. Her name was Marguerite Bendt. She ran the Surgery Department with an iron hand. She would tell the doctors off. If they were late, she would get very upset."

William J. Glover, MD.
General Surgeon, retired
Mercy Hospital
(began in approximately 1947 in Gary)

It's been *Said* in 2009...

"Three of my favorite physicians were the three doctors who had almost 100% of their patients on 3North where I worked right after graduation. Dr. James Reynolds, Dr. John Brincko, and Dr. Sam Richter were partners and physician surgeons in genitourinary practice (GU). They were just wonderful physicians to work with and for."

Evelyn Charbonneau Ryan, R.N.
Infection Control, retired
Mercy Hospital
(began in 1957 in Gary)

IT'S BEEN *Said* IN 2009...

"Dr. Alvin Jahns was an excellent orthopedist with great surgical skills. Dr. Dale Olson was Dr. Johns' associate. Both Drs. Johns and Olson were born in Gary and went to Horace Mann High School."

John T. Scully, M.D., INTERNIST, RETIRED
MERCY HOSPITAL | (BEGAN IN 1955 IN GARY)

IT'S BEEN *Said* IN 2010...

"Dr. Joseph Carbone used to take care of my children. He was an outstanding pediatrician."

Jose H. Roig, M.D., OPHTHALMOLOGIST, RETIRED
MERCY HOSPITAL
(BEGAN IN 1967 IN GARY)

IT'S BEEN *Said* IN 2009...

"There were many fine physicians who acted as mentors for us and also instilled the fear of God in us when we went on rounds with them. We never knew what questions they would ask us; sometimes we were right on top of things, and sometimes we weren't, but they always made it a learning experience. The fear was not of their making, but our own. Names who come to mind are Dr. John Scully, Dr. Jack Kamen, Dr. Robert Milos, Dr. Leo Radigan and many more."

Connie McCarthy Blaine, R.N, BSHA, DIRECTOR OF QUALITY MANAGEMENT, RETIRED
ST. MARY MERCY HOSPITAL | (BEGAN IN 1963 IN GARY)

IT'S BEEN *Said* IN 2009...

"(I knew) the Goldstone brothers – Sidney Goldstone and Robert Goldstone. One family – two children, a husband and a wife – died in a plane crash in Florida, a private plane crash. The other Goldstone was very, very, affluent in those days. They had offices at 32nd and Broadway. My office building was the Goldstone Building. There was another one near IU on 33rd Street. It was a Goldstone building."

Vijay Dave, M.D., CARDIOLOGIST
MERCY HOSPITAL | (BEGAN IN 1977 IN GARY)

IT'S BEEN *Said* IN 2009...

"When I worked in ICU, I worked with Dr. Kamen who had become the ICU medical director. He was a great teacher. He loved the patients and he would take the time to teach us and we were always free to call him any time of the night if there was a problem. He would always come in – sometimes in his pajamas by putting his pants on over them."

Flora Dean Meeks, R.N, RADIOLOGY, RETIRED
MERCY HOSPITAL | (BEGAN IN 1960 IN GARY)

"The names of a number of physicians who were dedicated to St. Mary come right off the top of my head. The first is Dr. Jack Kamen. The second is Dr. Milton Bergal. The third one is Dr. A. S. Williams and fourth, of course, is Dr. Benjamin Grant."

Vijay Dave, M.D., CARDIOLOGIST
MERCY HOSPITAL | (BEGAN IN 1977 IN GARY)

Milton Bergal, M.D.

"Dr. Bob Martino and Dr. Charlie Yast have always been very faithful to Hobart Mercy. They were very ethical and highly respected by their doctor peers – both first class people in every way."

Robert J. Welsh, FORMER ST. MARY MEDICAL CENTER, ST. CATHERINE HOSPITAL BOARD MEMBER
ST. MARY MEDICAL CENTER CHAIRMAN OF THE BOARD (1997 – 2001)
CFNI BOARD MEMBER

Charles Yast, M.D.

"Dr. Bob Young was a superb ophthalomogist with great surgical skills and truly high ethical standards."

John T. Scully, M.D., INTERNIST, RETIRED | MERCY HOSPITAL | (BEGAN IN 1955 IN GARY)

"Dr. Mikhail Jeha is a very compassionate man. When it comes to his patients he is very, very compassionate, and he is still here."

Beverly Armenta., COORDINATOR RADIOLOGY SUPPORT, RADIOLOGY | MERCY HOSPITAL | (BEGAN IN 1972 IN GARY)

"Dr. Peter Bonaventura was an obstetrician/gynecologist who was loved dearly. He passed away from cancer. Everybody in the hospital just thought he was the best. His interactions with people, his bedside manner – he took time with you. He would sit and talk to you. You wouldn't see him for months and he seemed to remember everything. It was sad when he was gone."

Sharon Forszt, FORMER ADMINISTRATIVE ASSISTANT TO CEO
ST. MARY MEDICAL CENTER | (BEGAN IN 1975 AT ST. CATHERINE HOSPITAL)

"It's hard to single out standout physicians but one very good one is Dr. Raj Devanathan in Pulmonary. I think of the outstanding care he gives and how receptive he is to everything."

Scott A. Andrews, M.D., ORTHOPEDIC SURGEON
MEDICAL STAFF PRESIDENT, 2008-2010
(BEGAN IN 1994 IN HOBART)

BY THE WAY...

"I'm grateful and I'm honored to be an employee of St. Mary Medical Center. We were family and we are still family. I worked with Carmen Alfaro – good person. I was so glad to be able to work with her and Joni Bucko. These employees were like my mothers away from home."

Irene Pacheco, PATIENT FINANCIAL COUNSELOR, PATIENT FINANCIAL SERVICES
ST. MARY MEDICAL CENTER | (BEGAN IN 1973 IN GARY)

Dr. Leo Cooper stopped by a Gary hospital business office party in 1981 and is shown here (l-r) with Dr. Miriam Sonera, Carmen Alfaro and Irene Pacheco.

ENJOYING TIME OFF...
Seated at this 1970 Radiology holiday party at Broadmoor Country Club in Schererville are Dr. and Mrs. Aram Semerdjian.

THERE WHEN NEEDED
In 1979, Jean Sanders, Medical Records stenographer, would have choked on a piece of meat if it hadn't been for Robert Milos, M.D., performing the Heimlich maneuver on her during lunchtime in Hobart. The maneuver forced her diaphragm upward, compressed the air in her lungs and expelled the food blocking her airway. She is shown here "thanking" Dr. Milos for his quick action with the frightening incident.

Acts and Facts, JUNE 1979

"(A lady) who used to work downstairs in Medical Records had a total of seven stents placed in her heart. I didn't put them in – she had them done (elsewhere). She had chest pain and she was mad. She had tremors.

"A new medication came out – Ranexa – and I gave it to her. Within two weeks, she couldn't believe she felt so good. I was the first person to use it. I had maximum, extensive experience because we are involved in a lot of clinical trials.

"She had a tremor and went to Dr. Mark Simaga. He is very, very dedicated. He is an ideal doctor. He has nothing to do with financial gain and nothing to do with trying to show off. He is a brilliant doctor! He is very knowledgeable and a good human being.

Mark Simaga, M.D.

"Dr. Simaga put our patient on medication for tremors (that) were very bad. She felt better. Then she had headaches. Dr. Simaga did a CT scan and found out she had an aneurysm in a bad area of the brain. Dr. Simaga almost cried when he gave this news to her. He referred her to the University of Illinois in Chicago, UIC, to one of the top neurosurgery departments.

"She is going to have surgery. There is a high probability that when she has an angiogram, it will be dangerous. I will take off that day and be there. I promised. She nominated me as her healthcare representative so I can make the decision about her healthcare. I have more right than her children."

Vijay Dave, M.D., CARDIOLOGIST
MERCY HOSPITAL | (BEGAN IN 1977 IN GARY)

ALEXANDER S. WILLIAMS, M.D.

A 1990 *Post-Tribune* advertisement called "Partners with the Community," included this statement from Alexander S. Williams, M.D., about St. Mary Medical Center, Gary: "We are committed to quality healthcare and committed to the citizens of our community."
Reprinted by permission of the *Post-Tribune*, AUGUST 26, 1990

STEVE SIMPSON, M.D.

The same *Post-Tribune* advertisement included this statement from Steve Simpson, M.D.: "We ask the citizens of our community to assist us in providing the best healthcare possible by using the fine facilities of St. Mary Medical Center, Gary, and to demand the best – of our physicians, the hospital staff, and yourselves."
Reprinted by permission of the *Post-Tribune*, AUGUST 26, 1990

KESHAV D. AGGARWAL, M.D.

Another statement in the advertisement came from Keshav D. Aggarwal, M.D.: "St. Mary Medical Center has been taking care of Gary residents longer than anyone and we fully intend to continue our mission that our founder, Blessed Mary Katherine Kasper, envisioned."
Reprinted by permission of the *Post-Tribune*, AUGUST 26, 1990

ST. MARY MEDICAL CENTER
A MISSION OF MERCY, A CENTURY OF CARE

IT'S BEEN *Said* IN 2009...

"Starting with the point that the medical field consumes 18% of our gross national product, healthcare's significance goes everywhere from the individual's health and well being to what it means to a community to have a hospital. A good solid medical system has significant economic, social and spiritual implications for a community."

John Birdzell
FORMER PRESIDENT OF LAKESHORE HEALTH SYSTEM
(BEGAN IN 1985 WITH ANCILLA SYSTEMS INCORPORATED)

IT'S BEEN *Said* IN 2009...

"I have seen this place grow up from what we call 'the box' which was just the old building. Then they built this addition here and then the next addition, the Patient Tower. I remember when this was just all view; there was nothing there and... we have sort of grown up together. It has gotten better with each successful year as far as the facility and the area we are in."

Joe Koscielniak, M.D.
ORTHOPEDIC SURGEON
MERCY HOSPITAL (EXTERN)
(BEGAN IN 1984 IN HOBART)

IT'S BEEN *Said* IN 2009...

ON THE HORIZON
"Whether you like it or not, stem cells are in our future. Genetic manipulation is on the horizon in terms of the potential to grow heart muscle, to grow arteries and restore heart muscle, restore blood supply – maybe reverse strokes in a more effective manner. Which particular directions they'll take and which end up being superior are difficult to say but the sky's the limit."

Jack Ziegler, M.D., CARDIOLOGIST
ST. MARY MEDICAL CENTER | (BEGAN IN 1982 IN HOBART)

WITH GRATIFICATION AND PURPOSE

IT'S BEEN *Said* IN 2009...

Jack Ziegler, M.D.

"I think the 1980s were the initiation of the ideas on how we could intervene and help people. The 1990s were the development and implementation of those theories to a fuller degree. What's exciting is that this is not just something to be done at a large medical center and academic center. These technologies can be done in a small, local community hospital. They can be done effectively and efficiently and with accuracy and good results without having to transfer our patients. All of that has been brought by the support of Community Healthcare System and the Ancilla System before that. Without the monies to provide those technologies, we wouldn't be able to do it."

Jack Ziegler, M.D., CARDIOLOGIST
ST. MARY MEDICAL CENTER | (BEGAN IN 1982 IN HOBART)

IT'S BEEN *Said* IN 2010...

"I believe the hospital is in wonderful, good condition now. I feel the laboratory services and anatomic pathology services at St. Mary Medical Center have reached a very high standard and continue to excel in every respect for the present people in charge."

Earl J. Mason, Ph.D., M.D., FORMER DIRECTOR OF THE LABORATORY, RETIRED
MERCY HOSPITAL | (BEGAN IN 1965 IN GARY)

IT'S BEEN *Said* IN 2009...

"Healthcare is important because in order to accomplish other tasks people have to be healthy. It is our duty as medical people to make sure that the care is given freely. I understand the business end of it. You hear the term 'philosophical differences' all the time – with accountants who want you to charge the patients and then take care of them and you have the nursing staff and medical staff that are more concerned about taking care of the patients. Those philosophical differences are what cause much conflict in medicine today. I honestly do not know that there is a bridge for it.

"The Sisters understood accounting but if they had to lean toward something they would lean toward taking care of the person. Their presence is still here. The spirit of the family is still here."

Peggy Kamysz, R.N, MPA, INFORMATION TECHNOLOGY
ST. MARY MEDICAL CENTER | (BEGAN IN 1982 IN GARY/HOBART)

IT'S BEEN *Said* IN 2009...

"We knew this would be a wonderful addition to Hobart, that it would help the rural area grow. Any city that has a hospital is held at a higher regard because you draw people from other areas. We drew from Portage, from Lake Station, from New Chicago, from Merrillville – before Broadway Methodist had opened.

"I don't believe the shopping center across the street would have been developed had it not been for the hospital. I'm president of the Redevelopment Board and we're starting to redevelop the 61st Avenue corridor and we regularly meet with hospital administrators on how that's going."

Margaret Kuchta, MAYOR OF HOBART, 1988 –1992
ST. MARY MEDICAL CENTER VOLUNTEER
LONGTIME HOBART RESIDENT, COMMUNITY ADVOCATE

A Community without a Hospital

IT'S BEEN *Said* IN 2009...

"A community without a hospital is not a community. It impoverishes people who find it more difficult to access healthcare. I have been most appreciative in my dealings with Ancilla who had the wisdom and the stamina, motivation, courage to really move forward and help us understand fully the need to move in some of these directions.

"We call this a community hospital. And if it is truly a community hospital and these others really are serving their communities then I would say to the people, 'Own those institutions. Make them your own. Make them the places of excellence in the area of that hospital where there is need for people willing to help others to access that care that is there for them. Help them also help others to access it.'"

Sister Jolise May, PHJC, GENERAL SUPERIOR OF THE INTERNATIONAL CONGREGATION OF THE POOR HANDMAIDS OF JESUS CHRIST | DERNBACH, GERMANY

IT'S BEEN *Said* IN 2009...

"I don't think the community would let the hospital go away. We would keep it here. I think there is enough public concern and citizens who would really work to keep it if something happened. What would have been adequate 50 years ago is not adequate today and what is adequate today will not be adequate 50 years from now."

Virginia Curtis, LONGTIME HOBART COMMUNITY ADVOCATE/HISTORIAN

Heritage and Tradition

"The hospital is the city that never sleeps for it is the great theater of every man. It sees him through every stage of his existence, from the cradle to the grave, and for that space of life in between."

~BISHOP JOSEPH DURICK
NASHVILLE, TENNESSEE

When St. Mary Medical Center's counterpart, Mercy Hospital, stood as a primitive structure along one of Gary's dirt roads in the early 1900s, the Poor Handmaids of Jesus Christ worked by the light of hanging oil lamps and sought the warmth of coal furnaces as typhoid fever patients were turned away from the filled-to-capacity 20-bed facility.

And today – imagine. The Hobart hospital exists as the largest employer in the community followed by the school system. The 85-acre site has given way to a helipad, digital mammography, the latest Axia LIF spinal fusion surgery, and futuristic technology. Antibiotics are plentiful and physicians specialize in their fields as never before. By acquisition, St. Mary Medical Center now belongs to the three-hospital Community Healthcare System, locally and nationally recognized in a variety of categories.

After a century of care – 103 years in 2010 to be exact – the focus remains the same – that patient care is second to none. As the book confirms, the hospital in Hobart stands by its heritage and tradition. From the past, it also looks to the future, destined to become St. Mary Medical Center – a mission of mercy with many centuries of care.

Index

Index

Index

Index

Index

Index

Index

Index

Roz Jevtic and Mary Fetsch

MARKETING DEPARTMENT...

If it is said that cobbler's children are the last to get shoes, so too is the St. Mary Medical Center Marketing Department the last to have a photo taken for this history book! Just as this project is going to print, Director of Marketing and Community Relations Mary Fetsch (seated) and Marketing Assistant Roz Jevtic (standing) are ensconced in preparations for the opening of the hospital's new Emergency Department in September, 2010. With a nudge from book Editor Debra Jenkins, they took time out for a quick pose and literally became the very last entry in this publication. Thank you, Mary and Roz, for the time you devoted to taking photos of others, unearthing historical data, recommending resources, and lending an extra hand with St. Mary Medical Center – A Mission of Mercy, a Century of Care.